Essentials of Soil Mechanics and Foundations:
Basic Geotechnics

third edition

DAVID F. McCARTHY, P.E.

PRENTICE HALL, Englewood Cliffs, New Jersey 07632

Library of Congress Cataloging-in-Publication Data

McCarthy, David F.
 Essentials of soil mechanics and foundations.

 Bibliography: p.
 Includes index.
 1. Soil mechanics. 2. Foundations. I. Title.
TA710.M29 1988   624.1'5   87-17445
ISBN 0-13-287889-5

Editorial/production supervision and
  interior design: David Ershun
Cover design: Photo Plus Art
Manufacturing buyer: Peter Havens

Prentice-Hall International (UK) Limited, *London*
Prentice-Hall of Australia Pty. Limited, *Sydney*
Prentice-Hall Canada Inc., *Toronto*
Prentice-Hall Hispanoamericana, S.A., *Mexico*
Prentice-Hall of India Private Limited, *New Delhi*
Prentice-Hall of Japan, Inc., *Tokyo*
Prentice-hall of Southeast Asia Pte. Ltd., *Singapore*
Editora Prentice-Hall Do Brasil, Ltda., *Rio de Janeiro*

Contents

6 MOVEMENT OF WATER THROUGH SOIL: PRACTICAL EFFECTS: FLOW NETS AND SEEPAGE, DRAINAGE, FROST HEAVE   107

Preface to the Third Edition

This edition is intended to carry on the function of the earlier editions, introducing the basic theories and applications of soil mechanics and foundations (or geotechnics) to students in the civil engineering, technology, architectural, and construction undergraduate programs. The nature and content of the material will also make this edition a useful reference for the practitioner.

This edition represents an updating of topics covered in the earlier works as well as some clarifications. Numerous minor changes have been accomplished. A major change has been made in the section covering shallow foundation design considerations and procedures, to better reflect current general practice.

The body of the text, the illustrative examples, and student work problems continue to use both U.S. Customary Units and SI Units, representing the dual-language status noted to prevail within the practitioner's sector of the geotechnical profession in the United States. Undoubtedly, the slow adoption of the SI system by practicing engineers relates to the wealth of reference information still in U.S. Customary units (in design manuals and building codes, for example) but it is also the result of a difficulty in translating the "feel" and intuition gained from experience into new numerical terms, particularly terms where mixed units apply (e.g., stress, density, unit weight, various property coefficients).

The assistance and contributions of others have been important to all the editions of this text. Illustrations, photographs, and text items provided by others continue to be acknowledged where such materials appear. The library staff of Mohawk Valley Community College, SUNY, Utica, New York, continued to prove resourceful in securing desired references. Mrs. Patricia Klossner continued her earlier role in developing the final manuscript. My colleagues and family continued to demonstrate understanding and provide encouragement. A documented thank you to all is not out of order.

Preface to the Second Edition

It is intended that this edition will continue as an educational instrument to introduce theories and applications basic to the field of soil mechanics and foundations. The text is directed to the level of course work found in civil engineering, civil and construction technology, and architectural undergraduate programs. Due to the nature of the topics, however, a considerable amount of the material has direct application to practical usage; practitioners who are not soils or foundations experts should find such sections of the text informative and useful.

The significant difference between the present work and the first edition is the expansion of topics; chapters on the subjects of slope stability, lateral pressures and retaining structures, and loads on buried conduits have been added, while Chapter 1, relating to geology, has been revised. Chapters from the first edition that deal with basic theory have been retained with little alteration; chapters dealing with application have been modified primarily to include developments since the first edition was written. Following the style of the first edition, illustrative problems have also been integrated into the discussion of topics presented in the new chapters. Many of this edition's illustrative problems are worked in SI Units, but many are also worked in U.S. Customary Units, a reflection on the present-day dual-language status of the geotechnical engineering profession in the United States.

Two individuals are deserving of acknowledgment because of the extent of their contribution to this second edition. Dr. Herman S. Muskatt, Department of Geology at Utica College of Syracuse University, provided a detailed review of the original geology-related Chapter 1, suggesting modifications and additional items which are now included to make the chapter more precise and more complete. Professor Francis H. Collopy of Northern Essex Community College, Haverhill, Massachusetts, a conscientious reviewer of the manuscript for the first edition and the expansion chapters for this second edition, offered suggestions relating to topic coverage and presentation which have been incorporated into the present work.

Contractors, consulting engineers, manufacturers and publishers are the source of a number of the illustrations and photographs included in this edition. Acknowledgments are provided where such materials appear, but a special word is in order to document the gracious attitude of these contributors.

The major portion of the new material included in this second edition was developed during a sabbatical leave from Mohawk Valley Community College, SUNY, Utica, New York. The efforts of the college administration and colleagues toward arranging that leave are appreciated. The library staff at the college was exceptionally helpful in locating and securing many references, and their assistance is gratefully acknowledged.

The preparation of the typed manuscript again became the responsibility of Mrs. Patricia Klossner, whose experience with the manuscript for the first edition helped ease the burden of planning. The author's family witnessed the development of the new work with patience and tolerance, plus some subtle humor—in perspective, not undesirable traits.

Preface to the First Edition

This text has been developed as an educational instrument to introduce the theory and application of soil mechanics to students intending to enter the planning, design, or field phases of the construction profession.

In its function as an introductory level text, the material is limited to basic principles. Advanced topics are beyond its intended scope. Advanced mathematics have been avoided. Detail has been restricted to ensure that major concepts do not become masked or lost. For the student, the text establishes the importance of soil mechanics to the design and construction profession. The practitioner and teacher will find that the methods presented for analysis and evaluation apply to many practical problems.

Illustrations and photographs provided by contractors and manufacturers to complement the written text have been acknowledged where presented. The opportunity to use them is greatly appreciated. Soiltest, Inc., and Acker Drill Co., Inc., deserve special mention for the considerable material made available during the text's development. Many diagrams and photographs relating to soil-boring methods appear in Will Acker's book, *Basic Procedures for Soil Sampling and Core Drilling*, a recommended reference where detailed information on drilling and boring techniques is required. Important to the manuscript, and deserving of acknowledgment, are the reviews, suggestions, and materials provided by former colleagues at Dames and Moore and at Empire Soil Investigations—Thomsen Associates.

The preparation and editing of a technical manuscript requires time and patience. To this end, the skill of Mrs. Patricia Klossner was essential and not unappreciated. The efforts of Mrs. Sue Fox Hill and Miss Laurene Allen, involved during the manuscript's formative stage, require acknowledgment. A special note of gratitude is due Mrs. Grace Messere of Mohawk Valley Community College for her interest and assistance throughout the various stages of the book's development. Also deserving of recognition are the patience and understanding of the author's family, whose life-style was uncomplainingly altered throughout the text's gestation period.

Units

Soil mechanics is a field where U.S. Customary Units (also referred to as British or English units) and metric units have commonly been used in the past. The international system, SI Units (the international metric system), is proposed as the system for eventual worldwide usage. Although many countries have accomplished the change to the SI system, the process is still going on in the United States. At present, students and practitioners in the geotechnical field obtain information and operate in the dual language of Customary and SI Units. Sole use of the SI system in a text intended for teaching and for a reference is not yet warranted. Within the body of this text, dual units are used; the method for working illustrative problems has been divided approximately evenly between the two systems.

The fundamental dimensions and properties used in developing a scientifically based measuring system are units of force (F), mass (M), time (T), linear distance (L), and angular distance (R). The units for these fundamental factors, expressed for the SI system and the U.S. Customary Units system, are tabulated here:

Fundamental Property or Factor	SI System (Base Unit)	U.S. Customary (Base Unit)
Force (F)	newton	pound
Mass (M)	(kilo)gram	slug
Time (T)	second	second, minute
Linear distance (Length, L)	meter	foot
Angular distance (R)	radians	degree

Where large or small units are involved, it is convenient to use the following prefixes in written and oral presentations:

Oral Term	Written Symbol	Indicated Multiplication Factor
mega	M	10^6 (one million times greater)
kilo	k	10^3 (one thousand times greater)
centi	c	10^{-2} (a hundredth part)
milli	m	10^{-3} (a thousandth part)
micro	μ	10^{-6} (a millionth part)

Thus, the term *kilonewton* indicates a force of one thousand newtons, the term *millimeter* indicates a length of one one-thousandth of a meter, and so on. The use of the well-established *centi-* prefix is discouraged in the SI system.

Other terms derived from the fundamental units to identify various physical properties, conditions, and occurrences are in common use in the geotechnical and other scientific fields (e.g., area, volume, stress, pressure, velocity, acceleration, energy, density, unit weight). The following compilation of terms with usually applied units, and the relationship between the SI and U.S. Customary systems, should prove useful.

Property or Term	SI Units	U.S. Customary Units	Equivalencies

Length, L	meter, m	ft (also inches, yards, miles)	1 m = 3.281 ft
			1 mm = .0394 in.
			    = .00328 ft
			1 ft = 0.348 m
			1 in. = .0254 m
			    = 25.4 mm
			1 yd = 0.91 m
			1 km = 0.621 mile
			1 mile = 1610 m = 1.61 km

Area, L^2	sq. m, m^2	ft^2 (also $in.^2$, yd^2, sq. miles, acre)	$1\ m^2$ = 10.764 ft^2
			    = 1.196 yd^2
			$1\ mm^2$ = $10.764 \times 10^{-6}\ ft^2$
			    = .00155 $in.^2$
			$1\ ft^2$ = 0.093 m^2
			$1\ in.^2$ = 645.16 mm^2
			$1\ yd^2$ = 0.836 m^2
			$1\ km^2$ = 0.386 square miles
			1 sq. mi = 2.59 km^2
			1 acre = 43,560 ft^2
			    = 4047 m^2
			    = 0.4047 hectare
			1 hectare = 2.471 acre
			1 hectare = 10,000 m^2

Volume, L^3	cu. m, m^3 (also liter, where 1 liter = 1,000 cm^3)	ft^3 (also cu. yd, gallon)	$1\ m^3$ = 35.32 ft^3 = 1.31 yd^3
			61023.4 $in.^3$
			$1\ cm^3$ = .061023 $in.^3$
			$1\ ft^3$ = .0283 m^3 = 28.3 liter
			$1\ in.^3$ = 16.39 cm^3
			$1\ yd^3$ = 0.765 m^3
			1 liter = 1,000 cm^3 = 0.263 gal
			    = .0354 ft^3
			1 gal = 3.8 liter = .0038 m^3
			    = 0.134 ft^3
			$1\ m^3$ = 263 gal

Property or Term	SI Units	U.S. Customary Units	Equivalencies
Mass, M	kilogram, kg (gram in metric)	Slug (note: units for slug are lb-sec^2/ft) also lb-mass (lbm)	1 slug = 14.59 kg 1 kg = .0685 slug
Force, F ($F = ML/T^2$)	newton, N (dyne in metric)	lb, ton, (note: lb and ton also indicate weight)	1 N = 0.2248 lb 1 kN = 224.8 lb 1 kN = 0.1124 ton 1 lb = 4.448 N = 453.6 gram force 1 ton = 8.896 lcN 1 dyne = 1×10^{-5} N = 2.25×10^{-6} lb
Stress, Pressure (F/L^2)	N/m^2 (also Pascal, Pa, where 1 Pa = 1 N/m^2, and bar, where 1 bar = 10^5 Pa)	lb/ft^2, psf (also ton/ft^2, tsf, and kip/ft^2, ksf and lb/in.^{2}, psi)	1 N/m^2 = .0209 psf 1 kN/m^2 = 20.89 psf = 0.145 lb/in.^{2} 1 psf = 47.88 N/m^2 = 48 Pa 1 psi = 6.895 kN/m^2 1 tsf = 95.76 kN/m^2
Density (mass density) (M/L^3)	ρ (rho) in kg/m^3, mg/m^3	ρ in lbm/ft^3, and slugs/ft^3	1 Mg/m^3 = 62.4 lbm/ft^3 1 lbm/ft^3 = .0157 Mg/m^3
Unit weight (F/L^3, M/L^2T^2)	γ (gamma) in kN/m^3 (dynes/cm^3 for metric)	γ in lb/ft^3, pcf	1 kN/m^3 = 6.36 pcf = .00368 pci 1 pcf = 157 N/m^3
Velocity (L/T)	m/sec	ft/sec, fps ft/min, fpm	1 m/sec = 3.28 fps 1 cm/sec = 1.97 fpm 1 fps = 0.305 m/sec 1 fpm = 5.08 mm/sec
Acceleration (L/T^2)	m/sec^2	ft/sec^2	1 m/sec^2 = 3.28 ft/sec^2 1 ft/sec^2 = 0.348 m/sec^2
Angle measurement	radians	degrees	1 rad = 57.3 deg 1 deg = .01745 rad

Nomenclature

The tabulation that follows indicates the nomenclature used throughout this text. Generally, the notation and symbols are standard for the soil mechanics professions. Some dual use of nomenclature does exist (the use of the same symbol for different factors). This practice is continued, for certain nomenclature has become well established in soil mechanics use, and it is felt not advisable to arbitrarily assign new notation. Fortunately, repeated nomenclature only occurs with different topics, and the potential for confusion is remote.

A	area (in.^{2}, ft^2, cm^2, m^2)
A_{tip}	end area of pile tip (ft^2, m^2)
$\overset{\circ}{A}$	Angstrom unit (1 $\overset{\circ}{A}$ = 10^{-8} cm)
AASHTO	American Association of State Highway and Transportation Officials
ASCE	American Society of Civil Engineers
ASTM	American Society for Testing and Materials
a_v	coefficient of compressibility (ft^2/lb, or cm^2/gm)
B	footing width, pile or pile group width (ft, m)
B_c	diameter or breadth of a buried conduit (ft, m)
B_d	width of trench in a buried conduit analysis (ft, m)
b_c, b_γ, b_q	base tilt factors, foundation design (dimensionless)
C_c	compression index (dimensionless)
C_r	slope of recompression curve from consolidation test (dimensionless)

C_u	uniformity coefficient for sands (dimensionless)
C_d, C_c, C_n, C_t	load coefficient, buried conduits (dimensionless)
c	unit cohesion or shear strength of cohesive soils (lb/ft^2, kip/ft^2, N/m^2; also kg/cm^2 has been used)
c_h	coefficient of consolidation for horizontal drainage (ft^2/day, month, or year; cm^2/min, hour, day, or month)
c_v	coefficient of consolidation for vertical drainage (ft^2/day, month, or year; cm^2/min, hour, day, month)
D, d	diameter of soil particles (in., cm, mm)
D	depth (ft, m)
D_c	critical depth for pile penetration (ft, m)
D_f	depth of footing (ft, m)
D_r	relative density of cohensionless soil (percent)
D_{10}	effective particle size, diameter of the 10 percent finer size (cm, mm)
D_{60}	particle size corresponding to 60 percent finer (cm, mm)
D_c, D_γ, D_q	foundations depth factor (dimensionless)
E	modulus of elasticity (lb/in.^{2}, lb/ft^2, N/m^2)
E_m	Menard pressuremeter modular (kN/m^2)
e	void ratio (dimensionless)
Eff.	efficiency of pile driving hammer (decimal, fraction, percent)
F	force (lb, kip, ton, N; kg has also been used)
FS and SF	factor of safety or safety factor (dimensionless)
f	skin friction or adhesion between pile and soil (lb/ft^2, kip/ft^2, N/m^2)
G	soil shearing modulus (lb/in.^{2}, lb/ft^2, N/m^2)
G_w	specific gravity of water (dimensionless)
G_s	specific gravity of soil solids (dimensionless)
g	acceleration of gravity (ft/sec^2, cm/sec^2)
H	height or thickness (ft, m)
H	vertical distance from top of a conduit to the ground surface in a buried conduit analysis (ft, m)
H_e	height above a buried conduit where settlement of earth zone overlying the conduit becomes equal to the settlement of adjacent soil zones (ft, m)
H_{dr}	longest drainage path
H_w, h	height of water, head of water (ft, m)
ΔH	settlement (in., cm)
h_c	height of capillary rise
l	electrical current (amperes)
I_B, I_W	influence factor for determining subsurface stress (dimensionless)
I_r	soil rigidity index, foundation design (dimensionless)
i	hydraulic gradient (dimensionless)
i	inclination angle for earth slopes
i_c, i_γ, i_q	load inclination factors, foundation design (dimensionless)
K	permeability (ft^2, m^2)

K	lateral earth pressure coefficient (dimensionless)
K_o	lateral earth pressure coefficient for at-rest condition (dimensionless)
K_a	lateral earth pressure coefficient for the active pressure condition (dimensionless)
K_p	lateral earth pressure coefficient for the passive pressure condition (dimensionless)
k	coefficient of permeability (ft/min, day; cm/sec, min)
k_{bc}	foundation shape factor for determining bearing capacity from pressuremeter test results (dimensionless)
K_v	modulus of subgrade reaction (kip/ft^3, N/m^3)
ksf	kips per square foot (one kip equals 1,000 lb)
L, l	length (ft, m)
LI	liquidity index (dimensionless)
LL	liquid limit (percent)
M	mass (gm, kg)
M_s	slope stability factor (dimensionless)
m_v	coefficient of volume compressibility (ft^2/lb, m^2/N; cm^2/kg has also been used)
N	normal force (lb, kip, ton, N; kg has also been used)
N	blow count from standard penetration test
N_c, N_γ, N_q	bearing capacity factors for foundation design (dimensionless)
$N_{cs}, N_{\gamma s}$	bearing capacity factors for footings on slopes (dimensionless)
N_d	number of equipotential drops in flow net analysis (dimensionless)
N_f	number of flow channels in flow net analysis (dimensionless)
N_s	stability number used in slope stability analysis (dimensionless)
n	porosity (dimensionless)
PI	plasticity index (percent)
PL	plastic limit (percent)
P_A	lateral force acting against a vertical structure which results from active lateral earth pressure condition (lb/ft of length, N/m of length)
P_p	lateral force acting against a vertical structure which results from passive lateral earth pressure condition (lb/ft of length, N/m of length)
P_Q, P_q	lateral pressure against a vertical structure as a result of a concentrated load Q or line load q located on the surface behind the structure (#/ft^2, N/m^2)
Pa	lateral pressure acting against a vertical structure, resulting from active earth pressure condition (lb/ft^2, N/m^2)
P_p	lateral pressure acting against a vertical structure, resulting from passive earth pressure condition (lb/ft^2, N/m^2)
P_l	limit pressure value used with pressuremeter analysis (kN/m^2)
P_w	water pressure (lb/ft^2, gm/cm^2, N/m^2)
pcf	pounds per cubic foot (unit weight or density) (lb/ft^3)
psf	pounds per square foot (pressure) (lb/ft^2)

Q	total water flow (ft^3, cm^3, m^3, gal)
Q, Q_t	total load (lb, kip, ton, N; kg has also been used)
$q_{ultimate}$, q_{ult}	ultimate unit soil bearing pressure (lb/ft^2, kip/ft^2, ton/ft^2, N/m^2; kg/cm^2 has also been used)
q_{design}	design value of soil bearing pressure (lb/ft^2, kip/ft^2, N/m^2; kg/cm^2 has also been used)
q_c	static cone resistance (kg/cm^2)
q	volume of water flowing per unit time (gal/min, ft^3/min, cm^3/min)
R	correction factor to obtain bearing capacity of inclined foundation (dimensionless)
R_H	hydraulic radius (ft)
r	radius (ft, m)
r_c	settlement ratio on buried conduit analysis (dimensionless)
r_u	pore pressure ratio, ratio of pore water pressure to overburden soil pressure, for slope stability analysis (dimensionless)
r_c, r_γ, r_q	soil bearing capacity reduction factors (dimensionless)
S	degree of saturation (percent)
S	set, penetration of driven pile per hammer blow (in., cm)
S	total shearing force or resistance developed on the sliding surface of an assumed moving soil mass (lb, kN)
S_t	sensitivity (dimensionless)
S_o	elastic compression of pile (in., cm)
SPT	standard penetration test blow count (blows)
s_c, s_γ, s_q	shape factors, shallow foundations (dimensionless)
T_h	time factor for horizontal drainage (dimensionless)
T_s	value of surface tension (lb/ft, dyne/cm)
T_v	time factor for vertical drainage (dimensionless)
t	time (sec, min, hour, day, month, year)
U	percentage of consolidation (percent)
u	neutral stress due to water pressure (lb/ft^2, N/m^2; kg/cm^2 has also been used)
V	volume (ft^3, cm^3, m^3)
V, v	velocity (ft/s, m/s)
V	electrical potential difference in soil resistance studies (V, volts)
W	weight (lb, N; gm and kg have also been used)
W	width (ft, m)
W_c	weight of soil on buried conduit (lb/ft of conduit length, kN/meter of conduit length)
W_h	weight of pile hammer ram (lb, ton; N; kg has also been used)
w	water content (percent)
z	depth or vertical distance (ft, m)
α (alpha)	factor expressing ratio of adhesion to cohesion for clay (dimensionless)
α	creep factor used in pressuremeter settlement computations (dimensionless)
β (beta)	soil resistivity (ohm-ft)

β	skin friction factor for piles embedded in clay (dimensionless)
β	steepest safe inclination angle for earth slopes
η (eta)	fluid viscosity, poises $\dfrac{\text{dyne-sec}}{\text{cm}^2}$, $\dfrac{\text{N-sec}}{\text{m}^2}$, $\dfrac{\text{lb-sec}}{\text{ft}^2}$
η	coefficient for silt and clay soils applied when calculating foundation settlement from static cone penetration data (dimensionless)
γ (gamma)	unit weight (lb/ft^3, dynes/cm^3, N/m^3)
γ_{dry}	dry unit weight of soil
γ_{total}, γ_t	total unit weight of soil including water content
γ_{sat}	unti weight of saturated soil
γ_{sub}	submerged unit weight of soil
γ_w	unit weight of water (62.4 pcf, 9.81 kN/m^3, 980 dynes/cm^3)
λ (lambda)	friction coefficient in pile foundation analysis (dimensionless)
λ_c, λ_d	foundation shape factors used in pressuremeter settlement computations (dimensionless)
μ (mu)	micron (one micron = 0.0001 cm)
μ′	coefficient of sliding friction between soil backfill and natural soil in trench construction (dimension)
ν (nu)	poissons ratio
φ (phi)	angle of internal friction (deg)
ρ (rho)	density (kg/m^3, gm/cm^3, slugs/ft^3)
ρ′	used in buried conduit analysis to indicate ratio of conduit vertical projection above trench bottom to the original conduit diameter (dimensionless)
σ (sigma)	normal stress (lb/in.^2, lb/ft^2, kip/ft^2, ton/ft^2, N/m^2; kg/cm^2 has also been used)
σ_1, σ_2, σ_3	principal (normal) stresses (lb/in.^2, lb/ft^2, kip/ft^2, N/m^2; kg/cm^2 has also been used)
σ_h	horizontal stress (lb/ft^2, N/m^2; kg/cm^2 has also been used)
σ_v	vertical stress or overburden stress (lb/ft^2, N/m^2; kg/cm^2 has also been used)
$\bar{\sigma}_v$	effective vertical stress, effective overburden stress (lb/ft^2, N/m^2; kg/cm^2 has also been used)
$\bar{\bar{\sigma}}_v$	effective vertical stress of influence used in pile capacity analysis (lb/ft^2, N/m^2)
σ_{vo}	original overburden stress (lb/ft^2, N/m^2; kg/cm^2 has also been used)
τ (tau)	shear stress (lb/ft^2, N/m^2; kg/cm^2 has also been used)
θ (theta)	inclination angle of inclined foundation or inclined load on footing (deg)
θ	angle of slope in earth dams
tan δ (delta)	coefficient of friction (dimensionless)

## chapter 1

Origin and Characteristics of Soil Deposits

Soil is the material that mankind—from earliest times to the present—has known will influence its survival. Soil is the ground on which we stand. We build with soil. We have relied on soil to support structures and the paths of transportation. We depend on soil to grow our food and provide the products we use for living, protection, and comfort. We have trusted the soil to be stable and permanent. In some of these presumptions, we have been incorrect.

This text studies soil as a material that is used to build with or on, and as a material of the environment that may act in combination with other forces of nature or of civilization to effect structures and landforms; this is the field of *geotechnics*. In this introductory study of geotechnics, the agricultural aspects of soil are not considered, with the exception of discussions relating to vegetation used as a means for erosion control and as a factor influencing the creation of present-day soil types.

The earth's crust is composed of soil and rock. *Rock* can be defined as a natural aggregate of minerals that are connected by strong bonding or attractive forces; for this reason, rock is often considered a consolidated material. *Soil* may be defined as the unconsolidated sediments and deposits of solid particles that have resulted from the disintegration of rock. To the construction industry and the engineering profession, however, soil is also assumed to include the residue of vegetable and animal life, including industrial wastes.

Soil is a *particulate* material, which means that a soil mass consists of an accumulation of individual particles that are bonded together by mechanical or attractive means, though not as strongly as for rock. In soil (and in most rock), voids exist between particles, and the voids may be filled with a liquid, usually water, or a gas, usually air. As a result, soils are often referred to as a three-phase material or system (solids plus liquid plus gas).

ROCK: THE SOURCE OF SOILS

Most of the nonorganic materials that are identified as soil originated from rock as the parent material. Rock types are grouped into three major classes—igneous, sedimentary, or metamorphic—determined by their origin or method of formation. The type of soil that subsequently develops relates to the rock type, its mineral components, and the climatic regime of the area.

Igneous rock resulted from the cooling and hardening of molten rock called *magma,* which originated deep within the earth. Molten magma that escaped to, and near to the surface of the earth through volcanoes and fissures in the earth's crust (termed *lava*) cooled quickly. As a result of rapid cooling, the mineral components solidified in small crystals and possessed a fine interlocking texture. In some situations, the cooling was so rapid that a crystal-free, glassy texture resulted. The molten materials (lava) that cooled rapidly at or near the earth's surface are called extrusive or volcanic rock types and include the *basalts, rhyolites,* and *andesites.*

Molten rock trapped deep below the surface of the earth (magma) cooled slowly. The mineral components formed in large interlocking crystals, and coarse-textured rocks resulted. These rocks are classified as intrusive or plutonic types and include the *granites,* the most common, as well as the *syenites, diorites,* and *gabbros.*

Many of the chemical combinations in igneous rocks are unstable in the environment existing at the earth's surface. Upon exposure to air, water, chemicals in solution in water, freezing temperatures, varying temperatures, and erosive factors, the rock minerals break down to the soil types existing today. Rock whose chief mineral is quartz or orthoclase (potassium feldspar), minerals with high silica content, decomposes to predominantly sandy or gravelly soil with little clay.[1] Granites, syenites, and rhyolites are in this category. Because of the high silica content, these rocks are classified as acidic.

Rocks whose minerals contain iron, magesium, calcium, or sodium, but little silica, such as the gabbros, diabases, and basalts, are classified as basic rocks. These rocks decompose to the fine-textured silt and clay soils.

Generally, the acidic rocks are light-colored, while the basic rocks are very dark. Intermediate colors reflect an intermediate chemical composition. Rock types intermediate between acidic and basic include the *trachytes, diorites,* and *andesites.* Because of their mineral components, diorite and andesite easily break down into the fine-textured soils.

The clay portion of fine-textured soil is the result of primary rock minerals decomposing to form secondary minerals. The clays are *not* small fragments of the

---

[1]According to the engineering definition, coarser soils include sands and gravels and are particles larger than 0.074 mm. The fine-textured silt and clay soils are smaller than 0.074 mm. The 0.074-mm size is close to the smallest particle size observable with the unaided eye under normal conditions. Most clay particles are smaller than 0.002 mm. Chapters 3 and 4 further discuss soil type and classification.

original minerals that existed in the parent rock. Because of this change, the properties and behavior of clay soils are different from the gravel, sand, and silt soils, which *are* still composed of the primary rock minerals.

Rocks that are *acidic* (not *basic*) such as the granites, are considered to be good construction materials.

Sedimentary rocks are formed from accumulated deposits of soil particles or remains of certain organisms that have become hardened by pressure or cemented by minerals. Pressure sufficient to harden or solidify a soil deposit results from the weight of great thicknesses of overlying material. Under this pressure, the deposit is compacted and consolidated, and strong attractive bonds are established. Cementing minerals such as silica, calcium carbonate, and the iron oxides are abundant in soil as a result of rock weathering, and when dissolved in the water circulating through a soil deposit they precipitate out onto the soil particles. Other cementing may be obtained from within the mass by solution or chemical change of materials. Sedimentary-type rocks include the limestones and dolostone (dolomites),[2] shale (claystone, siltstone, mudstone), sandstone, conglomerate, and breccia.

Geologic conditions in past historic times have had a very significant effect on the location and type of sedimentary rocks that exist across North America today. In earliest prehistoric times, most of what is now the United States was under water (Fig. 1-1). Gradually, much of the land rose. Accumulated sediments in these shallow seas eventually became the limestones, shales, and sandstones of today. As a consequence of the layered manner of soil deposition, many sedimentary rocks are easily recognized today because of their stratified appearance (Fig. 1-2).

Shales are formed predominantly from deposited clay and silt particles. The degree of hardness varies, depending on the type of minerals, the bonding that developed, and the presence of foreign materials. The hardness is generally due to external pressures and the particle bonds that resulted, not to cementing minerals. Many shales are relatively stable when exposed to the environment, but some expand or delaminate (the layers separate) after contact with water or air. Weathering breaks down shale to fragments of varying size. These fragments, in turn, may be quickly reduced back to clay-particle sizes. The properties of shale are quite important to the construction industry, for it is estimated that shale represents approximately 50 percent of the rock that is exposed at the earth's surface or closest to the surface under the soil cover. Sound shale can provide a good foundation material. Its use as a construction material is questionable, however, because of its tendency to break down under handling, abuse, and weathering.

Sandstone is predominantly quartz cemented together with mostly silica, but also calcium carbonate, or iron compounds. Sandstones are generally considered good construction materials. *Conglomerate* (cemented sand and gravel) and *breccia* (cemented angular rock fragments) are similar to sandstone.

Limestone is predominantly crystalline calcium carbonate (calcite) formed under water. This rock material forms as a result of chemicals precipitating from

---

[2]Historically, the term *dolomite* has referred to both the rock-forming mineral $CaMg(CO_3)_2$ and sedimentary rock. *Dolostone* is a recent proposal for designating the rock material, to avoid confusion.

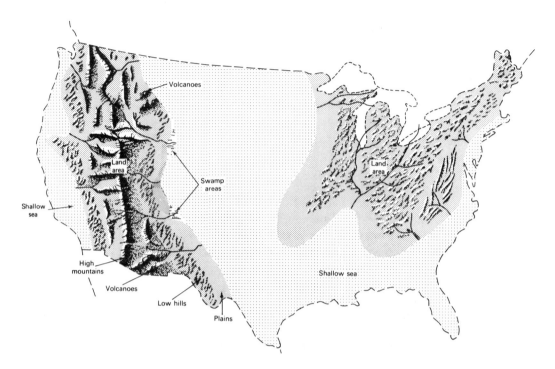

Figure 1-1 Generalized geographic map of the United States for period approximately 100 million years ago. Sediments deposited in shallow seas became sedimentary rock that exists in such areas today. (*Source:* U.S. Department of the Interior, Geological Survey)

Figure 1-2 Sedimentary rock in central New York State showing stratified formation.

solution and from the remains of marine organisms and action of plant life. Because of their sedimentary nature, limestones frequently include impurities such as clays and organic material. The degree of hardness and durability of limestones varies. Some limestone formations are very sound, but some limestones are very soluble with the result that the formation contains many cavities.

Dolostone is a variety of limestone, but harder and more durable. *Marl* and *chalk* are softer forms of limestone.

Weathering of limestones can produce a soil that includes a large range of particle sizes, but the fine-grained soils predominate. Limestone is a good foundation material, provided that the formation is sound and free of cavities. Sound limestone is considered a good construction material.

Frequently, because of the manner of deposition of the original rock-forming sediments, sandstone and shale, or limestone and shale, and sometimes sandstone, limestone, and shale are interbedded.

Metamorphic rock results when any type of existing rock is subject to metamorphism, the changes brought about by combinations of heat, pressure, and plastic flow so that the original rock structure and mineral composition are changed. *Plastic flow* for rock refers to slow viscous movement and rearrangement within the rock mass as it changes and adjusts to the pressures created by external forces. Under these conditions, limestone is changed to *marble,* and sandstone to *quartzite.* When subject to metamorphism, shale is transformed to *slate* or *phyllite.* Higher levels of these factors change the shale, or slate, to *schist.* Because of the processes affecting their formation, slates and schists become foliated rocks (that is, layered as in a folio). *Gneiss* is a foliated rock with distinctive banding that results from the metamorphosis of sedimentary rock or basalt or granite. Despite their possibly different origin, a distinction between gneisses and schists is not always clear. These two rock types on occasion appear to be gradational.

Metamorphic rocks formed from sound igneous or sedimentary rocks can be good materials for construction. But schist, gneiss, and slate are questionable construction materials because the foliated or banded structure can act to originate planes of weakness that affect strength and durability.

Upon weathering, some metamorphic rocks break down to soil types comparable to that which would be derived from the original igneous or sedimentary-type rock. Others reflect the changes brought about by metamorphism. Gneiss and schist decompose to silt–sand mixtures with mica. Soils from slates and phyllites are more clayey. Soils derived from marble are similar to those resulting from limestone. Decomposition of quartzite generally produces sands and gravels.

The processes of rock changing to soil, soil changing to rock, and alteration of rock are continuous and occur simultaneously. The process of change or alteration takes place over long periods of time, and there is no set sequence in which changes occur.

There are many rock types. To establish a proper perspective, the construction industry's concern is generally not with rocks' names but with their properties. In-place properties such as hardness and possible presence of fractures or fissures affect drilling, blasting, and excavation operations. The suitability for use as a foundation for structures is related to strength, durability, and possible presence of cavities or of fractures and fissures. The commercial value of excavated and crushed rock for fill and as an ingredient of concrete is influenced by soundness and durability. In a general way, desirable and undesirable properties have been associated with the different rock types.

SOIL CATEGORIES

Soils can be grouped into two broad categories—residual or transported—depending on the method of deposition.

Residual soils (sedentary soils) have formed from the weathering of rock or accumulation of organic material and remain at the location of their origin. The weathering process may be attributed to mechanical weathering or chemical and solution weathering. Mechanical weathering refers to physical disintegration resulting from the effects of wind, rain, running water, ice and frost wedging, and tectonic forces (earthquakes). Chemical and solution weathering is rock decomposition due to chemical reactions in the rock minerals that occur from exposure to the atmosphere, temperature changes, water, or other materials. Climate topography, drainage, and vegetative cover have great influence on the chemical-solution weathering process. Residual soils are primarily the result of chemical-solution weathering.

In the United States, three geographic areas are known for extensive deposits of residual soils—the Piedmont Province of the Southeast, the Pacific Northwest, and the central states south of the Ohio and Missouri rivers.

Residual soils can include particles having a wide range of sizes, shapes, and composition, depending on the amount and type of weathering and the minerals in the parent rock. However, aged formations typically include a preponderance of fine-grained particles (silt or clay) whose mineral composition and behavioral properties relate to the mineral composition of the parent rock: For example, the clays of the Piedmont have derived from deeply weathered metamorphic rock while the residual clays of the Pacific Northwest and the area south of the Ohio and Missouri rivers have evolved from deeply weathered sedimentary and volcanic rock. The thickness of residual soil existing at any particular location is affected by the rate of rock weathering and the presence or lack of erosive forces to carry the soil away after it is formed. A profile of residual material lying above the unweathered rock often shows the transitional stages of soil formation: Downward from the surficial zone of soil (a material that may bear little mineralogical resemblance to the parent rock), progressively lesser degrees of rock weathering and soil formation exist, until finally the unaltered rock is encountered. See Figure 1-3.

The rate of weathering is generally greater in warm, humid regions than in cool, dry regions. In the tropics, well-drained regions produce lateritic soils (soils with an absence of silica and alkalines, but enriched with iron and aluminum compounds; see Chapter 3), poorly drained areas show a prevalence of dark expansive montmorillonite clay, and andosols (allophanic soil, a soil with an indefinite

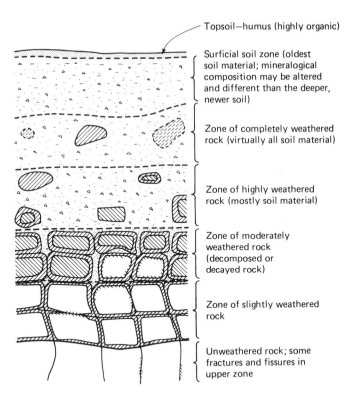

Topsoil—humus (highly organic)

Surficial soil zone (oldest soil material; mineralogical composition may be altered and different than the deeper, newer soil)

Zone of completely weathered rock (virtually all soil material)

Zone of highly weathered rock (mostly soil material)

Zone of moderately weathered rock (decomposed or decayed rock)

Zone of slightly weathered rock

Unweathered rock; some fractures and fissures in upper zone

Figure 1-3 Profile for residual soil area, indicating stages of transition from rock to soil.

mineral composition but rich in silica) develop over volcanic ash and rock. Thick residual soil formations have proved to be prone to landslides in periods of heavy rain fall.

Most residual soils can be used for construction projects, but often some care and special treatment is required. The behavioral properties of disturbed or reworked, wetted then dried, soil may be considerably different from those of undisturbed soil.

Transported soils are those materials that have been moved from their place of origin. Transportation may have resulted from the effects of gravity, wind, water, glaciers, or human activity—either singularly or in combination. Soil particles are often segregated according to size by, or during, the transportation process. The method of transportation and deposition has significant effect on the properties of the resulting soil mass, as discussed in subsequent sections of this chapter.

Gravity and Wind-Transported Soils Gravity is generally capable of transporting minerals only limited distances, such as down a hill or mountain slope, with the result that little change in the soil material is brought about by the transportation procedure.

Wind can move small particles by rolling or carrying them. Soils carried by wind and subsequently deposited are designated *aeolian* deposits. Particles of small sand sizes can be rolled and carried short distances. Accumulations of such wind-deposited sands often form dunes. Dunes are typically characterized by low hill and ridge formation. They generally occur in sandy desert areas and on the down-wind side of bodies of water having sandy beaches. Dune material is a good source of sand for some construction purposes, but if the particles are of uniform size and very weathered and rounded, the sand may not be highly suitable for all construction purposes.

Fine-textured soils, the silts and clays, can be carried great distances by wind. Silt soils in arid regions have no moisture to bond the particles together and are very susceptible to the effects of wind. Clay however, has sufficient bonding or cohesion to withstand the eroding effects of wind. Deposits of wind-blown silts laid down in a loose condition that has been retained because of particle bonding or cementing minerals is classified as *loess*. Significant loess deposits are found in North America, Europe, and Asia (Fig. 1-4a).

In the United States, great thicknesses of loess exist in the vicinity of the Mississippi River and the Missouri River. With these materials, accumulations have built up slowly, and grasses growing at the surface could keep pace with the rate of deposit. The resulting rootholes and grass channels that remain have created a soil that has a high porosity and cleavage in the vertical direction. Natural and man-made cuts in this material will stand with nearly vertical slopes, as illustrated in Figure 1-4b. However, if the soil is exposed to excessive water (becomes saturated or inundated), or is subject to severe ground vibrations, the soil's stable structure can be broken down. Subsidence or settlement results. Consequently, loess formations should be considered as poor foundation soils unless they can be protected from the effects of water and vibrations.

Volcanic eruptions have also produced "wind-transported" soils. The volcanic ashes carried into the air with the escaping gases are small fragments of igneous rock. The soil type expected to result will be related to the mineral characteristics of the igneous rock, as discussed earlier. Generally, remains of volcanic ash deposits are limited. Because of surface deposition, they are quickly affected by weathering agents.

Glacial Deposits Much of Canada and the northern United States in North America, as well as northern Europe and Asia, have been subjected to the past effects of massive moving sheets of ice, the continental glaciers (see Fig. 1-5). The most recent geological period of glaciation is referred to as the Great Ice Age, and scientists estimate that, generally, it covered the span of time extending from about 2 million years ago to about 10,000 years ago. Recent theories supported by evidence consider that extended glaciation occurred periodically even earlier throughout prehistoric times, in cycles apparently related to the significant variation that occurs in the earth's orbit (which gradually varies from nearly circular to elliptical, with the related change in distance between the sun and the earth being approximately 11 million miles), to variations in the tilt of the earth's axis with respect to the plane of the orbit (from about 21.5° to about 24.5°), and to a wobble about the axis of rotation. Conditions conducive to glaciation apparently develop on approximately 100,000-year cycles.

(a)

(b)

Figure 1-4 (a) Major loess deposits of the world (shaded areas); enlargement shows area of loess deposits in central United States. (b) Highway cut through loess deposit in Iowa shows natural vertical cleavage. (*Source:* Courtesy of Dr. H. S. Muskatt, Utica College of Syracuse University)

9

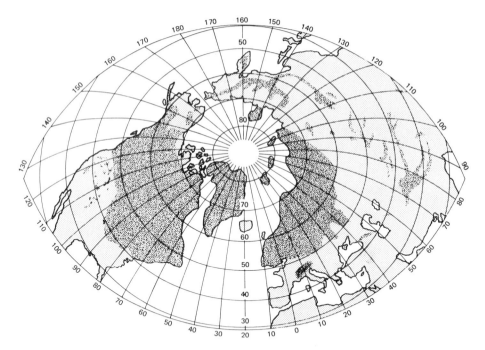

Figure 1-5 Areas of the Northern Hemisphere that have been covered by glacial ice (shaded areas). (*Source:* After Ernst Antevs, "Maps of the Pleistocene Glaciations," Geological Society of America, Bulletin 40, 1929)

The past periods of glaciation resulted in some present-day areas being covered once (Fig. 1-5), whereas some other areas were covered several times. Glaciers expanded and advanced over the land when climatic conditions permitted or contributed to the formation of ice. Glacial advance ceased when melting at its limits equaled the rate of expansion. When, because of climatic or other changes, the rate of melting exceeded the rate of growth, the glaciers receded or shrunk. Generally, glacier expansion or shrinkage and movement were slow. At present, only the polar regions of the planet remain covered by glacial ice, and for the present the condition is considered stable.

Considerable quantities of soil have been moved and deposited by or because of glacial action. Such deposits are referred to as *glacial drift.* But although glaciers moved vast quantities of soil and created a surface topography, the major topographical features such as mountain ranges or plains areas are not the direct result of glaciers. Indirectly, however, major topographical features have very likely been affected by the continental glaciers. The glaciers were several thousand feet thick in many areas, and this had two very significant effects: The tremendous amount of water taken to form the glaciers lowered the level of the sea by some 400–500 ft (125–150 m), and the tremendous weight of the glaciers caused the land beneath them to depress. As a result of the lowering of the sea level, the continental limits of North America extended beyond its current limits. It is probable that much glacially eroded soil was dropped or washed to areas that are now under the sea.

Origin and Characteristics of Soil Deposits   Chap. 1

As a result of the land's being depressed, areas of low elevation were subsequently flooded. After the glaciers retreated and the areas were relieved of their weight, the land rose in elevation. Rock and soil deposits that had been carried to and formed in the low flooded areas rose to create new land surfaces. Many lake areas became diminished in size or disappeared entirely. Great Salt Lake in Utah, for instance, is the shrunken remains of a 20,000-square-mile (50,000-km²) glacial lake that once had a depth in excess of 1000 ft (300 m).

As a glacier grew or advanced, it gathered and pushed soil ahead of it or enveloped and gathered the soil into itself. All sizes of particles were picked up and mixed together, with no sorting according to size. Some of the material picked up was subsequently dropped during the advance, either under the glacier or in front of it, and then overrun by the continued movement. When a glacier advance stopped, soil being pushed by the glacier and soil being freed by the melting process accumulated in front of the glacier. When the glacier receded, all soil trapped in the melting ice was dropped. Such direct glacial deposits are a heterogeneous mixture of all soil sizes and are termed *glacial till.*

The land form or topographic surface resulting after a glacier receded is called a *ground moraine* or *till plain.* The hills and ridges of till that formed at the front of the glacier and marked its farthest advance are *terminal moraines* (Fig. 1-6). *Recessional moraines* are hills or ridges that represent deposits along the front of a glacier where it made temporary stops during the recession process. (Long Island, located in the northeastern United States, illustrates such a glacial landform of geographical importance;[3] the western segment provides approximately half the land area for New York City, and the island houses one of the world's highest population densities.) Debris dropped along the side of a glacier as it moved through a valley is termed a *lateral moraine.* Long low hills of till that extend in the direction of the glacial movement are called *drumlins.*

Where the till material was dropped under the glacier and overrun, it became very dense and compact, and can provide excellent foundation support. The suitability of a till material for construction purposes, such as for a compacted earth fill, depends on the quantity and range of sizes of the soil particles; till deposits that have a preponderance of coarse particles are good construction materials, whereas deposits containing large percentages of silt and clay materials are, generally, relatively difficult to handle and compact.

Where an area was subjected to repeated glacial action, early deposits could be overlain by the more recent glacial till, or the original deposits may have been moved and redeposited by the more recent glacier as a new landform. As a result, the original source of a material may be difficult to determine. In some situations, however, the color may provide information about its source. With reference to glacial deposits in the northern United States, material gathered by glaciers from the Hudson Bay area in Canada is gray, whereas soils picked up from glaciers

[3]Present-day Long Island is actually the result of two glacial actions, one forming the eastern or outer section (Ronkonkoma Ridge) and the other forming the western or inner section (Harbor Hill Ridge).

(a)

(b)

Figure 1-6 (a) The development of a terminal moraine and outwash plain in front of a glacier; (b) aerial photo of glacier showing developing moraine and outwash area.

Origin and Characteristics of Soil Deposits   Chap. 1

originating in the area northwest of the Great Lakes are red in color as a result of the high iron content in the original soils of that area.

Even while the glaciers covered a land area, there were streams and rivers of water flowing on the surface of the glaciers and in subterranean tunnels eroded within the glaciers. These flowing bodies of water carried material picked up from the land surface or eroded from the glaciers (Fig. 1-7). Some such soil was ultimately carried to the front of the glacier, but much was also dropped along the routes of flow and where the water became trapped within the glacier or between a glacier and valley wall.

Soils deposited by the surface and subsurface glacial rivers, to remain in the form of long winding ridges (Fig. 1-8), are called *eskers*. These deposits, sorted and stratified, are usually mostly coarse-grained. The range of particle sizes can vary considerably in cross-section or over short distances, however. Nevertheless, eskers can provide a good source of coarse-grained soils for construction purposes, but the uniformity of gradation should not be expected to be consistent at different locations within the esker. Eskers frequently followed along locations of low ground elevation, such as river valleys. As a result, they often represent paths of good foundation soils across areas where poor soil deposits, such as fine-grained soil sediments or marshes, have subsequently accumulated. Such paths of coarse-grained soils ideally suit the requirements for highway subgrades because of their good drainage characteristics, low susceptibility to frost heave, and ease of handling during the construction process.

Kames provide soil deposits somewhat similar to eskers; they are the remains of material dropped along the boundaries of a glacier and a valley wall (kame terrace), or in holes in a glacier. The resulting landform has the shape of knobs or small hills. As with eskers, the gradation of soils from kames should be expected to be variable.

In some areas where kame terraces and outwash plains exist, the surface topography is further affected by depressions called *kettle holes*. Kettle holes apparently formed when great blocks of ice remained after a glacier receded and became buried by the glacial soil. When the ice melted, a hole or depression in the soil surface resulted. When water-filled, the depressions are *kettle lakes*.

Figure 1-7 Flowing water on a glacier and resulting effect on landform.

Soil Categories   **13**

Figure 1-8 Esker, a ridgelike deposit of granular soil at the location of a former glacial river. (*Source:* Courtesy of Thomas D. Maneen)

River Deposits Flowing bodies of water are capable of moving considerable volumes of soil by carrying the particles in suspension or by rolling, sliding, and skipping them along the river bottom. The largest-diameter particle that can be carried in suspension is related to the square of the velocity of the flowing water. Coarser particles being carried in suspension are dropped when a decrease in the water velocity occurs, as when the river deepens, widens, or changes direction. Finer particles remain in suspension to be deposited in quieter waters. Thus, river deposits are segregated according to size. For most rivers the volume of water that flowed and the volume of soil that was transported were variables that changed as land drainage forms changed or as seasonal variations in precipitation occurred.

All soils carried and deposited by rivers are classified as *alluvial deposits*. However, glacial soils carried by rivers created from melting glacial waters and subsequently sorted and dropped according to size to create deposits of stratified glacial drift are referred to as *glaciofluvial deposits* or *stratified drift*.

Glacially created rivers were developed from water escaping at the edge of a glacier or from trapped water breaking through a recessional moraine left by a receding glacier. Upon leaving the glacier or moraine area, the flowing water rapidly fanned out over a broad area of land, temporarily flooding it. With the resulting decrease in the flow velocity, the larger soil particles dropped out, forming fan- or delta-shaped flat beds of predominantly sand and gravel soils. Overlapping deltas of coarse soils spread over broad areas create land forms classified as *outwash plains* (see Fig. 1-6). The finer soil particles remained in suspension in the escaping water. Subsequently these too settled out where the velocity of flow slowed or the water became ponded.

At locations where a heavily loaded natural or glacial river broadened or encountered flatter terrain so that its velocity decreased, coarse soil particles dropped out to form submerged spreading triangular-shaped deposits termed *alluvial fans*. The alluvial fans are good sources of sand and gravel for construction purposes.

Rivers flowing through broad flat valleys have often overflowed their banks during periods of flooding. When this occurred, the overflow velocity quickly diminished, and the heavier gravel and sand particles dropped out in the vicinity of the bank, forming low ridges termed *natural levees*. The broad lowland areas on either side of the river were also flooded over, but the materials dropped in the areas were the finer-grained soils. These are *floodplain deposits* (Fig. 1-9).

Where rivers bend or curve to change direction, the velocity of the flowing water can vary considerably between the inside and outside edges of the curve. These natural curves are called *meander bends*. Erosion may take place along the outside, while deposition takes place on the inside. The deposits are the coarser soils, generally sorted according to size. Constant erosion along the outside of a bend while the inside is being built up with sediments causes the river to migrate laterally. The old river locations provide good sources of coarse soils for construction and are good foundation sites.

When a river shortcuts a large bend when eroding a new route, the old channel left behind is cut off from new flow, and the trapped water forms an *oxbow lake* (Fig. 1-10). Such lakes eventually fill with predominantly fine-grained soils carried by low-velocity flood waters or surface runoff. These areas become poor foundation sites.

Lake areas were created in natural basins in the topography or, in glacial areas, in depressed reservoirs created between a terminal (or recessional) moraine and a retreating glacier. Natural lakes and glacial lakes often covered vast areas of land. The coarsest soil particles (sands) carried by rivers feeding into the lake would fall out of suspension quickly after entering the lake area because of the sharp decrease of velocity. Such coarse soil deposits, termed *lake deltas* because of the resulting shape of the deposit, are good sources of sand and gravel for construction purposes. Fine-grained particles remained in suspension and were carried to the body of the lake, where they eventually settled out. The larger particles (fine sand and silt) settled out first, while the smaller particles (clay) continued to remain in suspension. After the waters in the lake quieted, as in

Figure 1-9 Cross-section of floodplain deposit.

Soil Categories

Figure 1-10 Aerial photo of meandering river and forming oxbow lakes.

Origin and Characteristics of Soil Deposits   Chap. 1

Alternate layering of silt and clay soil (**varied** clays) in qiuet lake area

Stream or river flow feeding lake

Gravel and coarse sand deposited in river bed

Sands (deposited close to lake shore)

Clays   Silts   Silt and fine sand

Figure 1-11 Cross-section of soil deposits in a lake area, indicating typical alternate layering of silt and clay soil.

periods of little or no flow into the lake, the clay settled out. Alternating layers of these fine-grained deposits built up as the variation of water flowing into the lake area continued (Fig. 1-11). If the lake area were extremely large, the coarser silt particles might settle out in areas close to the shore while the clays settled out in the quiet central areas of the lake. Frequently, the basin eventually filled with soil, or drained and left the lake deposit if the trapped water found or eroded an outlet. Soil formations remaining at the locations of former lake areas are termed *lacustrine deposits*. When layers are less than one cm in thickness, the sediments are described as *laminated*. Deposits of such fine sand–silt and clay layering are termed *laminated clay*. Laminations that have been deposited over a one-year period are *varves*. Unless such lake sediments were subject to the weight of a new glacier during a new glacial advance or to other overburden pressures, they are weak and compressible and make poor foundations. However, the deltas of coarse soils dropped when the flowing waters entered the lake area provide good foundation support and soils for construction use.

At some former glacial lake locations, the silt–clay soil near the surface has become firm because of drying (desiccation). This can give the illusion of a strong deposit with good foundation capabilities. Such an area may be suitable for carrying roadways and light structures, but foundations for larger and heavier structures generally cannot be satisfactorily supported.

In some areas where flowing waters carried fine-grained soils to ocean or sea water areas, some types of clay particles flocculated in the presence of the salt water.[4] The silt and clay then settled out of suspension at about the same rate, creating deposits of *marine clays*. Despite their classification, marine clays may actually consist of more silt than clay. The marine clays are typically gray or blue-gray in color. Frequently, these deposits contain the shells or remains of shells from marine life. Much of the seaboard area of the northeastern United States and southeastern Canada has such deposits. Because of the method of deposition, marine clay deposits are generally weak and compressible, and are therefore poor foundation materials. Where the land covered by the marine clays has subsequently elevated to be above sea level, there is an additional danger that the sodium (from the seawater) that reacted with the clays to cause them to flocculate may have

[4]Flocculation may be defined as the development of an attraction between and bonding of individual particles to form larger particles.

Soil Categories   **17** been leached from the soil by percolating rainwater. The result is that the clays suffer a loss in strength and become sensitive to disturbance, and land areas that had been stable become unstable.

Beach Deposits   Ocean beach deposits are predominantly sand materials, and are constantly being changed by the erosive and redistributing effects of currents and wave action. These same curents and wave action keep silt and clay particles in suspension and carry them to the deeper, quieter, offshore areas, where they eventually settle out. Long ridges of sand that form slightly offshore are termed *bars* (Fig. 1-12). When the formation that develops includes two or more submerged ridges, they are *longshore bars*. Such deposits have been built up by the breaking waves. When a small exposed ridge forms offshore from a gently sloping beach, the formation is termed an *offshore bar* or *island bar* (also called barrier beach or barrier island). A *barrier bar* is a depoist that almost completely blocks the entrance to a bay. A sand or sand–gravel accumulation that is connected to the shore and extends into open water like a finger is a *spit*.

Marine sands are somewhat rounded and smooth, particularly the larger particles, and the deposit at a particular location may consist of particles of uniform size. Such factors, plus the corrosion potential due to salinity, may affect their usefulness for certain construction purposes, such as making quality concrete. Generally, however, such sands are potentially good sources of materials for construction purposes, particularly for waterfront and marine structures, because excavation is generally uncomplicated and transportation will be economical if barges or hydraulic pumping techniques (through pipelines) can be used.

Swamp and Marsh Deposits   Swamps and marshes develop in stagnated areas where limited depths of water accumulate, or where periodic inundation and drying occurs because of fluctuations in the groundwater level, and where vegetation has the chance to grow. The soils that subsequently form on the surface of swamp areas are generally of high organic content (from the decaying vegetation)

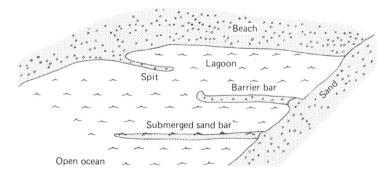

Figure 1-12   Types of sandbar deposits along a shoreline.

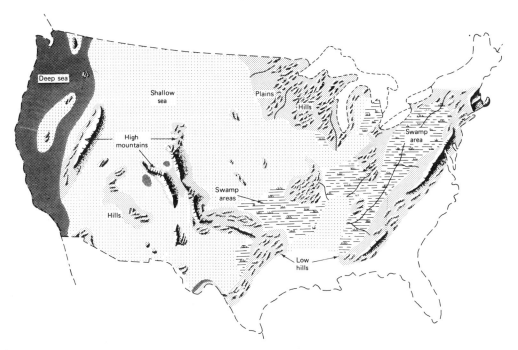

Figure 1-13 Generalized paleogeographic map of the United States approximately 200 million years ago, indicating extensive swamp areas that subsequently formed into coal deposits. (*Source:* U.S. Department of the Interior, Geological Survey)

and soft and odoriferous. Accumulations of decomposed or partially decomposed aquatic plants in swamp or marsh areas are termed *muck* or *peat*. Muck, geologically older than peat, is almost fully decomposed vegetation and is relatively dense. Peat includes partially decomposed vegetation and is normally spongy and relatively light. These materials are generally weak and highly compressible. Muck or peat deposits may be buried beneath the ground surface if the marsh area is subsequently overlain by glacial or alluvial materials. Peat has been used as a fuel in many areas of the world.

In an early geologic period of time, when much of the present United States was covered over by shallow seas, an eastern section of the continent was generally a low swampy area where heavy vegetation flourished (Fig. 1-13). Because of subsequent geologic changes, these lush forest areas slowly became flooded and covered over. While they were being destroyed, however, vast accumulations of partially decomposed forest vegetation were also being deposited. Subsequently, heat and pressure due to depth of burial changed these deposits to the extensive coal beds found throughout Pennsylvania, West Virginia, Tennessee, Illinois, and Kentucky.

For a summary and overview of the interrelationships between rock and soil formations, see Table 1-1.

TABLE 1-1 SUMMARY AND OVERVIEW: INTERRELATIONSHIP BETWEEN ROCK AND SOIL FORMATIONS

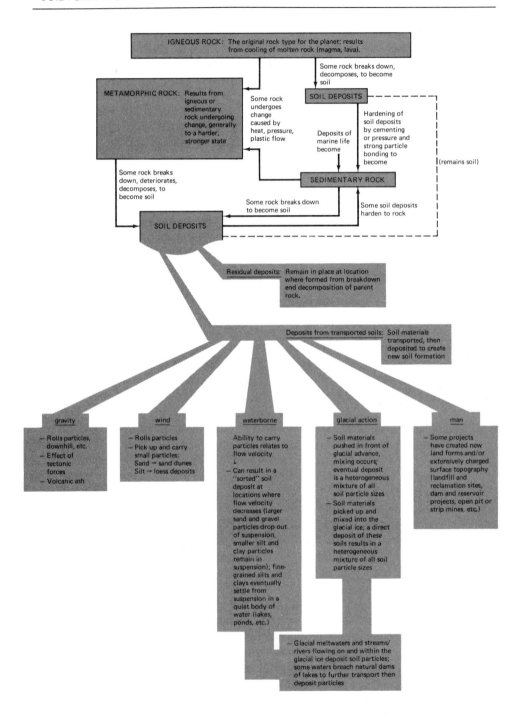

PLATE TECTONICS

The theory of plate tectonics deals with the development, formation, and changes occurring to the earth's land and ocean areas on a long-term, large-scale basis. Plate tectonics relates to the recent recognition that the outer shell of the earth is made up of a small number of large, thick plates that mesh together like pieces of a gigantic puzzle (see Fig. 1-14), but that also move somewhat independently of each other. Continents and oceans are carried (float) on these plates. The phenomenon of plate movement has had a profound effect on what constitutes today's continents, including the type and location of rock and soil materials, mineral deposits, and animal and plant life. Very significantly, areas near plate boundaries coincide with the most active earthquake and volcanic regions of the world.

In macroscopic terms, the earth's interior consists of a core, mantle, and outer crust, concentrically zoned, as depicted by Figure 1-15. The uppermost region of the mantle possesses properties important to the plate tectonics theory. The outer zone, ranging from about 70 to 150 km thick and termed the *lithosphere* (rock sphere), consists of dense and hard brittle rock materials. Generally, the lithosphere is thickest beneath continental mountain masses. Underlying the lithosphere is a 200- to 250-km thick zone of dense, semisolid, or plastic rock material termed the *asthenosphere* (weak rock). The rock materials making up the lithosphere and asthenosphere actually are similar, with the demarcation between zones being established on the basis of a difference in condition. Material in the lower asthenosphere increases in hardness and rigidity, grading to become the more solid material characteristic of the deeper mantle.

Continental and ocean crusts of relatively light density rock material (in comparison to the rock material of the mantle) top the lithosphere. The crust underlying continental areas is thicker and less dense than oceanic crust; continental crust ranges from about 20 to 60 km in thickness (thickest beneath mountain areas), whereas ocean crust is generally on the order of 10 km thick.

The areal boundaries of the shell-like plates are the result of discontinuities or fractures that have developed in the lithosphere. At some locations, these plates of lithosphere are moving apart (diverging); at other regions the plates are moving toward each other (converging) or sliding past each other. The plates are rigid and tend to not change shape with time. Changes result only at zones where convergence or divergence occurs; the process of plate convergence and divergence will be described in later paragraphs.

The causes of plate movement are not known, but it has been hypothesized that regions of the asthenosphere and underlying mantle are in motion because of a temperature difference between the earth's core zone and the outer mantle (similar to the way heated air moves by convection through a cool room), with the lithosphere being carried along by the asthenosphere. What *is* established is that the plates of lithosphere have been in motion for a long period of the earth's history, and that the plates have been moving relative to each other.

Continental and ocean crusts atop the lithosphere move with the lithosphere. The position and orientation of continent-supporting plates has been changing with respect to other continental plates and with respect to location on the earth's

Figure 1-14 Major plates of the lithosphere and general direction of movement. (*Source:* After J. F. Dewey, "Plate Tectonics," copyright May 1972 by Scientific American, Inc. All rights reserved.)

———— Ridge axis

———|—— Transform

▲▲▲ Subduction zone

- - - - Uncertain plate boundary

——→ Direction of plate motion

22

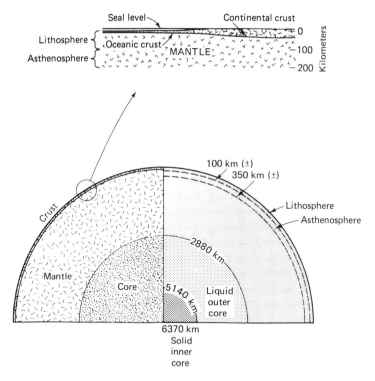

Figure 1-15 Cross-section depicting composition of the earth (numerical distances indicate approximate depths from the earth's surface).

surface. Similarly, ocean areas have been changing; some of these changes have been so extensive that oceans have been both created and destroyed. Figure 1-16 illustrates the relative position of continental areas and oceans through the past 200-million-year period, and an expectation for the future.

A *rift* develops where plates of lithosphere are moving apart, creating the condition where molten rock from the asthenosphere rises to create new lithosphere and crust; volcanism is involved. Plate divergence and the creation of new lithosphere in ocean ridge zones may be referred to as *sea-floor spreading*. Plate boundaries identified as *ridges* and *rises* (Fig. 1-14) represent locations where plates are spreading apart. Most of the currently known locations of major plate divergence occur in what is now ocean area. It is likely that early in the earth's history the spreading of some plates began under continental areas, but the widening separations filled with shallow crust, had low surface elevation, and were flooded over.

The surface area of the earth remains approximately constant with time. The creation of new lithosphere where plates diverge must be balanced by an equivalent loss of lithosphere at other plate boundaries. Such losses occur at locations where plates converge, by having one plate subduct (dip) below the other. The subducted section of lithosphere passes into or through the asthenosphere, where it is absorbed. Boundaries where subduction occurs are identified as *trenches* in Figure

Plate Tectonics

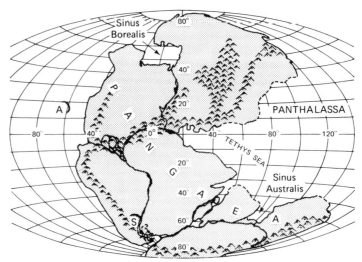

Figure 1-16 Location and position of continents and oceans over past 200-million-year period, on basis of plate movements. (*Source:* After R. S. Dietz and J. C. Holden, "The Breakup of Pangaea," copyright October 1970 by Scientific American, Inc. All rights reserved.) (a) Universal land mass pangaea may have looked like this 200 million years ago. Panthalassa was the ancestral Pacific Ocean. The Tethys Sea (the ancestral Mediterranean) formed a large bay separating Africa and Eurasia. The Appalachian, Alps, and Ural mountain ranges were already ancient by this time. The Rockies and Andes were in existence, but were relatively young. These ranges probably developed as a result of collisions between continental plates predating pangaea (plates are shown lightly shaded).

(b) After 20 million years of drift (180 million years ago), the northern group of continents, collectively known as Laurasia, has split away from the southern group, known as Gondwana. The latter has started to break up: India has been set free by a Y-shaped rift, which has also begun to isolate the Africa–South America land mass from Antarctica–Australia. The Tethyan trench (hatched lines in black), a zone of crustal uptake, runs from Gibralter to the general area of Borneo. Black lines and black arrows denote megashears, zones of slippage along plate boundaries. The white arrows indicate the vector motions of the continents since drift began.

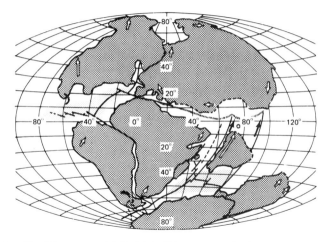

(c) After 65 million years of drift (135 million years ago), the North Atlantic and the Indian Ocean have opened considerably. The birth of the South Atlantic has been initiated by a rift. The rotation of the Eurasian land mass has begun to close the eastern end of the Tethys Sea. The Indian plate continues its northerly movement.

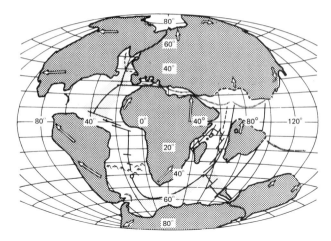

(d) After 135 million years of drift (65 million years ago), the South Atlantic has widened into a major ocean. A new rift has carved Madagascar away from Africa. The rift in the North Atlantic has switched from the west side to the east side of Greenland. The Mediterranean Sea is clearly recognizable. Australia still remains attached to Antarctica. An extensive north–south trench (not shown) must also have existed in the Pacific to absorb the westward drift of the North American and South American plates.

1-14. Ocean crust will be carried along when its supporting plate of lithosphere is being subducted, but continental crust does not subduct because of its light density; ocean crust is thus destroyed by subduction and created where plate divergence occurs, but continental crusts tend to be permanent.

Boundaries where plate edges slide past each other are classified as *transform*

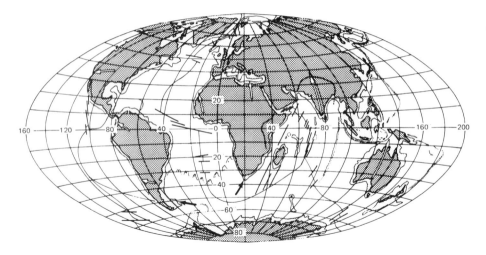

(e) World as it looks today was produced in the past 65 million years. Nearly half of the Atlantic Ocean floor was created in this geologically brief period. India completed its flight northward by colliding with Asia, and a rift has separated Australia from Antarctica. The North Atlantic rift finally entered the Arctic Ocean, fissioning Laurasia. The Antilles and Scotia area now occupy their proper positions with respect to neighboring land masses. Extrapolation indicates that, 50 million years into the future, the Atlantic (particularly the South Atlantic) and the Indian Ocean will continue to grow at the expense of the Pacific. Australia will drift northward and begin rubbing against the Eurasian plate. The eastern portion of Africa will split off. Baja California and a sliver of California west of the San Andreas fault will be severed from North America, to begin drifting to the northwest.

faults. Such locations are identified as faults on Figure 1-14. Surface area is neither created nor destroyed at such plate edges.

When two plates carrying continental crust converge, a subduction of one lithosphere plate occurs, but its continental crust is too lightweight and thick to be carried along. The result is that the two continental masses stay afloat but undergo a condition of collision over a sustained period, causing the crust material to fold slowly, accordion style, and giving rise to a mountain range (for instance, the Himalayas). Regions near the boundary where two continent-supporting plates converge are earthquake zones but are not volcanically active. Earthquakes relate to the quick release of strains (deformations) that build up within the lithosphere and crust as a result of the plate sections moving past each other.

Where two ocean plates converge, or where an ocean plate dips below a plate carrying continental crust, the boundary region becomes an area of active volcanism and earthquake (for instance, the Andes Mountains of South America). Apparently the volcanic activity relates to the surface breakthrough of a rising, relatively low-density magma, which is created when ocean crust, carried into the asthenosphere on the lithosphere plate being subducted, melts (Fig. 1-17). Mountain ranges near the boundary where a continental plate overrides a subducting oceanic plate, such as the Andes, may be the product of volcanism, or the result of horizontal compression and folding that continental crust experiences because of the plate convergence.

Transform faults occur at plate boundaries originally created by divergence or convergence. The sliding of one plate past another causes earthquake activity but no volcanism. Transform faults develop where a section of plate boundary is aligned with the general direction of the plate's movement. At some locations the fault is of great length—for example, the San Andreas fault near the west coast of the United States. More prevalently, however, numerous limited segments of transform fault are incorporated into the plate boundaries of the ocean ridges and rises identified in Figure 1-14, a condition brought about by the irregular fracturing of lithosphere where plate spreading is taking place.

Recent evidence suggests that plate movement does not occur at a steady state, as was earlier believed. New crust formed along rift boundaries assumes the north–south magnetism in effect at the time molten magma cools. It has been established that, for reasons as yet unexplained, the magnetism of the earth has reversed numerous times during the planet's existence—170 times in the last 76 million years: These changes in magnetic direction might be related to the cyclic large variations in the earth's orbit discussed in the section on "Glacial Deposits," pages 8–13. Variations found in the width and directional magnetism of the bands of new crust adjacent to ocean rifts provide a reference to the past rate of

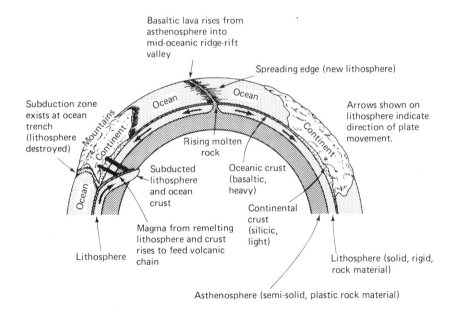

Figure 1-17 Movement of lithospheric plates—plate divergence and plate subduction.

plate movement. The causes of plate acceleration and deceleration are not yet understood. The movements of the major plates are related, whereby the plates speed up or slow down together. Of significance, volcanic activity and the mountain building process increases during the periods of plate acceleration. In the past, apparently each period of acceleration and deceleration extended over several millions of years. The earth is probably in a session of accelerated plate movement at the present time.

The plate tectonic theory assumes that the various geologic processes associated with the formation of rock and soil materials as discussed in the early part of this chapter have been ongoing simultaneously with plate movements. If we recognize that the global position of a continent influences the conditions and forces of nature that the land becomes subjected to, such as climate, including temperature and moisture; effects of oceans if nearby, including chances of inundation; and exposure to glacial, volcanic, and earthquake activity, it becomes evident that much of the earth's currently existing rock and soil represents the influence of plate movements.

EFFECT ON DESIGN AND CONSTRUCTION

Many large land areas have been formed with soils deposited primarily by one of the transportation methods described in this chapter. One area may be underlain by glacially deposited soils, another by lake or marine deposits, another by river deposits.

It is not unusual, however, to have stratification of soils that have been deposited by different methods. For instance, a glacial till may be covered with a glacial outwash or other alluvium. Soft lake deposits are known to exist over compact glacial till or river deposits of sands and gravels. Coarse soil alluvium may overlie soft lake deposits or marine clays. In areas that have been subjected to repeated glaciation, stratification of different types of glacially transported soils having different properties can exist. The result is that loose or soft soils may overlie compact or firm soils, and vice versa.

In areas blanketed by residual soil, the character of the material will vary with depth, and both depth and properties can vary across limited horizontal distances. A residual soil formation may be covered by a transported soil, or reduced by erosive and other transportive forces.

The type and condition of soil deposits underlying any proposed construction site must be an important consideration to the engineering and construction personnel concerned with the project, for it is the soil, or rock, that provides the support for the structure. Proper design for a structure includes investigation and evaluation of soil conditions underlying the proposed structure. However, knowledge of geology and the manner in which land forms and the soils in them have been created, as discussed throughout this chapter, can frequently serve to provide a preliminary evaluation of an area and the potential advantages or problems.

PROBLEMS

1-1. Name the three main classes of rock and describe how they originated.

1-2. What factor of formation most influences the texture of igneous rocks?

1-3. What visual properties can frequently be used to distinguish between acidic rocks and basic rocks?

1-4. Describe the two typical processes that occur to transform soil sediments into sedimentary rock.

1-5. What processes occur to cause metamorphosis of rocks?

1-6. What type of bedrock formations would be thought to offer good foundation support for structures? What types would be more suspect of being possible poor bedrock materials?

1-7. What are loess soils and what is the potential danger of loss of stability in loess deposits?

1-8. Indicate the soil types to be expected in a glacial terminal moraine.

1-9. Indicate why sand or gravel deposits are frequently found along old river and stream locations.

1-10 What effect does the shape of a channel have on stream flow and the related carried or deposited soil sediments?

1-11. How do natural levees originate? What is the major soil type expected in a natural levee?

1-12. What soil types would be expected in a river or stream delta?

1-13. Describe the process by which a glacial lake is formed.

1-14. How can lakes exist at elevations above the ground water table?

1-15. Why are naturally filled-in lake locations often thought of as areas that offer poor support for building foundations?

1-16. How do eskers differ from drumlins with regard to formation and soil types?

1-17. In glacially affected areas, what type of glacial formations represent possible good sources of sands and gravels for the construction industry?

1-18. Does an area covered by glacial till represent a location of advantage or disadvantage to the building and construction industry?

1-19. Do soils typical of beach deposits represent any advantage or disadvantage to the building and construction industry?

1-20. What is the potential danger to stability in areas where the land is formed from marine clays?

1-21. On the basis of known lithosphere plate boundaries:
   (a) Identify the major continental areas likely to experience earthquakes in the future.
   (b) Identify the continental areas likely to experience active volcanic activity in the future.

chapter *2*

Soil Composition
Terminology and Definitions

Soil deposits comprise the accumulated solid particles of soil or other materials plus the void spaces that exist between the particles. The void spaces are partially or completely filled with water or other liquid. Void spaces not occupied by fluid are filled with air or other gas. Since the volume occupied by a soil bulk may generally be expected to include material in the three states of matter—solid, liquid, and gas—soil deposits are referred to as three-phase systems.

Significant engineering properties of a soil deposit, such as strength and compressibility, are directly related to or at least affected by basic factors such as how much volume or weight of a bulk soil is solid particles or water or air. Information such as soil density (weight per unit volume),[1] water content, void ratio, degree of saturation—terms defined in the following sections—is used in calculations to determine the bearing capacity for foundations, to estimate foundation settlement, and to determine the stability of earth slopes. In other words, such information helps to define the condition of a soil deposit for its suitability as a foundation or construction material. For this reason, an understanding of the terminology and definitions relating to soil composition is fundamental to the study of soil mechanics.

---

[1]In soil mechanics, the term *density* has frequently been used to indicate unit weight—that is, pounds per cubic foot. For the metric system, unit weights should be expressed as dynes per cubic centimeter, whereas kilonewtons per cubic meter are used with the SI system.

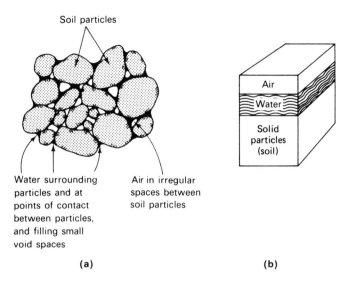

Soil particles

Water surrounding
particles and at
points of contact
between particles,
and filling small
void spaces

Air in irregular
spaces between
soil particles

Air

Water

Solid
particles
(soil)

(a)

(b)

Figure 2-1 (a) Actual soil bulk consisting of soil particles, water, and air; (b) phase diagram representation of soil bulk.

SOIL COMPOSITION: ANALYTICAL REPRESENTATION

Bulk soil as it exists in nature is a more or less random accumulation of soil particles, water, and air space, as shown in Figure 2-1a. For purposes of study and analysis it is convenient to represent this soil mass by a phase or block diagram, with part of the diagram representing the solid particles, part representing water or other liquid, and another part air or other gas, as shown in Figure 2-1b.

Weight–Volume, Mass–Volume Relationship On the phase diagram, the interrelationships of weight and mass to the volume that make up the soil system being analyzed can be shown. The relationships are summarized in Figure 2-2.

As the diagram shows, the total *weight* W_T of the soil volume is taken as the sum of the weight of solids W_s plus water W_w. In practical problems, all weighings

Figure 2-2 Relationship between volume and weight/mass of a soil bulk.

are made in air, and the weight of air (in the voids) measured in air (the earth's atmosphere) is zero. If the gas is other than air, it may have a measurable weight, but it would normally be very small compared to the total weight of soil plus water and therefore can be neglected without causing serious error.

$$W_T = W_s + W_w \qquad (2\text{-}1a)$$

Similarly, for measurement of mass

$$M_T = M_s + M_w \qquad (2\text{-}1b)$$

The total *volume* of the soil bulk includes the volume occupied by solids plus water (or liquid) plus air (or other gas). The total space occupied by water and air may collectively be indicated as the volume of voids.

$$V_T = V_s + V_w + V_a = V_s + V_v \qquad (2\text{-}2)$$

where V_T = total volume.
  V_s = volume of soil solids.
  V_w = volume of water.
  V_a = volume of air.
  V_v = volume of voids.

The relationship between weight and volume, for any material (x), is

$$W_x = V_x G_x \gamma_w \qquad (2\text{-}3a)$$

while for mass and volume

$$M_x = V_x G_x \rho_w \qquad (2\text{-}3b)$$

where W_x = weight of the material (solid, liquid, or gas).
  V_x = volume occupied by the material.
  G_x = specific gravity of the material, a dimensionless value.
  γ_w = unit weight of water at the temperature to which the problem refers. (In most soils work, γ_w is usually taken as 62.4 pcf, 980 dynes/cm³ or 9.81 kN/m³ regardless of temperature. In experimental work, accurate values are used.)[2]
  M_x = mass of the material.
  ρ_w = density of water, 1 gm/cm³, 1 Mg/m³ or 1.95 slugs/ft³ (note 1 slug = 1 lb-sec²/ft).

---

[2]The gram is a unit of mass, whereas the pound is a unit of weight or force. A value of grams per cubic centimeter is density (by definition, density is mass per unit volume and is given the symbol ρ). Unit weight is force or weight per unit volume. Unit weight and density are therefore *not* identical, but they are related by the expression $\gamma = \rho g$, where g is the acceleration of gravity. In soil mechanics work the terms are often taken to have synonymous meaning. Since comparative values of unit weight of density are normally sought to relate to other properties, this practice does not cause complications. To overcome this discrepancy between γ and ρ, unit weights based on a gram measurement can be expressed as gram-force (gf) per unit volume.

For soil mechanics problems, then,

$$W_s = V_s G_s \gamma_w \tag{2-4a}$$

$$M_s = V_s G_s \rho_w \tag{2-4b}$$

$$W_w = V_w G_w \gamma_w = V_w \gamma_w \quad \text{since } G_w = 1 \tag{2-5a}$$

$$M_w = V_w G_w \rho_w = V_w \rho_w \tag{2-5b}$$

The specific gravity of most commonly occurring rock or soil materials is between 2.30 and 3.10. For many deposits, the specific gravity of soil solids lies within the range of 2.60 to 2.75.

BASIC TERMS RELATING TO SOIL COMPOSITION AND CONDITION

The unit weight of a soil γ is conventionally expressed as pounds per cubic foot, or kilonewtons per cubic meter. Unit weights are reported as wet unit weight γ_{wet} or dry unit weight γ_{dry}:

$$\text{Wet unit weight,} \quad \gamma_{wet} = \frac{W_T}{V_T} \text{ (pcf, kN/m}^3) \tag{2-6a}$$

$$\text{Dry unit weight,} \quad \gamma_{dry} = \frac{W_s}{V_T} \text{ (pcf, kN/m}^3) \tag{2-6b}$$

From the definition, it can be seen that the wet unit weight includes the weight of water as well as soil particles in a soil volume. The dry unit weight is based on only the weight of soil solids in the soil mass.

Soil density, ρ, expressed in kilograms per cubic meter or grams per cubic centimeter, also can be in terms of a wet or dry value, whereby

$$\text{Wet density,} \quad \rho_{wet} = \frac{M_T}{V_T} \text{ (kg/m}^3, \text{gm/cm}^3) \tag{2-7a}$$

$$\text{Dry density,} \quad \rho_{dry} = \frac{M_s}{V_T} \text{ (kg/m}^3, \text{gm/cm}^3) \tag{2-7b}$$

To relate a value given in grams per cubic centimeter (i.e., density) to pounds per cubic foot (i.e., unit weight), multiply by 62.4.*

By definition, water content w is the ratio of the weight of water in a soil

---

*Note 1 gm/cm^3 is the equivalent of 62.4 lb/ft^3. Since $W = mg$, the weight for one gram of mass is: $W = (1 \text{ gm})(980 \text{ cm/sec}^2) = 980$ dynes (where 1 dyne $= 10^{-5}$ N $= 0.2248 \times 10^{-5}$ lb, and 980 dynes $= .002203$ lb). Therefore, the weight for one cm^3 of water is 980 dynes $= 0.00203$ lb/cm^3, and the weight for one ft^3 of water $= (.002203 \text{ lb/cm}^3)(28,317 \text{ cm}^3/\text{ft}^3) = 62.4$ lb/ft^3.

volume to the weight of soil solids, or of the mass of water in a soil to the mass of solids.

$$w\% = \frac{W_w}{W_s} \times 100\% \quad \text{or} \quad \frac{M_w}{M_s} \times 100\% \qquad (2\text{-}8)$$

where $w\%$ = water content expressed as a percentage.
  W_w = weight of water.
  W_s = weight of dry soil.
  M_w = mass of the water.
  M_s = mass of the soil.

(*Cautionary note:* Water content is *not* weight of water divided by the total weight W_T, nor mass of water divided by total mass M_T.)

The relationship of water content and weight of dry soil to total wet weight of a soil volume is as follows:

$$W_T = W_s + W_w \qquad \text{(from Eq. 2-1)}$$

and since

$$W_w = \left(\frac{w\%}{100\%}\right) W_s \qquad \text{(from Eq. (2-8)}$$

$$W_T = W_s + \left(\frac{w\%}{100\%}\right) W_s$$

$$= W_s\left(1 + \frac{W\%}{100\%}\right)$$

then, by rearranging, obtain

$$W_s = \frac{W_T}{1 + \dfrac{w\%}{100\%}} \qquad (2\text{-}9a)$$

In a similar manner

$$M_s = \frac{M_T}{1 + \dfrac{w\%}{100\%}} \qquad (2\text{-}9b)$$

These equations enable the dry soil weight (or mass) to be easily determined when the wet weight or mass of a large soil sample is known and the water content is determined from a small representative portion taken from the sample. This procedure for determining dry soil weight or mass is frequently used in laboratory and construction work.

Two terms, *void ratio* and *porosity*, express a relationship between the volumes in a soil material occupied by solids and nonsolids. Void ratio e is

$$e = \frac{\text{Vol. of voids}}{\text{Vol. of solids}} = \frac{V_v}{V_s} \qquad (2\text{-}10)$$

Void ratio is expressed as a decimal. Porosity n, conventionally expressed as a percentage, is

$$n\% = \frac{\text{Volume of voids}}{\text{Total volume}} \times 100\% = \frac{V_v}{V_t} \times 100\% \qquad (2\text{-}11)$$

The relationship between void ratio and porosity is

$$e = \frac{\dfrac{n\%}{100\%}}{1 - \dfrac{n\%}{100\%}} \qquad (2\text{-}12a)$$

$$n\% = \frac{e}{1 + e} \times 100\% \qquad (2\text{-}12b)$$

The term *degree of saturation*, S, indicates the portion of the void spaces in a soil material (bulk) that is filled with water. Degree of saturation is expressed as a percentage.

$$S\% = \frac{V_w}{V_v} \times 100\% \qquad (2\text{-}13)$$

Full saturation, or 100 percent saturation, indicates that all voids are filled with water. A soil can remain 100 percent saturated even though its water content is changed if the soil experiences compression or expansion (since compression or expansion indicates a decrease or increase in void spaces).

With reference to a phase diagram as shown in Figure 2-3, other useful weight–volume relationships can be developed.

Since

$$V_T = V_s + V_v, \text{ and with } e = \frac{V_v}{V_s}, \text{ obtain}$$

$$V_T = V_s + eV_s = V_s(1 + e) \qquad (2\text{-}14a)$$

or

$$V_s = \frac{V_T}{1 + e} \qquad (2\text{-}14b)$$

Figure 2-3 Phase diagram used to develop equations applicable to weight–volume relationship.

Basic Terms Relating to Soil Composition and Condition

Also, since
$$\gamma_{dry} = \frac{W_s}{V_T} \qquad \text{(from Eq. 2-7)}$$

$$\gamma_{dry} = \frac{V_s G_s \gamma_w}{V_T} = \frac{V_s G_s \gamma_w}{V_s(1+e)} = \frac{G_s \gamma_w}{(1+e)} \qquad (2\text{-}15)$$

For a fully saturated soil, the unit weight becomes

$$\gamma_{sat} = \frac{W_T}{V_T} = \frac{W_s + W_w}{V_s(1+e)} \qquad \text{(from Eq. 2-6)}$$

$$= \frac{V_s G_s \gamma_w + V_w \gamma_w}{V_s(1+e)} = \frac{V_s G_s \gamma_w + e V_s \gamma_w}{V_s(1+e)}$$

$$= \frac{(G_s + e)\gamma_w}{(1+e)} \qquad (2\text{-}16\text{a})$$

For a partially saturated soil, the wet unit weight, γ_{wet} (or γ_{total}), becomes

$$\gamma_{wet} \text{ (or } \gamma_{total}) = \frac{W_T}{V_T} = \frac{V_s G_s \gamma_w + V_w \gamma_w}{V_s(1+e)} = \frac{V_s G_s \gamma_w + (SV_v)\gamma_w}{V_s(1+e)}$$

$$= \frac{V_s G_s \gamma_w + S(eV_s)\gamma_w}{V_s(1+e)} = \frac{(G_s + Se)\gamma_w}{1+e} \qquad (2\text{-}16\text{b})$$

A very informative relationship can be obtained by proper substitution of terms into Equation 2-5.

$$W_w = V_w G_w \gamma_w = V_w \gamma_w \qquad \text{(from Eq. 2-5a)}$$

or
$$V_w = \frac{W_w}{\gamma_w}$$

Dividing both sides by V_s gives

$$\frac{V_w}{V_s} = \frac{W_w}{V_s \gamma_w}$$

Multiplying the left term by $\dfrac{V_v}{V_v}$ gives

$$\frac{V_w}{V_s} \times \frac{V_v}{V_v} = \frac{W_w}{V_s \gamma_w}$$

and
$$\frac{V_w}{V_v} \times \frac{V_v}{V_s} = \frac{w W_s}{V_s \gamma_w}$$

$$S \cdot e = w \left(\frac{W_s}{V_s \gamma_w} \right)$$

$$Se = w G_s \qquad (2\text{-}17)$$

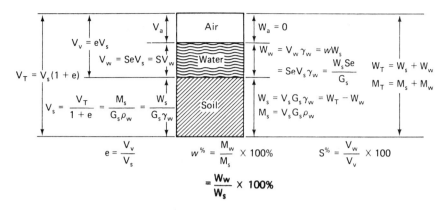

Figure 2-4 Summary of weight–volume and mass–volume equations.

In this equation, both the S and w terms are expressed as percent. For a given soil and unit weight, this equation shows the relationship between void ratio and water content, and the limiting water content that can be obtained.

A summary of the weight–volume and mass–volume equations most frequently used in solving problems is presented in Figure 2-4. In performing the analysis to determine weight or volume properties, it is extremely helpful to sketch the phase diagram, and indicate on the diagram that information which is known (from given data or as it is developed). This procedure helps to guide the analyst through the proper steps or equations necessary for a complete solution and will eliminate unnecessary computations.

ILLUSTRATION 2-1. A sample of soil obtained from a test pit is one cubic foot in volume and weighs 140 lb. The entire sample is dried in an oven and found to weigh 125 lb. Calculate the water content, wet unit weight, and dry unit weight.

$$\text{Weight of water} = W_w = 140 - 125 = 15 \text{ lb}$$

$$\text{Weight of dry soil} = W_s = 125 \text{ lb}$$

$$\text{Total volume of sample} = V_T = 1.0 \text{ ft}^3$$

$$\text{Wet unit weight} = \gamma_{\text{wet}} \text{ or } \gamma_{\text{total}} = \frac{W_T}{V_T} = \frac{140 \text{ lb}}{1.0 \text{ ft}^3} = 140 \text{ pcf}$$

$$\text{Dry unit weight} = \gamma_{\text{dry}} = \frac{W_s}{V_T} = \frac{125 \text{ lb}}{1.0 \text{ ft}^3} = 125 \text{ pcf}$$

$$\text{Water content} = w\% = \frac{W_w(100\%)}{W_s} = \frac{15 \text{ lb}}{125 \text{ lb}}(100\%) = 12\%$$

Basic Terms Relating to Soil Composition and Condition

ILLUSTRATION 2-2. Determine the wet density, dry unit weight, void ratio, water content, and degree of saturation for a sample of moist soil which has a mass of 18.18 kg and occupies a total volume of 0.009 m³. When dried in an oven, the dry mass is 16.13 kg. The specific gravity of the soil solids is 2.70.

$$\text{Wet density, } \rho = \frac{M_t}{V_t} = \frac{18.18 \text{ kg}}{0.009 \text{ m}^3} = 2020 \text{ kg/m}^3$$

$$\text{Dry unit weight, } \gamma_{\text{dry}} = \frac{W_s}{V_t} = \frac{M_s g}{V_t} = \frac{(16.13 \text{ kg})(9.81 \text{ m/sec}^2)}{0.009 \text{ m}^3} = 17.58 \text{ kN/m}^3$$

$$\text{Water content, } w\% = \frac{M_w}{M_s} \times 100\% = \frac{(18.18 - 16.13) \text{ kg}}{16.13 \text{ kg}} \times 100\%$$

$$= 12.7\%$$

$$\text{Void ratio, } e = \frac{V_v}{V_s} = \frac{0.0031 \text{ m}^3}{0.0059 \text{ m}^3} = 0.53$$

$$\left[\text{where } V_s = \frac{M_s}{G_s \rho_w}\right.$$

$$= \frac{16.13 \text{ kg}}{(2.70)\left(1.0 \frac{\text{gm}}{\text{cm}^3} \times 10^6 \frac{\text{cm}^3}{\text{m}^3} \times 0.001 \text{ kg/gm}\right)}$$

$$= \frac{16.13 \text{ kg}}{2.70 \times 10^3 \frac{\text{kg}}{\text{m}^3}} = 0.0059 \text{ m}^3$$

$$\text{and } V_v = V_t - V_s$$

$$= 0.009 \text{ m}^3 - 0.0059 \text{ m}^3$$

$$= 0.0031 \text{ m}^3]$$

$$\text{Degree of saturation, } S\% = \frac{wG_s}{e} = \frac{(12.7\%)(2.70)}{(0.53)} = 64.7\%$$

ILLUSTRATION 2-3. A 150-cc sample of wet soil has a mass of 250 g when 100 percent saturated. When oven-dried the mass is 162 g. Calculate the dry density, dry unit weight, water content, void ratio, and G_s.

$$\rho_{dry} = \frac{M_s}{V_t} = \frac{162 \text{ g}}{150 \text{ cm}^3} = 1.08 \frac{\text{g}}{\text{cm}^3}$$

and

$$\gamma_{dry} = (1.08 \text{ g/cm}^3)\left(62.4 \frac{\text{lb/ft}^3}{\text{g/cm}^3}\right) = 67.5 \text{ pcf}$$

$$w\% = \left(\frac{M_w}{M_s}\right)(100\%) = \left(\frac{250 \text{ g} - 162 \text{ g}}{162 \text{ g}}\right)(100\%) = 54.3\%$$

$$V_w = \frac{M_w}{G_\gamma \rho_w} = \frac{250 \text{ g} - 162 \text{ g}}{(1.0)(1.0 \text{ g/cm}^3)} = 88 \text{ cm}^3 = V_v \text{ for this problem, since for}$$
$$100\% \text{ saturation all voids are filled with water}$$

$$V_s = V_T - V_v = 150 \text{ cm}^3 - 88 \text{ cm}^3 = 62 \text{ cm}^3$$

$$e = \frac{V_v}{V_s} = \frac{88 \text{ cm}^3}{62 \text{ cm}^3} = 1.42$$

$$G_s = \frac{M_s}{V_s \rho_w} = \frac{162 \text{ g}}{(62 \text{ cm}^3)(1.0 \text{ g/cm}^3)} = 2.61$$

ILLUSTRATION 2-4. Laboratory test data on a sample of saturated soil show that the void ratio is 0.45 and the specific gravity of soil solids is 2.65. For these conditions, determine the wet unit weight of the soil and its water content.

This sample is saturated; thus all voids are filled with water.

$$e = \frac{V_v}{V_s} = 0.45$$

but V_v and V_s are not known. On the phase diagram, assume that V_s is unity. Therefore

$$V_T = V_s + eV_s = 1.0 + 0.45 = 1.45$$

As a result, $W_s = V_s G_s \gamma_w = (1.0)(2.65)(62.4 \text{ pcf}) = 165 \text{ lb}$

and $W_w = V_w \gamma_w = (0.45 \text{ ft}^3)(62.4 \text{ pcf}) = 28 \text{ lb}$

from which

$$W_T = W_s + W_w = 165 \text{ lb} + 28 \text{ lb} = 193 \text{ lb}$$

$$\gamma_{\text{wet}} = \frac{W_T}{V_T} = \frac{195 \text{ lb}}{1.45 \text{ ft}^3} = 133 \text{ pcf}$$

$$w\% = \frac{W_w}{W_s}(100\%) = \left(\frac{28 \text{ lb}}{165 \text{ lb}}\right)(100\%) = 17\%$$

SUBMERGED SOIL

In many soil mechanics problems it is necessary to determine the net intergranular weight, or *effective* weight, of a soil when it is below the groundwater table. (In this context, *intergranular* refers to the weight or force that acts at the point, or on the surfaces, where soil particles are in contact.) For this "underwater" condition, the soil solids are buoyed up by the pressure of the surrounding body of water, and the submerged soil weight becomes less than for the same soil above water. The effective soil weight then becomes the unit weight of the soil material when it is weighed under water. The water in the voids has zero weight (when submerged, all voids can be assumed to be filled with water), and the weight of the soil solids is reduced by the weight of the water they displace. Therefore, a submerged weight (W_{sub}) equals the soil weight above water minus the weight of water displaced, or

$$W_{\text{sub}} = V_s G_s \gamma_w - V_s G_w \gamma_w = V_s \gamma_w (G_s - G_w)$$

$$W_{\text{sub}} = V_s \gamma_w (G_s - 1) \tag{2-18}$$

Since unit weight is total weight divided by total volume,

$$\gamma_{\text{sub soil}} = \frac{W_{\text{sub}}}{V_{\text{total}}} = \frac{V_s \gamma_w (G_s - 1)}{V_s(1 + e)}$$

$$\gamma_{\text{sub soil}} = \frac{(G_s - 1)}{(1 + e)} \gamma_w \tag{2-19}$$

Equation 2-19[3] indicates that an accurate determination of the submerged soil weight requires that the specific gravity of the soil solids and the void ratio be known. Unfortunately, in terms of time and expense, some testing or physical analysis is required to determine the specific gravity, which in turn is used to compute the void ratio. Also unfortunately, insofar as analytical studies for practical soil mechanics problems are concerned, void ratios and soil weights vary somewhat even in "uniform deposits." Because of this fact, the effort to make highly accurate

---

[3] As a word of caution, it is pointed out that γ_{sub} is not equal to γ_{dry}, the dry unit weight of soil. The term γ_{dry} conventionally is restricted to indicate dry soil and does not include the effect of buoyancy as caused by submergence.

determinations of submerged soil weights is rarely undertaken when studies and designs are done. Instead, satisfactory estimates, which can be made from knowing a wet weight, are frequently utilized. For most soils, and fortunately for ease of computation, the submerged weight is on the order of half the wet soil weight above the water table. The most notable exception to this rule is for soils containing significant decomposed vegetation or organic material.

$$\gamma_{sub\ soil} = \tfrac{1}{2}\gamma_{wet\ soil} \quad \text{(approximately)} \tag{2-20}$$

For many practical problems, errors resulting from applying this simplification are negligible. Where accuracy is required, Equation 2-19 should be used. However, for the situation where the soil above the water table is 100 percent saturated, Equation 2-19 for the submerged unit weight becomes (simple and exact)

$$\gamma_{sub\ soil} = \gamma_{sat.\ soil} - \gamma_w$$

$$\gamma_{sub\ soil} = \gamma_{sat.\ soil} - 62.4 \quad \text{(in pcf)} \tag{2-21}$$

ILLUSTRATION 2-5. An undisturbed, one-cubic-foot volume of soil obtained from a test pit is found to have a wet weight of 103.2 lb. The dry weight of the sample is 84.5 lb. What would be the effective unit weight of such a soil if it were submerged below the groundwater table? The specific gravity of the soil is determined to be 2.70.

By Equation 2-20, the effective submerged weight is approximately

$$\gamma_{sub} = \tfrac{1}{2}\gamma_{wet} = \tfrac{1}{2}(103.2\ \text{pcf}) \cong 52\ \text{pcf}$$

An accurate determination is as follows:

$$V_s = \frac{W_s}{G_s\gamma_w} = \frac{84.5\ \text{lb}}{(2.70)(62.4\ \text{pcf})} = 0.50\ \text{ft}^3$$

$$V_v = V_T - V_s = 1.0\ \text{ft}^3 - 0.50\ \text{ft}^3 = 0.50\ \text{ft}^3$$

$$e = \frac{V_v}{V_s} = \frac{0.50}{0.50} = 1.00$$

$$\gamma_{sub} = \left(\frac{G_s - 1}{1 + e}\right)\gamma_w \qquad \text{(from Eq. 2-19)}$$

$$= \left(\frac{2.70 - 1}{1 + 1.0}\right)(62.4\ \text{pcf}) = 53.2\ \text{pcf}$$

or, submerged weight,

$$W_{sub} = V_s\gamma_w(G_s - G_w) = (0.50)(62.4\ \text{pcf})(1.70) = 53.2\ \text{lb}$$

and for a volume of one cubic foot,

$$\gamma_{sub} = \frac{W_{sub}}{V_T} = \frac{53.2\ \text{lb}}{1.0\ \text{cf}} = 53.2\ \text{pcf}$$

Submerged Soil

ILLUSTRATION 2-6. Assume that a one-cubic-foot volume of soil similar to the soil from the preceding illustration is excavated from a location below the water table. The soil is now 100 percent saturated. What saturated weight would be expected?

$$\gamma_{sub} = \gamma_{sat.} - \gamma_w$$

or $\quad \gamma_{sat.} = \gamma_{sub} + \gamma_w = 53.2 \text{ pcf} + 62.4 \text{ pcf} = 115.6 \text{ pcf} \qquad$ (from Eq. 2-21)

PROBLEMS

2-1. A sample of soil obtained from a construction site is found to have a wet weight of 27.5 lb. When completely dried, the soil weighs 24.3 lb. What is the water content of the soil sample?

2-2. A sample of soil obtained from a borrow pit has a wet weight of 35 lb. The total volume occupied by the sample when in the ground was 0.30 ft³. A small portion of the sample is used to determine the water content. When wet, the sample weighs 150 g. After drying, it weighs 125 g.
(a) What is the water content of the sample?
(b) Determine the wet and the dry unit weights of the soil in the borrow pit.

2-3. The mass of a dried soil sample is 250 g, as determined on a laboratory balance (scale). When immersed in water, the soil particles displace 95 cm³, and this is then the volume of soil solids. Using this data, determine the specific gravity of soil solids.

2-4. A one-cubic-foot sample of undisturbed soil is found to have a dry weight of 107 lb. If the specific gravity of soil solids is 2.70, what is the void ratio of the sample? What is the porosity?

2-5. A dry sand is placed in a container having a volume of ¼ ft³. The dry soil weight is 27 lb. If the specific gravity of soil solids is 2.75, what is the void ratio of the sand in the container?

2-6. A dry sand is placed in a container having a volume of 0.30 ft³. The dry weight of the sample is 31 lb. Water is carefully added to the container so as not to disturb the condition of the sand. When the container is filled, the combined weight of soil plus water is 38.2 lb. From these data, compute the void ratio of the soil in the container, and the specific gravity of the soil particles.

2-7. What will be the dry unit weight of a soil whose void ratio is 1.20, where the specific gravity of soil solids is 2.72?

2-8. A sand is densified by compaction at a construction site so that the void ratio changes from 0.80 to 0.50. If the specific gravity of solids is 2.70, what is the increase in the dry unit weight of the sand?

2-9. Demonstrate that $e = n/(1 - n)$ when n is used as a decimal.

2-10. An undisturbed sample of clay is found to have a wet weight of 63 lb, a dry weight of 51 lb, and a total volume of 0.50 ft³. If the specific gravity of soil solids is 2.65, determine the water content, void ratio, and degree of saturation.

2-11. A clay sample has a wet mass of 417 g and occupies a total volume of 276 cm³. When oven dried, the mass is 225 g. If the specific gravity of soil solids is 2.70, calculate the water content, void ratio, and degree of saturation.

2-12. Given the following data for an undisturbed soil sample

$$G_s = 2.69, \qquad e = 0.65, \qquad w = 10\%$$

determine wet unit weight, dry unit weight, and degree of saturation.

2-13. A saturated sample of undisturbed clay has a wet mass of 700 g. The sample has a total volume of 425 cm³. When dry, the soil mass is 450 g. What is the specific gravity of the soil solids?

2-14. A sample of soil obtained from beneath the ground water table is found to have a water content of 20 percent. If it is assumed that the specific gravity of most soil particles is within the range 2.60–2.75, what is the approximate void ratio of the soil sample?

2-15. In an undisturbed soil formation, it is known that the dry soil weight is 115 pcf. The specific gravity of the soil particles is 2.75.
(a) What is the saturated wet unit weight of the soil?
(b) What is the effective submerged weight of the soil?

2-16. An undisturbed soil sample has a wet unit weight of 120 pcf when the water content w is 15 percent. The specific gravity of the soil particles is 2.65.
(a) Approximate the effective submerged weight of this soil.
(b) Determine the effective submerged weight, using the exact formula.

chapter *3*

Soil Types and Soil Structure

The term *soil*, as generally used, refers to the accumulation of particles of disintegrated rock, and, frequently, also man-made materials. Because of the experienced wide variation in characteristics and behavior, soil has been subdivided into categories based on the materials' physical properties. In nature, soils are made up of particles of varying size and shape. Size and, to some extent, shape are factors that have been found to be related to or to affect the material behavior of soil to some degree. Consequently, soil categories or types have been developed that are basically referenced to size. To distinguish between soils where size cannot be discerned visually (the particles are too small), an additional property, plasticity (or nonplasticity), is used as a criterion.

Study has proved that a soil's important behavioral properties are not always controlled by particle size and plasticity. Soil structure and mineralogical composition, and the intereffect with water, may also have significant influence on the properties and behavior deemed important for design and construction. Under certain conditions, simple typing of the soil provides adequate information for design and construction, whereas certain other conditions require that detailed information about the soil's composition and structure be determined.

MAJOR SOIL TYPES

The major categories of soil are *gravel, sand, silt,* and *clay.* There is not unanimous agreement on the exact division between each of these major soil types, but gravel and sand *are* universally considered as *coarse-grained* soil, for the individual par-

44

ticles are large enough to be distinguished without magnification. Silts and clays are considered as *fine-grained soil* because of their small particles—too small, for the most part, to be seen unaided.

The most commonly used divisions for classifying soils for engineering and construction purposes are shown in Table 3-1. On a comparative basis, the division sizes between gravel and sand (4.76 mm or 2.00 mm), and sand and silt–clay (0.074 mm or 0.05 mm) are actually quite close. As a result, lack of agreement on these division sizes normally does not cause serious problems.

Particles larger than gravel are commonly referred to as *cobbles* or *boulders*. Again, no unanimous agreement exists on range of sizes. When gravel extends up to the 8-inch (20-cm) size, anything larger would be termed a boulder. Where the 3-inch (8-cm) size, or thereabouts, is taken as the upper size for gravel, the sizes between 3 inches and 8 inches may be designated as cobbles, and anything larger than 8 inches as boulders. However, 6 inches or 12 inches (15 cm or 30 cm) may also be taken as the division between cobbles and boulders. As for sands and gravels, these discrepancies usually do not cause serious problems. Conventionally, when a construction project requires a particular material, it has become standard practice to indicate the soil or aggregate requirements on the basis of size, instead of or in addition to classification.

Therefore, it is apparent that particle size alone serves as the basis for classification of sands, gravels, cobbles, and boulders.

The classification of a fine-grained soil as either a silt or a clay is not done on the basis of particle size but, rather, is based on the plasticity or nonplasticity of the material. Clay soil is plastic over a range of water content; that is, the soil can be remolded or deformed without causing cracking, breaking, or change in volume, and will retain the remolded shape. The clays are frequently "sticky." When dried, a clay soil possesses very high strength (resistance to crushing). A silt soil possesses little or no plasticity and, when dried, has little or no strength. If a small sample of moist silt is shaken easily but rapidly in the palm of the hand, water will appear on the surface of the sample but disappear when shaking stops. This is referred to as *dilatancy*. When a sample of moist clay is similarly shaken, the surface will not become wetted.

The reason for the difference in behavior between clay and silt relates to the difference in mineralogical composition of the soil types and particle shape. Silt

TABLE 3-1 SIZE RANGE FOR SOIL TYPES

Soil type	Upper size limit	Lower size limit
Gravel	Varies from 3 in. up to about 8 in. (8 cm–20 cm)	4.76 mm (about 0.20 in.) as determined by a #4 U.S. Standard Sieve) or 2.00 mm (#10 U.S. Standard Sieve)
Sand	4.76 mm or 2.00 mm	0.074 mm (#200 U.S. Standard Sieve) or 0.050 mm (#270 U.S. Standard Sieve)
Silt and clay	0.074 mm or 0.05 mm	None

soils are very small particles of disintegrated rock, as are sands and gravels, and possess the same general shape and mineralogical composition as sands and gravels (which are nonplastic). The clay minerals, however, represent chemical changes that have resulted from decomposition and alteration of the original rock minerals. The effect is that their size and shape are significantly different from those of other types of soil particles. This is discussed further in a following section.

Naturally occurring soil deposits most generally include more than one soil type. When they are classified, all the soil types actually present should be indicated, but the major constituent soil type should dominate the description, while the soils of lesser percentage are used as modifying terms; for example, a material that is mostly sand but includes silt would be classified as a silty sand, whereas a silt–clay mixture with mostly clay would be termed a silty clay.

Although a soil may be predominantly coarse-grained, the presence of silt or clay can have significant effect on the properties of the mixture. Where the amount of fine-grained material exceeds about one-third of the total soil, the mixture behaves more like a fine-grained soil than a coarse-grained soil.

The condition also exists where small fragments of decomposed vegetation are mixed with the soil, particularly fine-grained soils. Organic material mixed with the nonorganic soil can have striking detrimental effects on the strength and compressibility properties of the material. The presence of organic material should be carefully watched for. A foul odor is characteristically though not always associated with such soils, as is a blackish or dark gray color. Soils in this category are designated as *organic* (i.e., *organic silt* or *organic clay*) in comparison to a nonorganic designation for soil free of decomposed vegetation.

PARTICLE SHAPES AND SIZES

Particles in the sand, gravel, and boulder categories are considered as "bulky grain," indicating that particle dimensions are approximately equal; that is, the dimension in a length, width, and thickness direction would be of the same order of magnitude (that is, one dimension is no more than two or three times larger or smaller than another dimension). Individual particles are frequently very irregular in shape, depending somewhat on the rock they were derived from, their age, and exposure to weathering and transporting processes. Generally, a new particle is "angular" and rough-surfaced, and is then modified with time and exposure to become more smooth-surfaced and rounder. The various stages of transition—angular, subangular, rounded—are illustrated in Figure 3-1. Generally, the angular particles possess better engineering properties, such as higher shear strength, than do weathered and smooth particles.

Particles in the silt category, though classified as "fines" along with the clays, are still angular or bulky in shape and of the same mineralogical composition as the coarse-grained soils. Because of the mineralogical compositions, such particles rarely break down to less than 2μ in size (one μ, i.e., one micron, equals 0.001 mm).

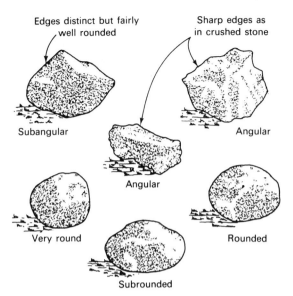

Figure 3-1 Shapes of granular soil particles [1].

The mineralogical composition of true clay is distinctly different from the mineral components of the other soil types, inviting the distinctions *clay minerals* and *nonclay minerals*. Almost all clay minerals are crystalline minerals (having an orderly, sheetlike molecular arrangement) that are capable of developing cohesion (because of an attraction and bonding between soil sheets and water) and plasticity. Clay particles may be made of many sheets on top of one another. Clay particles are mostly found in sizes less than 2μ or easily break down to this size. It is emphasized, however, that it is the mineral type and not the small size that is primarily responsible for the high cohesion and plasticity that clays possess. Where particles of nonclay minerals have been broken down to smaller than 2μ, the clay properties are not developed.

Because of the sedimentary origins of fine-grained soil deposits, and the overlap in sizes of the clay and nonclay minerals, it is unusual to find natural deposits of pure clay mineral soils. Very frequently, so-called clay deposits are actually a mixture of clay minerals and nonclay minerals. Because of this, the term *clay mineral* has been used to prevent confusion when one is designating a naturally occurring soil deposit consisting of fine-grained soils that have the general properties of cohesion and plasticity.

The clay minerals themselves can and do vary in their composition and, therefore, in their behavior properties. The building blocks, or constituent sheets, that combine to form most of the different types of clay mineral are the *silica tetrahedral* sheet (Fig. 3-2) and *alumina octahedral* sheet (Fig. 3-3).

The silica tetrahedron consists of four oxygen ions and one silicon ion. The molecular arrangement is such that the four oxygens are spaced and located at what would be the corners and tip of a three-dimensional, three-sided pyramid, with the silicon located within the pyramid. Oxygen ions at the base are shared by

Figure 3-2 Assembly of atoms forming the basic clay mineral sheet–silica tetrahedrol [97].

adjacent tetrahedrons, thus combining and forming the sheet. The thickness of a silica sheet is 5×10^{-7} mm, or 5 Angstrom units (one Angstrom unit or 1 Å $= 1 \times 10^{-7}$ mm).

The alumina octahedron consists of six oxygens and one aluminum. Three of these oxygens are in the top plane of the octahedron, and three are in the bottom plane. The aluminum is within the oxygen grouping. It is possible that the aluminum ion may be replaced with magnesium, iron, or other neutral ions. To obtain a valence balance, some of the oxygens may also carry a hydrogen ion (resulting in a hydroxyl at some oxygen locations). The alumina sheet is also 5×10^{-7} mm or 5 Å units thick.

It also happens that oxygens from the tip of a silica tetrahedron can share in an alumina sheet, thus layering sheets. Different arrangements of sheets then can

Figure 3-3 Assembly of atoms forming the basic clay mineral sheet–alumina octahedron [97].

combine to form the different clay minerals. The composition and typical properties of the more commonly occurring clays are summarized in Table 3-2.

Although the thickness of a clay mineral sheet is limited, the dimensions in the length and width direction are not. As a result, the clay minerals have a flat, platelike shape (like an irregular sheet of paper), where the length and width can be several tens or several hundreds times the thickness.

CLAY AND WATER

The surfaces of clay mineral particles have a net electrical charge that is negative, while the edges have positive and negative charges. This results from the molecular grouping and arrangement of ions. However, the charges are not uniform, but vary in intensity at different locations on the particle. Because of the extremely small size of clay particles and the very high ratio of particle surface to particle mass, the forces of electrical charge have a profound effect on the behavior of particles coming in association with other particles and water (or other fluids) present in the soil. And because of the manner of development or deposition, clay deposits almost always exist in the presence of some water.

The engineering behavior of coarse particles, because of a comparatively low ratio of particle surface to mass, are not significantly affected by surface electrical charges.

Clay mineral particles would, by themselves, tend to repel each other because of the net negative charges, unless edge-to-surface contact were made (positive to negative would attract). Because of the net negative charge, however, the particles will attract cations (positive ions) such as potassium, sodium, calcium, and aluminum from moisture in the soil (ions present as a result of solutions from rock weathering), so as to obtain an electrically balanced or equilibrium condition.

Because of the net positive charge of the cations, they in turn can also attract negative charges. As a result of this phenomenon, water becomes bonded to the cations. Water, though neutral, has its oxygen and hydrogen atoms spaced in such a manner that the center of gravity of the positive and negative electrical charges do not coincide. The resulting molecule has a plus charge acting at one end and a negative charge acting at the opposite end, similar to a bar magnet. Water molecules are thus considered *polar molecules* (Fig. 3-4). The negative tips of water molecules are attracted and held to the cation, which in turn is held by the clay particle. The resulting effect is that significant water (significant with respect to the size and weight of the clay particle) becomes "bonded" to the clay. Water molecules are also held to the particle surface, where they become attracted directly to a location of negative charge.

Additional water molecules then also become attracted to the clay particle because of a chainlike arrangement of negative ends to positive ends of molecules, and by hydrogen bonding (the condition where hydrogen atoms in water are shared with hydrogen atoms in the clay).

The state or nature of the water immediately surrounding a clay particle is not clearly understood by soil scientists, but it is generally known to possess prop-

TABLE 3-2 BASIC PROPERTIES OF SOME TYPICAL CLAYS

Clay mineral	Composition	Layer thickness	Shape of mineral, general properties, and comments
Kaolinite	One silica, one alumina sheet. Very strongly bonded together.	7.5 Å	The most prevalent clay mineral. Very stable, with little tendency for volume change when exposed to water. Kaolinite layers stack together to form relatively thick particles. Particles are plate-shaped. Form from crystalline rocks in humid climates.
Halloysite	One silica, one alumina sheet make up the layer. Has sheet of water molecules between layers. (Similar to kaolinite except for sheet of water.)	10 Å	Sheets of halloysite curl into tubes. Strength and plasticity are significantly affected by drying and removal of the water. After drying, the clay mineral will not reinstate a water layer if again exposed to water. Caution is required in identifying this mineral and in using remolded (and rewetted) samples in the laboratory testing to determine properties. Dried halloysite has characteristics of kaolinite. Rewetted samples appear stronger and less plastic than naturally wetted halloysite.
Illite	Alumina sheet sandwiched between two silica sheets to form the layer. Potassium provides the bond between layers.	10 Å	Irregular flake shape. Generally more plastic than kaolinite. Does not expand when exposed to water unless a deficiency in potassium exists. Illite clays seem most prevalent in marine deposits and soil derived from micaceous rock (schists, etc.).
Montmorillonite (also identified as smectite)	Alumina sheet sandwiched between two silica sheets to form the layer. Iron or magnesium may replace the alumina in the aluminum sheet; aluminum may replace some silicons in the silica sheet (isomorphous substitution). Weak bond between layers.	9.5 Å	Irregular plate shapes or fibrous. Because of the weak bond between layers and the negative charge resulting because of isomorphous substitution, the clay readily absorbs water between layers. This mineral has a great tendency for large volume change because of this property. Montmorillonite forms mostly from ferromagnesium rock in areas where high temperatures exist and rainfall is abundant; also from decomposition of volcanic ash.
Chlorite	Layers formed of alumina sheet sandwiched between two silica sheets, but layers are bonded together with an alumina sheet.		Irregular plate shapes. Nonexpanding. Formed from well-drained soils and micaceous rocks in humid areas.

Note: 1 Å = 1×10^{-7}mm.

50

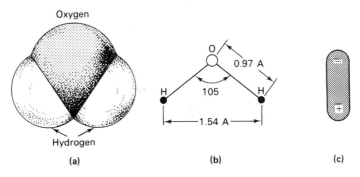

Figure 3-4 (a) Model of water molecule; (b) relative location of atoms in the water molecule; (c) polar representation of water molecule.

erties different from liquid water. It may be in a very dense and viscous state. It *is* certain, however, that this water is very strongly attracted to the clay particle.

The attraction for cations necessary to balance the negative charge of the clay extends beyond the surface layer of molecules surrounding the particle. The further from the particle surface, though, the weaker the attraction becomes, and, therefore, the concentration of cations becomes lessened. The resulting effect is that water molecules are still attracted to the clay particles, indirectly, but the further from the particle, the weaker the attraction. At a distance beyond where cation and, therefore, water molecules are attracted to a clay particle, water in the soil is considered "loose" or "normal" pore water.

The distance from the clay particle surface to the limit of attraction is termed the *diffuse double layer* (Fig. 3-5). This term originates from the belief that immediately surrounding the particle a thin, very tightly held layer of water, perhaps 1×10^{-6} mm (10 Å) thick exists, and a second, more mobile, diffuse layer extends beyond this first layer to the limit of attraction. Molecular movement in the outer layer (or outer zone), and probably also in the tightly held layer, continually occurs, however. The water that is held in the diffuse double layer is frequently termed *adsorbed water* or *oriented water*, to differentiate it from normal pore water, which is not oriented.

The plasticity that clay soils possess is attributed to the attracted and held water. And, as a restatement, water molecules are attracted because of their dipole structure. The unusual properties of plasticity possessed by clays result because of the unusual molecular structure and the common presence of water in soil deposits. Experiments performed with clay using nonpolar liquid in place of water have resulted in a "no-plasticity" condition similar to that noted for coarse-grained sandy soil.

SOIL STRUCTURE

The particle arrangement of the equidimensional particles—gravel, sand, and silt—has been likened to arrangements that can be obtained by stacking marbles or oranges. For similar-sized spherical particles, a loose condition (condition with a

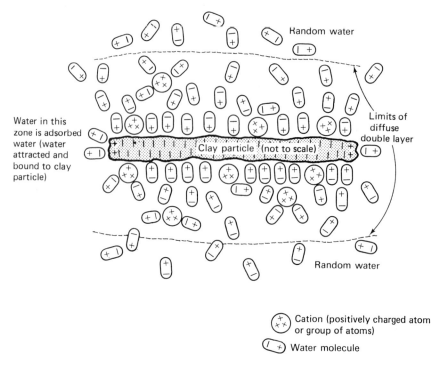

Random water

Water in this zone is adsorbed water (water attracted and bound to clay particle)

Clay particle (not to scale)

Limits of diffuse double layer

Random water

Cation (positively charged atom or group of atoms)

Water molecule

Figure 3-5 Adsorbed water and cations in diffuse double layer surrounding clay particle.

high void ratio) is obtained from an arrangement as shown in Figure 3-6a. A dense condition (condition with a low void ratio) is obtained from an arrangement as in Figure 3-6b.

Actual soil deposits are made of accumulations of soil particles having at least some variation, but more frequently great variation, in particle sizes. As a result, the soil structure is not quite like that presented in Figure 3-6. Generally, the greater the range of particle sizes, the smaller the total volume of void spaces there will be. For a given soil deposit, however, a range of conditions between loose and dense is possible. Typical values for different types of soil mixtures are tabulated in Table 3-3.

In relating the volume of void spaces to properties desirable for building construction purposes, it is generally recognized that the smaller the void ratio (or the denser the material), the higher the strength and the lower the compressibility will be.

(a) Loose

(b) Dense

Figure 3-6 Schematic diagram of grain arrangement for loose and dense granular soils.

Soil description	Range of void ratio		Range of unit weight				
	e_{max} (loose)	e_{min} (dense)	Condition (moisture)	γ_{min} pcf (loose)	γ_{max} pcf (dense)	$\gamma_{min} \frac{kN}{m^3}$ (loose)	$\gamma_{max} \frac{kN}{m^3}$ (dense)
Well-graded fine to coarse sand	0.70	0.35	Saturated	125	140	19.5	22
			Dry	95	120	15	19
Uniform fine to medium sand	0.85	0.50	Saturated	120	130	19	20.5
			Dry	85	110	14	17.5
Silty sand and gravel	0.80	0.25	Saturated	115	145	18	22.5
			Dry	90	130	14	17
Micaceous sand with silt	1.25	0.75	Saturated	110	125	17	19.5
			Dry	75	95	12	15

Coarse soil in an initially loose condition may be prone to quick volume reductions and loss of strength if subjected to shock or vibrations, unless there is some cementing at points of particle contact or "cohesive strength" provided by moisture menisci (discussed further in Chapter 10).

Experiences indicate that it is possible for sands or silts to be deposited in such a manner that an unusually loose or honeycomb structure results. Grains settling slowly in quiet waters, or a loosely dumped mass of moist soil, can develop a particle-to-particle contact that bridges over relatively large void spaces within the mass and can carry the weight of the overlying material. Possible particle arrangements are shown in Figure 3-7.

The presence of flake-shaped particles, such as mica flakes, in a coarse soil has significant effect on the void ratio, density, and compressibility of a deposit. The flake-shaped particles are capable of bridging over open spaces so that relatively large void ratios develop. When subject to external loading, however, the flakes are incapable of providing great support, bending or breaking, and rearranging under load.

For coarse-grained soils and silts, the mass of an individual particle is relatively great compared to the surface area. Therefore, the effect of gravity has the most influence over the arrangement of deposits of such soils. (The effect of electrical charges on the particle surface is negligible.) Conversely, the clay particles, because

Figure 3-7 Honeycomb structure in a granular soil.

Soil Structure

of their large surface-to-mass ratio, are more affected by the electrical forces acting on their surfaces than by gravity forces.

Clay deposits developed from clay particles that have settled out of suspension in a fresh-water or salt-water environment tend toward a *flocculated structure*, whereby the attraction and contact between many of the clay particles is through an edge-to-face arrangement. Clays settling out in a salt-water solution tend to a structure more flocculent than do clays settling out in a fresh-water situation. Salt water (oceans are approximately a 3.5 percent saline solution) acts as an electrolyte in which the repulsion between particles is reduced. With respect to other particles, particle sedimentation then occurs with a random orientation, creating the flocculent structure. Sedimentation in a weaker electrolyte, such as fresh water (fresh surface or subsurface water is not "pure") produces a structure where some parallel orientation of settled particles occurs, but the overall structure is flocculent; see Figures 3-8a and 3-8b. Clay particle sedimentation occurring in ponds and wetlands where organic decay is taking place will result in highly flocculent structures.

Clay deposits with flocculent structures will have high void ratios, low density, and probably high water contents. The structure, however, is quite strong and resistant to external forces because of the attraction between particles. But if the environment surrounding the clays is changed, such as by having the salts leached from the deposit (as has occurred where ocean deposits have been raised to above sea level and fresh water subsequently has percolated through the soil, leaching out the salts with it), the attraction and strength between particles can be markedly decreased.

Clays that have been further transported after being deposited (as from glacial action, or when used in man-made earth fills) are reworked or remolded by the transportation process. The particle structure that develops from remolding is a more parallel arrangement or orientation of particles than existed in the flocculent condition, as shown in Figure 3-9. Such a particle arrangement is considered a *dispersed* or *oriented* structure.

When used for construction, clays that were in a flocculent condition before

Figure 3-8 Schematic diagram of types of particle orientations [00].

Dispersed-type structure
(face to face contact)

Figure 3-9 Schematic diagram of particle orientations.

use generally lose some strength as a result of remolding. Subsequent to remolding, and with the passage of time, however, the strength increases, though not back to the strength of the originally undisturbed clay. Reasons for this increase appear to be related to a time-dependent rebuilding from the remolded, dispersed structure toward a less dispersed, more flocculent structure. In the dispersed condition, the equilibrium of forces between particles is disturbed. With time, the particles become sufficiently reoriented (only very small movements are necessary) to reacquire a structure in which the forces between particles are again in equilibrium (but not as originally structured; see Fig. 3-10). This phenomenon of strength loss–strength gain, with no changes in volume or water content, is termed *thixotropy*. Thixotropy has been defined as a "process of softening caused by remolding, followed by a time-dependent return to the (original) harder state." The degree of difference between the undisturbed strength and remolded strength, and the extent of strength gain after remolding, are affected by the type of clay minerals in the soil. Generally, the clay types that absorb large quantities of water, such as the montmorillonites, experience greater thixotropic effects than do the more stable clay types, such as kaolinite.

For many construction situations, thixotropy is considered a beneficial phenomenon, since with the passing of time soil structures (dams, highway embankments, etc.) and disturbed foundation soils get stronger and presumably safer. However, the phenomenon also causes its problems; construction sites may be quickly transformed into a mire of mud when construction equipment travels across the area, making handling of equipment and materials very difficult. Thixotropic influences have also affected piles driven in clay soils when the driving operation caused remolding and weakening of the clay surrounding the pile. The soil strength is sometimes recovered relatively quickly. This has been experienced where a pile has initially been driven part of its length, and attempts at continued driving after a one- or two-day wait have met with considerable resistance due to the increasing adhesion (directly related to a clay's strength) along the pile surface. This is one reason that piles embedded in cohesive soils should be fully driven whenever possible.

SOME SPECIAL SOIL CATEGORIES

To those in the construction industry, the term *special soil* implies a soil type with a property or behavior that is considered unusual and therefore requires special treatment. The loessal soils discussed in Chapter 1 are in this category, for the in-place structure of this aeolin deposit makes it susceptible to collapse if it is exposed

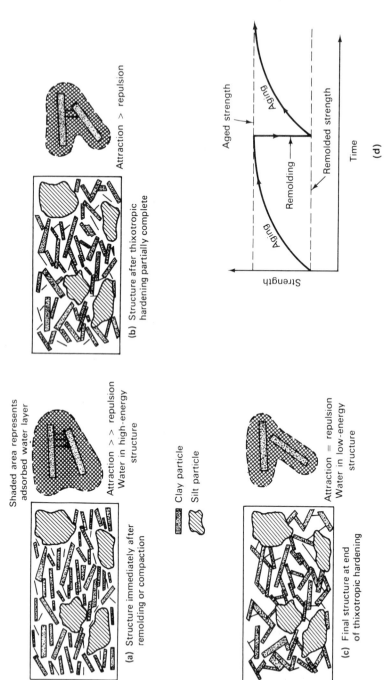

Shaded area represents
adsorbed water layer

Attraction > > repulsion
Water in high-energy
structure

(a) Structure immediately after
remolding or compaction

Attraction > repulsion

(b) Structure after thixotropic
hardening partially complete

▨ Clay particle
▨ Silt particle

Attraction = repulsion
Water in low-energy
structure

(c) Final structure at end
of thixotropic hardening

(d)

Figure 3-10 Schematic diagram of thixotropic structure change in a fine-grained soil [000].

56

to excessive amounts of water. Correspondingly, the design and construction of facilities in loessal areas should include means for either protecting the foundation soil from water or otherwise compensating for its adverse effects.

Some clay soils are prone to large volume changes which are directly related to changes in water content, shrinking in dry seasons and swelling in wet seasons or when otherwise in the presence of water. Such soils are termed *expansive clays* or *swelling clays*. Clays including the montmorillonite mineral are particularly noted for their high volume change characteristic. The expansive force of a swelling montmorillonite clay can lift pavements and light structures. A common construction practice in areas where expansive clays exist is to keep the soil beneath a structure stable by providing protection against changes in the moisture content. Additives that provide a source of calcium, such as lime or lime materials, have also been used to stabilize expansive clays; for example, crushed clamshells have been mixed with the natural clay soil used for road bases in the Gulf Coast region of the United States.

Dispersive clays and *lateritic soils* also represent materials which require special consideration, as discussed in the following sections. *Permafrost*, the permanently frozen ground which exists near the earth's polar regions, is discussed in Chapter 6. A discussion of radon gas, a health hazard, is also presented.

Dispersive Clays Fine-grained soils that will deflocculate in still water and erode if exposed to low-velocity water are termed *dispersive clays*.[1] Ordinary clays typically do not erode in the presence of water unless the flow velocity is relatively high (e.g., more than about 3 or 4 ft/sec). Areas blanketed by natural deposits of dispersive clays characteristically show steep erosion gullies and eroded tunnels, though not always. Embankments constructed with dispersive clays similarly experience the development of gullies and tunnels. Critically, the presence of dispersive clay in earthen dams, engineered and otherwise, has been the reason for piping (leakage through eroded tunnels) of such great magnitude that major repair became necessary to keep the structures functional; frequently the piping condition developed very soon after the initial pooling of the reservoir.

A clay's susceptibility to dispersion has been found to be related to the presence of cations (sodium, calcium, magnesium, potassium) in the soil pore water. Generally, repulsive forces between clay particles that act to cause deflocculation decrease as the concentration of ions increases. However, repulsion increases as the quantity of sodium ions increases; the thickness of the diffuse double layer of water adsorbed to the soil particles is relatively great when monovalent sodium ions are present, and the distance-related attractive forces that exist between particles are thus weakened. Usually, in a clay–water system, the repulsive forces and the tendency toward dispersion increase as the concentration of ions increases along

---

[1]Note that the terms *dispersive clay* and *dispersed structure* for clay refer to different properties. The similarity of terms is unfortunate, but when each term is used in proper context the description will be understood. Simply stated, dispersive clay refers to an easily eroded clay, whereas dispersive structure refers to a positional relationship between particles; a clay having a dispersed structure may or may not be dispersive (easily eroded).

Some Special Soil Categories

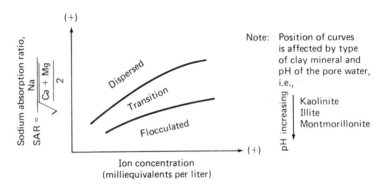

Figure 3-11 Qualitative relationship between ion concentration and dispersivity.

the series calcium–magnesium–potassium–sodium–lithium (e.g., a clay high in sodium is more dispersive than one having a high concentration of calcium and little sodium). Figure 3-11 expresses a qualitative relationship between cations present in a clay deposit and the tendency for dispersion; laboratory tests used to indicate dispersive tendencies are discussed in Chapter 4.

The piping that occurs in compacted earth dams that have been constructed of dispersive clay may originate at locations where water enters minuscule cracks, such as those that would develop from settlement or hydraulic fracturing. In the presence of water, the exposed clay particles quickly go into suspension, and a progressive erosion rapidly results. Where the presence of a dispersed clay has not been recognized during construction, dams have experienced piping as the first reservoir filling was under way, or soon after filling has been completed. Relating to the effect of ion concentration, earth dams that have satisfactorily retained reservoirs of salt water for long periods have been known to develop piping problems quickly when fresh water replaced the salt water, a result of the dilution of the ion concentration in the dam's clay.

The erodibility of dispersive clay can be reduced through the use of hydrated lime or aluminum sulfate admixtures, 1–2 percent by weight. Where core zones of dams must be constructed of dispersive clays, soil transition–filter zones that border the dispersed clay can be designed to control erosion and seal concentrated leaks. The use of geofabrics (geotextiles) can also be investigated as an erosion control.

Laterites The term *laterite* or description *lateritic soil* refers to a category of residual soil formed from the weathering of igneous rock under conditions of high temperature and high rainfall such as those typically occuring in tropical regions, where the decomposition process results in a soil leached of silica (SiO_2) and calcium carbonate but retaining high concentrations of iron and aluminum sesquioxides (Fe_2O_3, Al_2O_3). An Al_2O_3/SiO_2 ratio of one-half or greater is one criterion used to classify a soil as lateritic. Calcium, magnesium, and potassium contents are very low. Laterites are frequently reddish in color, but not always, and all reddish tropical soils are not lateritic. Extensive areas of Asia, South America, and Africa are blanketed with lateritic soils. Concerning their engineering behavior, these soils have been found to possess some unusual properties when compared to soils existing in the temperate regions of the world. Agriculturally, most lateritic soils typically contain only meager concentrations of the nutrients considered necessary for productive farming.

Deposits of lateritic soils may be found in a hard or cemented state, particularly in areas where vegetation is sparse or has been removed. The cementation, attributed to the presence of free iron oxide in the soil, is such that the hardened soil can be quarried and used as a bricklike material for building construction purposes.

Generally, with a tropical residual soil the weathering process is not complete, and material can exist at all stages between fresh rock and soil. However, lateritic soils seem to be typified by a gap grading, existing with a prevalence of gravel-sized and clay materials but having very limited sand and silt-sized particles. When used as a construction material, these weathered soils often have been found to be unstable, subject to further breakdown during handling and testing or excavation and placement. It appears that the soils from a damp regime are more apt to change physical properties than are soils from an arid region; soil from the damp environment has never been dehydrated but becomes so after exposure to air, an occurrence that has a weakening effect. Further, there is great possibility of significant changes in properties if a laterite is completed dried and then wetted. Reworking a lateritic soil at a given water content frequently alters properties such as plasticity and compaction characteristics. It has become apparent that widely used correlations between soil classification index properties and the subsequent engineering behavior, established primarily from experiences with soils formed in the temperature regions of the world, cannot be relied on to predict behavior of soils formed in tropical areas.

In their native regions, lateritic soils have, of economic necessity, been used as construction material for road bases and embankment structures, and to support foundations. Experience has proved that these materials can serve successfully when protected from percolating or migrating water and the effects of heavy repetitive loadings. Properties can be improved by the use of common admixtures such as cement and lime.

Radon   Radon is a radioactive gas whose presence is related to rock, soil and waste material whose composition includes uranium, radium or polonium. Radium and polonium, products of decay (the progeny) from naturally occurring uranium, in turn decays into radon. Radon gas is invisible, odorless, and tasteless, and is soluble in water. As radon gas decays into solid particles of lead and bismuth, it emits small amounts of radiation. Naturally occurring radon gas exists in low concentration in many areas of the earth without causing harm. On the basis of information obtained from experiences with highly radioactive materials, however, medical and health specialists fear that inhaling air that includes high concentrations of radon for extended periods could cause the type of serious health problems associated with excessive exposure to radiation and carcinogens. Where waterborne, the dissolved radon apparently represents a direct hazard only after it separates and becomes airborne.

Unusual concentrations of radon have been encountered in and near uranium mines, at locations where uranium or phosphate tailings (i.e., waste materials and by-products of mining operations) exist, at disposal sites for manufacturing processes that included uranium–radium materials, in some geologic areas underlain by extensive deposits of granite and sillimanite (aluminum silicates), and from granular soil deposits resulting from glacially transported granitic debris. In open space at such locations, health may not be affected because dangerous concentrations do not accumulate. But significant hazard to health is anticipated where high concentrations accumulate indoors (in houses and at places of work) when a building is constructed over uranium-bearing rock, soil, or waste material, and where radioactive materials have been used to manufacture material used for the building construction (e.g., masonry building blocks made with radioactive phosphate slag). Concentrations of airborne radon at or exceeding 2 picocuries per liter of air (pCi/l) typically are taken as the condition requiring a remedial action.[2] The radon gas works its way into the building through construction joints or other openings in contact with the earth. Domestic water will be the source of radioactive material if the surface or subsurface supply has absorbed radon; for example, the radon becomes airborne when the water is sprayed. A concentration of 10,000 pCi per liter of water is taken as the threshold level requiring a remedial action.

The inset article on radon in buildings on pages 60–61 reviews current mitigation procedures for handling a radon presence in residential buildings.

RADON IN BUILDINGS

The only way to know if a building has a radon problem is to measure. There are several techniques that can be used. Because radon concentrations in buildings vary widely on a daily basis, the most appropriate methods for characterizing radon are those that give a short-term (4–7 days) measurement. Activated carbon detectors are commonly used for this purpose. Longer term methods (more than 30 days) are valuable in determining the long-term success of a radon mitigation effort. Alpha-sensitive detectors are used to make these measurements. Continuous monitors that use scintillation flasks are more expensive instruments that are powerful aids in locating radon entry routes and making a quick determination of the effectiveness of mitigation techniques.

Radon mitigation techniques fall into one of two broad categories: Either prevent the radon from entering the building or exhaust it with ventilation air if it does enter.

---

[2]The *curie* (Ci) is the unit to indicate radioactivity. Radioactivity is the release of particles or radiation from the nucleus of an unstable atom as it is in the process of transforming to a stable atom. The release can be alpha particles, beta particles, or gamma radiation. One curie represents 3.7×10^{10} disintegrations per second, that is, the release of 3.7×10^{10} alpha particles or beta particles per second, or 3.7×10^{10} photons per second of gamma radiation. One picocurie represents 1×10^{-12} Ci, or $(3.7 \times 10^{10}) (1 \times 10^{-12}) \times (60) = 2.2$ disintegrations per minute.

Prevent Entry

A first step is to try to seal the leaks in the basement, slab, or crawlspace that allow soil gas entry. This should be done with a durable material that will adhere to concrete. One part polyurethanes have been found to be effective for this. The typical entry points are at the floor–wall joint, through floor drains and sump holes, and around plumbing penetrations.

A second method used to prevent gas entry is to isolate and ventilate the source. An example of this would be the sealing and insulating of a crawlspace ceiling and then adding passive or fan powered ventilation to the crawlspace. This essentially diverts the soil gas from the crawlspace to the outside of the building. Another common example is sealing the cracks and openings in the floor slab or block wall and using a fan and ductwork to evacuate air from inside the block wall or from beneath the slab. An interior subslab drainage system lends itself to this technique. The methods that combine sealing and powered evacuation have been very successful at reducing even high radon concentrations in buildings.

Dilution by Ventilation

If, for one reason or another, the foregoing methods are not suitable for radon mitigation, the air inside the building can be changed at a higher rate. The problems with increasing the air exchange rate include the increased energy costs for heating and cooling and comfort, and the possibility of causing freezing pipes. Most of these problems can be overcome through a combination of using heat recovery ventilation, ventilating as near to the radon sources as possible, and not using ventilation to mitigate problems that would require more than two air changes per hour.

Contributed by Terry Brennan, principal, Camroden Associates, Rome, NY; Cochairman, ASTM Radio-nuclide Task Group.

PROBLEMS

3.1. Clay is a soil material that possesses plasticity in the presence of water. What does the term *plastic* mean in relation to clay soils?

3.2. What is the essential reason for the difference in behavior of natural clays and other soil types such as silts and sands?

3.3. Comment on the difference between the shape and size of clay particles compared to other soil types such as silts and sands.

3.4. What are the "building blocks" of most clay minerals? Comment on the comparative length–width–thickness dimensions of a typical clay particle.

3.5. Referring to the attraction that typically exists between water and clay particles, what is adsorbed water?

3.6. Describe what is meant by the dipole nature of a water molecule. How is this related to adsorbed water and plasticity in a clay soil?

3.7. Why does the presence of water in a soil have so much greater an effect on clays than on sand or gravel materials?

3.8. In a general way, the strength of a coarse-grained soil is related to the soil deposit's structure (or particle orientation) and void ratio (or density). What is this relationship?

3.9. **(a)** Briefly describe the difference in a flocculent structure and a dispersed structure in clay soils.

   (b) What type of structure is most likely expected in a clay deposit that has resulted in a naturally occurring underwater environment?

   (c) What type of structure would be expected where a clay had been used for a compacted fill on a construction project?

3.10. With regard to the *thixotropy* phenomenon in clay soils, what is it and what causes it?

## chapter 4

Index Properties and Classification Tests, and Soil Classification Systems

As an aid to the engineering profession and the design–construction field, soils have been divided into basic categories or classifications based on certain physical characteristics. But because of the range of characteristics for the different soil variations that exist in nature, classification categories have been, of necessity, relatively broad in scope. All of a soil's properties are not checked to obtain a classification. Consequently, for proper evaluation of a soil's suitability for construction or foundation use, information about its properties in addition to classification is frequently necessary. Those properties that do help to define a soil's engineering qualities and that are used to assist in determining accurate classification are termed *index properties*. The tests necessary to determine index properties are *classification tests*. Index properties include those characteristics that can be determined relatively quickly and easily and that will have bearing on items of engineering importance such as strength or load-supporting ability, tendency to settle or expand, and effect of water and freezing conditions.

INDEX PROPERTIES

Index properties refers to those properties of a soil that indicate the type and condition of the soil, and provide a relationship to structural properties such as the strength and the compressibility or tendency for swelling, and permeability.

Generally, for coarse-grained soils, properties of the particles and the relative state of compaction are most significant. For fine-grained soils, the consistency (firm or soft) and plasticity are particularly important. The index properties that

TABLE 4-1 INDEX PROPERTY AND RELATED CLASSIFICATION TEST

Soil type	Index property	Classification test
Coarse-grained	Range of particle sizes and distribution of sizes	Particle-size distribution (mechanical analysis) by sieving or sedimentation test
	Shape of particles	Visual
	Presence of fine-grained particles	From mechanical analysis (usually from use of a fine-mesh sieve)
	In-place density and relative state of compaction	In situ density determination, and relative density test
	Classification	From mechanical analysis, or visual identification based on grain size
Fine-grained	Consistency (strength and type of structure in the undisturbed state)	Field or laboratory evaluation of unconfined compressive strength or shear strength (cohesion)
	Change in consistency due to remolding	Unconfined compressive strength or cohesion for the remolded soil
	Water content	Water content
	Plasticity	Atterberg limits (liquid limit and plastic limit)
	Classification	From visual identification and Atterberg limits
	Presence and type of clay	Indirectly from determination of plasticity and change in consistency, and/or directly from a clay mineral analysis

provide the desired information for coarse-grained and fine-grain (as elsewhere) soils are summarized in Table 4-1.

It should be recognized that in studies and analyses for construction projects it frequently is not necessary to determine all the index properties for the soil. Properties to be determined relate to the information that is needed and how such information eventually is to be used. For example, a clay mineral analysis requires very specialized equipment and is not performed in studies for foundation designs, unless the soils are unusual.

For organic soils, it is important to know of the presence and at least the approximate amount of organic material because of its influence on compressibility and strength.

For all soils, the description should include the color. Color may have bearing on the mineralogical composition and is also extremely useful for determining homogeneity of a soil deposit and as an aid for identification and correlation during field construction.

CLASSIFICATION TESTS

Particle Size Distribution (Mechanical Analysis)   This classification test determines the range of size of particles in the soil and the percentage of particles in each of the sizes between the maximum and minimum.

TABLE 4-2 COMMON SIEVE TYPES AND MESH OPENINGS

Sieve size designation	U.S. Standard		Tyler Standard		British Standard	
	Inches	Millimeters	Inches	Millimeters	Inches	Millimeters
#4	0.187	4.76	0.185	4.70	—	—
#8	0.0937	2.38	0.093	2.362	0.081	2.057
#10	0.0661	1.68	0.065	1.651	0.0661	1.676
#20	0.0331	0.84	0.0328	0.833	—	—
#40	0.0106	0.42	—	—	—	—
#60	0.0098	0.25	0.0097	0.246	0.0099	0.251
#100	0.0059	0.149	0.0058	0.147	0.0060	0.152
#200	0.0029	0.074	0.0029	0.074	0.0030	0.076
#270	0.0021	0.053	0.0021	0.053	—	—
#400	0.0015	0.037	0.0015	0.038	—	—

Two methods are in common use for obtaining the necessary information. Sieving is generally used for coarse-grained soils, and a sedimentation procedure is used for analyzing fine-grained soils. Sieving is a most direct method for determining particle sizes, but there are practical lower limits to sieve openings that can be used for soils. This lower limit is approximately at the smallest size attributed to sand particles. Information on sieves in common use is shown in Table 4-2.

In the sieve analysis, a series of sieves (screens) having different-sized openings are stacked with the larger sizes over the smaller (Fig. 4-1). The soil sample being tested is dried, clumps are broken, and the sample is passed through the

Figure 4-1 Set of sieves being assembled. Sieves shown are U.S. Standard Sieves, typically used in laboratories.

Classification Tests

series of sieves by shaking. Larger particles are caught on the upper sieves, and the smaller particles filter through to be caught on one of the smaller underlying sieves. The weight of material retained on each sieve is converted to a percentage of the total sample. The resulting data are conventionally presented as a grain- or particle-size distribution curve plotted on semilog coordinates, where the sieve size opening is on a horizontal *logarithmic* scale, and the percentage (by weight) of the size smaller than a particular sieve opening is on a vertical *arithmetic* scale. Results may be presented in tabular form also. A detailed procedure for performing the sieve analysis is presented in the *ASTM* (American Society for Testing and Materials) *Testing Manual*, under ASTM Test Designation D-422. A typical presentation is shown in Figure 4-2. Note the "reversal" of the logarithmic scale (size increases from right to left).

Most soil grains are not of an equal dimension in all directions. Hence, the size of a sieve opening will represent neither the largest nor the smallest dimension of a particle, but some intermediate dimension. As an illustration, assume a brick-shaped particle whose length, width, and thickness are different. The dimension that controls whether or not the particle passes through the sieve opening is the intermediate dimension, assuming the particle is aligned so that the greatest dimension is perpendicular to the sieve opening.

Sieve tests can be performed in a laboratory or in the field (at the area being explored, such as a proposed borrow pit or construction site).

The appearance of the particle-size distribution plot depends on the range and amounts of the various sizes of particles in the soil sample. These, in turn, have been affected by the soil's origin or the method of deposition. Well-graded soils (a distribution of particles over a relatively large range of sizes) produce a longish straight curve (see Fig. 4-3a). A uniform soil (soil having most of the particles of approximately similar size) plots as shown in Figure 4-3b. A gap-graded soil (an absence of intermediate sizes) plots as in Figure 4-3c.

The grain-size plot can provide an indication of a soil's history. A residual deposit has its particle sizes constantly changing with time as the particles continue to break down, and typically produces grain-size curves as shown in Figure 4-4. The curves shown in Figures 4-5a and 4-5b represent glacial and glacial–alluvial

Figure 4-2 Particle-size or grain-size distribution curve.

Index Properties and Classification Tests   Chap. 4

(a) Well-graded soils   (b) Uniform soil

(c) Gap-graded soil (absence of
intermediate-size particles)

Figure 4-3 Shape of particle-size distribution curve expected for described soil type.

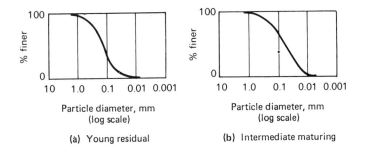

(a) Young residual   (b) Intermediate maturing

(c) Fully maturing

Figure 4-4 Typical particle-size curves for residual soils.

Classification Tests   **67**

(a) Galacial

(b) Galacial–alluvial

Figure 4-5 Typical particle-size curves for transported soils.

deposits. River deposits may be well-graded, uniform or gap-graded, depending on the water velocity, the volume of suspended solids, and the river area where deposition occurred.

Certain properties of *clean sands* have been related to particle diameters. The *effective size* of a sand is taken as the particle size corresponding to the 10 percent passing size from the grain-size curve, and is indicated as D_{10}. It is this size that is related to permeability and capillarity. Another relation, the ratio D_{60}/D_{10}, is termed the *uniformity coefficient* C_u, and provides a comparative indication of the range of particle sizes in the soil (see Fig. 4-6). Sand having a wide range of particle sizes is considered well graded and has C_u values greater than 10. A uniform soil has C_u values less than about 5.

The procedure commonly used for obtaining particle-size distribution information for silts and clays is the sedimentation method. In this method, the soil is placed into a solution with distilled water, and the soil particles are permitted to settle out of the solution. As settling occurs, the average specific gravity of the solution decreases. Readings of specific gravity or related property by use of a hydrameter, made at different time intervals, provide an indication of the weight of soil remaining in solution and also information on the sizes of particles that have settled out of the solution (see Fig. 4-7). Most conventionally, the test data are reduced to provide particle diameters and the percentage (weight) that is finer than

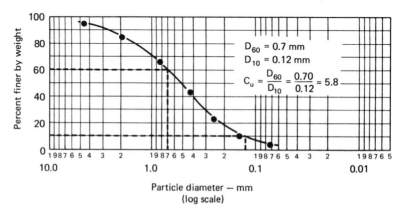

Figure 4-6 Determining uniformity coefficient from particle-size curve.

　　　　Index Properties and Classification Tests　　Chap. 4

(a)   (b)

Figure 4-7 (a) Hydrometer used to determine specific gravity of a soil-water solution being inserted into the solution; (b) diagram showing change in hydrometer depth as soil particles settle out of solution.

a particular size by using the Stokes equation for spheres falling freely in a fluid of known properties. This application is not absolutely correct, since most fine-grained soil particles are not round; in fact, most clay particles are flat or plate-shaped. The method is, therefore, more applicable to silts than to clays. Nevertheless, the method is in wide use, for it is felt to be a practical way to obtain reasonable approximations of the particle-size distribution for fine-grained soils. Resulting effects are not serious, since particle-size distribution is not used for evaluation of the significant engineering properties of fine-grained soils. Details on the method to determine the particle-size distribution by using the sedimentation test (hydrometer method) are described by ASTM Test Designation D-422.

In-Place Density, In-Place Unit Weight   The term *in-place density* refers to the volumetric weight, usually expressed as pounds per cubic foot, kilonewtons per cubic meter, or megagrams per cubic meter, of a soil in the undisturbed (or in situ) condition or in a compacted fill. (Actually, pounds per cubic foot and kilonewtons per cubic meter indicate unit weight whereas megagrams per cubic meter, Mg/m^3, indicates density. Historically, the term in-place density has been widely used for years to refer to the field procedure for determining volumetric weight, but with the advent of the SI system, improper use of weight and mass terms has become more noticeable; correct usage is evolving slowly. For reference, the density of water is one Mg/m^3, that is, $1,000,000 \ gm/m^3$.) Generally, for the coarse-grained soils, the greater the density, or unit weight, the better the shear strength and the lesser the tendency for compression (settlement). In-place density or unit weight determinations are made of borrow pit soils so as to estimate the volume of shrinkage or swell that will occur as the soil is transported or compacted in place at a fill location. Where compacted earth fills are being constructed, it is standard practice to make in-place density or unit weight determinations of the soil after it is placed

Classification Tests   **69**

Glass or
plastic
jar holds
sand

Density plate
(metal)

Sand cone
(metal)

Figure 4-8 Sand-cone and balloon apparatus for determining in-place density. (*Source*: Balloon apparatus courtesy of Soiltest, Inc.)

to determine whether the compaction effort has been adequate or if more compaction is required.

Of the equipment and methods used for making in-place density or unit weight determinations,[1] the sand cone method and the rubber balloon method have been in extensive use (see Fig. 4-8). With these methods, a small test area is selected and a volume of compacted soil is dug up and weighed. The sand cone equipment or the balloon equipment is used to determine the volume of the dug hole. Knowing soil weight (or mass) and corresponding volume permits the unit weight (or density) to be calculated.

A modern development for making in-place density and unit weight determinations involves the use of nuclear equipment (Fig. 4-9). Through controlled use of a nuclear material, gamma rays (photons) are emitted into the tested soil. These photons collide with electrons in the soil materials, some being scattered and some being absorbed. The quantity of photons reaching a detection device (part of the test equipment) relates to the soil density. To determine water content, a neutron-emitting material and detector are used. Compared to the other methods of making in-place density determinations, a significant advantage of the nuclear method is the rapid speed with which results are obtained. Detailed information on nuclear moisture-density test equipment is included in Chapter 12.

Relative Density For a granular soil, the shear strength and resistance to compression are related to the density (or unit weight) of the soil; higher shear strength and more resistance to compression are developed by the soil when it is in a dense or compact condition (high density) than when it is in a loose condition (low density). In a dense condition, the void ratio is low; in a loose condition, the void ratio is high. To evaluate the relative condition of a granular soil, the in-place void ratio can be determined and compared to the void ratio when the soil is in its densest condition and when it is in the loosest condition (see Fig. 4-10). This comparison is the relative density D_R. Relative density is expressed as a percentage.

[1]More detailed discussion of the procedures and equipment for performing in-place density testing is included in Chapter 12.

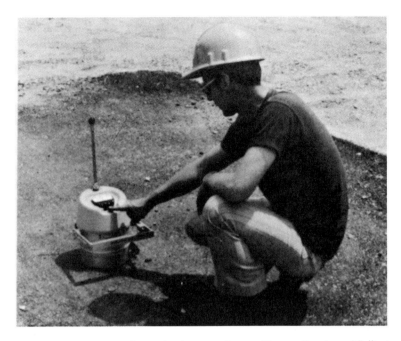

Figure 4-9 Nuclear moisture-density meter in use. (*Source*: Courtesy of Soiltest, Inc.)

High values indicate a dense or compact material; low values represent a loose material.

$$D_R^\% = \frac{e_{\max} - e_0}{e_{\max} - e_{\min}} \times 100\% \qquad (4\text{-}1)$$

where $e_{\max}$ = void ratio of the soil in its loosest condition.

$e_{\min}$ = void ratio of the soil in its densest condition.

e_0 = void ratio of the soil in the natural condition or condition in question.

The maximum density (or minimum void ratio) is determined in the laboratory by compacting the soil in thin layers in a container of known volume and subsequently weighing the soil. The compaction is achieved by applying a vibratory and

Figure 4-10 Relative conditions of a granular soil.

Classification Tests

compressive force simultaneously. The compressive force needs to be sufficient to compact the soil without breaking the individual particles of soil. Because of the irregular size and shape of granular particles, it is not possible to obtain a zero volume of void spaces. Practically, there will always be voids in a soil mass.

The minimum density (or maximum void ratio) can be determined in the laboratory by carefully letting the soil slowly flow into the test container through a funnel. When this task is carefully performed, the soil will be deposited and remain in a loose condition, from whence the loose density and void ratio can be calculated.

In terms of dry unit weights (which are more convenient to work with), relative density is

$$D_R^\% = \frac{\dfrac{1}{\gamma_{\min}} - \dfrac{1}{\gamma_0}}{\dfrac{1}{\gamma_{\min}} - \dfrac{1}{\gamma_{\max}}} \times 100\% \tag{4-2}$$

where $\gamma_{\min}$ = dry unit weight (or density) in the loosest condition.
$\gamma_{\max}$ = dry unit weight in the densest condition.
γ_0 = dry unit weight in the condition in question.

Typical relative density values are presented in Table 4-3.

ILLUSTRATION 4-1. An undisturbed sample of fine sand is tested in the laboratory and found to have a dry weight of 8 lb, a total volume of 0.07 ft³ and a specific gravity G_s of 2.70. Other laboratory tests were performed to determine the maximum and minimum density for the sand. At the maximum density, it is determined that the void ratio is 0.35; at the minimum density the void ratio is 0.95. Determine the relative density of the undisturbed sample.

Void ratio of undisturbed sample e_0:

$$V_T = 0.07 \text{ ft}^3$$

$$V_s = \frac{W_s}{G_s \gamma_w} = \frac{8 \text{ lb}}{(2.70)(62.4 \text{ pcf})} = 0.0474 \text{ ft}^3$$

$$V_v = V_T - V_s = 0.070 - 0.0474 = 0.0226 \text{ ft}^3$$

$$e_0 = \frac{V_v}{V_s} = \frac{0.0226 \text{ ft}^3}{0.0474 \text{ ft}^3} = 0.476$$

$$D_R = \frac{e_{\max} - e_0}{e_{\max} - e_{\min}} = \frac{0.95 - 0.476}{0.95 - 0.35} = 0.79 = 79\%$$

Dry unit weight of soil $= \dfrac{W_s}{V_T} = \dfrac{8.0 \text{ lb}}{0.07 \text{ ft}^3} \approx 115 \text{ pcf}$

In its natural condition, the soil is probably dense (see Table 4-3).

Index Properties and Classification Tests   Chap. 4

TABLE 4-3 REPRESENTATIVE VALUES OF RELATIVE DENSITY

Descriptive condition	Relative density, %	Typical range of unit weight	
		pcf	kN/m³
Loose	<35	<90	<14
Medium dense	35–65	90–110	14–17
Dense	65–85	110–130	17–20
Very dense	>85	>130	>20

Water Content For coarse- and fine-grained soils, water content can have a significant effect on the soils' behavioral properties when used for construction purposes. By definition and as previously described, water content (w) is the ratio of the weight of water in a soil to the dry weight of the material. As a result, in laboratory and field work the weight of water in the test sample has to be determined. Conventionally this is done by drying the original wet sample, recording the wet and dry weights, and performing the required calculation.

One device, the Speedy Moisture Tester (Fig. 4-11), bases its operation on the reaction that occurs between a carbide reagent and soil moisture to determine a soil's water content. The wet soil sample is placed in a sealed container with calcium carbide, and the pressure generated by the vaporized moisture is then related to water content. This method provides a rapid procedure for determining moisture content and is finding increased usage in laboratory and field work.[2]

Figure 4-11 Speedy moisture tester: Speedy Kit including tester chamber, scales, and reagent for vaporizing soil moisture.

[2]Somewhat unfortunately, the Speedy moisture reading is expressed as a percentage of the soil's wet weight. Conversion to moisture content by dry weight can be performed using the relationship

$$w\% = \frac{w_{sp}}{1 - w_{sp}} \times 100\%$$

where w_{sp} is the moisture content obtained with the Speedy device, expressed as a decimal.

Classification Tests

Consistency of Clays *Consistency* refers to the texture and firmness of a soil and is often directly related to the strength. Consistency is conventionally described as *soft, medium stiff* (or *medium firm*), *stiff* (or *firm*), or *hard*. These terms, unfortunately, are relative and have different meanings to different observers. For standardization, it is reasonable and practical to relate consistency to strength. With clays, shear strength is discussed in terms of cohesion and unconfined compressive strength. The unconfined compressive strength is obtained by imposing an axial load to the ends of an unsupported cylindrical sample of clay and determining the load that causes shear failure in the sample. Unconfined compression tests can be performed in the laboratory or in the field. The unconfined compressive strength is, under practical conditions, twice the cohesion (or shear strength) of a clay soil. The cohesion can be determined in a laboratory strength test. For a consistency classification in the field or laboratory, special soil testing equipment such as a vane-shear device or pocket penetrometer provides means of making quick and easy determinations (Fig. 4-12). A tabulation of strength values for various consistency terms is shown in Table 4-4.

It is well established that the strength of a clay soil is related to its structure. If the original structure is altered because of changes in particle arrangement (from reworking or remolding) or chemical changes, the strength of the altered clay is less than the original strength. *Sensitivity* is the term that provides an indication of remolded strength related to original strength. When remolded, the strength of a clay is affected by the water content. At lower water contents, strength is generally

Figure 4-12 Testing equipment for making strength or consistency determinations on cohesive soils.

Index Properties and Classification Tests   Chap. 4

TABLE 4-4 CONSISTENCY AND STRENGTH FOR COHESIVE SOILS

Consistency	Shear strength, T/SF or Kg/cm² (kN/m²)	Unconfined compressive strength, T/SF or Kg/cm² (kN/m²)	Feel or touch
Soft	Less than 0.25 (<24)	Less than 0.5 (<48)	Blunt end of pencil-sized object makes deep penetration easily.
Medium (medium stiff or medium firm)	0.25–0.50 (24–48)	0.50–1.0 (48–96)	Blunt end of pencil-sized object makes half-inch penetration with moderate effort.
Stiff (firm)	0.50–1.0 (48–96)	1.0–2.0 (96–190)	Blunt end of pencil-sized object makes moderate penetration (about one-quarter in.).
Very stiff (very firm)	1.0–2.0 (96–190)	2.0–4.0 (190–380)	Blunt end of pencil-sized object makes slight indentation; fingernail easily penetrates.
Hard	Greater than 2.0 (>190)	Greater than 4.0 (>380)	Blunt end of pencil-sized object makes no indentation; fingernail barely penetrates.

Classification Tests

greater. However, sensitivity should be based on comparison of remolded to un-disturbed soil strength at an identical water content.

$$\text{Sensitivity } S_t = \frac{\text{Unconfined compressive strength, undisturbed clay}}{\text{Unconfined compressive strength, remolded clay}} \quad (4\text{-}3)$$

For most clays, sensitivities range between 2 and 4. Clays considered *sensitive* have S_t values between 4 and 8. Clays classified as *extrasensitive* have values between 8 and 16. Clays with sensitivity values greater than 16 are classified as *quick* clays. Such clays are very unstable. Normally, clays with a high degree of sensitivity possess a very flocculent structure in the undisturbed condition.

Consistency in the Remolded State and Plasticity   In the remolded state, the consistency of a clay soil varies in proportion to the water content. At higher water content, the soil–water mixture possesses the properties of a liquid; at lesser water contents, the volume of the mixture is decreased and the material exhibits the properties of a plastic; at still lesser water contents, the mixture behaves as a semisolid and finally as a solid.

The water content indicating the division between the liquid and plastic state has been designated the *liquid limit*. The division between the plastic and semisolid state is the *plastic limit*. The water content at the division between the semisolid and the solid state is the *shrinkage limit*.

At water contents above the shrinkage limit, the total volume of the soil–water mixture changes in proportion to change in water content. Below the shrinkage limit, there is little or no change in volume as water content varies (Fig. 4-13).

Definition of the various states of consistency and the establishment of criteria to determine these various states were first formally proposed by A. Atterberg, a Swedish soil scientist, in the early twentieth century. Initially intended for agricultural use, the method has been adapted for engineering use in classifying soils. Although the limit values (water contents) have little direct meaning insofar as engineering properties of soils are concerned, correlations between liquid or plastic limits and engineering properties have been established over the years to aid in evaluating a soil for use as structural fill (dams, embankments, landfills), for highway construction, and for building support.

The liquid limit is taken as the water content at which the soil "flows" (like a viscous liquid). Special equipment and procedures, defined in ASTM Test Designation D-423, are required for determining the liquid limit (see Fig. 4-14). The plastic limit is the water content where the soil can just be rolled into a $\frac{1}{8}$-inch diameter thread before crumbling, as described in ASTM Test Designation D-424.

Various designations have been used to indicate the liquid and plastic limit. Using LL and PL for liquid limit and plastic limit, respectively, provides an easily understood terminology that has little chance of misinterpretation.

The *plasticity index* (PI) is the numerical difference of the liquid and plastic limits, and indicates the range of water content through which the soil remains plastic. For proper evaluation of a soil's plasticity properties, it has been found desirable to use both the liquid limit and plasticity index values. Engineering soil

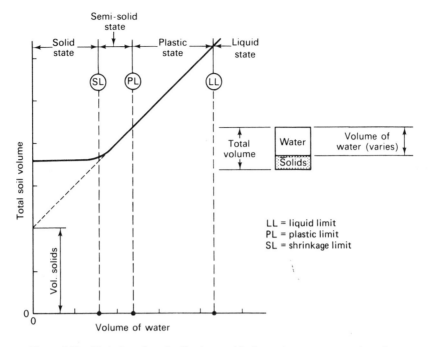

Figure 4-13 Variation of total soil volume with change in water content for a fine-grained soil (for soil in remolded state).

Figure 4-14 (a) Liquid limit trial being performed; (b) details of liquid limit device; (c) soil thread being rolled to determine plastic limit.

Classification Tests

77

classification systems use these values as a basis for classifying the fine-grained soils.

For fine-grained soils, determining the natural water content (the water content of a soil in an undisturbed condition in the ground) and relating it to the plastic and liquid limits can provide an indication of the soil's consistency and/or sensitivity potential. One such relationship is the *liquidity index*, LI:

$$LI = \frac{w\% - PL\%}{LL\% - PL\%} = \frac{w - PL}{PI} \tag{4-4}$$

where w is the natural water content of the soil. A value less than one indicates that the natural water content is less than the liquid limit. A very low value for the LI, or a value near zero, indicates that the water content is near the plastic limit, where experience has shown that the sensitivity will be low and the cohesive strength relatively high (a stiff or hard consistency). As the natural water content approaches or exceeds the liquid limit, the sensitivity increases. The undisturbed strength still very much depends on the undisturbed structure. Negative values of the LI are possible and normally indicate a desiccated (dried) hard soil.

Presence of Clay Minerals   The presence of even small amounts of certain clay minerals in a soil mass can have significant effect on the properties of the soil. Identifying the type and amount of clay mineral may be necessary in order to predict the soil's behavior or to develop methods for minimizing detrimental effects.

The identification of clay minerals requires special techniques and equipment and trained personnel. Many different techniques are available. Some are useful for identifying only a particular type of clay, whereas other methods are suitable for identifying several types of minerals. These techniques include microscopic examinations, X-ray diffraction, differential thermal analysis, infrared absorption, optical property determination, and electron micrography. Description of these techniques and equipment is beyond the scope of this text; further information is available in publications dealing with clay mineralogy. Even with the techniques available to today's soil scientists, the accurate determination of some clay minerals is not possible. Generally, however, qualitative if not quantitative identifications can be made that are adequate for many engineering problems.

A somewhat indirect method of obtaining information on the type and effect of clay mineral in a soil is to relate plasticity to the quantity of clay-sized particles. It is known that for a given amount of clay mineral the plasticity resulting in a soil will vary for the different types of clays. One relationship is *activity*, defined as

$$\text{Activity} = \frac{\text{Plasticity index, \%}}{\text{Percentage of clay sizes, \%}} \tag{4-5}$$

For this analysis, the percentage of clay sizes is that portion of the soil, by weight, consisting of particle sizes below 0.002 mm. Such information is available from the conventional hydrometer analysis used to determine a particle-size distribution. Activity, therefore, can be determined from standard laboratory tests. Clay materials with kaolinite, a stable clay mineral, will have low activity, whereas those soils with montmorillonite, known to be a type subject to large volume changes depending on available water, will have a high activity value. Limited study has also indicated the possibility of a relation betwen activity and shear strength. A relative activity classification is as follows:

Activity	Classification
< 0.75	Inactive clays
0.75–1.25	Normal clays
> 1.25	Active clays

Testing for Dispersive Clay   On the basis of testing many clay soils for dispersion (dispersive clays as described in Chapter 3), the relationship between the presence of ions and susceptibility to deflocculation shown in Figure 4-15 has been proposed. Atomic absorption spectroscopy or flame photometry is used to determine the ion concentrations. Unfortunately, a clay's tendency to disperse is not indicated by conventional soil classification tests such as the Atterberg limits. The atomic absorption spectroscope and flame photometer are not ordinarily found in soil mechanics laboratories; simple *qualitative* tests, using standard laboratory equipment, capable of being performed in the field have been developed and are outlined next. Judgment is involved when evaluating some of the results but generally the tests are good indicators.

1. *Soil Conservation Service Dispersion Test*: This procedure, also known as the double hydrometer test, compares the percentage of soil sample particles smaller than 0.005 mm as determined by a conventional hydrometer analysis

Figure 4-15   Relationship of pore water salts and soil dispersion. (*Source*: After Sherard, Dunnigan, and Decker [000]).

(where a deflocculating agent is used and the soil sample is mechanically agitated prior to test) and as determined when a similar sample is exposed to a plain distilled water environment without being agitated, whence

$$\% \text{ dispersion} = \frac{\% \text{ finer than 0.005 mm in plain water test}}{\% \text{ finer than 0.005 mm in conventional hydrometer test}}$$

A percentage dispersion greater than 35 percent is used to indicate a dispersive clay soil.

2. *Crumb Test*: A small sample of soil (one cm or less in diameter) preserved at the natural water content is placed in a beaker of distilled water. The reaction in terms of a colloidal cloud around the crumb is an indication of the soil's tendency to disperse; no cloud indicates a nondispersive material.

3. *Pinhole Test*: The test soil is compacted, and distilled water is then made to flow through a one-mm-diameter hole in the sample. The test can be set up in the permeameter apparatus used for permeability determinations, using pea gravel filters at the ends of the test sample. With a dispersive clay, the hole erodes and the flowing water discharge is colored, whereas for a non-dispersive soil the hole does not enlarge and the water discharge remains clear.

Other Properties Where a soil is to be used to support building foundations or other types of buried structures (such as pipelines, tunnels, and storage vaults), it is good practice to have pH and soluble sulfate determinations made, so as to obtain information on the corrosion potential to buried metal (piles or piping) or the deteriorating effect on concrete foundations.

CLASSIFICATION SYSTEMS

Soil classification systems have been devised primarily to facilitate the transfer of information between interested parties. In the engineering and construction field, the broad general properties of concern relate to the performance or usefulness for supporting structures and the handling or working qualities of a soil. Because of the wide variation in properties and behavior of soils, classification systems generally group together in relatively broad categories the soils that have similar features or properties that are considered to be of importance. As a result, a classification system is not necessarily an identification system in which all pertinent engineering properties of a material are determined. Because of this, soil classification should not be used as the sole basis for design or construction planning.

Historically, the most widely used method of classifying soils has been through visual identification, the size of soil grains and the plasticity of the soil being used as the basis for indicating the soil type. To a great degree, the refined and more recently developed classification systems that rely on laboratory-determined properties for accurate identification still use these two criteria as the basis for indicating soil type.

The desirable requirements for a satisfactory engineering soil classification system include:

1. There should be a limited number of different groupings, so that the system is easy to remember and use. Groupings should be on the basis of only a few similar properties and generally similar behavioral characteristics.

2. The properties and behavioral characteristics should have meaning for the engineering and construction profession. Generally, the properties should, at least crudely, relate to a soil's handling characteristics, shear strength, volume change characteristics, and permeabilty.

3. Descriptions used for each grouping should be in terms that are easily understood and are in common use for indicating the soil type and its properties. Symbols or shorthand used to describe the grouping should easily relate to the soil type. Coded symbols are not desirable.

4. Classification into any grouping should be possible on the basis of visual identification (generally limited to differentiating between particle sizes, coarse- and fine-grained soils, and plasticity) without special tests or equipment being necessary.

The Unified Soil Classification System satisfies the above requirements of a classification system and is the system that is coming into prevalent use in the engineering and construction fields. This system is shown in Figure 4-16. Classifications are on the basis of coarse- and fine-grained soils, and retain the four common groupings of soil—gravel, sand, silt, and clay. The symbols are easily associated with the classification, being simply the first letter of the soil type (except for silt, which has the designation M, from *mo*, the Swedish word for silt). Refinement in grouping is based upon a coarse soil's being well or poorly graded, and a fine-grained soil being of a high or low plasticity. What at first appears to be a large number of groupings are in fact very logical categories. Experience has proved that previously untrained personnel very quickly learn the system and use it with accuracy. The Unified System includes the use of a plasticity chart for aiding classification of fine-grained soils.

Another system familiar to those in the engineering and construction fields is the AASHTO (American Association of State Highway and Transportation Officials) Classification System (Fig. 4-17), which has been in wide use for highway construction work. The criteria for the groupings are logical, but shortcomings include the requirement for laboratory testing in order to determine a classification, and the difficulty in using code designations and remembering the requirement for each of the designations. To obtain an indication of the relationship between the Unified and AASHTO systems, a comparison is presented in Table 4-5.

Unified Soil Classification System
(ASTM Designation D-2487)

Major division			Group Symbols	Typical Names	Classification Criteria
Coarse-grained soils More than 50% retained on No. 200 sieve	Gravels 50% or more of coarse fraction retained on No. 4 sieve	Clean gravels	GW	Well-graded gravels and gravel-sand mixtures, little or no fines	$C_u = D_{60}/D_{10}$ Greater than 4 $C_z = \dfrac{(D_{30})^2}{D_{10} \times D_{60}}$ Between 1 and 3
			GP	Poorly graded gravels and gravel-sand mixtures, little or no fines	Not meeting both criteria for GW
		Gravels with fines	GM	Silty gravels, gravel-sand-silt mixtures	Atterberg limits plot below "A" line or plasticity index less than 4
			GC	Clayey gravels, gravel-sand-clay mixtures	Atterberg limits plot above "A" line and plasticity index greater than 7
	Sands More than 50% of coarse fraction passes No. 4 sieve	Clean sands	SW	Well-graded sands and gravelly sands, little or no fines	$C_u = D_{60}/D_{10}$ Greater than 6 $C_z = \dfrac{(D_{30})^2}{D_{10} \times D_{60}}$ Between 1 and 3
			SP	Poorly graded sands and gravelly sands, little or no fines	Not meeting both criteria for SW
		Sands with fines	SM	Silty sands, sand-silt mixtures	Atterberg limits plot below "A" line or plasticity index less than 4
			SC	Clayey sands, sand-clay mixtures	Atterberg limits plot above "A" line and plasticity index greater than 7
Fine-grained soils 50% or more passes No. 200 sieve	Silts and Clays Liquid limit 50% or less		ML	Inorganic silts, very fine sands, rock flour, silty or clayey fine sands	
			CL	Inorganic clays of low to medium plasticity, gravelly clays, sandy clays, silty clays, lean clays	
			OL	Organic silts and organic silty clays of low plasticity	Check plasticity chart
	Silts and Clays Liquid limit greater than 50%		MH	Inorganic silts, micaceous or diatomaceous fine sands or silts, elastic silts	
			CH	Inorganic clays of high plasticity, fat clays	
			OH	Organic clays of medium to high plasticity	
Highly organic soils			Pt	Peat, muck and other highly organic soils	Fibrous organic matter; will char, burn, or glow

(Classification on basis of percentage of fines: Less than 5% Pass No. 200 sieve — GW, GP, SW, SP; More than 12% Pass No. 200 sieve — GM, GC, SM, SC; 5% to 12% Pass No. 200 sieve — Borderline classification requiring use of dual symbols)

(a)

Plasticity chart for the classification of fine-grained soils.
Tests made on fraction finer than No. 40 sieve.

(b)

Figure 4-16 Unified Soil Classification System (ASTM Designation D-2487).

General Classification*	Granular Materials (35 percent or less passing No. 200)							Silt-Clay Materials (more than 35 percent passing No. 200)			
	A-1		A-3	A-2				A-4	A-5	A-6	A-7
Group Classification	A-1-a	A-1-b		A-2-4	A-2-5	A-2-6	A-2-7				A-7-5 A-7-6
Sieve analysis percent passing:											
No. 10	50 max										
No. 40	30 max	50 max	51 min								
No. 200	15 max	25 max	10 max	35 max	35 max	35 max	35 max	36 min	36 min	36 min	36 min
Characteristics of fraction passing No. 40:											
Liquid limit				40 max	41 min	40 max	41 min	40 max	41 min	40 max	41 min
Plasticity index	6 max		N.P.[b]	10 max	10 max	11 min	11 min	10 max	10 max	11 min	11 min
Usual types of significant constituent materials	Stone fragments —gravel and sand		Fine sand	Silty or clayey gravel and sand				Silty soils		Clayey soils	
General rating as subgrade	Excellent to good							Fair to poor			

[a]Classification procedure: With required test data in mind, proceed from left to right in chart; correct group will be found by process of elimination. The first group from the left consistent with the test data is the correct classification. The A-7 group is subdivided into A-7-5 or A-7-6 depending on the plastic limit. For PL < 30, the classification is A-7-6; for PL > 30, A-7-5.

[b]N.P. denotes nonplastic.

Figure 4-17 American Association of State Highway and Transportation Officials Soil Classification System (AASHTO Designation M-145).

TABLE 4-5 APPROXIMATE EQUIVALENT GROUPS OF
AASHTO AND UNIFIED SOIL CLASSIFICATION SYSTEMS

AASHTO	Unified
A-2-6	GC, SC
A-2-7	GC, SC
A-3	SP
A-4	ML, OL
A-5	MH
A-6	CL
A-7-5	CL, OL
A-7-6	CH, OH

PROBLEMS

4-1. Indicate the difference between index properties of a soil and classification tests.

4-2. The following information is obtained from a sieve analysis to determine the range of particle sizes in a granular soil sample.

Sieve size	Sieve opening (mm)	Percent filter by weight
# 4	4.76	96
# 10	2.00	80
# 20	0.84	52
# 40	0.42	38
# 60	0.25	25
# 100	0.149	12
# 200	0.074	5

Present the information as a grain-size curve on semilog coordinates of percent finer versus particle diameters. From the plot, determine the uniformity coefficient C_u.

4-3. (a) An in-place density determination (in-place unit weight) is made of a sand in a borrow pit using a balloon type density apparatus. A sample dug from a test hole is found to weigh 8.5 lb. The volume of the test hole is 0.065 ft³. From these data, compute the wet unit weight of the soil.

   (b) This soil is found to have a water content of 15 percent. Compute the dry unit weight of the soil and, by referral to Table 4-3, indicate the probable condition of the natural material.

4-4. A sand at a borrow pit is determined to have an in-place dry unit weight of 115 pcf. Laboratory tests performed to determine the maximum and minimum unit weights give values of 122 pcf and 102 pcf, respectively. From these data, what is the relative density of the natural soil?

4-5. An undisturbed sample of sand has a dry weight of 4.20 lb and occupies a volume of 0.038 ft³. The soil solids have a specific gravity of 2.75. Laboratory tests performed to determine the maximum and minimum densities indicate void ratios of 0.42 at the maximum density and 0.92 at the minimum density. Compute the relative density of this material.

4-6. A fine-grained soil is found to have a liquid limit of 70 percent and a plastic limit of 38 percent.
   (a) What do the percentages for these limit values represent?
   (b) What is the plasticity index for this soil?
   (c) On the plasticity chart for the Unified Soil Classification System, what soil type is this?

4-7. A silt–clay soil has a plastic limit of 25 and a plasticity index of 30.
   (a) If the natural water content of the soil is 35 percent, what is the liquidity index?
   (b) What soil type is this, according to the Unified Soil Classification System?

4-8. A fine-grained soil is found to have a liquid limit of 90 percent and a plasticity index of 51. The natural water content is 28 percent.
   (a) Determine the liquidity index and indicate the probable consistency of the natural soil.
   (b) Classify this soil according to the Unified Soil Classification System.

4-9. A saturated 100-cc clay sample has a natural water content of 30 percent. It is found that the shrinkage limit occurs when the water content is 19 percent. If the specific gravity of soil solids is 2.70, what will the volume of the sample be when the water content is 15 percent?

4-10. A clay soil is found to have a liquid limit of 75 percent, a plastic limit of 45 percent, and a shrinkage limit of 25 percent. If a sample of this soil has a total volume of 30 cc at the liquid limit and a volume of 16.7 cc at the shrinkage limit, what is the specific gravity of the soil solids?

4-11. Limit tests performed on a clay indicate a liquid limit of 67 percent and a plastic limit of 32 percent. From a hydrometer analysis to determine particle sizes, it is found that 40 percent of the sample consists of particles smaller than 0.002 mm. From this information, indicate the activity classification for this clay, and the probable type of clay mineral.

## chapter 5

Movement of Water Through Soil: Basic Principles
Permeability and Capillarity

Natural soil deposits, as they exist at most locations, include water. Under many conditions, the soil water is not immobile but does move or is capable of moving through the ground. Moving water affects the properties and behavior of soil and can influence both construction operations and the performance of completed construction. Since groundwater conditions are frequently encountered on construction projects, those in the construction profession have found it necessary to understand the manner in which movement of water through soil can occur and its possible effects. The discussion on permeability and capillary action in soil in this chapter relates to type and manner of water movement. The discussion on drainage, seepage, and frost heave in Chapter 6 relates to the practical effects of water movement.

PERMEABILITY

Soil, being a particulate material, has many pore or void spaces existing between the solid grains because of the irregular shape of the individual particles. In a mass of particles that are rounded and roughly equidimensional in shape, such as the gravels, sands, and silts, or are platey or flakelike, such as clays, the pore spaces are interconnected. Fluids (and gases) can travel or flow through the pore spaces in the soil. Thus, soil deposits are porous, and the material is considered a *permeable* material. It should be realized that flow is occurring through the void spaces between particles, and not actually *through* the particles themselves (see Fig. 5-1).

Figure 5-1 Schematic diagram indicating manner in which water flows through soil.

• water

Factors Affecting Flow   The actual path taken by a fluid particle as it flows through void spaces from one point toward another is a tortuous and erratic one in most soils because of the random arrangement of the soil grains. It is highly probable that the direction of flow and velocity of flow vary considerably.

The factors that can affect the flow of a fluid through soil are known, but the *influence* of all factors has not been clearly established. These factors include:

1. The pressure difference existing between the two points where flow is occurring
2. The density and viscosity of the fluid
3. The size, shape, and number of pore openings
4. The mineralogical, electrochemical, or other pertinent properties of the fluid and the soil particles, which affect the attraction between the two materials

The effects of items 3 and 4 on flow are the most difficult to evaluate, partly because of the tremendous variation that occurs in natural deposits (even in homogeneous soils) and partly because of insufficient knowledge.

In many engineering and construction problems, the concern is primarily with the *quantity* of fluid, usually but not always water, that is flowing through or out of a soil mass. The seepage *velocity* is frequently sufficiently low that no problems result because of this factor, and it may not even require consideration. An exception is where the velocity is great enough to cause movement of the soil particles, or erosion; this problem is discussed in Chapter 6 on flow nets. For the situation where the *quantity* of flow is to be determined, an *average discharge velocity* is assumed. This is a fictitious velocity compared to the actual velocity of flow. The discharge velocity is simply the volume of fluid flow per unit of time divided by the total area (soil plus voids) measured normal to the direction of flow. If an average *seepage velocity* (average actual velocity of flow) is desired, it can be obtained by dividing the average discharge velocity by n, the porosity of the soil (recall that porosity n equals V_v/V_T).

Experimental studies have shown that fluid flow is affected by the shape and dimensions of the channel through which flow is occurring. To relate these effects to flow velocity, the terms *hydraulic radius* and *shape factor* have been developed.

Permeability   **87**

Hydraulic radius R_H provides a relation between the cross-sectional area of flow and the channel walls that are in contact with the fluid;

$$R_H = \frac{\text{Area of flow}}{\text{Wetted perimeter}} \qquad (5\text{-}1)$$

The coefficient that reflects the shape factor is C_S. For a circular tube flowing full (Fig. 5-2), the hydraulic radius is one-half the tube diameter and $C_S = \frac{1}{2}$.

Cross-section of flow area
= πr^2
Wetted perimeter
= $2\pi r$

$R_H = \frac{\pi r^2}{2\pi r} = \frac{r}{2} = \frac{1}{2}r$

Figure 5-2 Hydraulic radius for pipe flowing full.

To indicate how *permeable* a porous material will be to *any* flowing fluid, the term K, permeability, is used. Mathematically,

$$K = C_S R_H^2 n \qquad (5\text{-}2)$$

where n = porosity of the material. It should be understood this term applies *only to the material* through which the flow could occur. It reflects the effect of the size, shape, and number of flow channels, and is completely independent of any fluid properties.

To indicate the ease or difficulty that a particular *fluid* will encounter when flowing through a permeable material, the properties of the fluid are incorporated with K, the properties of the permeable material, to provide a *coefficient of permeability k* (the lowercase letter is used for this term), where

$$k = K\frac{\gamma}{\eta} \qquad (5\text{-}3)$$

where γ = unit weight of the fluid (e.g., pcf, kN/m³).
η = viscosity of the fluid.

This relation permits a coefficient of permeability to be determined for any fluid whose properties are known.

Darcy's Law for Flow   In the mid-eighteenth century, H. Darcy performed experiments to study the flow of water through sands. With an arrangement represented by Figure 5-3, it was found that the quantity of water flowing through the soil in a given period was proportional to the soil area normal to the direction of flow and the difference in levels indicated in the piezometers (open standpipes), and inversely proportional to the length of soil between piezometers through which flow took place. Mathematically,

$$\frac{Q}{t} \propto \frac{(\Delta h) \times (A)}{L} = (\text{a constant}) \times \frac{(\Delta h) \times (A)}{L}$$

Figure 5-3 Darcy's sand filtration experiment.

where Q = volume of water flowing through the soil in a time t.
  t = time period for the volume Q to flow.
  Δh = $h_1 - h_2$.
  A = cross-sectional area of the soil sample.
  L = length of soil through which flow occurs.

The factors A and L relate to the volume occupied by the soil but not to its properties. The value of Δh relates to the pressure acting to force the water to flow through the soil. The constant of proportionality, a factor that indicates if the volume of flow is to be great or small, relates to the ease or difficulty with which the water moves through the soil. This constant of proportionality is k, Darcy's *coefficient of permeability*. This is the same coefficient of permeability indicated in Equation 5-3, but attributed to Darcy, who first established it. Consequently,

$$\frac{Q}{t} = k\frac{(\Delta h)(A)}{L} \tag{5-4}$$

which is Darcy's law. The ratio of $\Delta h/L$ is termed the hydraulic gradient i, and therefore

$$\frac{Q}{t} = q = kiA \tag{5-5}$$

where q = volume of flow per unit time.
  The units of k are length per unit time; i is dimensionless (length divided by length); area is in square units.
  For steady flow, the volume of flow q passing a point is equal to the product of flow velocity v and the cross-sectional area A through which flow occurs;

$$q = Av \tag{5-6}$$

where units of v are length or distance per unit of time.
  From Equations 5-5 and 5-6, an expression for velocity of flow is obtained.

$$q = kiA,$$

and

$$v = ki \tag{5-7}$$

Permeability   **89**

This is a theoretical average velocity, and will be lower than an actual velocity. Its determination is of use in practical problems, however, where only order of magnitude is required.

Laminar and Turbulent Flow   The movement of a fluid through a channel or pore space can be described as laminar or turbulent flow, depending on the path followed by the flowing water particles. Laminar (layered) flow indicates that adjacent paths of water particles are parallel, even when changing direction, and the paths never cross. This is an orderly flow with no mixing. Turbulent flow indicates a disorderly random path for moving water particles, with lines of movement crossing and frequently moving at an angle with or contrary to the general direction of flow. A high degree of mixing occurs.

Velocity has direct bearing on whether a flow is laminar or turbulent.

Darcy's law for fluid flow applies provided that the flow is laminar. In soils, the velocity of flow is affected by the size of the void opening as well as the hydraulic gradient i. Studies show that for soils in the coarse sand and finer range, and frequently for small gravel, laminar flow occurs provided that the hydraulic gradient is 5 or less. In practical soil mechanics work, Darcy's law thus has a wide range of application.

Effect of Soil Type   The volume of water that can flow through a soil bulk is related more to the size of the void openings than to the number or total volume of voids. This is shown by observing that the values of k for coarse soils are greater than for fine-grained soils (even though void ratios are frequently greater for the fine-grained soils) along with the knowledge that voids in a soil mass are approximately of the same size as the particles themselves.

This phenomenon of higher permeability in coarse-grained soil can be explained, at least in part, by the manner in which water flows through a conduit. The fluid flow measured at increments of distance extending between the walls of the conduit indicates that the velocity varies from a very low value adjacent to the wall of the conduit (or against the soil particle) to a maximum at the center of the conduit, as indicated in Figure 5-4. This variation in flow is caused by the friction developed at the conduit wall and the viscous friction developed in the moving fluid. For fine-grained soil, where void spaces are very small, all lines of flow are physically close to the "wall of the conduit," and therefore only low-velocity flows occur. In clays, flow in already small "flow channels" is further hampered because some of the water in the voids is held, or adsorbed, to the clay particles, reducing the flow area and further restricting flow.

Velocity at wall = $V_{min.}$
Velocity at center = $V_{max.}$

Figure 5-4   Variation of flow velocity across the cross-section of a tube.

TABLE 5-1 TYPICAL RANGES OF PERMEABILITY FOR DIFFERENT SOIL TYPES

Soil type	Relative degree of permeability	k, coefficient of permeability (cm/sec)	Drainage properties
Clean gravel	High	$1\text{--}10$	Good
Clean sand, sand and gravel mixtures	Medium	$1\text{--}10^{-3}$	Good
Fine sands, silts	Low	$10^{-3}\text{--}10^{-5}$	Fair–poor
Sand–silt–clay mixtures, glacial tills	Very low	$10^{-4}\text{--}10^{-7}$	Poor–practically impervious
Homogeneous clays	Very low– practically impermeable	$<10^{-7}$	Practically impervious

Note: To convert cm/sec to ft/min, multiply cm/sec by 2; that is, 1 cm/sec = 2 ft/min; also ft/day = cm/sec $\times$ 3 $\times$ 10^3.

Typical ranges of permeability for different soil types and resulting drainage characteristics are listed in Table 5-1.

Empirical Relationships Considerable information on the flow of fluids through porous media has been obtained from studies of flow through tubes and conduits. From such information, attempts have been made to relate permeability to a soil's grain size. Practically, such a relationship appears more possible for sands and silts than for clays, because of the particle size, shape, and overall soil structure. One of the more widely known relationships is

$$k = 100 D_{10}{}^2 \tag{5-8a}$$

where k is given in centimeters per second and D_{10} is the 10 percent particle size, expressed in centimeters, from the grain-size distribution analysis (from the curve resulting from plotting percent finer by weight versus particle diameters).[1] This relationship was developed from the work of Hazen on sands.[2] This expression applies *only* to uniform sands in a relatively loose condition.

More recent studies to evaluate the permeability and filter properties of sands [217] have determined a relationship between the D_{15} size and the k value for *dense* or *compacted sands*. A close approximation for coefficient of permeability based on the D_{15} size is

$$k = 0.35 \, (D_{15})^2 \tag{5-8b}$$

when D_{15} is expressed in millimeters and the k value is in centimeters per second. The permeability for *loose sands* will be greater than indicated by Equation 5-8b.

[1]See Chapter 4, the section on particle-size distribution curve.

[2]Originally included in "Some Physical Properties of Sands and Gravels with Special Reference to Their Use in Filtration," Allen Hazen, 24th annual report of the State Board of Health of Massachusetts, 1892, and numerous subsequent engineering manuals, including reference [177].

For sands where the C_u value is less than about 10, the k value for the loose condition can be estimated as 1.5–3 times the equation value. When the C_u value is more than 10, the permeability for a loose sand can be considerably greater (5–15 times greater) than the value indicated by Equation 5-8b.

Permeability Tests   Much of the available information from studies of flow through uniform porous media is not directly applicable to soils because of the variation in the size and shape of void spaces in a soil mass. For soil, it has been found to be more practical and accurate to evaluate flow directly through use of laboratory or field tests on the soil in question. Experience has shown that for a given soil a relationship exists between permeability and void ratio. Generally, a semilog plot (e plotted on an arithmetic scale, k plotted on a logarithmic scale) produces approximately a straight line for most soils. Thus, permeability tests can be performed on a soil at two or three widely different void ratios, and the results can then be plotted. Permeability at intermediate void ratios would be determined by interpolation (see Fig. 5-5).

The permeability of a soil deposit is significantly affected by its in-place structure. A loose granular (coarse-grained) soil would have a higher void ratio than a dense soil, and therefore would permit greater flow. Clays are very significantly affected by structure. Even at similar void ratios, a clay with an undisturbed flocculated structure will possess larger void openings than the same clay having a remolded dispersed (or oriented) structure, with the result that the permeability is many times greater for the flocculated soil (see Fig. 5-6).

Extremely important is the significance of stratification. In layered soils, the permeability measured for flow across layers can be greatly different from that for flow parallel to the layering. Fine-grained deposits, such as clay or alternating layers of silt and clay, have a permeability in the direction parallel to bedding of the layers (often, such bedding is approximately horizontal) many times the permeability of cross-bedding flow. Thus, the use of undisturbed test samples, where the sample has retained its original structure and is tested so that flow through the sample is in the correct direction (to correspond to horizontal or vertical flow, as will actually occur in the field), is important if reliable results are to be obtained.

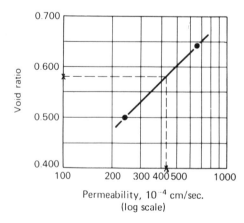

Figure 5-5   Void ratio versus permeability plotted on semilog coordinates.

Undisturbed flocculent structure   Remolded or dispersed structure

Figure 5-6 Cohesive soil with flocculent structure will have higher permeability than soil with dispersed structure.

This also points out an important consideration regarding use of test data: Data from remolded samples may not apply to field conditions if the natural soil remains undisturbed, or test data from undisturbed samples may not apply if, in the field, the soil is to be disturbed and rehandled (as in placing a compacted fill).

Conditions other than the size and number of voids will affect the quantity of flow through a soil deposit. Trapped air or gases prevent flow, whereas seams, cracks, fissures, and cavities that exist in a soil deposit increase the opportunity for fluid movement. Field investigations need to provide information on the presence of these conditions if reliable measures of flow through the soil mass at a construction site are to be obtained. For this reason, *field permeability tests* are felt to provide more accurate information than laboratory tests. Field testing has its disadvantages, however. Costs and time involved are usually greater than for a laboratory test, and the field test provides only information on conditions in the limited proximity of the test location.

In practice, determining permeability from field or laboratory tests or from indirect analytical methods is for *order-of-magnitude* use only. This is realistic when it is realized that subsurface conditions and soil properties most probably vary over even short horizontal distances, that soil conditions and properties are generally not known in all areas of influence at a site, and that frequently external factors causing or affecting flow are not accurately known during planning and design.

Laboratory Permeability Tests Two of the more conventional laboratory permeability tests are the constant-head test and the falling-head test. Schematic diagrams showing each of these methods, and the mathematics to calculate the coefficient of permeability, are shown in Figures 5-7 and 5-8.

The constant-head permeability apparatus (permeameter) is in wide use for testing the coarse-grained soils, such as sands, where the volume of flow through the soil will be relatively large. For fine-grained soils, such as silt and clay, the falling-head permeameter is generally used. In the constant-head test, permeability is computed on the basis of fluid that passes through the soil sample. In the falling-head test, permeability is computed on the basis of fluid flowing into the sample. The reason for the distinction is simple. In a fine-grained soil, a very limited volume of fluid will flow through the sample. With the constant-head test, time is required to accumulate the fluid volume necessary to perform computations. Extreme care

Permeability   **93**

Constant head

Note:
t is time for
volume of
water, Q, to
flow through
sample.

Δh

Porous filters

Soil
sample

L

Q

Cross-sectional

area = $A = \frac{\pi}{4} D^2$

Sample
diameter = D

Spring

Constant head test: $\frac{Q}{t} = kiA$

$$k = \frac{Q}{t} \cdot \frac{1}{iA} = \frac{Q}{t} \cdot \frac{L}{A(\Delta h)}$$

Figure 5-7 Constant-head permeability test: Representation of permeameter and definition of related terms.

Time when water level
is at h, is t_1

(t_1)

a = area of standpipe

Time when
level is at
h_2 is t_2

h_1

(t_2)

h_2

A = cross-sectional area
of soil sample

L

Soil
sample

Falling head test: $k = \dfrac{L}{(t_2 - t_1)} \cdot \dfrac{a}{A} \cdot \ln \dfrac{h_1}{h_2}$

or $\qquad k = \dfrac{(2.303)L}{(t_2 - t_1)} \cdot \dfrac{a}{A} \log_{10} \dfrac{h_1}{h_2}$

Figure 5-8 Falling-head permeability test: Representation of permeameter and definition of related terms.

would be required to prevent leaks in the apparatus and evaporation of discharged water. With the falling-head method, the duration of the test is shortened, and there is no concern about the volume of discharge. Care is required, however, to prevent evaporation of water in the inlet tube.

Darcy's coefficient of permeability is the factor for a condition of steady flow through a soil. In performing laboratory permeability tests it is essential that volumes be measured only after steady flow has been occurring for some period. It is important to assure that no air or other gases are trapped within the soil to interfere with flow. A vacuum may be required to remove trapped air. In general, the constant-head test is easier to perform, and requires less skill and experience than the falling-head test. Care is required during testing of fine granular soils (such as in the fine sand range) to prevent the particles from being carried along with the discharging water. Details for performing permeability tests are presented in the *ASTM Procedures for Testing Soils*.

ILLUSTRATION 5-1. A constant-head permeability test is performed on a sample of granular soil. The test setup is as indicated in Figure 5-7. The length of soil sample is 15 cm and the cross-sectional area is 10 cm². If a 24-cm³ volume of water passes through the soil sample in a 3-minute period, when Δh is 30 cm, compute the coefficient of permeability.

Use
$$k = \left(\frac{Q}{t}\right)\left(\frac{L}{A\,\Delta h}\right)$$

where Q = 24 cm³.
t = 3 minutes.
L = 15 cm.
A = 10 cm².
Δh = 30 cm.

$$k = \left(\frac{24\text{ cm}^3}{3\text{ min}}\right)\left(\frac{15\text{ cm}}{10\text{ cm}^2 \times 30\text{ cm}}\right)$$
$$= 0.4\text{ cm/min} = 0.006\text{ cm/sec.}$$

ILLUSTRATION 5-2. A falling-head permeability test is performed on a silty soil. The test setup is as shown in Figure 5-8. For the test data summarized below, what is the coefficient of permeability for this sample?

Sample length = 8 cm.
Cross-sectional area of sample = 10 cm².
Area of standpipe = 1.5 cm².
Height of water in standpipe at start of test period h_1 = 100 cm.
Height of water in standpipe at end of test period h_2 = 90 cm.
Time for change from h_1 to h_2 = 60 min.

Permeability

use
$$k = \frac{(2.303)L}{t_2 - t_1}\left(\frac{a}{A}\right)\log\frac{h_1}{h_2}$$

$$k = \frac{(2.303)(8 \text{ cm})}{60 \text{ min}}\left(\frac{1.5 \text{ cm}^2}{10 \text{ cm}^2}\right)\log\frac{100 \text{ cm}}{90 \text{ cm}}$$

$$= 0.00212 \text{ cm/min} = 3.5 \times 10^{-5} \text{ cm/sec}$$

Where consolidation tests are performed on soil samples (Chapter 9), the permeability test can be adapted to determine the rate of flow through the consolidation sample, and the coefficient of permeability computed from these data. Alternatively, the coefficient can be determined from the consolidation data obtained to calculate the rate of consolidation of the soil (described in Chapter 9).

Field Permeability Tests   Field permeability tests offer the advantage of testing undisturbed soil in the natural location with respect to the ground surface, water table, and other factors that could influence the rate of flow. Various methods for determining permeability are available, depending, among other things, on the soil's being above or below the ground water table. The methods described herein are of the type where a cased boring is made into the soil that is to be tested. The casing and related equipment necessary are of the type normally used by soil-boring contractors. Whenever possible, it has been found expedient to perform field permeability tests during the investigative stage of planning a project, at the time that the subsurface investigation (soil borings) is being made.

Essentially, the field permeability test involves obtaining a record of the time that it takes for a volume of water to flow out of, or into, the boring casing. A schematic presentation of different conditions and the related equations for calculating the coefficient of permeability is shown in Table 5-2.

On a practical note, simple field permeability tests of the types depicted in Table 5-2 are considered appropriate for evaluating granular and silt soils. The low coefficient of permeability associated with clays and silt–clay mixtures would involve a long time period for the field test and require consideration of various additional factors such as evaporation, etc.

CAPILLARITY

The *groundwater table* (or *phreatic surface*) is the level to which underground water will rise in an observation well, pit, or other open excavation into the earth. All voids or pores in soil located below the groundwater table would be filled with water (except possibly for small isolated pockets of trapped air or gases). In addition, however, soil voids for a certain height above the water table will also be completely filled with water (full saturation). Even above this zone of full saturation, a condition of partial saturation will exist.

TABLE 5-2 METHODS FOR PERFORMING FIELD PERMEABILITY TESTS [71]

Cased hole, soil flush with bottom.

$$k = \frac{0.024\,Q}{RH}$$
where Q = gal/min
R = feet
H = feet
k = ft/min

Used for permeability determinations when water is above or below bottom of casing. Q is quantity of water to keep casing filled

Cased hole, soil flush with bottom.

$$k = \frac{2\pi R}{11(t_2 - t_1)} \ln \frac{H_1}{H_2}$$
For D from 6" to 60"

Used for permeability determination at shallow depths below the water table. May yield unreliable results in falling-head test with silting of bottom of hole.

Cased hole, uncased or perforated extension of length L.

$$k = \left[\frac{R^2}{2L(t_2 - t_1)} \times \ln\left(\frac{L}{R}\right) \ln\left(\frac{H_1}{H_2}\right) \right]$$
For $\frac{L}{R} > 8$

Used for permeability determinations at greater depths below water table.

Cased hole, column of soil inside casing to height L.

$$k = \frac{2\pi R + 11L}{11(t_2 - t_1)} \ln\left(\frac{H_1}{H_2}\right)$$

Principal use is for permeability in vertical direction in anisotropic soils.

Any water in soil located above the water table is referred to as *soil moisture*. The phenomenon in which water rises above the groundwater table against the pull of gravity but is in contact with the water table as its source is referred to as *capillary rise*. The water associated with capillary rise is *capillary moisture*.

Water in Capillary Tubes   The basic principles of capillary rise in soils can be related to the rise of water in glass capillary tubes (tubes with very small diameters) under laboratory conditions. When the end of a vertical capillary tube is put in contact with a source of water, the water rises up in the tube and remains there. The rise is attributed to the attraction between the water and the glass and

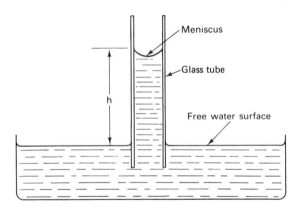

h

Meniscus

Glass tube

Free water surface

Figure 5-9 Capillary rise and water meniscus in a glass tube.

to a *surface tension*[3] which develops at the air–water interface at the top of the water column in the capillary tube. This surface tension can be thought of as an infinitely thin but tough film, such as a stretched membrane. (The surface tension phenomenon is one of the reasons that small insects can "walk" on water.) The water is "pulled up" in the capillary tube, to a height regulated by the diameter of the tube, the magnitude of the surface tension, and the density of the water.

The attraction between the water and capillary tube affects the shape of the air–water interface at the top of the column of water. For water and glass, the shape is concave downward; that is, the water surface is lower at the center of the column than at the walls of the tube. The resulting curved liquid surface is termed the *meniscus* (Fig. 5-9).

The column of water in the capillary tube has risen above the surface of the water supply and against the pull of gravity. For a condition of equilibrium, the effect of the downward pull of gravity on the capillary column of water has to be resisted by the ability of the surface film to adhere to the wall of the capillary tube and hold the column of water. This wall adhesion must equal the surface tension of the fluid. If T_s is the value of surface tension, expressed in units of force per unit length, the vertical loading that can be supported is

$$(\text{Tube circumference}) \times (T_s) \times (\cos \alpha)$$

[3]The kinetic theory explains the surface tension phenomena (all molecules are in motion and the speed or kinetic energy increases as temperature increases, and molecules attract each other at close range). Within the body of a liquid, a molecule of water will be subject to attractions that are equal in all directions because of the surrounding molecules. At the surface of a body of water (the air–water interface) the water molecules are subject to an unequal force in the direction of the body of water, since in the air (gaseous state) the molecules are widely dispersed and, in total, exert a lesser attractive force. The normal molecular motion of the water molecules is thereby restricted by the unbalanced pull (attraction). The resulting net effect between the natural molecular motion and unbalanced attraction is that the surface zone of the water acts as a stretched membrane (i.e., a membrane in tension). If the attractions internal to the body of water (cohesion) are less than the attractions between the water and a solid (adhesion), then the water surface curves outward (from the body of water) where the water is in contact with the solid, producing a curved meniscus. Since glass materials (and soil particles) are solids that possess a polar surface, the result is an attraction or adhesion between the water molecules and the surface of glass (or soil particles).

where α is the angle formed between a tangent to the meniscus and the capillary wall. With water and glass, the meniscus at the wall of the capillary tube is tangent to the wall surface, and the angle α is zero degrees. Therefore, cos α is one, and the column weight that is capable of being supported because of surface tension is

$$(2\pi r)(T_s)$$

where r is the radius of the capillary tube.

The weight of the column of water in the capillary tube is

$$(\pi r^2) \times (h) \times (\rho) \times (g)$$

where h = height of the column of water.

ρ = density of water, mass per volume, taken as 1 gm/cm³ or 1.95 slugs/ft³.

g = acceleration of gravity, 980 cm/sec² or 32.2 ft/sec².

If h_c is the maximum height of capillary rise that can occur for prevailing physical conditions (such as for a particular temperature), equilibrium requires that

$$(2\pi r)(T_s) = (\pi r^2 h_c)(\rho)(g) = \pi r^2 h_c \frac{\text{(weight)}}{\text{(volume)}} \quad \text{[4]}$$

$$= \pi r^2 h_c \gamma_w$$

where γ_w = unit weight of water, taken as 62.4 pcf, 9.81 kN/m³ or 980 dynes/cm³. [5] The maximum height of capillary rise is then

$$h_c = \frac{(2\pi r)(T_s)}{(\pi r^2)(\rho)(g)} = \frac{2T_s}{(r)(\rho)(g)}$$

$$h = \frac{2T_s}{r(\gamma_w)} = \frac{4T_s}{d(\gamma_w)} \qquad (5\text{-}9)$$

where d = the diameter of the capillary tube.

The value of T_s for water varies according to temperature. At normal room temperatures, T_s is close to 0.005 lb/ft, 0.064 N/m or 73 dynes/cm. In applying the development of capillary rise in tubes to capillary rise in soils, these values for T_s are sufficiently accurate for many practical problems. Thus, the equation for capillary rise can be expressed as

$$h_c = \frac{0.31}{d} \text{ cm (approximately)} \qquad (5\text{-}10)$$

provided that d is in centimeters.

[4]Since weight equals mass times acceleration of gravity ($W = mg$), the product of ρg equals $\frac{\text{(mass)}}{\text{(volume)}} \times (g)$, or $\frac{\text{weight}}{\text{volume}}$. Also see footnote, p. 32.

[5]Recall the dyne is a unit of force; units are $\frac{\text{g-cm}}{\text{sec}^2}$.

Capillarity

ILLUSTRATION 5-3. Compute the height of capillary rise for water in a tube having a diameter of 0.005 cm.

In metric units:

$$h_c = \frac{4T_s}{(d)(\rho)(g)} = \frac{(4)(73 \text{ dynes/cm})}{(0.005 \text{ cm})(1 \text{ gm/cm}^3)(980 \text{ cm/sec}^2)}$$

$$\cong 60 \text{ cm} \cong 2 \text{ ft}$$

In customary or British units:

$$d = 0.005 \text{ cm} = \frac{0.005 \text{ cm}}{\left(2.54 \frac{\text{cm}}{\text{in.}}\right)\left(12 \frac{\text{in.}}{\text{ft}}\right)} = 1.64 \times 10^{-4} \text{ ft}$$

$$\text{and } h_c = \frac{4T_s}{d\gamma_w} = \frac{(4)(0.005 \text{ lb/ft})}{(1.64 \times 10^{-4} \text{ ft})(62.4 \text{ pcf})} \cong 2 \text{ ft}$$

There *are* situations, however, where the temperature effects should be considered. Generally, as temperature increases, the value of T_s decreases, indicating a lessening height of capillary rise under warm conditions or an increasing height of capillary rise for conditions of falling temperatures. At freezing, T_s for water is about 76 dynes/cm.

Note from the terms of Equation 5-9 that the height of capillary rise is not affected by a slope or inclination in the direction of the capillary tube, or by variations in the shape and size of the tube at levels below the meniscus (Fig. 5-10). But for water migrating up a capillary tube, a large opening can prevent further upward movement in an otherwise small-diameter tube. The determining factor is the relation between the size of the opening (tube diameter) and the particular height of its occurrence above the water supply.

In the capillary tube, at the level equal to the free surface of the water in the supply pan, the hydrostatic pressure in the water is zero. Hydrostatic pressures increase below that free water surface according to the relationship

$$p_w = \gamma_w Z \qquad (5\text{-}11)$$

where Z = the depth below the water surface.

p_w = the fluid pressure at the depth Z.

Figure 5-10 Capillary heights of capillary tubes of various shapes are the same if their menisci diameters are the same.

Conversely, hydrostatic pressure measured in the capillary column *above* that free water surface is negative, according to the relationship

$$p_w = -\gamma_w h \qquad (5\text{-}12)$$

where h = the distance measured upwards, from the free water surface. The negative sign indicates that water pressures in the capillary tubes are at less than atmospheric pressure. As a result, water in the capillary columns is said to be in *tension*. The maximum negative pressure, or capillary tension, exists at the maximum height of rise h_c. If the pressure at the water surface in the supply pan depicted in Figure 5-10 is atmospheric pressure, p_a, the pressure in the capillary water just beneath the meniscus, point c, is $p_a - h_c \rho g$. By substitution of terms

$$p_a - h_c \rho g = p_a - \left(\frac{2T_s}{r\rho g}\right)(\rho g) = p_a - \frac{2T_s}{r},$$

or $2T_s/r$ less than the pressure existing just above the meniscus.

As the column of water stands in the capillary tube, "hanging" by the surface tension at the meniscus, the *weight* of the column is transferred to the walls of the capillary tube, creating a compressive force in the walls. An effect of this occurrence within soil deposits is discussed in a later section, "Effects of Surface Tension."

Capillary rise is not limited to tube, or enclosed, shapes. If two vertical glass plates are placed so that they touch along one end and, in plan, form a "V," a wedge of water will rise up in the "V" because of the capillary phenomena (Fig. 5-11). The height of rise relates to the attraction between the water and plates and the physical properties of the water, as in tubes, but also to the angle formed by the "V." The significance of this type of capillary rise is discussed in the following section, "Capillary Rise in Soil."

Capillary Rise in Soil   In soils, the shapes of void spaces between solid particles are unlike those in capillary tubes. The voids are of irregular and varying shape and size, and interconnect in all directions, not only the vertical. These properties make the accurate prediction of the height of capillary rise in soil almost impossible. However, the features of capillary rise in tubes are applicable to soils insofar as they facilitate an understanding of factors affecting capillarity, and help to establish an order of magnitude for capillary rise in the different types of soils.

Figure 5-11 Capillary rise in corner formed by glass plates.

Capillarity

ILLUSTRATION 5-4. Limited laboratory studies indicate that for a certain silt soil, the effective pore size for height of capillary rise is $\frac{1}{5}$ of D_{10}, where D_{10} is the 10 percent particle size from the grain-size distribution curve. If the D_{10} size for such a soil is 0.02 mm, estimate the height of capillary rise.

$$d = \text{effective capillary diameter} = \tfrac{1}{5}D_{10} = \tfrac{1}{5}(0.02 \text{ mm})$$

$$= 0.004 \text{ mm} = 0.0004 \text{ cm}$$

$$h_c = \frac{0.31}{d} \qquad \text{(from Eq. 5-10)}$$

$$= \frac{0.31}{0.0004 \text{ cm}} = \frac{0.31}{4 \times 10^{-4} \text{ cm}}$$

$$= 7.75 \times 10^2 \text{ cm} = 775 \text{ cm} \cong 25 \text{ ft}$$

Review of Equation 5-9 indicates that even relatively large voids will be filled with capillary water if the soil is close to the source of water, that is, the groundwater table. As the distance from the water table increases, only the smaller voids would be expected to be filled with capillary water. The larger voids represent interference to upward capillary flow and would not be filled. Consequently, the soil closest to the water table but above it is fully saturated as a result of capillarity. Above this zone of full saturation lies a zone of partial saturation due to capillarity (see Fig. 5-12). The height to which capillary water rises is termed *capillary fringe*.

In the upper zone of the capillary fringe, where partial saturation exists, capillary movement occurs through the capillary tube phenomenon but may also occur in the wedges of the capillary "V" formed where soil particles are in contact (similar to the "V" formed by vertical plates discussed in the preceding section; see Fig. 5-13).

Since void spaces in soil are of the same order of magnitude as the particle sizes, it follows that the height of capillary rise would be greater in fine-grained soils than in coarse-grained soils. For orders of magnitude, relative values of capillary rise for different type soils are presented in Table 5-3.

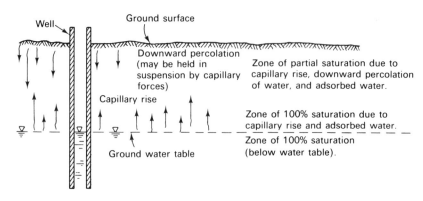

Figure 5-12 Distribution of soil moisture in a soil profile.

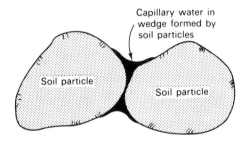

Figure 5-13 Wedge of capillary water at point of contact between particles.

Temperature plays an important practical role in the capillary rise in soil. The height of rise is greater at lower temperatures than at high temperatures. Demonstrations of this fact have frequently been observed in construction performed in a cool season following a warm season (i.e., in the fall at locations in the northern hemisphere). Cool temperatures cause an increase in migration of water toward the surface. Frequently the additional moisture increases the difficulty in handling or working with the soil, or creates a muddy surface, which makes the moving of equipment a problem. *Horizontal migration* of water can also occur near a heated building. Water may move from beneath a structure in cold seasons if the presence of the structure affords some protection from cold temperatures. If the building itself contributes to a lowering of the ground temperature, as in a poorly insulated cold-storage warehouse, frozen foods processing plant, or ice skating rink, capillary flow will be induced towards the building.

Attempts at establishing a relationship between height of capillary rise for a given soil and some aspect of the soil's grain size or void ratio have been made. The general applicability and accuracy of proposed relationships appear to be limited to providing estimates of order of magnitude.

Time Rate of Capillary Rise The time necessary for the expected maximum height of capillary rise to occur requires consideration in some practical problems, such as where a structural fill has been placed for highways, buildings, or other purposes. On the basis of typical void sizes, clay and fine silt soils will have significant heights of capillary rise. However, the time period required for the rise to occur may be so great that other influences, such as evaporation and change in groundwater level, also have to be considered.

TABLE 5-3 REPRESENTATIVE HEIGHTS OF CAPILLARY RISE IN SOILS

Soil type	Approximate capillary heights	
	cm	ft
Small gravel	2–10	0.1–0.4
Coarse sand	15	0.5
Fine sand	30–100	1–3
Silt	100–1000	3–30
Clay	1000–3000	30–90

Capillarity

The term indicating the *rate* of capillary rise is *capillary conductivity* or *capillary permeability*, k_{cap}. Factors known to affect a soil's capillary conductivity are void sizes, moisture content, and temperature in the soil. Generally, capillary conductivity is greater at higher moisture contents and lower temperatures. Absolute values of capillary conductivity are not available. Though not identical to Darcy's coefficient of permeability, the *relative rates* of capillary conductivity can be thought of in terms of the comparative values for permeability—that is, rapid for coarse soils, low and very low for silts and clays.

Suspended Capillaries   Water attempting to percolate downward through a soil (such as percolating surface water from rain or melting snow) or pore water resulting from a formerly higher water table can be held suspended in the soil voids because of the same surface tension phenomenon responsible for capillary rise. For this, the column of water would have a meniscus at both ends of the suspended column. Each meniscus would be in tension. The maximum length of a column would be controlled by the same factors affecting height of capillary rise.

Elimination of Capillary Water in Soil   For capillary rise to occur, the existence of an air–water interface is required. Capillary water will not exist in soil at a level below the groundwater table. It follows that a condition of capillarity will cease where submergence of a soil zone occurs.

Capillary water can be removed from a soil by evaporation. As a result, capillary water can represent a very mobile category of water where the evaporation is continually replaced by new capillary water.

Effects of Surface Tension   At the location of the meniscus the surface tension imposes a compressive force onto the soil grains in contact with the meniscus that is equal in magnitude to the weight of the water in the capillary column, as indicated in the earlier discussion for capillary tubes. This effect applies to both a meniscus resulting from capillary rise and for pore water suspended above a capillary zone. The compressive force is imposed throughout the soil particles in contact with the "held column" of water, and serves to compress or shrink the soil.

In clays, this phenomenon results where the groundwater table drops subsequent to the time the clay deposits were formed. Such "drying" of an area can cause compressive forces within the clay mass of such great magnitude that the affected soil zone becomes firm and strong. This is referred to as drying by desiccation, and the clays are referred to as *desiccated clays*. A land area formed by clay deposits that were originally soft and weak may have a firm crust or upper layer overlying the still soft and weak deeper clays because of desiccation. The thickness and strength of a desiccated zone has frequently been found sufficiently adequate that road and light building structures could be satisfactorily supported by it.

Typical magnitudes of compressive stress that can result in fine-grained soils are tabulated in Table 5-4.

In partially saturated granular (coarse-grained) soils, the surface tension phenomenon also contributes to the strength of the mass. At partial saturation, all

TABLE 5-4 REPRESENTATIVE VALUES OF COMPRESSIVE STRESS RESULTING FROM CAPILLARY FORCES

Soil type	Compressive stress		
	psf	Kg/cm^2	kN/m^2
Silt	200–2000	0.1–1.0	10–100
Clay	2000–6000	1.0–3.0	100–300

voids are not filled with water. The available water collects in the interstices adjacent to where soil particles touch, forming a wedge of moisture but leaving the center portion of the void filled with air. Thus, an air–water interface, or meniscus, is formed. The surface tension in the meniscus imposes a compressive force onto the soil particles, increasing the friction between particles and thus the shearing strength. The strength gain in granular soil due to partial saturation and the surface tension phenomenon is termed *apparent cohesion*. The strength gain can be quite significant, as the firm condition of sandy beach surfaces, which easily support the weight of vehicles, indicates. The menisci and surface tension, along with the apparent cohesion, will disappear when the soil is fully saturated.

PROBLEMS

5-1. Compute the value of the hydraulic radius for a circular pipe flowing half-full.

5-2. Calculate the value for the hydraulic radius for flow in an open channel where the bottom of the channel is 3 ft wide, the side slopes are 1 on 1 (slope of 1 ft horizontal to 1 ft vertical), and the depth of flow is 2 ft.

5-3. A thick fluid having a high viscosity and a thin fluid having a low viscosity are to be passed through a permeable material. Indicate the condition for which the resulting coefficient of permeability will be greatest and briefly explain why. For which condition (thick or thin fluid) is the quantity of flow through the material expected to be greatest?

5-4. The coefficient of permeability is generally greater for coarse soils (sands and gravels) than for fine-grained soils (silts and clays). What effect does particle size have on permeability?

5-5. What effect does the presence of adsorbed water in clay have on the coefficient of permeability for this type of soil?

5-6. In the flow of water through soil, what are the conditions necessary in order for Darcy's law to apply?

5-7. **(a)** Estimate the coefficient of permeability for a uniform sand where a sieve analysis indicates that the D_{10} size is 0.15 mm.
(b) The particle-size distribution curve for a sand indicates the D_{15} size is 0.19 mm. If the sand deposit is in the dense or compact state, estimate the coefficient of permeability.

5-8. Why might the permeability in fine-grained soil deposits be expected to be greater for horizontal flow than for vertical flow?

5-9. Briefly give reasons why the coefficient of permeability in an undisturbed clay deposit possessing a flocculent structure would be expected to be greater than if the same clay had a dispersed (remolded) structure.

5-10. A constant-head permeability test is performed in a laboratory where the soil sample is 25 cm in length and 6 cm² in cross-section. The height of water at the inflow end is maintained at 2 ft, and at 6 in. at the outlet end. The quantity of water flowing through the sample is 200 cm³ in 2 minutes.
(a) Make a sketch of the described conditions.
(b) What is the coefficient of permeability in centimeters per minute?

5-11. A constant-head permeability test is performed where the hydraulic gradient is 0.75. The cross-sectional area of the sample is 0.25 ft². The quantity of water flowing through the sample is measured to be 0.004 ft³/minute.
(a) What is the coefficient of permeability in feet per minute?
(b) What is the coefficient of permeability in centimeters per second?

5-12. How much water will flow through a soil mass in a 5-minute period when the sample length is 15 cm, the cross-section is 2 cm by 2 cm, and a constant head of 2 ft is maintained? The soil has a k value of 1×10^{-2} cm/sec.

5-13. A falling-head permeability test is performed on a fine-grained soil. The soil sample has a length of 12 cm and a cross-sectional area of 6 cm². The water in the standpipe flowing into the soil is 60 cm above the top of the sample at the start of the test. It falls 5 cm in 30 minutes. The standpipe has a cross-section of 2 cm².
(a) Make a sketch of the described conditions.
(b) What is the coefficient of permeability in centimeters per second?
(c) What is the coefficient of permeability in feet per minute?

5-14. A field permeability test is performed by measuring the quantity of water necessary to keep a boring casing (pipe) filled. The distance from the top of the casing to the bottom (in the ground) is 10 ft. The groundwater table is below the bottom of the casing. The casing has an inside diameter of 6 in. In a 10-minute period, one gallon of water was used to keep the casing filled. What is the coefficient of permeability for the soil at the bottom of the casing?

5-15. A field permeability test indicates that the coefficient of permeability for a certain soil is 2×10^{-5} cm/sec. Is this a relatively high or low coefficient of permeability? What type of soil would this probably be?

5-16. To what height would water rise in a glass capillary tube that is 0.01 mm in diameter?

5-17. What is the water pressure just under the meniscus in a capillary tube where the water has risen to a height of 6 ft?

5-18. A glass capillary tube is 0.001 mm in diameter.
(a) What is the theoretical maximum height of capillary rise for a tube of this size?
(b) What compressive pressure results in the capillary water just under the meniscus?

5-19. In a silt soil, the D_{10} size is 0.01 mm. If the effective pore size for estimating capillary rise is taken as $\frac{1}{5}$ of D_{10}, approximately what height of capillary rise will occur?

5-20. Why is it expected that the maximum height of capillary rise is greater for fine-grained soils than for coarse-grained soils?

5-21. How is the height of maximum capillary rise of water in soil affected by temperature?

5-22. Explain how capillarity is related to the dried and firm condition frequently observed to exist in the surface zone of fine-grained soil deposits.

5-23. Indicate the ways that capillary water and the effects of capillarity can be removed from a soil.

## chapter 6

Movement of Water Through Soil: Practical Effects

Flow Nets and Seepage, Drainage, Frost Heave

The handling of mobile and stationary underground water during construction operations, and making provisions so that the effects of its presence will not interfere with the function of completed structures are of vital concern to the construction profession. The following discussion on flow nets and seepage, drainage, and frost heave relates to the practical aspects of controlling groundwater during and after construction.

FLOW NETS AND SEEPAGE

Flow of Subsurface Water   The flow of water beneath the ground surface through all soils except coarse gravel and larger materials occurs as laminar flow; that is, the path of flow will follow a regular pattern, with adjacent paths of water particles all flowing parallel. For this condition, Darcy's law for water traveling through soils can be applied to determine the rate and quantity of flow, and the seepage forces that result from this flow. In its most direct form, Darcy's law is

$$q = kiA \tag{6-1}$$

(as developed in Chapter 5, Eq. 5-5), where q is the quantity of flow in a unit time period (or rate of flow), k is the coefficient of permeability for the soil, A is the cross-sectional area of the soil through which flow is occurring (normal to the direction of flow), and i is the hydraulic gradient (the difference in the energy head of water between two points divided by the distance between the same two points), all as previously defined in Chapter 5.

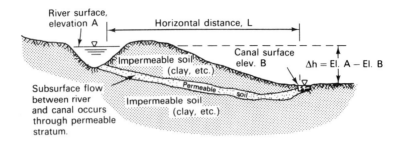

River surface, elevation A

Horizontal distance, L

Impermeable soil (clay, etc.)

Canal surface elev. B

Δh = El. A − El. B

Subsurface flow between river and canal occurs through permeable stratum.

Impermeable soil (clay, etc.)

Permeable soil

Figure 6-1 Instance in which direct application of Darcy's law can be used to determine underground flow.

When underground water is flowing over a relatively long distance and within a soil zone having well-defined boundaries, such as that shown in Figure 6-1, the quantity of flow can be determined by using the foregoing expression directly.

ILLUSTRATION 6-1. A river and a canal run parallel to each other but at different elevations, as indicated by Figure 6-1. If the difference in the water surface elevations is 16 ft, the horizontal distance is 400 ft, and the thickness of the permeable stratum is 6 ft, compute the seepage loss between river and canal, per mile of river-canal length. Permeability $k = 1.0$ ft/day.

$$q = kiA = k \frac{\Delta h}{L} A = (1.0 \text{ ft/day}) \frac{16 \text{ ft}}{400 \text{ ft}} (6 \text{ ft} \times 5280 \text{ ft/mi})$$

$$= 1,270 \text{ ft}^3/\text{day/mile of length}$$

The Need for Flow Nets and Flow Net Theory Where the zones of flow or directions of flow are irregular, where water enters and escapes from a permeable zone of soil by traveling a short distance, or where the flow boundaries are not well defined (a boundary being the separation between where flow does and does not occur), it may be necessary to use flow nets to evaluate flow. Flow nets are a pictorial method of studying the path that moving water follows. Darcy's law can be applied to flow nets to evaluate the effects of flow.[1]

For a condition of laminar flow, the path that the water follows can be represented by *flow lines*. In moving between two points, water tends to travel the shortest distance. If changes in direction occur, the changes take place along smooth curved paths. A series of flow lines to represent flow through a soil mass would be parallel except where a change in the size of an area through which flow occurs takes place. Figure 6-2 shows flow lines for water seeping through a soil in a simple laboratory model.

Flow of water occurs between two points because of a difference in energy (usually expressed as head of energy or as pressure). Since it is the *relative* energy difference between two points, energy head can be referenced to an arbitrary datum

---

[1]A scale drawing is necessary where actual quantities of flow are to be calculated or the effects of flow are to be determined.

Figure 6-2 Laboratory seepage tank showing flow lines indicating path of water flowing through the soil.

for convenience. The total head of any point is that resulting from the sum of velocity head, potential head, and pressure head.[2] For water flowing through soil, velocity head is neglected, since it is small compared to potential and pressure head.[3] In Figure 6-3a piezometers (open standpipes) inserted at points A and B would have the water level rise to the elevations shown. This figure shows the pressure and potential energy heads.

At certain points on different flow lines, the total energy head will be the same, as seen in Figure 6-3a. Lines connecting points of equal total energy head can be drawn, and are termed *equipotential lines* (see Fig. 6-3b). It becomes apparent that there is no gradient to cause flow between points on the same equipotential line. On a flow net, equipotential lines must cross flow lines at right angles, since they represent pressure normal to the direction of flow. The flow lines and equipotential lines together form the flow net, and are used to determine the quantities and other effects of flow through soils.

When seepage analyses are made, flow nets can be drawn with as many flow lines as desired. The number of equipotential lines will be determined by the number of flow lines selected. A general recommendation is to use the fewest flow lines that still permit reasonable depiction of the flow path along the boundaries and within the soil mass. For many problems, three or four flow channels (a channel being the path between adjacent flow lines) are sufficient.

Development of the Flow Net—Isotropic Soil[4]

Figure 6-4 shows a condition where flow occurs through a soil mass. Flow occurs because of the difference in total energy head caused by the unequal heights of water.

   1. To begin the flow net, establish the boundaries of the soil mass through which the flow occurs and conditions at the boundaries. In Figure 6-4, lines a–b

---

[2]From the Bernoulli equation for steady irrotational (or laminar) flow, total head, $H = v^2/2g + p/\gamma + Z$, where v = velocity of flow, g is the acceleration of gravity, p is pressure, γ is the unit weight of the fluid flowing and Z is the vertical distance between the point where the pressure p is determined and a reference elevation or datum.

[3]Because the velocity head can be assumed negligible, the total head difference between two points along a path of flow is equal to the difference in height that water in open tubes would rise—for example, $\Delta h = h_1 - h_2$ as defined in Chapter 5 and shown by Figure 5-3. Thus, flow occurs because of differences in total energy head.

[4]When applied to fluid flow, the term *isotropic* implies that soil permeability is equal in all directions.

Flow Nets and Seepage

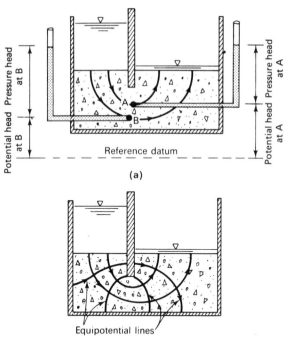

Potential head at B | Pressure head at B

Reference datum

(a)

Potential head at A | Pressure head at A

Equipotential lines

(b)

Figure 6-3 Points of similar energy head indicated on flow lines, and drawing of the flow net by addition of equipotential lines.

and c–e–f–d are drawn to represent flow lines at the boundary. Line c–a is an equipotential line with total head equal to h_t. Line b–d is an equipotential line with (as elsewhere) total head equal to h_0. These four lines establish the boundaries for flow through the soil in this problem. Note the line that indicates the variation in head between the ends of the soil mass.

2. Next sketch in intermediate flow lines parallel to those flow lines along the boundaries. Start by spacing the flow lines an equal distance apart in the sections where it is known that the flow lines will be parallel to each other (where the direction of flow is in a straight line and not curved) (see Fig. 6-5).

3. After the flow lines have been selected, locate a point of equal total energy

h_t

Variation in energy head

h_0

Reference datum

Figure 6-4 Laboratory seepage tank showing soil and water conditions, and boundaries for flow.

Figure 6-5 Intermediate flow lines between flow boundaries.

head on each flow line. A line connecting these points will be an equipotential line (see Fig. 6-6). Draw additional equipotential lines, selecting a spacing so that the distances y_1, y_2, y_3 permit the proportion

$$\frac{y_1}{l_1} = \frac{y_2}{l_2} = \frac{y_3}{l_2}$$

to be maintained. Note the corresponding changes in total head at each equipotential line (Fig. 6-7).

4. Apply Darcy's law, $q = kiA$. Since a volume (of flow) is to be determined, width as well as length and height of soil mass must be considered. For convenience, assume a thickness (perpendicular to the page) of unity. Let the flow past y_1 be q_1, the flow past y_2 be q_2, and the flow past y_3 be q_3. Referring to Figure 6-7, and noting that i (the hydraulic gradient) is the difference in head divided by the distance between the points where the head is measured, or $\Delta h/\Delta L$, (where l_1, l_2, are ΔL), obtain

$$q_1 = (k)\frac{\Delta h_1}{l_1}(y_1)(1)$$

$$q_2 = (k)\frac{\Delta h_2}{l_2}(y_2)(1)$$

$$q_3 = (k)\frac{\Delta h_2}{l_2}(y_3)(1)$$

Figure 6-6 Equipotential lines to establish the flow net.

Flow Nets and Seepage   **111**

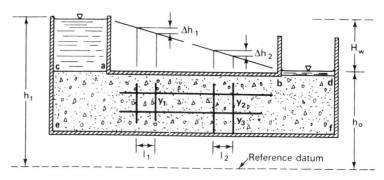

Figure 6-7 The developing flow net indicating relationship of pressure head differences between equipotential lines.

Since y_1 and y_2 are bounded by the same flow lines, q_1 and q_2 must be equal, because flow is continuous. Also, since the ratios of the sides of each block are equal, y_3 is equal to y_2 and therefore q_3 equals q_2.

If all the blocks are proportional, the quantity of flow between flow lines is equal, and it follows that Δh_1 equals Δh_2.

In flow net solutions, the blocks are usually drawn as squares, although actually only the proportionality of distances between the two sides of a block must be maintained. By using squares, however, the ratio of the sides (height/length ratio) is one, and the expresssion for flow becomes

$$q_1 = k\Delta h$$

where Δh is the total head divided by the number of equipotential line pressure drops $\mathcal{N}_d$, or

$$\Delta h = \frac{H_w}{\mathcal{N}_d}$$

Total flow is the summation of the flow in each flow channel or $q = q_1 + q_2 + q_3 + \ldots$, which is also q_1 times the number of flow channels $\mathcal{N}_f$, or $q_1 \mathcal{N}_f$.
Therefore,

$$q = q_1 \mathcal{N}_f = k\Delta h \mathcal{N}_f = k \frac{H_w}{\mathcal{N}_d} \mathcal{N}_f$$

or
$$q = kH_w \left(\frac{\mathcal{N}_f}{\mathcal{N}_d}\right) \quad \text{(for isotropic soil)} \tag{6-2}$$

In constructing flow nets for most problems, it is improbable that the figures resulting from the assumed flow lines and equipotential lines will all be squares. The requirement for this condition is that, for each block, the distance across the center of the block between flow lines must equal the distance between the two equipotential lines, and the equipotential lines must cross the flow lines at right angles. Figure 6-8 traces the steps used in drawing a flow net for a practical problem, and shows the computations to determine seepage.

(a)

L' = 50'

H_w = 18'

k = 1 ft/day

Permeable stratum

Impermeable stratum

(b)

(c)

H_w = 18'

Seepage = $q = kH_w \left(\dfrac{N_f}{N_d}\right)$

$= (1 \text{ ft/day})(18 \text{ ft})(\tfrac{3}{9})(1 \text{ ft of width})$

$= 6 \text{ ft}^3/\text{day/ft of width}$

(d)

Figure 6-8 Steps in drawing a flow net: (a) scale drawing of conditions; (b) trial flow lines; (c) trial equipotential lines; (d) final flow net and related seepage computation.

Boundaries for the Flow Net Figure 6-9 provides illustrations of typical flow net problems. These illustrations can serve as a guide to establish the boundaries of flow and the general pattern of a flow net for many types of problems. For problems like that shown in Figure 6-8, the upper boundary is the flow line following along the base of the structure. The lower boundary is a flow line that, for appli-

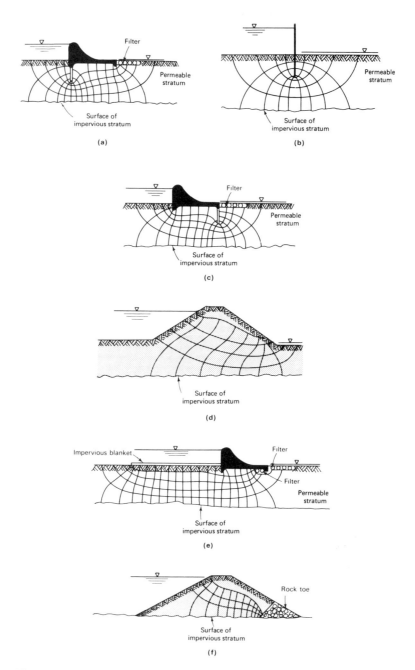

Figure 6-9 Flow nets for representative seepage problems: (a) masonry dam with sheetpile cutoff at heel; (b) sheetpile; (c) masonry dam with sheetpile cutoff and filter at toe; (d) earth dam; (e) masonry dam with upstream impervious blanket and downstream filter; (f) earth dam with downstream rock toe filter.

Figure 6-10 Seepage through an earth dam; definition of terms necessary to locate seepage outbreak.

cation to the flow net, is a line following along the surface of the impermeable stratum. The locations and directions of other flow lines within these boundaries are selected by using the methods described earlier.

Earth dams represent the condition in which the upper limit of flow is not defined by a natural boundary.[5] In some cases, such as homogeneous earth dams situated on an impervious stratum (see Fig. 6-10), seepage will outlet on the dam's downstream face. The flow line representing the upper limit of seepage moving through the dam is approximately parabolic in shape. The point where the seepage breaks out onto the downstream face can be established from

$$a = \frac{d}{\cos \theta} - \sqrt{\frac{d^2}{\cos^2 \theta} - \frac{h^2}{\sin^2 \theta}} \qquad (6\text{-}3)$$

(for slope angles, θ, less than 30°)[6]

where values of a, d, and h are defined in Figure 6-10. The method used to establish the shape and position of the upper line of seepage through the dam is outlined in Figure 6-11. After the upper flow line is established, the remainder of the flow net can be sketched. The quantity of seepage can be estimated using the methods discussed previously. The effect of seepage forces is discussed in a later section of the chapter.

Flow Nets for Nonisotropic Soil The method of flow net analysis discussed above applies for the frequently found condition in which the soil permeability in the horizontal and vertical directions is similar. In stratified soil deposits, however,

[5]The method for studying seepage through earth dams is presented in Arthur Casagrandes's paper "Seepage Through Dams," which appeared in the *Journal of the New England Water Works Association*, June 1937. This paper has been reprinted in *Contributions to Soil Mechanics, 1925–1940*, Boston Society of Civil Engineers, Boston, Mass.

[6]Earth dams typically have slopes flatter than 2 horizontal to 1 vertical—that is, flatter than 30°.

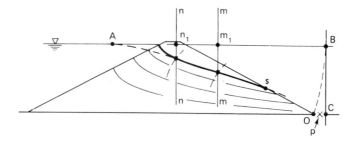

1. Establish point A and swing an arc OB having the radius AO (point O will be the focus of the parabola);

2. Draw vertical line BC (this will be the directrix of the parabola);

3. Locate point p midway between O and C;

4. Draw the vertical line m-m in the general location indicated, and determine the horizontal distance from line BC to line m-m;

5. Using point O as a center, swing an arc with radius m_1B to intersect line m-m. This intersection establishes a point on the parabolic flow line;

6. Draw the vertical line n-n in the general location indicated, and determine the distance n_1B;

7. Using point O as a center, swing an arc with radius n_1B to intersect line n-n. This intersection establishes another point on the parabolic flow line;

8. Continuing the procedure just outlined, establish as many additional points as necessary to sketch the total length of flow line between A and s;

9. Modify the beginning section of the flow line freehand. The freehand line must intersect the upstream face of the dam at a right angle;

10. The parabolic flow line is assumed to follow the downstream face of the dam below point s;

11. Other flow lines are sketched in, assuming a shape generally similar to the upper seepage line.

Figure 6-11 Procedure for locating the upper seepage line for flow through an earth dam.

the horizontal and vertical coefficients of permeability may differ; usually the horizontal permeability is greater than the vertical. In such instances, the methods for drawing the flow net need to be modified. Use of a *transformed section* is an easily applied method that accounts for the different rates of permeability. Vertical dimensions are selected in accordance with the scale desired for the drawing. Horizontal dimensions, however, are modified by multiplying all horizontal lengths by the factor $\sqrt{k_v/k_h}$, where k_v and k_h are the vertical and horizontal coefficients of permeability, respectively. A distorted diagram results, with shortened horizontal dimensions, as illustrated in Figure 6-12. The conventional flow net is then drawn on the transformed section using the procedures presented previously.

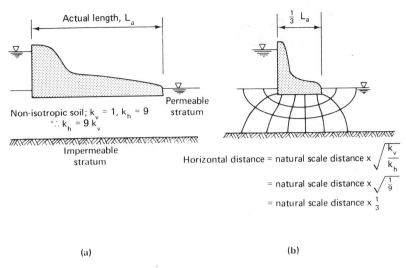

Figure 6-12 Method of drawing the transformed section and flow net for noni-sotropic soil conditions: (a) actual section (to scale); (b) transformed section (distorted scale).

For flow through the nonisotropic soil, the seepage equation becomes

$$q = H_w \left(\frac{\mathscr{N}_f}{\mathscr{N}_d}\right)\sqrt{k_v k_h} \quad \text{(for nonisotropic soils)} \tag{6-4}$$

The values for $\mathscr{N}_f$ and $\mathscr{N}_d$ in this equation are taken directly from the transformed section.

Uplift Forces   For the problem of seepage beneath a structure such as a dam, the uplift force acting on the base of the structure because of this seepage can be evaluated from the flow net. The pressure acting at the upstream and downstream ends of the structure (and at selected in-between points if necessary) is determined and a pressure diagram is made. The total uplift force (per unit of width perpendicular to the drawing) is then the area of the pressure diagram (see Fig. 6-13).

Other Seepage Forces   Water seeping beneath a structure and then escaping by flowing upward at the downstream end imposes an upward force on the soil. If the upward force is sufficiently great, soil particles will be carried away by the escaping water. There follows an illustration of how the flow net can be used to determine if the pressure of the escaping water is great enough to erode the soil. The submerged unit weight of soil is

$$\gamma_{\text{sub}} = \left(\frac{G_s - 1}{1 + e}\right)\gamma_w \tag{2-18}$$

If the value of G_s (specific gravity of soil) is about 2.7 and the void ratio is about 0.70 (both reasonable values), the submerged weight of the soil would be about

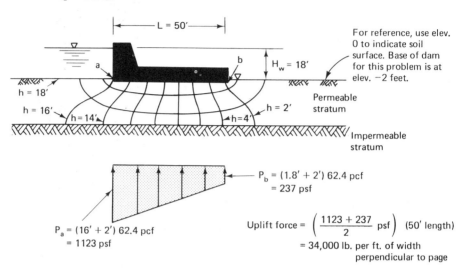

Note:
In this figure, the h values on the equipotential lines indicate the height above the ground surface to which the water level in a piezometer would rise.
Pressure head drop across adjacent equipotential lines =
$$\frac{H_w}{N_d} = \frac{18\ ft}{9\ drops} = 2\ ft/drop.$$

L = 50'

For reference, use elev. 0 to indicate soil surface. Base of dam for this problem is at elev. −2 feet.

a   b H_w = 18'

h = 18'

Permeable stratum

h = 16'

h = 14'   h = 4'   h = 2'

Impermeable stratum

$P_b = (1.8' + 2')$ 62.4 pcf
= 237 psf

$P_a = (16' + 2')$ 62.4 pcf
= 1123 psf

Uplift force = $\left(\dfrac{1123 + 237}{2}\ psf \right)$ (50' length)
= 34,000 lb. per ft. of width perpendicular to page

Figure 6-13 Procedure used to compute uplift pressure acting on base of a masonry dam.

equal to the weight of water. The hydraulic gradient between the last two equipotential lines is the difference in pressure head across these two points divided by the distance between these equipotential lines, or $\Delta h/l$. The pressure difference between the two equipotential lines is Δh times the unit weight of water, γ_w. If the hydraulic gradient is unity, the upward force due to the moving water is equal to the unit weight of water. There then exists an upward pressure of 62.4 psf acting on a soil where gravity effects a downward pressure of 62.4 psf. This is a fully buoyant condition in the soil. A slightly greater uplift pressure would carry away soil particles. For this reason, an escape or exit hydraulic gradient of about unity or greater is usually considered an indication that erosion may occur. To prevent erosion, the pattern of flow could be modified to reduce the pressure of the escape gradient (increasing the length of flow either by making the structure larger or by embedding sheeting beneath the structure are two alternatives), or a coarse material of carefully graded particle sizes that is not susceptible to erosion by the escaping water could be placed beneath the tip of the structure (a soil filter).

ILLUSTRATION 6-2. A masonry dam having a sheetpiling cutoff at the upstream end is located at a reservoir site, as indicated by the sketch. Draw a flow net for the subsurface flow and compute the seepage. Also calculate the uplift force acting on the base, and the escape gradient of the water at the downstream tip of the dam.

Uplift Force on Base

$$p_A = (5\ \text{ft} + 7\ \text{ft})\gamma_w$$

$$p_B = (5\ \text{ft} + 2\ \text{ft})\gamma_w$$

$$\text{Uplift} = \left(\frac{p_A + p_B}{2}\right)(L) = \frac{(12\ \text{ft} + 7\ \text{ft})(62.4\ \text{lb/ft}^3)(48\ \text{ft})}{2}$$

$$= 29,200\ \text{lb per foot of width (perpendicular to page)}$$

Escape Gradient at Downstream Tip

Δh between last two equipotential lines = 2.0 ft, and

$l = 6$ ft

$$i = \frac{\Delta h}{l} = \frac{2}{6} = 0.33\ \text{(therefore erosion not expected)}$$

(Figure 6-14 shows a dam where foundation erosion did occur.)

Practical Considerations   The correct drawing of a flow net can be a tedious operation, particularly in the case of nonuniform soil conditions. Fortunately, even crudely drawn flow nets can provide reliable information on quantities of seepage and uplift pressures. Proper evaluation of an escape gradient requires a correct and carefully drawn flow net, however. For flow nets, as well as for all seepage studies, it should be expected that there will be a variation in the coefficient of permeability for the soil in the seepage zone under study. For practical problems, answers obtained from a seepage analysis should be considered as approximate, and are not to be believed as being precise.

Quicksand   The dreaded quicksand condition occurs at locations where a sand or cohesionless silt deposit is subjected to the seepage force caused by an upward flow of groundwater. This condition can occur in depressions of areas where the water table is high (close to the ground surface) or where artesian conditions exist. The upward gradient of the water is sufficient to hold the soil particles in suspension, in effect creating a material with the properties of a heavy liquid. A no-support condition exists even though the soil gives the appearance of being firm ground.

The suction or pull attributed to quicksand is in reality gravity exerting its normal effect, but in a heavy liquid environment whose viscous properties also exert "drag" on a thrashing body. Theoretically, a person falling into a quicksand area can float as in water.

Since the quicksand condition is caused by the forces of seepage and not some mystical property of the soil, elimination of the seepage pressure will return the soil to a normal condition capable of providing support.

Number flow channels, $N_f = 4$
Number pressure drops, $N_d = 10$ (note feet of head acting at each equipotential line).

$$\Delta h = \frac{H_w}{N_d} = \frac{20'}{10'} = 2.0 \frac{\text{ft.}}{\text{drop}}$$

Number flow channels, $\mathcal{N}_f = 4$.

Number pressure drops, $\mathcal{N}_d = 10$ (note feet of head acting at each equipotential line, where

$$\Delta h = \frac{h}{\mathcal{N}_d} = \frac{20.0 \text{ ft}}{10} = 2.0 \frac{\text{ft}}{\text{drop}} \Bigg)$$

Seepage

$$q = kH_w \frac{\mathcal{N}_f}{\mathcal{N}_d} \quad (\text{width}), \quad \text{or}$$

$$q = \left(0.01 \frac{\text{ft}}{\text{min}}\right)(20 \text{ ft})\left(\frac{4}{10}\right)(1.0 \text{ ft wide})$$

$$= 0.8 \frac{\text{ft}^3}{\text{min}} \text{ per foot of width}$$

Flow Nets and Seepage   **119**

(a) Dam viewed from the downstream side (upper right section of photo is drained lake area).

(b) Closeup of downstream face and toe of dam.

(c) Foundation cavity approximately 2 feet deep that developed as a result of piping. Light near center of photo is daylight from back (upstream) side of the dam.

Figure 6-14 Small dam that experienced underdam erosion of its foundation due to seepage and piping.

Flow Nets and Seepage

DRAINAGE

Among the more common problems in construction work is the need to handle subsurface water encountered during the construction sequence, and to handle subsurface water after construction so that the completed facililty is not damaged nor its usefulness impaired.

During construction, lowering of the groundwater table and removal of water from working areas is desirable from the standpoint of better working conditions for workers and equipment. In some cases dewatering may be necessary to ensure that proper construction can be obtained. Conditions at some locations require that the structure be protected from erosive effects of flowing groundwater to prevent the loss of foundation stability. Additionally, usable interior portions of structures located below groundwater elevation normally are required to be free from serious seepage or leakage.

Conditions Requiring Drainage   In planning excavations for construction projects that extend below the water table in soils where the permeability is greater than about 1×10^{-5} ft/min (or 5×10^{-6} cm/sec), it is generally anticipated that at least some continuous drainage or dewatering procedures will be required if the work area is to be kept dry for construction. Excavations in the more impermeable soil types may remain dry after an initial dewatering, especially if the excavation is to remain open for only a limited time. (For all soil conditions, the actual amount of seepage expected would be affected by the depth below the water table and by the period of time that the excavation is to be open, as well as by the soil properties.)

Dewatering Shallow Excavations   For construction of shallow foundations and for other excavations of limited depth made in coarse soil, open drainage or interceptor ditches can be an expedient and relatively inexpensive method for lowering the groundwater table a slight distance. The interceptor ditch has to penetrate deeper than the elevation of the work area because of the pattern that the underground water surface takes (termed the *drawdown curve*) in the area surrounding the interceptor ditch. Water collecting in such ditches normally has to be pumped out of the ditch for disposal. Since gravity flow is relied on to bring the water to the ditch, the continued inflow is dependent on the water level in the ditch being kept low. With this method, it is common to construct small pits in the ditch, termed *sumps*, for locating the necessary pumps (sump pumps).

Where shallow foundations are to be installed at just about the water table elevation, it has frequently been found possible to obtain sufficient lowering of the water level to permit working in the dry by locating sump pits within, or immediately adjacent to, the foundation excavation.

The drawing down of the water table can also be accomplished by constructing a series of sump pits (Fig. 6-15), or, if greater depth is required, some type of drainage wells around the construction area and pumping the water from these pits or wells.

Subsurface water that flows in an upward direction into an excavation area that is being dewatered imparts a seepage force that tends to loosen the soil,

Figure 6-15 Shallow drawdown of water table by use of interceptor ditches and sump pit in excavation.

reducing the soil strength. The change in strength should be considered in designing excavation bracing and foundations.

Dewatering Intermediate Depths Where excavations in coarse-grained and silty soils are to extend more than a few feet below groundwater level, open ditches or pits are not practical, and more advanced methods are used. Discussion of some methods follows.

Well points. For dewatering to intermediate depths (to about 30 ft or 9 m, but more if sufficient area is available for installing the necessary equipment), well-point systems are normally used. Basically, a well point is a closed-end pipe or tube, having perforations along its lower end, that is installed to the desired depth below the water table (see Fig. 6-16). Groundwater entering the well point through the perforations is pumped to the surface through a riser pipe connected to the well point (Fig. 6-17). For construction dewatering, the well-point perforations are provided with a protective screen or filter to prevent soil particles from

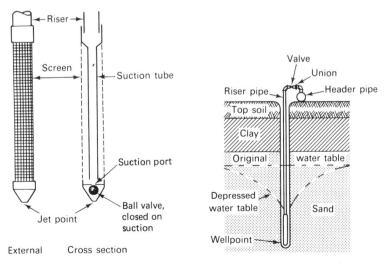

Figure 6-16 A well-point assembly.

Figure 6-17 Installed well point.

clogging the perforations. Well points are conventionally installed in drilled holes or, most usually, by jetting. In jetting, water is pumped through (into) the riser and discharges through special openings at the tip of the well point, an action that displaces the soil below the tip of the point. This procedure is continued until the desired penetration is achieved.

To dewater an area, a series of well points is installed around the perimeter of the area. The groundwater level within the perimeter will be lowered when the well-point system is put in operation. The spacing of the well points varies according to the soil type and depth of dewatering. Spacings conventionally vary between 3 and 10 feet (1–3 m). Each well-point riser is connected by hose or pipe to a horizontal header or collector pipe, which is connected to a pump. Usually, many risers are connected to a common header. Well-point systems are usually rented from specialty contractors who also install the system. With most contractors, the riser pipes are about 2 inches (5 cm) in diameter, and headers are 6–12 inches (15–30 cm), depending on the flow to be handled.

Normally, the screen provided with the well point is sufficient to keep medium sands and coarser materials from clogging the perforations. Where finer soils are to be dewatered, it is necessary also to provide a sand filter around the well point. The sand filter has the added benefit of acting to increase the size of the well point, permitting easier and greater flow into the point. To obtain a filter, it is necessary to create a hole having a larger diameter than the well point, prior to or when installing the well point and riser. The sand filter and backfill are then placed around the installed riser. A large-diameter hole can be formed by providing an attachment to the well point so that it can still be jetted to the desired depth, or by installing a casing by jetting or other method, after which the well point and surrounding sand filter are installed and the casing is pulled. For normal requirements, the sand filter material consists of a uniform graded medium to coarse sand.

The horizontal extent of the soil zone surrounding a well point that will show lowering of the groundwater table is affected by the depth of the well point and the permeability of the soil. Generally, the horizontal distance that is affected increases as permeability of the soil increases. The drawdown curve values shown in Table 6-1 can be used to estimate the horizontal distance that will be influenced by well-point dewatering.

With the type of pumping equipment conventionally used for well points, the

TABLE 6-1 APPROXIMATE SLOPE OF DRAWDOWN CURVE DUE TO A SINGLE ROW OF WELL POINTS

Soil being dewatered	Slope of drawdown curve, %[a]
Coarse sand	1–3
Medium sand	2–5
Fine sand	5–20
Silt–clay	20–35

[a]Refer to Figure 6-18 and recall that percentage slope is vertical change (ft or m) per 100 units of horizontal length (ft or m).

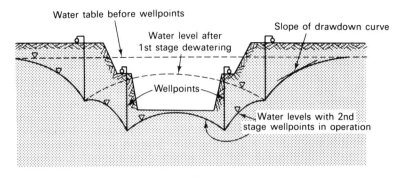

Figure 6-18 Multistage well-point operation.

depth of dewatering that can be achieved by a single line of well points located around the perimeter of an excavation is about 18–20 ft (6–7 m). This is due to the limit on the practical lifting, or suction, capacity of the pumping equipment. Lowering the water table through a greater distance may require the use of a two (or more) -stage (multistage) installation. Where a two-stage installation is required, the well points for the first stage of drawdown are located near the extreme perimeter limits of the area that can be excavated, and are put into operation. Well points for the second stage are subsequently located *within* the area that has been excavated, near to the bottom elevation that has been dewatered by the first stage. The second stage well points then lower the water table to the additional depth necessary to complete the excavation dry (see Figs. 6-18 and 6-19).

Although the principle on which well-point dewatering is based is a simple one, care and skill are required during installation and operation to obtain the intended results. Proper assembly of the piping system is particularly crucial, because if air leaks develop at connections, the efficiency of the pump suction is reduced.

Vacuum dewatering. Where well points are in use, flow to the well point is by gravity. In the coarser soils (soils with less than 25 percent of particles smaller

Figure 6-19 Installed two-stage well-point system in operation. (Courtesy of Moretrench American Corporation)

Drainage   **125**

than 0.05 mm) gravity flow is normally adequate to achieve dewatering. For silts, gravity flow is restricted because of capillary forces that tend to hold the pore water. It has been found, however, that by applying a vacuum to the piping system, satisfactory dewatering of silty soils can be achieved. For maximum efficiency, the vacuum dewatering system requires that the well point and riser be surrounded to within a few feet of the ground surface with filter sand and that the top few feet be sealed or capped with an impervious soil or other material. By having the pumps maintain a vacuum pressure, the hydraulic gradient for flow to the well points is increased. With this system, closer well-point spacings are required than for the conventional system.

Where suction pumps are used to draw the collected groundwater from the well points, as is common, the practical maximum height of lift is about 15–18 ft (5–6 m). Where an excavation is to extend more than this distance below the groundwater table, it will be necessary to dewater the area in two or more stages. With multistage dewatering, the well points for the first stage are installed on a perimeter line outside of the actual excavation area required for the construction and put in operation. Excavation proceeds within the perimeter formed by the well points to the depth where groundwater is encountered. Well points for the second stage are next installed within this excavation to further lower the water table for the actual construction area.

Electro-osmosis. Sand and the coarser silt soils usually can be dewatered by using gravity draining or vacuum-assisted well points. In fine silts, clay, or coarse-grained–fine-grained mixtures, the effective permeability may be too low to obtain a successful dewatering by using well-point methods. Drainage of such low-permeability soils may be achieved by electro-osmosis, provided that no more than 25 percent of the soil particles are smaller than 0.002 mm.

The basic principle of electro-osmosis is as follows: If a flow of direct current electricity is induced through a saturated soil between a positive and negative electrode (anode and cathode, respectively), pore water will migrate toward the negative electrode. If a well or well point is made the cathode, collected water drained from the soil can be removed by pumping as with a conventional well-point system.

Movement of water towards an electrically negative terminal occurs because of the attraction of the cathode for positive ions (cations) that are present in groundwater. Cations in pore water are the result of dissolved minerals going into solution with the groundwater. The cations concentrate around the negatively charged surface of clay particles to satisfy the electrical charge on the particle. These cations, in turn, attract the negative "end" of "dipole" water molecules. As the cations are drawn to the cathode, water molecules held to the cation follow.

In a field installation it is considered most beneficial to locate the anode close to the excavation perimeter and place the cathode further back, so that the direction of drainage is away from the excavation. This arrangement eliminates the danger that seepage forces caused by the draining water could act to cause the exposed slopes of the excavation to slide or slough in toward the excavation (construction area).

Figure 6-20 Summary: Relation between method for dewatering soil and range of particle sizes [7].

Because of techniques involved, the required special equipment, and the high electric consumption, drainage by electro-osmosis is expensive compared to gravity drainage methods. Consequently, the method is used only when other methods cannot be applied.

Deep Drainage   If excavations are to extend deep below the groundwater table, or to penetrate through a deep permeable stratum, well points may not be applicable because of the limits to which well points can raise water. For this situation, deep wells and deep well pumps (jet or venturi pumps) can be used. Deep wells are frequently relatively large diameter (on the order of 2 ft or 60 cm) drilled holes. A perforated protective casing is installed, and the deep well pump is then placed inside the casing near the bottom. Coarse filter material is placed between the outside of the casing and the walls of the drilled hole.

Consolidation Drainage   *Consolidation* refers to the process that occurs in clay deposits when the development of compressive stresses in the soil mass from external loading causes the soil to undergo a reduction in volume (due to a reduction in void spaces) that is simultaneously accompanied by water in the soil pores' being expelled to permit the decrease in voids. Thus, subsurface drainage of fine-grained soils by consolidation can be achieved by imposing a surface load onto an area. In general, a reduction in water content results in an increase in the shear strength of the clay. Unfortunately, the rate of drainage is quite slow in clay soils because of the low coefficient of permeability.

Sand drains represent one method that has been used with success to accelerate the rate at which consolidation drainage occurs in fine-grained materials. The method is based on reducing the distance that pore water has to travel to escape from the consolidating soil. Sand drains are vertical columns of freely draining sand installed so as to penetrate the soil strata to be consolidated. In clays, the permeability in the horizontal direction is frequently many times the vertical permeability because of the stratified manner in which clay deposits have been formed. The presence of relatively closely spaced sand drains thus reduces the distance that pore water must travel to escape and also permits an easier (horizontal) drainage path. In draining from the clay, water flowing to the sand drains is under pressure as a result of the external loading that is applied to cause the consolidation (usually an earth fill to act as a surcharge). Therefore, the water can flow upward as well as downward in the sand drain. Further details on the mechanics of the drainage that occurs in sand drains and wick drains (a related, more recent development) is presented in Chapter 9.

Drainage after Construction   Preventing groundwater from seeping into a structure or through a structure after it has been built may be necessary in order to obtain proper use of the structure or to protect it from damage.

In some cases, the dewatering methods used during construction can be kept in use to protect the structure. Normally, however, this procedure is not followed; the equipment or methods may interfere with the usefulness of the finished project, may be too expensive for long-term use, or may be impractical in some other way.

When it is known that a usable part of a structure will be located below the groundwater table, it is desirable to build the facility using waterproof design and construction techniques. One of the desirable features for a subaqueous structure is to have all seams and joints provided with water stops, and/or to have the structure built with no seams or joints wherever possible. For example, in small conventional buildings, concrete basement walls and floors can be poured monolithically. Admixtures also are available to make concrete more resistant to water penetration; similarly, chemical coatings are available to waterseal the surface of concrete.

Foundation Drains   Where groundwater will be flowing in the vicinity of the structure, provision can be made so that the water will be quickly carried away from the building area, and at worse only a limited height of groundwater buildup against the exterior will occur. With adequate provisions, the large hydrostatic pressures that tend to force seepage entry thus will not develop. A method for achieving this control when the depth below the water table is not too great is with foundation drains, conventionally placed around the building exterior at footing level and adjacent to the footing (see Fig. 6-21). Such drains should not be lower

Figure 6-21   Footing drain tile installation for disposing of groundwater against a basement wall.

than the bottom of the footing. Where there is concern over the ability of the exterior drain to handle the expected groundwater, the foundation drains may be located on the interior side of the foundation as well. With a high water table, it may also be desirable to place interceptor drains at some short distance from the building and at an elevation higher than the footings so that the water table is lowered in stages.

The installed drain normally consists of pipe provided with perforations or installed with open joints so that groundwater can enter into the pipe. Gravel and/or sand filter material must surround the drain pipe so that soil particles tending to be carried along by the inflowing water are prevented from clogging the drain pipe openings or causing erosion. Criteria for filter material are presented in subsequent paragraphs.

An outlet for collected water is a necessity; preferably disposal will be by gravity flow to a storm drain system or other drainage facility such as a ditch, dry well, or pool located at an area of lower elevation than the building. If disposal by gravity flow is not possible, drainage water will have to be directed to a sump pit or other collector and pumped to a disposal.

Blanket Drains   Where a basement is to be located below groundwater level, a blanket or layer of filter material can be placed beneath the floor slab to provide a highly permeable drainage path for removal of groundwater acting against the bottom of the slab (see Fig. 6-22). Providing an escape path serves to reduce uplift pressures and the possibility for seepage to occur through the floor. The blanket connects to a sump where collected water is pumped out, or to drainage pipes where disposal occurs by gravity flow. The filter blanket normally consists of a sand layer placed over the natural subgrade soils, and a coarser, small gravel or crushed rock layer through which most of the horizontal flow is intended to take place.

Figure 6-22   Details of a blanket drain beneath a concrete floor.

Figure 6-23 Highway and airfield drains: (a) interceptor drain for highway constructed in a sidehill (after Cedergren [00]); (b) interceptor drain for highway in flat terrain [00]; (c) typical airport runway interceptor drains (Civil Aeronautics Administration); (d) typical open-shoulder ditch for roads.

130

Interceptor Drains   In paved highways and airfield runways, the design frequently calls for interceptor trench drains located parallel to the shoulder, as shown in Figure 6-23. The purpose of the drains is to lower the groundwater table to a level beneath the pavement and to permit easy lateral drainage (escape) for water finding its way into the coarse base material provided beneath the pavement (water resulting from upward migration from capillarity and from infiltration through cracks, joints or voids in the pavement).

The intent of the drainage facility is to keep the base and subgrade soils dry so that they will maintain high strength and stability. With coarser soils, the intent is probably achieved quite successfully. In fine-grained soils, the degree of achievement is questionable. Most probably, a groundwater table in such soils is not significantly lowered because of the material's low permeability. However, the drainage ditches do serve to prevent excess pore water pressures from building up in the subgrade soils (excess pore water pressures have the effect of weakening the soil). The drains also provide a means for disposal of surface and near surface water, and will intercept underground flow trying to enter the roadway from the side areas.

Similarly, paved and unpaved roads will benefit somewhat from even open drainage ditches located adjacent to shoulder areas (see Fig. 6-23d). Such ditches handle surface water, provide a lateral drainage outlet for soil near the level of the road surface that helps prevent the development of excess pore water pressures, intercept surface and near surface water flowing toward the roadway area from the sides, and provide storage for plowed snow and a flow channel for melting snow so that it does not run onto the roadway.

Flow through a Structure   In some types of structures, such as earth dams and dikes, it is known that water will be flowing through the structure after it is put in use. The design of the structure, therefore, considers the effect that such flow will have on the stability of the structure. Flow is not prevented but, rather, is permitted and directed so as not to create a stability problem. For instance, in a homogeneous earth dam or dike, flow is typically as indicated in Figure 6-24. If the velocity of the water flowing through the structure is too great, erosion and instability of the downstream side will result. The placement of a toe drain or of an underdrain blanket that consists of coarse materials helps direct the flow to

Figure 6-24   Pattern of flow through a homogeneous earth dam.

Drainage   **131**

(a) Earth dam with rock fill toe

(b) Earth dam with downstream drain

Figure 6-25 Flow through an earth dam modified by toe drain or underdrain: (a) earth dam with rock fill toe; (b) earth dam with downstream drain.

those areas that will not erode or lose stability because of the flowing water (Fig. 6-25).

There are basically similar situations encountered in building construction, where localized underground flow occurs through seams or a stratum of pervious soil (frequently referred to as underground springs) and presents a potential seepage problem for the structure. Providing some type of drainage conduits for the flow to pass around or through the structure is frequently technically more desirable and less expensive than attempting to cut off or stop the flow. The main precaution to be observed is that the flow conduit be designed so that seepage forces do not affect the building, and soil erosion does not occur.

Filter Design   Water flowing towards a drainage structure must be able to enter the drain easily and quickly but must not be permitted to carry with it small soil particles that could eventually clog the drain, or cause erosion or cavitation in the areas surrounding the drain. As a result, where a drainage structure is open to the soil, it is necessary to provide a *drainage filter*. Sand and gravel blends are typically used for such filters.

To permit quick easy flow into the drain facility, and to "draw" water to the drain, it is necessary to have the permeability of the filter material considerably greater than the permeability of the surrounding natural soil. To satisfy this criterion, a ratio between particle sizes for the filter material and natural soil has been established; viz.,

$$\frac{D_{15} \text{ of filter material}}{d_{15} \text{ of natural soil}} \text{ should be 4 or greater.}$$

To prevent particles of *natural sandy* soils from migrating into the filter material and eventually clogging it, the following ratios of particle sizes should be used as design criteria:

$$\frac{D_{15} \text{ of filter material}}{d_{85} \text{ of natural soil}} \text{ is less than 5.}$$

$$\frac{D_{50} \text{ of filter material}}{d_{50} \text{ of natural soil}} \text{ is less than 25.}$$

$$\frac{D_{15} \text{ of filter material}}{d_{15} \text{ of natural soil}} \text{ is less than 20.}$$

Of these criteria, the D_{15}/d_{85} ratio is considered to be the most important and indicative of filter performance.

In these ratios, the D_{15}, d_{15}, and so on, values refer to the particle dimensions obtained from a particle-size distribution curve (e.g., the D_{15} or d_{15} refers to the particle size for which 15 percent of the soil material, by weight, is smaller). In the past, filter design criteria have suggested that natural and filter materials have parallel but transposed particle-size distribution curves, but this feature of filters has been found to be unnecessary and perhaps even undesirable.

Where a sand and gravel filter is to be in contact with a *fine-grained soil*, some additional criteria beyond those just outlined should be applied to the selection of filter materials. For fine clays (a d_{85} range of 0.03–0.10 mm), the D_{15} for the filter should not exceed 0.5 mm. For fine-grained silt (a d_{85} range of 0.03–0.10 mm) with low cohesive strength and low plasticity (liquid limit less than about 30), the D_{15} for the filter should not exceed about 0.3 mm. For sandy silts and clays having noticeable sand content (a d_{85} range of 0.1–0.5 mm), a sand filter material is adequate when the D_{15}/d_{85} ratio is less than 5. The D_{50}/d_{50} and D_{15}/d_{15} ratios should *not* be considered when selecting a sand or a sand–gravel filter that will be in contact with the fine-grained soils described.

To ensure that filter particles will not enter and clog the drain structure, where holes or slots are provided for the entry of water, the following criteria should be followed:

For circular holes, the ratio

$$\frac{D_{85} \text{ of filter material}}{\text{Diameter of opening}} \text{ is greater than 1.2.}$$

For slotted openings, the ratio

$$\frac{D_{85} \text{ of filter material}}{\text{Width of slot}} \text{ is greater than 1.4.}$$

For proper performance, the filter material must surround the drain, under as well as over. The filter material should also be compacted so that it does not settle. To help minimize any tendency for fine particles to migrate through the filter, and to drain as much water as possible, the holes or slots in the drain structure should be placed facing downward, or as near to downward as possible, so that the flow into the drain facility is *not* downward but instead is laterally or slightly upward.

If the natural soil is fine-grained, it may be necessary to provide a filter that consists of two or more layers, each having a different gradation. The material closest to the drain would be coarsest, with the outer material filter that is next to the natural soil being less coarse. For the situation in which two or more filter materials are used, the criteria presented earlier for filter and natural soil would also apply between any two adjacent filter materials.

Separation and Drainage with Synthetic Fabrics The use of fabrics in construction projects is a relatively new development but one whose application is becoming more widespread because of the increasing variety of fabric types and properties available, as well as the ease of handling.

Construction fabrics are clothlike or sheetlike, relatively thin and flexible, and usually available in wide sheets or rolls. Most of the fabrics used for construction work (often described as *geofabrics* or *geotextiles*) are the nonwoven materials made with synthetic fibers (most common are the nylon, polypropylene, and polyester fibers).[7] Since they are manufactured, the different synthetic fabrics can be made to possess different properties; for example, fabrics over a range of strengths or a range of permeabilities are available. Accordingly, fabrics have been found adaptable for use in the earthwork and drainage control phases of construction where separation or protection of earth materials is necessary, and where movement of underground or surface water must be directed or prevented.

The concern for separation of soil materials is significant in works such as zoned earth dams, roadways, airfields, and railroads. With projects of this nature, one zone of material is designed to be coarser than an adjacent zone (e.g., an earth dam may consist of a fine-grained soil core with shell zones of coarse material, whereas a roadway base of coarse granular material rests on a subbase or subgrade of finer soil). Means to prevent migration of fine material into the coarse material, or intrusion of coarse material into the fine material, is necessary. Fabrics can be used at the boundary between such different soil materials to maintain a separation but still permit the movement and passage of water (Figs. 6-26a, b). Fabrics similarly have application with foundation drains and underdrains (Fig. 6-26c). It has also been found that the presence of a fabric incorporated into a structure such as an earthen dam or a road pavement foundation acts as reinforcement, which helps to support and redistribute applied loads because of the material's tensile and shearing strength.[8]

Fabrics which possess low permeability or are impermeable can be used as buried or exposed linings to prevent seepage or infiltration in reservoir and impounding areas (Fig. 6-26d). The movement of water through an earth dike can be restricted by installing a fabric lining on the dike's upstream side. Seepage

---

[7]See inset, "The Materials and Manufacture of Synthetic Fabrics for Construction Projects," for details on the materials and classifications for synthetic fabrics (page 136).

[8]See Figure 12-26.

(a) Fabrics to maintain separation of different soils and carry seepage

(b) Fabric to reinforce roadbase and to maintain separation from subgrade

(c) Arrangement for foundation drain or pavement underdrain

(d) Fabrics to reduce seepage through or beneath an impounding structure

(e) Fabrics to drain water from soil behind a retaining wall

(f) Fabric with drains to hasten consolidation drainage of weak organic and fine-grained soil deposits

Figure 6-26 Representative uses of fabrics for separation and drainage.

Drainage

beneath a dam can be reduced by placing an impervious fabric to act as an upstream blanket. Conversely, fabrics with high planer permeability (ability to conduct flow within the thickness of the fabric) can be used as a passageway for water, and have application as protective drains where it is necessary to collect and carry seepage, such as within earth dams and behind retaining walls (Fig. 6-26e), and road and airfield pavement drains (Fig. 6-23).

With the increased use of fabrics on construction projects, the opportunity for manufacturers to provide technical advice and field assistance has correspondingly increased. With direct contacts, manufacturers have become aware that a market is available for composite products that are capable of outperforming plain fabrics or the conventional systems provided for particular needs (such as the subsurface drainage function). As a result, a number of manufacturers currently produce a prefabricated drainage envelope, or drainage system, which can be used for draining pavement subgrades, for retaining wall and bridge abutment drains, for wick drains (used to accelerate soil consolidation), and for protecting basement

---

THE MATERIALS AND MANUFACTURE OF SYNTHETIC FABRICS FOR CONSTRUCTION PROJECTS

Synthetic fabrics used for construction projects typically are manufactured from polymers, such as the polyesters, polypropylenes, polyethylenes, or nylons. Fabrics developed from filaments of polyester or polypropylene are most widely used. Some fabrics use bicomponent fibers (fibers of two or more polymer types). Compared to natural fibers, the polymer synthetics offer relative durability in the presence of elements commonly encountered in construction (e.g., moisture).

The fabric filaments (fibers or strands) may be obtained by an *extrusion* process or by the *slit-film* process. Extruded filaments result when a heated and liquefied polymer is forced through small openings, such as the holes in a spinnerette. The extruded strands cool and solidify and are then ready to be combined to form fabric. In the slit-film process, the polymer is melted and forced (extruded) into a thin sheet, or film. When cooled and solidified, the polymer sheet is cut (slit) into thin strips, which are wound onto storage bobbins.

Filaments are assembled into fabric using either a *woven procedure* or a *nonwoven procedure.* Woven fabric is obtained by the conventional technique of weaving warp yarn (filaments extending in the long direction of the weave) and filler yarn (filaments in the transverse or cross direction). Properties of the woven fabric are controlled or affected by the spacing of the warp and filler yarns, as well as by the size and properties of the filaments. Generally, strength-related properties of the completed woven fabric (tensile strength, resistance to distortion and tearing, etc.) tend to be bidirectional.

The nonwoven procedures include the *spun–bonded* technique and the *dry–laid–nonwoven* process.

In the spun–bonded process, continuous filaments resulting from extrusion of polymer through a spinnerette are randomly laid down in a circular pattern on a laydown belt to form the fabric web. The web strands can be bonded together using a *needle-punching* procedure, by *heat bonding*, or by *resin (chemical) bonding.* The needle-punching procedure involves use of a needle loom containing a number of barbed needles. The barbed needles repeatedly punch through the fabric web, forcing the randomly laid-down strands to interlock mechanically. The needles have the barbs designed so strands are grabbed only on the downward stroke. The resulting fabric texture is soft, with a noticeable thickness.

To heat bond a fabric, the unbonded web is passed through heated rollers in order to cause strand surfaces to melt and fuse together at points of contact. The fuse bonding is retained after the fabric cools. With resin bonding, the unbonded web is treated with a liquid cementing resin that adheres strands at their points of contact when the fabric passes through heated rollers. Excess resin is subsequently removed from the fabric.

Dry–laid–nonwoven fabrics are manufactured from staple fibers, which are fibers having limited length (typically, fiber lengths range between 1.5 and 6 inches, or 4–15 cm). The fibers are laid down on a moving belt by a cross-lapper, so to create a crisscross layering of short strands (staple). The staple is bonded by either needle punching, heat, or resin.

The manufactured fabric is wound into rolls for storage and shipping. Roll widths vary according to manufacturer and product, but many products are in the 12- to 16-foot-wide range (4–5 meters). At the construction site, the fabric is unrolled and cut if necessary. Large areas are covered using multi rolls. The edge and end seams are mechanically sewed, glued, fused, or simply overlapped.

Some generalities exist concerning properties, performance, and suggested uses for synthetic fabrics. (*Note:* some degree of caution is warranted with generalities; exceptions are to be expected. Furthermore, not all of a fabric's properties are a consideration for use.) Needle-punched fabrics generally are considered more flexible than chemically and heat-bonded fabrics. Nonwoven fabrics are generally considered to have similar strength properties across all directions in the plane of the fabric, whereas woven fabrics are probably strongest in the direction of fabric strands. Fabrics manufactured from continuous filaments generally are considered stronger than fabrics made with staple fibers of similar material. Polyester filaments have good resistance to ultraviolet rays (sunlight), but unprotected polypropylene is subject to deterioration. Polyesters are not expected to be damaged from exposure to diesel fuels, but polypropylenes could be. Polyester fabrics generally retain better flexibility at low temperatures than do polypropylene fabrics.

walls from seepage. Designers and contractors are also experimenting with drainage envelopes as a method for venting radon gas present in soil around buildings. Generally these composite systems consist of an outer layer of filter fabric and an interior core to act as the passageway to transmit groundwater and gases entering the system. Advantages of the properly designed composite system are relative ease of handling and installation, long effective service life, and lower cost than for a conventional drainage installation (e.g., drain pipe and granular fill placed in a trench). It is expected that the development of special products involving synthetic fabrics will continue as the opportunity to compete with conventional procedures or material is recognized.

Land Drainage   One of the earliest methods for reclaiming flat expanses of marginal wetland areas for use consisted of constructing a network of deep drainage ditches to lower the water table and obtain a stable surface suitable for agriculture and for supporting light structures. With a network of drainage ditches, drainage is by gravity, and best results are obtained in soils with relatively high coefficients of permeability. In clays or fine silts, where permeability is low and capillary forces holding the pore water are high, drainage from gravity effects will be limited. Water can be replaced by normal precipitation as quickly as drainage occurs. However, where the subsurface soils include strata or seams of coarse soils, as frequently exist in coastal and lake ares, predominantly fine-grained soil deposits have been drained. The drainage ditch network, generally laid out in some form of grid pattern, requires outletting to areas of elevation lower than the draining area.

Effects of Drainage   Water flowing toward a drain also causes seepage forces that act on the soil particles. These forces are capable of moving soil particles, particularly small particles. Unless the migration of particles by a properly functioning filter is prevented, the small particles will be washed into the drain, eventually eroding soil from the area surrounding the drain. This occurrence could cause the drainage structure to collapse because of inadequate support from the surrounding soil. This process is referred to as *internal erosion*.

If an open drainage system (i.e., open ditches) causes seepage forces to act toward an open excavation, there is the possibility that the forces will precipitate a sloughing-in of the soil embankment.

Normally, removing water from soil (particularly a fine-grained soil) will increase the shear strength of the soil, in effect making the soil mass stronger. Lowering of a water table, however, also results in an increased effective vertical pressure acting on the soil mass, because the soil weight changes from a submerged weight to a saturated but unbuoyed weight. The usual result of an additional loading to the area within the zone of drawdown is settlement. The magnitude of the settlement depends on the amount of water table lowering and the strength and compressibility of the soil. If an undeveloped area (one with no buildings, etc.) is dewatered and the surface settles, usually no problems result. If developed areas are in the zone of drawdown, however, settlement of buildings and utilities in the area could occur.

If the settlement of structures adjacent to a construction site being dewatered is anticipated, effects can be minimized by the process of *recharging*. Recharging consists of pumping water back into the ground, usually with well points, in the area between where the endangered structures are located and where the dewatering takes place. Careful monitoring of groundwater levels is required for proper overall results.

Soil Percolation Rate

Soil percolation rate refers to the ease or difficulty with which soil accepts fluid, generally water, into it. It is a condition frequently of interest for planning private underground sewage disposal systems, such as the leach fields and leach pits for septic tanks. With a septic tank system, all sewage passes into the septic tank. The solids are retained, but the liquid is passed on for absorption into the earth.

The percolation rate can be related to the coefficient of permeability of a soil; the coarser, permeable soils are capable of accepting larger volumes of water and at a faster rate than fine-grained soils having low permeability. However, *percolation* and *permeability* do *not* refer to the same property of a soil. For example, a coarse soil having a high coefficient of permeability may have a low rate of percolation if the groundwater table is high and the soil is not capable of accepting additional water.

Procedures to check the percolation rate for a soil generally stipulate testing of the area and depth where the septic tank leach field or leach pit is to be located. For the common requirement that leach field drain lines be installed about 2 feet below the ground surface, percolation tests are performed about 30 inches (75 cm) below the surface. A small test hole, usually 6–12 inches (15–30 cm) in diameter, is dug at least 6 inches deep. The test hole area is saturated by filling the hole several times with water and letting it drain completely before beginning the actual test. For the test, the hole is filled with water and the time for the water level to drop a specified distance (e.g., from 6 inches deep to 5 inches deep, or from 15 cm to 12.5 cm) is recorded. A fast rate of drop indicates "good" percolation. A slow rate or no drop indicates poor percolation. Areas having poor percolation rates should not be used as leach fields. Details of the applicable methods for performing percolation tests should be obtained from local health department authorities, to ensure that procedures are in accord with their requirements.

FROST HEAVE IN SOILS

When soil is exposed to a freezing climate for a sufficient period of time, soil temperatures will eventually depress to below freezing. Temperatures will vary within the soil mass, being lowest where contact with the freezing source is made (usually this would be the ground surface in contact with freezing air temperatures, but the source of a freezing temperature could also be from the floor of a frozen

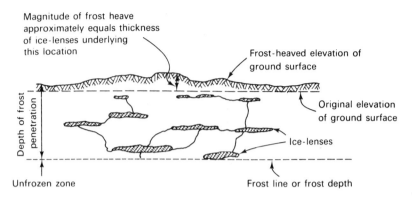

Magnitude of frost heave approximately equals thickness of ice-lenses underlying this location

Frost-heaved elevation of ground surface

Depth of frost penetration

Original elevation of ground surface

Ice-lenses

Unfrozen zone

Frost line or frost depth

Figure 6-27   Ice-lens formation in a frozen soil.

storage warehouse or ice rink) and gradually increasing with distance from the freezing source to reach the stable, above-freezing temperature that exists underground.

When freezing temperatures develop in a soil mass, most of the pore water in the soil also is subject to freezing.[9] As water crystallizes, its volume expands approximately 9 percent. In considering normal void ratios and the degree of saturation for soils in general, an expansion of the soil mass as a result of freezing might be expected to be on the order of 3 or 4 percent of the original volume. This may mean a vertical expansion on the order of 1–2 inches (2.5–5 cm) for an area with the climate that exists in the northern half of the United States. Experience indicates, however, that in some soil types the volume of expansion resulting during freezing periods, termed *frost heave*, is frequently considerably greater than could be expected from expansion of normal pore water. Frost heaves exceeding one foot (30 cm) are not uncommon.

Investigation of heaved soils indicates that pore water indeed has become frozen. However, much of the frozen water has been segregated in discontinuous layers, or lenses, throughout the frozen soil, and the volume of the water in the ice lenses is considerably greater than the volume of the original pore water. Further, the magnitude of ground surface heave has been found to approximately equal the combined thickness of ice lenses existing in the soil at the heave location (see Fig. 6-27).

Studies conducted at field sites and in the laboratory to investigate the frost heave phenomenon have been able to define conditions and occurrences responsible for the ice-lens formation, which is the basic cause of heaving.

As freezing temperatures develop, water in the *larger* voids of the frozen soil zone also becomes frozen. Such frozen water is potentially the start of an ice lens. Water remaining unfrozen in capillary size (very small) voids is subsequently attracted to such a beginning ice lens and enlarges the volume of the lens. The process

---

[9]This explains the "frozen-solid condition" noted for soil ground in cold weather. The frozen water is responsible for the strong bonding between soil particles; the soil particles generally experience no change as "freezing" temperatures occur, for they are already in the frozen or solid state.

Figure 6-28 Ice-lens formation by capillary movement of groundwater into zone of freezing.

of ice-lens growth continues as long as freezing temperatures prevail and free water can be attracted to the ice lens.

The development of ice-lens formations significant enough to cause large heaves to occur requires that a source of water be sufficiently close to the freezing zone of soil that it can be drawn into this zone. In the normal frost heave occurrence the source of water is the groundwater table, as illustrated by Figure 6-28. Upward movement from a water table to the freezing zone occurs through capillary rise. Water in fine capillary openings can continue to migrate through even a zone of subfreezing temperatures because of the depressed freezing point for water in small capillaries and water adsorbed to the surface of soil particles. In a "frozen" silty soil, it is known that there will exist some frozen water and some still liquid water with temperatures as low as, and possibly lower than, 25°F (-4°C).

All factors causing moisture migration through a frozen soil are not fully understood, but current theories attribute movement to a thermal gradient where capillary flow is in the direction of higher toward lower temperatures, and to osmotic flow.[10]

Height of capillary rise is quite limited in clean, coarse-grained soils, and unless a source of water is close to the zone of freezing soil, frost heave problems are normally not expected in such soils.

Theoretical height of capillary rise is greatest in the fine-grained silt and clay soils. Practically speaking, however, and under typical seasonal conditions of limited cold periods, ice-lens growth is affected by the *rate of capillary rise* in soil. In clay, this rate is so slow that under normal conditions sufficient water can not be obtained to cause ice-lens growth. Silts, however, have a relatively high rate of capillary rise, and water can migrate easily to the zone where ice lenses are forming. Silts, therefore, because of their potential for high capillary rise (distance) coin-

---

[10]Osmotic flow relates to the movement between liquid solutions having different ion concentrations. Simply stated, there is the tendency for the more dilute solution to flow into and mix with the highly concentrated solution. Water in soil normally has some concentration of cations because of dissolved minerals. Applied to the ice-lens phenomenon, crystallization of soil pore water may increase the ionic concentration; thus the more dilute free water in the soil would be attracted to the ice lens.

Frost Heave in Soils

cident with the potential for rapid rise, are conducive to ice-lens formation and frost heave. As a result, silts are termed *frost-susceptible* soils. Silt mixtures, such as silty sands and silty clays, are similarly regarded as frost susceptible. Because of the practical limitations on ice-lens growth within them, coarse-grained and clay soils are normally considered as *non-frost-susceptible* soils.

In summary, several simultaneously occurring conditions are required for the notorious frost heave problem to occur:

1. Presence of a frost-susceptible soil
2. Presence of freezing temperatures
3. Presence of a supply or source of water to help form and feed the ice lenses

The rate at which freezing temperatures penetrate the frost-susceptible soil has an effect on the total ice-lens formation and, consequently, on the frost heave of the ground surface. The maximum effects result when there is a gradual decrease in temperature as opposed to a rapid or flash decrease. The longer and the colder the freezing period, the greater will be the depth of frost penetration, and the greater the frost heave will be.

Damages from frost heave result in structures supported on the soils being heaved. Commonly, this includes roadways and pavements, and building foundations and exposed ground-level building slabs. The heaving force can be considerable; it has the ability to lift pavements, slabs, and building foundations. Because the magnitude of heave is rarely uniform over even short horizontal distances, cracking of pavements and slabs frequently occurs. In buildings, walls or floors may crack or distort so that doors, windows, and equipment supported on the walls may not operate properly. If heave is great enough, utility pipelines passing through or over the walls may be ruptured because of the movement.

Damage is not restricted to that resulting from the heaving. Much of the ice-lens volume represents new water introduced to the soil, and when the soil thaws from the surface downward in a warm period the free water cannot drain through the still frozen underlying soil. The effect is that the melting ice lenses significantly increase the water content of the soil, and loss of soil strength occurs. Loss of soil bearing and settlement follow. For building foundations not located below frost depths, the cycle of heaving in winter and settling in spring is potentially an annual occurrence that is capable of causing progressive damage.

Similar effects can occur in pavements and unprotected ground-level building slabs. In roadway surfaces, the effects are compounded by the repeated loadings applied to an area by vehicle movement. Under the action of traffic, the roadway surface will be broken up because of loss of underlying soil support. This is generally referred to as the spring breakup. Further, the soft soil will be displaced from the road base, causing holes and depressions, which are referred to as potholes or chuck holes.

It should also be realized that frost heave may have its effect where new construction takes place during freezing periods. For example, should the foundation soil for planned structural components such as footings, floor slabs, or pavements be in a frozen and heaved condition at the time of construction, the eventual thawing and settling of the soil can cause the component to experience settlement, distortion, or structural damage.

To prevent the effects of frost heave damage to buildings, it is common practice to construct foundations to a depth at least equal to the depth of frost penetration for the area. Such procedures might be thought to be necessary only in a frost-susceptible situation. If non-frost-susceptible soils exist at a building site or if there is no source of water, locating foundations below frost depth could be unnecessary unless required for other reasons. However, in natural soil deposits there should also be some suspicion that even "non-frost-susceptible" soils will have some properties that could make them susceptible. For example, many naturally occurring coarse-grained soils include some fines, or include seams or strata of finer, more susceptible material. Clay soils frequently have considerable silt content, or the clay deposit may include fissures and hairline cracks that can act as capillary tubes for the migration of water.

It should also be recognized that during the life of a structure, the depth of the groundwater table is subject to change.

In considering poor performance and damages that can result if frost heave should affect foundations, most designers and constructors are of the opinion that it is worth the relatively small extra expense to take precaution at the time of construction to install foundations for exterior elements below frost depth. Figure 6-29 shows maximum frost depth data prepared from information obtained across the United States.

For grade-level structures such as building slabs and highway pavements (no

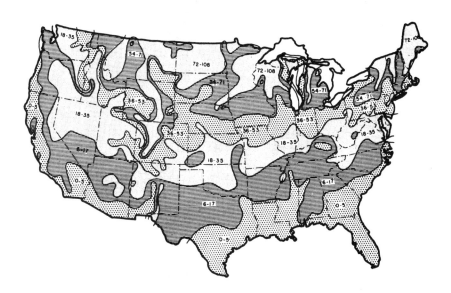

Figure 6-29 Maximum depth of frost penetration in inches (from Frost Action in Roads and Airfields, HRB Publication 211 [00]).

Frost Heave in Soils

deep foundations), other approaches to the control of the frost heave problem are taken. Control usually requires achieving at least one of the following:

1. Removing existing frost-susceptible soils to about frost depth
2. Removing or cutting off the water source that could feed ice-lens growth
3. Protecting the susceptible soil from freezing temperatures

For road or airfield pavements, the effort for control or protection has frequently included removing the frost-susceptible soils to frost depth and replacing them with a non-frost-susceptible material, or providing drainage facilities to keep the water table low in the vicinity of the pavement. For building slabs, replacing the frost-susceptible soil is frequently a practical solution.

Non-frost-susceptible soils for replacement purposes include coarse-grained soil (sand and sand–gravel mixtures) and clays. Coarse-grained soils are preferred because they are easier to place and compact, are less difficult to work with in inclement weather, and have other desirable properties when in place, such as easy drainage. To be non-frost-susceptible, studies and experience indicate that a *well-graded* granular soil should contain not more than 3 percent of particle sizes smaller than 0.02 mm,[11] while *uniform* granular soils can have up to about 10 percent of particle sizes smaller than 0.02 mm. Some ice-lens formation may still result with these soils, but such development will generally be of limited extent and tolerable.

Other methods for control of frost heave have included installation of a barrier at about frost depth to prevent upward capillary movement that could feed ice lenses. The barrier can be a very coarse soil of a thickness through which capillary rise cannot occur, an impermeable material such as a densely compacted clay layer, or a plastic or other fabric material through which water cannot penetrate. These methods appear most suitable for protecting limited areas, such as building slabs, or for highway fill sections. The methods are not considered practical for highway construction in areas of cut section or at-grade construction because of the expense of excavating and replacing subgrade soils that would be associated with installation of a barrier. Further, frost-susceptible subgrade soils may be difficult to replace and compact, especially in wet weather.

Successful protection has also been achieved by wrapping pavement subgrade soils within an impermeable membrane after they have been properly compacted, so as to keep the soil at a desired optimum moisture content and to prohibit ice-lens formation. A disadvantage of this method of control relates to costs of installing the membrane and placing the soil.

If the soil beneath a slab or pavement can be protected so that it does not freeze, there will be no frost heave problem. In the construction of frozen-storage warehouses, ice rinks, and similar facilities, insulation is placed between the soil subgrade and the floor of the facility, to protect the soil from the cold temperatures prevailing in the structure. Similar methods are adaptable for protecting exposed ground-level slabs for buildings. Various methods that have been used are illus-

---

[11]To retain a perspective on sizes, it is noted that the #200 sieve has openings of 0.074 mm; a #400 sieve has openings of 0.037 mm.

Figure 6-30 Some methods that have been used to insulate floor systems for refrigerated areas.

trated in Figure 6-30. For highways, some work has been done with providing insulating material beneath the pavement.

Permafrost   Permanently frozen ground, termed *permafrost*, exists in the northern areas of North America, Europe, and Asia, and across most of Greenland (see Fig. 6-31), a result of the severe climate in those areas. It is estimated that one-fifth of the earth's northern hemisphere is underlain by permafrost. The depth of frozen soil is on the order of 1000 ft (300 m) in regions corresponding to Alaska's North Slope, and probably extends to more than 3300 ft (1000 m) at the Arctic Circle.

The surface zone of soil in the permafrost regions thaws in summer (a condition that also occurs where permafrost is located beneath a structure that enables lost heat to penetrate the ground), but the deeper material stays frozen. The zone thawed by a summer climate refreezes the next winter. The soil depth that is subjected to seasonal cycles of thawing and freezing is termed the *active zone*.

Thawed soil in the active zone is usually weak and compressible because of the trapped water content. Structures built in permafrost areas should have their foundations installed in the permanently frozen earth that exists below the active zone, to protect the structure against seasonal movements that would otherwise result. These foundations must be designed to ensure that heat is not conducted through or by them to the permafrost that provides the support; insulating materials could be necessary along the vertical perimeter of the foundation and at the base. Similarly, to prevent building heat losses from thawing the permafrost, the floors and subsurface walls that would be in contact with the ground must be insulated, artificially cooled, or separated (with small buildings, the first floor can be elevated above the ground surface).

The subarctic plains have a characteristic vegetative cover of mosses and low shrubs underlain by mucklike soil, a combination termed *tundra*. This surficial blanket acts as an insulating material limiting the depth of summer thawing, and

Figure 6-31 Extent of permafrost zones in Northern Hemisphere [00].

therefore the active zone. A result of recognizing this beneficial effect of the tundra is that roadways for permafrost areas are now constructed on embankments of gravel, which act as a non-frost-susceptible insulating pad to keep the underlying soil frozen and stable. Equally significant, the presence of tundra has proved to be helpful in keeping sloped and hilly areas stable against slides.

PROBLEMS

6-1. A canal is located in an area where its route parallels that of a nearby river. The elevation of the water surface in the canal is +375 ft. In the river, the water surface is at elevation +345 ft. A stratum of coarse-grained soil 10 ft thick is sandwiched between relatively impermeable fine-grained soils, and extends between the canal and the river. The distance between the river and the canal is 500 ft, and the coefficient of permeability of the buried coarse stratum is 0.01 ft per hour.

(a) Make a sketch of the described conditions.

(b) Calculate the seepage loss from canal to river, in gallons per day per mile of river canal length.

6-2. What are flow nets and why are they used?

6-3. A concrete gravity dam is 100 ft long from upstream to downstream end. It is constructed on a stratum of sand–silt soil 40 ft thick. The coefficient of permeability for this soil is 0.1 ft/day. Rock underlies the soil stratum. The bottom of the dam is 6 feet below the soil surface.

(a) For the condition where the height of water against the upstream face of the dam is 45 ft above the soil surface, and the water level at the downstream end is just at the soil surface, draw the flow net for seepage beneath the dam and calculate the quantity of seepage in gallons per day per foot of width of dam.

(b) For the condition where the height of water against the upstream face of the dam is 35 ft above the soil surface, and the water level at the downstream end is 5 ft above the soil surface, draw the flow net for seepage beneath the dam and compute the seepage in gallons per day per foot of width of dam.

6-4. The vertically upward flow of groundwater (an artesian condition) occurs through a sand deposit where the void ratio is 0.60 and the specific gravity of soil particles is 2.65. What hydraulic gradient is necessary for a quicksand condition to develop?

6-5. The hydraulic gradient for an occurrence where there is a vertically upward flow of water through a sand mass is 0.95. If the specific gravity of the soil particles is 2.75 and the void ratio is 0.65, determine if a quicksand or erosion condition could develop.

6-6. Well points are to be used to dewater a large trench excavation that extends 35 ft below the surface of the water table. Assume that the bottom width of the trench excavation is 70 ft.

(a) Develop a simple sketch of the necessary well-point system. Use separate diagrams to show the progress of the necessary stages of installation.

(b) Assume that half the necessary lowering of the water table elevation is achieved with the outer row of well points. If the soil being dewatered is a fine to medium sand, approximately at what distance beyond the well-point location is the original groundwater table not affected by well-point pumping.

6-7. Indicate the intended functions for foundation drains, and the major requirements for design and installation so as to achieve a properly operating system.

6-8. What are the intended functions and limitations of interceptor drains as conventionally used for highway and airfield construction?

6-9. What are the primary reasons for having limitations on the sizes of particles used to construct drainage filters?

6-10. Briefly describe the conditions necessary and the resulting sequence of occurrences that typically take place in a frost heaving situation. Specify the soil type considered most susceptible to large frost heaves.

6-11. What methods are commonly used to prevent the occurrence of, or to offset the effects of, frost heave?

## chapter 7

Combined Stresses in Soil Masses
Stress at a Point and Mohr's Circle

When a body or mass is subjected to external loading, various combinations of *internal* normal and shear stresses are developed at the different points within the body or mass. Generally, data concerning internal stress conditions are used to determine deformations (in soils work, deformation is most frequently associated with settlement) and to check for the possibility of a material (soil) failure because the strength is exceeded. In performing a stress study, it is convenient to use methods from engineering mechanics for analyzing stress at a point. With these methods, stresses acting on any plane passing through the point can be determined. The combinations of normal and shear stress that develop will vary, depending on the plane being analyzed and the magnitude of the external loading. The "stress at a point" analysis is also applicable for determining the weakest plane or potential plane of failure in a material, not always easily evident, and for indicating the magnitude of the stresses that act on this plane. This type of analysis has particular application for soil and foundation studies, since stability failures in soil masses are the result of the shear strength of the soil being exceeded.

STRESS AT A POINT: ANALYTICAL DEVELOPMENT

The stresses acting on any plane passed through a point consist of a normal stress (compression or tension) and a shearing stress. Depending on the type of external loading causing the stress condition, it is possible for the shear *or* the normal stress, or both, to be zero on some planes. In soil problems, most external loadings are compression. (The downward weight of a structure supported by a soil mass would

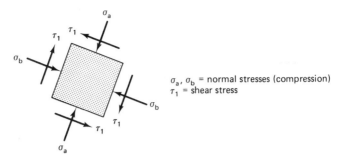

Figure 7-1 Incremental element with representative stresses assumed for analysis of "stress at a point."

be a compressive loading.) For a situation where the loading is compressive, normal stresses that develop on any plane would almost always have a value other than zero; some shear stress would act on all planes with the exception of two planes, where it will be zero (discussed in the following paragraphs).

If the combination of normal and shearing stresses acting on any two mutually perpendicular planes (orthogonal planes) are known, the combination of stresses acting on any other plane through the same point can be determined.

In analyzing stress at a point, it is convenient to assume an incremental element that represents the stress conditions at the point and to show the known stresses acting on it, as indicated in Figure 7-1.

For equilibrium, the sum of *forces* (not stresses) acting in any direction must equate to zero, and the rotational moments about any axis caused by forces similarly must equal zero. To satisfy this latter requirement, shear stresses acting on orthogonal planes must be equal in magnitude.

At the same point, but on a differently oriented element (actually a different plane passing through the identical location) the combination of normal and shearing stresses that act will be different (see Fig. 7-2). As will be shown, however, there is a relation between the normal and shear stresses acting on all planes (or orientation of elements) that pass through the same point.

Consider all the planes that can be passed through a point. On one particular plane, not yet defined, the shear stress will be zero, whereas the normal stress will be the maximum possible value of all the normal stresses acting on the various planes through that point. On a plane perpendicular to the plane just referred to,

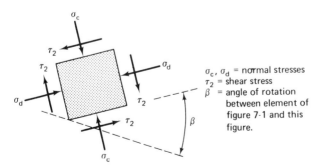

Figure 7-2 Method of rotating incremental element to determine stresses on different planes of study.

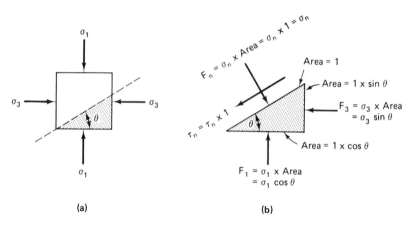

Figure 7-3 Basic step in determining stresses on a random plane through a point in terms of known principal stresses.

the shear stress will also be zero, but the normal stress that acts will be the least, or the minimum, of all the normal stresses acting on different planes through the point. These *maximum* and *minimum normal stresses* are called *principal stresses*. The planes on which they act are *principal planes*. The shear stress on a principal plane is *always* zero.

In many practical soil problems, the principal stresses act in the vertical and horizontal directions (or on horizontal and vertical planes), and are easily calculated. For instance, where the incremental element represents a point within a soil mass where the ground surface is horizontal, the vertical stress is due to the weight of the soil overburden at that point. This would be the effective unit weight of soil multiplied by the depth of the point below the ground surface. The horizontal stress is proportionate to the vertical stress. Thus, the magnitudes of the principal stresses are known, as are the orientations of planes on which the stresses act.

If the major and minor principal stresses are σ_1 and σ_3 respectively, the magnitude of a normal stress σ_n and shear stress τ_n on any other plane can be determined. Referring to the stressed element in Figure 7-3a and letting the area on the cut plane be unity (Fig. 7-3b), it is apparent that the area of the plane on which σ_1 acts becomes $(1) \times (\cos \theta)$, and the area on which σ_3 acts becomes $(1) \times (\sin \theta)$. The total normal *force* on the cut plane is $(\sigma_n) \times (1)$. The total force on the vertical surface is $(\sigma_3) \times (\sin \theta)$, and the total force on the horizontal surface is $(\sigma_1) \times (\cos \theta)$.

To determine σ_n and τ_n in terms of σ_1 and σ_3, the forces acting on the horizontal and vertical planes are resolved into components parallel and perpendicular to the cut plane (see Fig. 7-4). Summing forces parallel to σ_n (normal to the cut plane) gives

$$\sigma_n = \sigma_1 \cos \theta \cos \theta + \sigma_3 \sin \theta \sin \theta$$

$$= \sigma_1 \cos^2 \theta + \sigma_3 \sin^2 \theta$$

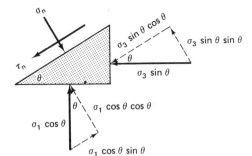

Figure 7-4 Resolution of principal stresses into components parallel and perpendicular to a random plane. This step is in preparation for determining stresses on the plane in terms of principal stresses.

and by trigonometric identity

$$\sigma_n = \sigma_1 \cos^2 \theta + \sigma_3 \sin^2 \theta = \frac{\sigma_1 + \sigma_3}{2} + \frac{\sigma_1 - \sigma_3}{2} \cos 2\theta \qquad (7\text{-}1)$$

Summing forces parallel to the cut plane in the direction of τ_n gives

$$\tau_n = \sigma_1 \cos \theta \sin \theta - \sigma_3 \sin \theta \cos \theta = (\sigma_1 - \sigma_3) \sin \theta \cos \theta$$

and by trigonometric identity,

$$\tau_n = (\sigma_1 - \sigma_3) \sin \theta \cos \theta = \left(\frac{\sigma_1 - \sigma_3}{2}\right) \sin 2\theta. \qquad (7\text{-}2)$$

From examination of Equation 7-2 it should be recognized that the maximum shear stress will occur on a plane that is 45° from the major principal plane ($\theta = 45°$), and will have a magnitude equal to $\frac{1}{2}(\sigma_1 - \sigma_3)$. On this plane, the normal stress is *always* $\frac{1}{2}(\sigma_1 + \sigma_3)$.

The previous developments apply to a two-dimensional stress analysis (stresses in a plane). In actuality, for soil problems the study of stress at a point involves a three-dimensional analysis. An incremental element with three principal stresses acting—σ_1, σ_2, and σ_3—is shown in Figure 7-5. For many practical conditions of loading, the intermediate stress, σ_2, is equal to σ_1, or to σ_3. For some situations, however, σ_2 may be a value intermediate between σ_1 and σ_3. As far as practical effects of the intermediate stress are concerned, it appears that there is some influence on the strength and stress–strain properties of the material, but its effect is not clearly understood. To keep a proper perspective, however, it is pointed out

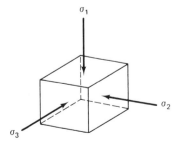

Figure 7-5 Three-dimensional incremental element showing principal stresses in mutually perpendicular directions.

Stress at a Point: Analytical Development

that the methods available for making determinations of the stresses within a soil mass that result from external loading are not highly refined. As a result, for most practical problems the degree of accuracy does not appear to be significantly diminished by neglecting the effect of the intermediate stress and working with the simpler two-dimensional condition (σ_1 and σ_3 only).

MOHR'S CIRCLE

The varying values of normal stress and shear stress corresponding to differing values of θ can be determined by using Equations 7-1 and 7-2. If the combination of normal and shear stress resulting from each value of θ is plotted as a point on a coordinate system where the horizontal axis represents normal stress and the vertical axis represents shear stress (Fig. 7-6a), the locus of many plotted points will form a circle (Fig. 7-6b).

This fact can be used to advantage. By working with simple properties of a circle, a graphical or pictorial method of solving for normal and shear stresses on any plane once the stresses on orthogonal planes are known is easily developed. The method simplifies the calculation necessary for determining stresses, and eliminates the need to work with cumbersome equations. The method is referred to as the Mohr's circle for determining stresses, after Otto Mohr (1835–1918), who is credited as the developer of the method.

In using Mohr's circle, a sign convention is required. For soil problems, compressive stresses are conventionally assumed to be positive, and shearing stresses that provide a clockwise couple are also considered positive (see Fig. 7-7).

For a stress combination like that shown in Figure 7-8a, σ_1 and σ_3 are the major and minor principal stresses. There is no shear stress acting on these major and minor principal planes. To construct the Mohr's circle for this combination (Fig. 7-8b), locate σ_1 (or 2500 psf) and σ_3 (or 500 psf) on the *horizontal axis* of the coordinate system (since the shear is zero). Next, establish the location (or value) for the center of the Mohr's circle, knowing that the diameter of the circle

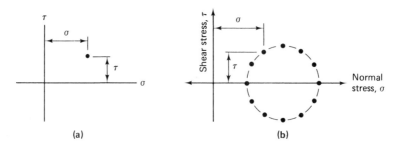

Figure 7-6 Method of representing the combination of normal and shear stresses acting on any plane through an incremental element on shear stress–normal stress coordinates: (a) single point represents stress combination on one plane; (b) stress combinations occurring on different planes through an incremental element provide points that form a circle.

Stresses shown on horizontal plane:
    positive normal stress
    positive shear stress

Stresses shown on vertical plane:
    negative normal stress
    negative shear stress

Figure 7-7 Sign convention assigned to stresses for the Mohr's circle analysis.

has a value equal to σ_1 minus σ_3. (This numerical difference between σ_1 and σ_3 is called the *deviator stress*.) For this illustration, the deviator stress is 2500 psf minus 500 psf, or 2000 psf. The radius of the circle is then 1000 psf, and the center of the circle will plot at 1500 psf, which is the value of σ_3 plus the radius. After the center of the circle and the diameter are established, the circle itself can be constructed; thereafter, the stress combination on *any* plane can be determined.

In working with the Mohr's circle, it is convenient to reference the plane under study to the major principal plane whenever possible. Remember that the major principal stress acts on the major principal plane; the angular measurement to the plane in question is made on the Mohr's circle by starting from the point representing the major principal stress. If the angle to be measured is formed by two radii, the angle is measured at the center of the circle. Because of the properties of a circle, the central angle on the circle must be twice the value of the angle θ measured on the original element (see Fig. 7-9). The direction of measurement from the principal plane to the cut plane on the element, clockwise or counterclockwise, is the same direction to be used on the Mohr's circle (see Fig. 7-9). By reference to the Mohr's circle diagram in Figure 7-10, the expressions for shear and normal stress for any point (representing any plane) can be reaffirmed. The normal stress coordinate is the value of the center of the Mohr's circle plus or

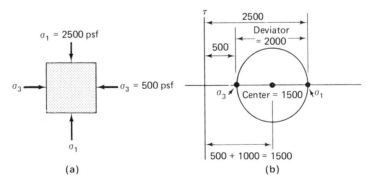

Figure 7-8 Representation of principal stresses acting at a point and the related Mohr's circle plot: (a) stresses acting on incremental element; (b) Mohr's circle plot.

Mohr's Circle

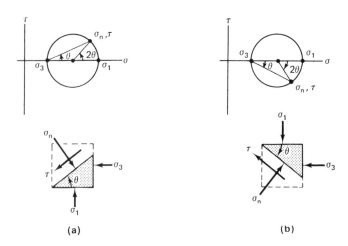

(a)   (b)

Figure 7-9 Relation of positions of planes on the incremental element to points on the Mohr's circle: (a) reference angle measured counterclockwise; (b) reference angle measured clockwise.

minus the horizontal projection of the radius. As shown in Figure 7-10, the normal stress would then be

$$\sigma_n = \frac{\sigma_1 + \sigma_3}{2} + \frac{\sigma_1 - \sigma_3}{2} \cos 2\theta$$

which agrees with Equation 7-1. The shear stress coordinate is the vertical projection of the radius, or

$$\tau_n = \frac{\sigma_1 - \sigma_3}{2} \sin 2\theta$$

which agrees with Equation 7-2.

As an illustration, to determine the magnitude of the normal and shear stress acting on a plane 45° from the major principal plane (Fig. 7-11), the angle measured

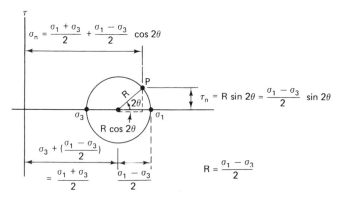

Figure 7-10 Establishment of the general equations for normal stress and shear stress from the Mohr's circle.

Combined Stresses in Soil Masses   Chap. 7

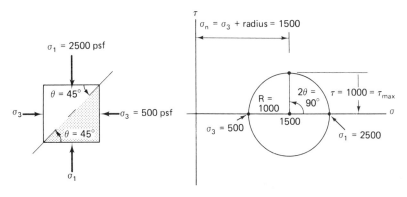

Figure 7-11 Use of Mohr's circle to determine the shear and normal stress acting on a plane 45° from the major principal plane.

at the center of the Mohr's circle would have to be twice 45°, or 90°. Note that, on the element, the angle θ is 45° measured counterclockwise, regardless of whether the top or bottom of the original element is used as the reference plane. On the Mohr's circle the central angle, 2θ or 90°, is also measured counterclockwise. If the principal stress equations developed previously are used, or by applying simple mathematics if the Mohr's circle is used pictorially, or by scaling if the graphical method is used, the value of the normal stress is found to be 1500 psf and the shear stress is 1000 psf.

From examination of the Mohr's circle, it should be evident that the maximum shear stress (in this case 1000 psf) always acts on the plane that is 45° from the major principal plane. Further, the maximum shear stress always has a magnitude equal to the radius of the Mohr's circle.

As a second illustration, with the same principal stresses used previously, assume that it is desired to find the stresses acting on a plane that is 60° clockwise from the major principal plane (Fig. 7-12). On the Mohr's circle, the central angle to be measured is 120°. Mathematically, from a pictorial Mohr's circle, the shear stress τ_n equals $(R) \times (\sin 60°)$, or $(1000 \text{ psf}) \times (0.866)$, which is 866 psf. The

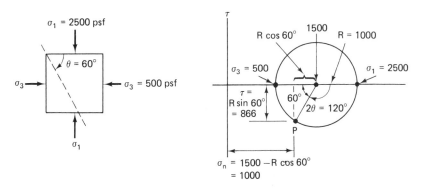

Figure 7-12 Use of Mohr's circle to determine stresses on a plane 60° clockwise from the major principal plane.

Mohr's Circle

Figure 7-13 Magnitude and direction of stresses acting on the plane studied in the Mohr's circle analysis of Figure 7-12.

normal stress σ_n is 1500 psf minus $(R) \times (\cos 60°)$, or 1000 psf, as shown in Figure 7-12. The 1500 psf value locates the center of the circle. On the desired plane, the stresses are as shown in Figure 7-13.

If the stress combination is to be determined on a plane measured with reference to the minor principal plane, the related angular measurement on the Mohr's circle is made from the minor principal stress, σ_3, as shown in Figure 7-14. The direction of the angle will be the same on the Mohr's circle as on the incremental element.

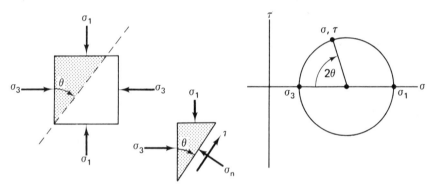

Figure 7-14 Method of locating the stress–combination point on the Mohr's circle when the minor principal plane is used as a reference.

The Mohr's circle pictorial or graphical method can similarly be used for determining principal stresses if the stress conditions for any two orthogonal planes other than principal planes are known. For an element where the normal and shear stresses are as shown in Figure 7-15 (note that the shear stresses on the mutually

Figure 7-15 An incremental element with stresses that are not principal stresses acting on principal planes.

Combined Stresses in Soil Masses   Chap. 7

Figure 7-16 Procedure for applying the Mohr's circle analysis to solve for principal stresses.

perpendicular planes are equal in magnitude), the Mohr's circle construction proceeds as follows (see Fig. 7-16):

1. On the Mohr's circle coordinates, establish the two points corresponding to σ_a, τ, and σ_b, τ.
2. Connect these points, thereby establishing the diameter of the Mohr's circle (Fig. 7-16a), and determine the coordinate for the center of the circle.
3. Calculate the value for the radius of the Mohr's circle (Fig. 7-16b).
4. The value of σ_1 (the major principal stress) is the circle radius added to the value established for the circle center. The value of σ_3 (the minor principal stress) is the radius subtracted from the coordinate for the circle center (Fig. 7-16c).

Mohr's Circle

5. The angle 2θ on the Mohr's circle is obtained from simple geometry, as shown in Figure 7-16d.

6. The orientations of the principal planes with respect to the original element are shown in Figure 7-16e.

7. Since the complete Mohr's circle is established, stresses on any other plane can be determined by using the methods covered previously.

ILLUSTRATION 7-1.   The major and minor principal stresses acting at a point are 50 psi compression and 10 psi compression, respectively. Draw the Mohr's circle for this stress combination, and determine the magnitude of shear and normal stress on the plane where shear is a maximum.

ILLUSTRATION 7-2.   At one point in a soil mass, the minor principal stress is 1000 psf. What is the maximum value possible for the major stress at this point if the shear stress cannot exceed 2000 psf?

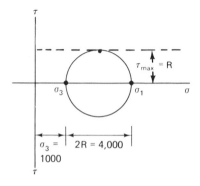

Combined Stresses in Soil Masses   Chap. 7

The maximum shear stress at a point is the value of the radius of the Mohr's circle; that is,

$$\text{Radius} = 2000 \text{ psf}$$

Since the major principal stress σ_1 is $\sigma_3 + 2R$,

$$\sigma_1 = 1000 + 2(2000) = 5000 \text{ psf}$$

PROBLEMS

7-1. At a point, the major principal stress is 5000 psf compression and the minor principal stress is 2000 psf compression.
  (a) Draw the Mohr's circle for this stress combination.
  (b) Find the maximum shear stress, and also indicate the value of normal stress acting on this same plane.
  (c) Determine the values of the normal and shear stress acting on a plane that is 60° from the major principal plane.

7-2. At a point, the major principal stress is 80 psi compression and the minor principal stress is 20 psi compression.
  (a) Draw the Mohr's circle for this stress combination.
  (b) What is the maximum shear stress acting at the point, and what value of normal stress acts on this same plane?
  (c) Determine the value of the normal and shear stress acting on a plane that is 60° from the minor principal plane.

7-3. The major and minor principal stresses acting at a point are 80 psi compression and 20 psi tension.
  (a) Draw the Mohr's circle for this stress combination.
  (b) What is the maximum shear stress acting at the point, and what value of normal stress acts on the plane?
  (c) Determine the value of the shear and normal stress acting on a plane that is 30° from the major principal plane.

7-4. At a point, the normal and shear stresses acting on one plane are 8000 psf compression and 2000 psf, respectively. On a perpendicular plane, the normal and shear stress combination is 2000 psf compression and 2000 psf.
  (a) Draw the Mohr's circle.
  (b) Determine the value of the principal stresses.
  (c) Find the angle between the plane on which the 8000 psf compressive stress acts and the major principal plane.
  (d) What is the maximum shear stress acting at the point?

7-5. The normal and shear stresses acting on one plane passing through a point in a soil mass are 120 psi compression and 25 psi, respectively. On an orthogonal plane the stresses are 40 psi compression and 25 psi.
  (a) Draw the Mohr's circle for this stress condition.
  (b) What are the principal stresses?

(c) Determine the angle between the plane on which the 120-psi stress acts and the major principal plane.

(d) What is the maximum shear stress acting at the point?

7-6. The major principal stress and deviator stress at a point are 100 kN/m² and 60 kN/m², respectively. What is the value of the maximum shear stress, and of the normal stress acting on the same plane?

7-7. For a minor principal stress of 50 kN/m², what is the maximum value possible for the major principal stress if the maximum shear stress is not to exceed 40 kN/m²?

7-8. In a soil where the ground surface is horizontal, the vertical stress acting at a point is 2000 psf and the horizontal stress is 1000 psf. If these stresses represent the principal stresses, what is the maximum shear stress acting at the point?

7-9. Given a soil mass with a level ground surface and a material having a unit weight of 120 pcf. The vertical pressure at any depth represents the major principal stress at that particular point. The lateral pressure acting at any point is one-half the vertical pressure and represents the minor principal stress.

(a) Determine the principal stresses acting at a depth of 10 ft below the ground surface and draw the Mohr's circle for these conditions.

(b) What is the value of the maximum shear stress at this depth?

7-10. A soil deposit exists with a level ground surface. The saturated unit weight of the soil is 125 pcf, and the water table is at the ground surface.

(a) Determine the principal stresses acting at a depth 15 ft below the ground surface that results from the effective (submerged) soil weight if the lateral pressure is 0.45 of the vertical pressure.

(b) What is the magnitude of the maximum shear stress at this depth?

## chapter 8

Subsurface Stresses

At a point within a soil mass, stresses will be developed as a result of the soil lying above the point and by any structural or other loading imposed onto that soil mass. The magnitude of the subsurface stress at a point is affected by the groundwater table if it extends to an elevation above the point.

In most foundation design problems, the safe bearing capacity of the soil (the ability to support structural load) and settlement (the soil volume change resulting from loading) that will develop under a given intensity of structural loading are major items of concern. For such analysis, the significant stresses are considered to be those acting in the vertical direction. In the design of vertical structures such as retaining walls, sheeting for braced excavations and waterfront structures, and some types of pile foundations, the soil stresses acting in the horizontal or lateral direction are the most significant.

STRESSES CAUSED BY THE SOIL MASS

Vertical Stresses   In a soil mass having a horizontal surface, the vertical stress caused by the soil at a point below the surface is equal to the weight of the soil lying directly above the point. Vertical stress thus increases as the depth of the soil overburden increases. The vertical stress can be calculated as the weight of a "column" of soil extending above a unit area (Fig. 8-1a). For a homogeneous soil having a wet unit volumetric weight of γ_t (normally expressed as pounds per cubic foot or kN/m^3), the stress σ_v (normally in pounds per square foot or kN/m^2) at a depth Z (ft or m) below the ground surface is

$$\sigma_v = \gamma_t Z \qquad (8\text{-}1)$$

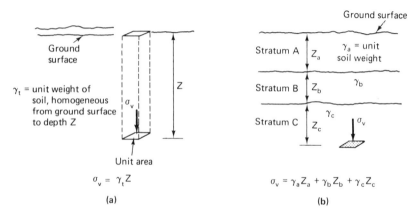

Figure 8-1 Vertical subsurface stress resulting from the soil mass.

If the soil mass is made up of strata of different soil types and the unit weights of the soil in each stratum are different, the vertical stress at a depth Z will be equal to the total weight of the different segments of the soil "column," as indicated by Figure 8-1b.

Effect of Groundwater Table   When a soil exists below the groundwater table, the submerged soil particles are subject to a buoyant force resulting from the hydrostatic water pressure, the same phenomenon that acts on any submerged solid. The submerged weight of the soil, γ_{sub}, is termed the *effective soil weight*, and the subsurface stress that results is termed the *effective stress*. Effective stress represents the actual intergranular pressure that occurs betwen soil particles. This effective stress is the stress that influences shear strength of the soil and volume changes or settlements.

If a condition exists where the *water table is at the ground surface* and the soil mass is homogeneous, the effective stress $\bar{\sigma}_v$ at a depth Z is

$$\bar{\sigma}_v = \gamma_{sub} Z \tag{8-2}$$

If the total weight of soil as it exists above the water table is γ_t (the total soil weight before the buoyant effects of submergence are considered), the effective stress is

$$\bar{\sigma}_v = \gamma_t Z - \gamma_w Z \tag{8-3}$$

where γ_w is the unit weight of water. (It is conventional to assume 62.4 pcf or 9.81 kN/m^3 for γ_w.) The last term of this equation is the total water pressure at the depth Z. Total water pressure at a point is termed the *neutral stress u*, for it acts equally in all directions. Neutral stress refers to any water pressure that develops at a point as caused by hydrostatic conditions. It is important to recognize that the neutral stress acts to *reduce* the intergranular stress that develops between soil particles. This condition frequently has an adverse effect on the strength of a soil. The effective stress for conditions just described can be expressed as

$$\bar{\sigma}_v = \gamma_t Z - u \tag{8-4}$$

To compute the effective stress for a condition where the *groundwater table lies below the ground surface*, and for the condition where strata of soils of different types and weights exist, two different approaches are possible. One approach involves determining the total soil pressure (disregarding buoyancy effects) and then subtracting the hydrostatic pressure (the neutral pressure) at the point being analyzed. The neutral pressure u is the unit weight of water γ_w, multiplied by the depth below the water table. A second approach is to determine directly the effective stress of the column of soil above the point by using the effective or submerged weight of all soil in the "column." Above the water table, the effective soil weight is the total soil weight, including the pore water; below the water table, the effective soil weight is the submerged or buoyant weight (see Fig. 8-2a).

Where the soil surface is below water (such as in oceans and lakes), the effective stress should be computed by using the submerged or effective soil weight multiplied by the depth measured from the soil surface (Fig. 8-2b).

A summary of the analytical procedures for computing subsurface stresses resulting from various soil and water table conditions, and numerical illustrations are presented in Figure 8-3.

Horizontal (Lateral) Stresses The magnitude of vertical stress is relatively simple to determine when the ground surface is level. When this condition does exist, it is also convenient to indicate horizontal (lateral) stresses that exist in a soil mass in terms of the soil vertical stress. The ratio of lateral stress to vertical stress, K, is termed the *coefficient of lateral earth pressure*. Mathematically,

$$K = \frac{\text{Horizontal soil pressure } \overline{\sigma}_h}{\text{Vertical soil pressure } \overline{\sigma}_v} \tag{8-5}$$

The use of effective pressures for determining the lateral pressure coefficient accounts for the influence of submergence where the soil deposit is wholly or partially below water or the water table (i.e., submerged unit weights are used when appropriate to determine $\overline{\sigma}_v$).

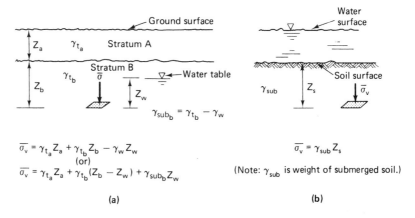

$$\overline{\sigma}_v = \gamma_{t_a} Z_a + \gamma_{t_b} Z_b - \gamma_w Z_w$$
(or)
$$\overline{\sigma}_v = \gamma_{t_a} Z_a + \gamma_{t_b}(Z_b - Z_w) + \gamma_{\text{sub}_b} Z_w$$

(a)

$$\overline{\sigma}_v = \gamma_{\text{sub}} Z_s$$

(Note: γ_{sub} is weight of submerged soil.)

(b)

Figure 8-2 Subsurface stress below water.

Stresses Caused by the Soil Mass

(a)

$\sigma_v = (120 \text{ pcf})(10 \text{ ft}) = 1200 \text{ psf}$

$= (18.84 \, \frac{kN}{m^3})(3.05 \text{ m}) = 57.5 \, \frac{kN}{m^2}$

(b)

$\bar{\sigma}_v = \gamma_{sub} Z = (\gamma_{saturated} - \gamma_w) Z$

$= (125 \text{ pcf} - 62.4 \text{ pcf})(12 \text{ ft}) = 751 \text{ psf}$

$= (19.63 \, \frac{kN}{m^3} - 9.81 \, \frac{kN}{m^3})(3.65 \text{ m}) = 35.8 \, \frac{kN}{m^2}$

(c)

$\bar{\sigma}_v = \gamma_t Z_a + \gamma_{sub} Z_b$

$= (120 \text{ pcf})(4 \text{ ft}) + (130 \text{ pcf} - 62.4 \text{ pcf})(10 \text{ ft})$

$= 480 \text{ psf} + 676 \text{ psf} = 1156 \text{ psf} = 55.5 \, \frac{kN}{m^2}$

(d)

$\bar{\sigma}_v = \gamma_{sub} Z_s = (\gamma_{sat} - \gamma_w) Z_s$

$= (110 \text{ pcf} - 62.4 \text{ pcf})(6 \text{ ft}) = 286 \text{ psf} = 13.7 \, \frac{kN}{m^2}$

$1 \text{ psf} = 0.048 \, \frac{kN}{m2} \; ; \; 1 \text{ pcf} = 0.157 \, \frac{kN}{m^3}$

Figure 8-3 Summary: Method to compute subsurface stress in a soil mass.

In a horizontal, uniform soil mass of infinite extent, the lateral movement of the soil at any depth is not possible, because the confining pressure is equal in all horizontal directions. Thus a state of static equilibrium exists and the soil is in the *at-rest condition*. The coefficient of lateral pressure for the at-rest condition is indicated by K_o.

The magnitude of K_o for a given soil mass is affected by the soil deposit's stress history. Soils that have been subjected to heavy loading at some time in their history, such as ~~now~~ dense granular (sand or gravel) deposits and hard overconsolidated[1] clays, would have had to develop resistance to high lateral stress

---

[1]Clays that at some past time were subject to loading greater than the weight of all currently existing overlying soil.

Subsurface Stresses   Chap. 8

TABLE 8-1 TYPICAL VALUES OF K_o

Soil type	K_o
Granular, loose	0.5–0.6
Granular, dense	0.3–0.5
Clay, soft	0.9–1.1 (undrained)
Clay, hard	0.8–0.9 (undrained)

in order to maintain stability. Deposits that have not been exposed to heavy loading, such as loose granular soils and soft normally consolidated or underconsolidated clays, would not have developed high lateral strength. Typically, then, dense granular soils and hard clays end up having lower values of K_o than do loose granular soils and soft clays. Such typical values are presented in Table 8-1. The topic of lateral pressures is discussed in greater detail in Chapter 16.

ILLUSTRATION 8-1.   The unit weight of the soil in a uniform deposit of loose sand is 100 pcf. Determine the horizontal stress that acts within the soil mass at a depth of 10 ft.

$$\sigma_v = \sigma Z = (100 \text{ pcf})(10 \text{ ft}) = 1000 \text{ psf}$$

$$\sigma_h = K_o\sigma_v = (0.5)(1000 \text{ psf}) = 500 \text{ psf}$$

where K_o is obtained from Table 8-1.

In soils below the water table, determination of the *total* lateral pressure requires that the hydrostatic pressure due to the water be added to the effective at-rest soil pressure computed by using a value from Table 8-1 and the effective soil weight.

ILLUSTRATION 8-2.   A concrete basement wall for a structure extends below the groundwater table. For conditions indicated by the sketch, calculate the total lateral pressure acting against the wall at a point 8 ft below the ground surface.

Ground surface

4′ γ = 120 pcf

8′ Z_w = 4′, Medium dense sand, k_o = 0.4

σ_h γ_{sub} = 60 pcf

Stresses Caused by the Soil Mass

$$\text{Soil pressure, } \overline{\sigma}_h \text{ at 8 ft} = K_o \gamma Z$$

$$= (0.4)[(4 \text{ ft} \times 120 \text{ pcf}) + (4 \text{ ft} \times 60 \text{ pcf})]$$

$$= 288 \text{ psf}$$

$$\text{Total lateral pressure} = K_o \gamma Z + \gamma_w Z_w = 288 \text{ psf} + (4 \text{ ft})(62.4 \text{ pcf})$$

$$= 538 \text{ psf}$$

STRESS WITHIN THE SOIL MASS RESULTING FROM VERTICAL SURFACE LOADING

Uniform Homogeneous Soils   When a vertical loading from a structure or other body is applied at the surface of a soil mass, new stresses are created within the mass. Because of shearing resistance developed within the soil, loading transferred to the soil mass will be spread laterally with increasing depth from the point or area of application (see Fig. 8-4). With increasing depth the area over which new stresses develop will increase, but the magnitude of the stresses will decrease. For an equilibrium condition, the sum of the new vertical stresses developed in the soil mass on any horizontal plane must equal the weight or force of the surface loading.

The manner in which the stresses become distributed throughout the soil mass is affected by the properties of the soil, including modulus of elasticity and Poisson's ratio, and any stratification of different soil types.

Boussinesq Stress Distribution   One of the methods in common use for calculating stresses that result in a soil mass from a surface loading is based upon the work of Boussinesq, a nineteenth-century French mathematician. Boussinesq assumed a homogeneous, isotropic material (properties the same in all directions) of semi-infinite extent (unlimited depth) and developed equations for the stress distribution resulting from a point load. Adapted to soil masses, the described conditions are as indicated by Figure 8-5. The vertical stress increase $\Delta\sigma_v$ resulting

Figure 8-4   Variation of vertical stress at different depths Z.

Figure 8-5 Definition of terms applicable to Boussinesq and Westergaard equations.

at a depth Z and a distance r, measured horizontally from where a point loading Q is applied, becomes

$$\Delta\sigma_v = \frac{3Q}{2\pi} \frac{Z^3}{(r^2 + Z^2)^{5/2}} = \frac{Q}{Z^2} \frac{3}{2\pi\left[1 + \left(\frac{r}{Z}\right)^2\right]^{5/2}} \tag{8-6a}$$

This equation indicates that as the depth increases the stress decreases. Similarly, the stress decreases as the horizontal distance from the point of loading is increased. For a given depth, the intensity of stress is greatest directly beneath the point of load application.

With the Boussinesq equation for vertical stress, the modulus of elasticity and Poisson's ratio are not required, which indicates that the stress is independent of these properties as long as the material is homogeneous and isotropic.

The suitability of using the Boussinesq equation for determining subsurface stresses in a foundation analysis depends on how closely the actual soil conditions and properties resemble the theory's original assumptions. For practical problems, conditions of a homogeneous and isotropic material are commonly assumed for homogeneous clay deposits, for man-made fills where the soil fill has been placed and compacted in thin layers, and for limited thicknesses of uniform granular soil deposits.

Westergaard Stress Distribution Some sedimentary soil deposits consist of alternating thin layers of sandy soil (coarse, relatively incompressible material) and fine-grained silt–clay soils (compressible material)—for example, stratified deposits such as laminated clays. For such conditions, the Westergaard equations provide a better means of evaluating the subsurface stresses. In his development, Westergaard assumed that thin layers of a homogeneous and anistropic material were sandwiched between closely spaced, infinitely thin sheets of rigid material that would permit compression but no lateral deformation. For the case where Poisson's ratio is zero, the equation for subsurface stress resulting from a concentrated point loading reduces to

$$\Delta\sigma_v = \frac{Q}{Z^2\pi\left[1 + 2\left(\frac{r}{Z}\right)^2\right]^{3/2}} \tag{8-7a}$$

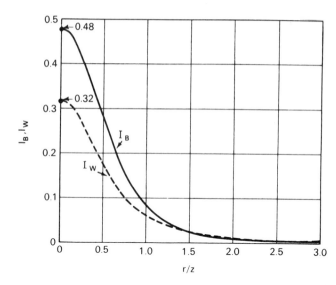

Figure 8-6 Values of I_B and I_w for calculating vertical stress resulting from surface load Q.

The terms Q, R, and Z are as defined for the Boussinesq equation, and as shown in Figure 8-5.

Computational Aides   With both the Boussinesq and Westergaard equations, the subsurface stress resulting from a given point load will be related to the Z and r distances, or the r/Z ratio. If the Boussinesq equation is written in terms of a stress influence factor I_B, which is related to r/Z as follows:

$$\Delta\sigma_v = \frac{Q}{Z^2}\frac{3}{2\pi\left[1 + \left(\dfrac{r}{Z}\right)^2\right]^{5/2}} = \frac{Q}{Z^2}I_B \tag{8-6b}$$

calculations for values of I_B for different r/Z ratios can be computed and presented as shown in Figure 8-6. The effort to determine a subsurface stress then becomes greatly simplified. Similarly, the Westergaard equation can be written in terms of an influence factor I_w as follows:

$$\Delta\sigma_v = \frac{Q}{Z^2\pi\left[1 + 2\left(\dfrac{r}{Z}\right)^2\right]^{3/2}} = \frac{Q}{Z^2}I_w \tag{8-7b}$$

and values of I_w versus r/Z ratios can be developed as presented in Figure 8-6.

ILLUSTRATION 8-3.   For Boussinesq conditions, what subsurface stress will result at a point 10 ft below where a 10,000-lb point load is applied?

$$Q = 10,000^\#$$

$$Z = 10'$$

$$\Delta\sigma_v$$

$$r = 0 \text{ ft}, \qquad Z = 10 \text{ ft}, \qquad r/Z = 0$$

For $r/Z = 0$, obtain $I_B = 0.48$ (from Fig. 8-6)

$$\text{and } \Delta\sigma_v = \frac{Q}{Z^2} I_B = \frac{10{,}000 \text{ lb}}{(10 \text{ ft} \times 10 \text{ ft})} (0.48) = 48 \text{ psf}$$

ILLUSTRATION 8-4. For the Westergaard conditions, what subsurface stress will result 10 ft below, and 10 ft horizontally, from where a 10,000-lb concentrated load is applied?

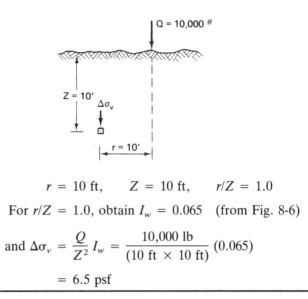

$$r = 10 \text{ ft}, \qquad Z = 10 \text{ ft}, \qquad r/Z = 1.0$$

For $r/Z = 1.0$, obtain $I_w = 0.065$ (from Fig. 8-6)

$$\text{and } \Delta\sigma_v = \frac{Q}{Z^2} I_w = \frac{10{,}000 \text{ lb}}{(10 \text{ ft} \times 10 \text{ ft})} (0.065)$$

$$= 6.5 \text{ psf}$$

Application for Foundation Loading   In construction practice, the condition of a concentrated point loading is rarely encountered. More commonly, building loads are supported on foundations that cover a finite area (square, rectangular, or round footing), or the structure itself directly imposes loading over a finite area (earth structures such as dams and dikes). The subsurface stresses that result from loading acting over an area can be determined by integration of Equation 8-6 or 8-7, where the loading on infinitely small increments of the foundation area can be assumed as point loads. The subsurface stress at a point is the summation of the effects resulting from all of the applied point loadings. Such integrations have been accomplished for uniform loads acting on square, rectangular, strip, and circular areas, and also for uniformly varying loads such as those developing from the weight of an earth structure having a sloped cross section (dams and dikes, for instance). Results are available in the form of charts, tables, and graphs in order to provide generalized solutions. In these presentations, the subsurface stresses are expressed as a percentage of the foundation loading intensity. Measurements of the depth and horizontal distance at which a subsurface stress acts are expressed in terms of the dimensions of the loaded foundation area. Subsurface stress con-

Stresses Within the Soil Mass Resulting from Vertical Surface Loading   **169**

ditions indicated by Boussinesq and Westergaard equations for commonly occurring foundation loadings are presented in Figures 8-7 and 8-8. The following example problems serve to illustrate the use of these figures.

ILLUSTRATION 8-5. A foundation supported on the surface of a uniform, homogeneous soil is 5 ft square and carries a loading of 125 kips. What subsurface stress increase occurs beneath the center of the foundation at a depth of 5 ft?

For uniform homogeneous soil, use Boussinesq conditions.

$$q = \frac{Q}{A} = \frac{125 \text{ kips}}{(5 \text{ ft} \times 5 \text{ ft})} = 5 \text{ ksf} = 5000 \text{ psf at base of foundation}$$

From Figure 8-7, $\Delta\sigma_v$ in terms of q is 34% for $\dfrac{\text{Depth}}{\text{Width}} = \dfrac{5 \text{ ft}}{5 \text{ ft}} = 1.0$

Therefore $\qquad \Delta\sigma_v = 0.34(5000 \text{ psf}) = 1750 \text{ psf}$

ILLUSTRATION 8-6. A circular storage tank is supported on soils that satisfy the Westergaard assumptions. What subsurface stress increase develops 10 ft beneath the edge of the tank? The tank is 20 ft in diameter, and the stored fluid material causes a pressure of 1000 psf at the tank base.

Surface load $q = 1000$ psf

$$\text{Ratio of depth/width} = \frac{10 \text{ ft}}{20 \text{ ft}} = 0.5$$

From Figure 8-8, $\Delta\sigma_v = 23\%$ of q

Therefore $\Delta\sigma_v = 0.23 \,(1000 \text{ psf}) = 230 \text{ psf.}$

The stress curves in Figures 8-7 and 8-8 show that the stresses beneath the center of a loaded foundation area will be greater than stresses beneath the edge of the foundation until a depth of about twice the foundation width is reached. Below this level, the stresses beneath the center and edge become practically equal.

Subsurface Stresses   Chap. 8

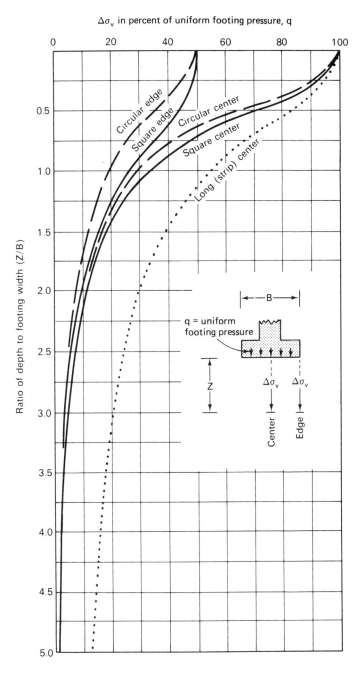

Figure 8-7 Variation of vertical stress beneath a foundation: Boussinesq analysis.

Figure 8-8 Variation of vertical stress beneath a foundation: Westergaard analysis.

Consequently, in making determinations of the stresses resulting from a foundation loading, it is suitable to assume a concentrated point loading, if convenient, where the subsurface depth is greater than twice the foundation width.

Sixty-Degree Approximation A method in wide use for making rough estimates of subsurface stresses resulting from a loaded foundation area is the so-called 60° approximation. In this method, it is assumed that the subsurface stresses spread out uniformly with depth, the stressed area increasing at a slope of 1 ft horizontally for each 2 ft of depth as measured from the edges of the foundation. These assumed conditions are sketched in Figure 8-9. At a given depth, the subsurface stress $\Delta\sigma_v$ is assumed to be uniform over the area stressed. The method differs from the Boussinesq and Westergaard theories in this respect. The stress at a depth Z then becomes

$$\Delta\sigma_v = \frac{Q}{(B + Z)(W + Z)} \tag{8-8}$$

This approximation method is incorrect in representing subsurface stresses as being uniform across a plane area. In a homogeneous soil, the computed subsurface stresses directly beneath the foundation will be less than indicated by the Boussinesq analysis, whereas at distances beyond the edges of the foundation the computed stress will be greater. This method's best application may be estimating stress conditions in deep layers below a foundation and for determining an order of magnitude in a preliminary analysis.

Layered Soils Having Different Properties The condition of soil deposits having uniform properties over a great vertical distance is not always found in practice. There frequently is encountered the situation where, within the zone (depth) that will be affected by structural loads, two or more layers of significantly different soils exist. For the condition of two different strata, the possibilities of relative properties include a firm upper layer overlying a soft layer, and the reverse.

For the condition where a firm layer overlies a soft layer (a dense sand above a compressible clay, or a surface zone of firm desiccated clay overlying the still saturated, softer and compressible lower zone of the clay), the firm layer tends to bridge over the softer layer, spreading out the area over which stresses are trans-

Figure 8-9 Method for approximating vertical stress increase resulting beneath a loaded foundation (60° approximation).

Stresses Within the Soil Mass Resulting from Vertical Surface Loading   **173**

ferred into the softer layer. This results in creating lower stresses in the soft material than would result for a homogeneous soil.

With a soft layer overlying a firm layer, the stresses reaching the deeper layer in the area directly beneath the foundation will be greater than that indicated for a uniform homogeneous deposit.

A diagram for determining how the variation in subsurface stress beneath a uniformly loaded circular area is affected by a two-layer soil mass appears in Figure 8-10. This diagram is for the special case where the thickness of the upper soil layer is equal to the radius of the loaded area.

The curves of Figure 8-10 can be used for approximating stress conditions

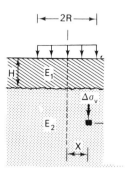

E = modulus of elasticity for soil

$\Delta\sigma_v$ in percent of uniform foundation pressure

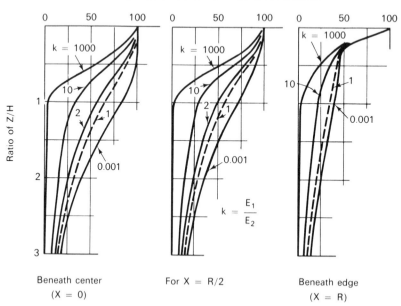

Figure 8-10 Variation of vertical stress beneath a circular foundation. Two-layer subsurface condition for condition where $R = H$.

Subsurface Stresses   Chap. 8

beneath a square area as well as the circular area by assuming foundation dimensions giving the same area as the circular foundation. The illustrative example presented below indicates the use of Figure 8-10.

ILLUSTRATION 8-7. A circular storage tank 20 ft in diameter is located in an area where soil conditions are as shown by the sketch. If the tank pressure at the soil surface is 500 psf, what stress results beneath the center of the tank at a depth of 15 ft?

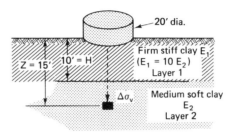

$$H = \text{radius} = 10 \text{ ft}$$

$$\text{Ratio of } \frac{Z}{H} = \frac{15 \text{ ft}}{10 \text{ ft}} = 1.5$$

$$k = \frac{E_1}{E_2} = 10$$

From Figure 8-10, $\Delta\sigma_v$ is 20 percent of surface load q

Therefore, $\Delta\sigma_v = 0.20(500 \text{ psf}) = 100 \text{ psf}$

Effect of Foundation Installation below Finished Grade In the practice of building design and construction, foundations are seldom placed directly on the ground surface. More usually, foundations are placed at some depth below the ground surface as protection against frost and seasonal soil volume changes, erosion, or other factors. In other words, some excavation is performed before the foundation can be constructed. The subsurface stresses developed in the soil below the foundation are determined by using the previously described methods, and the depth for computing the stress increase is measured from the base of the foundation.

The total stress at a point in the soil below the foundation is the sum of the stress caused by the soil overburden plus the stress due to the foundation loading. In many cases, a foundation excavation is backfilled to the ground surface or interior floor level after the foundation is constructed. For practical purposes, then, the stress caused by the soil remains equal to the original soil overburden.

If an excavation is made and not backfilled, the effect is to reduce the subsurface stresses. The reduction in stress can be computed by assuming that the excavation is a "foundation" whose loading is the weight of the excavated soil. The size of the "foundation" is the plan area of the excavation. The subsurface stress is determined as for a real foundation but is handled as a negative stress to

Stresses Within the Soil Mass Resulting from Vertical Surface Loading   **175**

be subtracted from the stress caused by the actual foundation that is ultimately installed in the excavation.

ILLUSTRATION 8-8.   A heavy materials storage building 30 ft by 30 ft is constructed with a basement that extends 6 ft below the ground surface. A foundation for an interior supporting column is constructed at floor level in the middle of the basement. The column footing is 4 ft square and carries a loading of 50 kips. What is the net stress change in the soil 5 ft below the middle of the basement floor? (For this example, neglect the weight of the concrete footing and floor.)

A "negative" foundation loading results from the basement excavation. Negative load is 6 ft deep × 120 pcf = 720 psf. For a foundation 30 ft × 30 ft placed at a depth 5 ft below the floor,

$$\frac{\text{Depth}}{\text{Width}} = \frac{5 \text{ ft}}{30 \text{ ft}} = 0.17$$

and the stress decrease $\Delta\sigma_v$ = 95 percent × 720 psf = −685 psf (percentage as determined from Fig. 8-7). Stress increase from column footing,

$$\left(\text{where } q = \frac{50 \text{ kips}}{4 \text{ ft} \times 4 \text{ ft}} = 3.14 \text{ ksf} = 3{,}140 \text{ psf}\right)$$

is $+\Delta\sigma_v$ = (25%)(3,140 psf) = +780 psf,

for the ratio of $\dfrac{\text{Depth}}{\text{Width}} = \dfrac{5 \text{ ft}}{4 \text{ ft}} = 1.25$ (ref. Fig. 8-7).

Therefore, actual stress increase,

$$\Delta\sigma_{v_{net}} = +780 - 685 = 95 \text{ psf}$$

Effect of Changing the Surface Grade

On large construction sites, the surface grade may be changed to improve the topography and to make the surface more suitable for the needs of the project. If the surface grade is lowered, this results in a reduction in the subsurface stresses. Where earth fill is placed to raise the surface level, an increase in the subsurface stresses results. When a uniform thickness of material is placed or removed over a large area, the subsurface stress increase or decrease is the product of the unit weight of the soil added or removed and the thickness involved. This subsurface stress change is constant with depth; it does not diminish with increasing depth, as for foundation loadings.

Where the thickness of fill or soil removal is variable, as is frequently the case, a limited area can be analyzed and the average thickness of soil added or removed can then be used to calculate the subsurface stress change for the area.

ILLUSTRATION 8-9.   A compacted fill for a shopping center development is placed over an area where soil conditions are as shown by the sketch. What stress increase results in the middle of the clay layer from the weight of the fill?

Since this is an areal fill (fill placed over a large area) the stress increase in the clay layer is

$$\Delta\sigma_v = (\gamma_{fill})(\text{height of fill})$$

$$= 125 \text{ pcf} \times 8 \text{ ft} = 1000 \text{ psf}$$

Subsurface stresses caused by foundations subsequently installed in fill or cut areas are computed by using the methods already presented. It is important to remember that the final total subsurface stress must reflect the changes caused by filling or lowering the surface of the site as well as the foundation loading.

ILLUSTRATION 8-10   Assume that a building foundation is constructed on the fill discussed in the previous illustration. If the footing is 5 feet square (5 ft by 5 ft) and carries a loading of 75 kips, what net stress results in the middle of the clay layer beneath the center of the footing? (Consider effects of fill *and* foundation loading.)

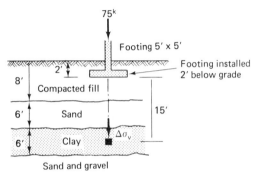

$$q_{footing} = \frac{75\ kips}{5\ ft \times 5\ ft} = 3\ ksf = 3000\ psf$$

$$Ratio\ of\ \frac{Depth}{Width} = \frac{15\ ft}{5\ ft} = 3$$

Estimate stress increase by either Boussinesq or Westergaard, $\Delta\sigma_v \approx 5\% \times q$ (percentage determined from Fig. 8-7 or Fig 8-8),

$$Therefore\ \Delta\sigma_v = 0.05\ (3{,}000\ psf) = 150\ psf\ from\ foundation$$

$$Stress\ increase\ from\ fill = 1000\ psf\ (previous\ illustration)$$

$$Total\ stress\ increase = 150 + 1000\ psf = 1150\ psf$$

PROBLEMS

8.1. At a planned construction site, subsurface sampling indicates that the wet unit weight of the soil is 123 pcf.
(a) Determine the effective vertical stress at the 12-ft depth if the water table is deep.
(b) Determine the effective vertical stress and the neutral stress at the 12-ft depth if the water table rises to within 6 ft of the ground surface.

8-2. At an offshore location, the soil surface is 30 ft below the water surface. Weighing of soil samples obtained in the investigation indicates the saturated unit weight to be 118 pcf. Determine the effective vertical pressure at a depth 55 ft below the water surface.

8-3. Determine the lateral earth pressure at a depth 20 ft (6.1 m) below the ground surface in a loose sand deposit. The wet unit weight of the sand is 115 pcf (18 kN/m³). What would the total lateral pressure be if the water table rose to the ground surface (in psf and kN/m²)?

8-4. A deep basement for a building is constructed in dense granular soil whose unit weight is 130 pcf (20.4 kN/m³). For a distance 10 ft (3 m) below the ground surface, determine the increase in total lateral pressure that results by having the water table change from a location below the basement level to the ground surface (in psf and kN/m²).

8-5. A 20-kip concentrated (point) load acts on the surface of a soil mass. Determine the vertical stress 10 ft below the ground surface at locations directly beneath the load, 10 ft horizontally from the load, and 20 ft horizontally from the load, for the
(a) Boussinesq condition.
(b) Westergaard conditions.

8-6. A 4-foot-square foundation (4 ft by 4 ft) located on the surface of a soil mass supports a total load of 96 kips. Determine the vertical stress resulting from the foundation loading at a depth 6 ft below the ground surface for locations beneath the center of the footing and beneath the edge of the footing, assuming
(a) the Boussinesq conditions apply.
(b) the Westergaard conditions apply.

8-7. A 4-foot-wide long (strip) footing carries a wall loading of 20,000 lb/ft of wall length.

What vertical stress increase results below the center of the footing at depths of 4, 8, and 12 ft, if

(a) the Boussinesq conditions apply.

(b) the Westergaard conditions apply.

8-8. An oil storage tank 50 ft in diameter imposes a maximum loading of 2500 psf onto the ground surface where the tank is supported. The soil underlying the tank has a unit weight of 125 pcf. For a depth 25 ft below the ground surface, compute the effective vertical stress when the tank is empty and when the tank is full, at locations beneath the center and the edge of the tank. Assume that the Boussinesq conditions apply.

8-9. Compare the stress increase resulting 8 ft below the center of a 10-foot-square foundation supporting 5000 psf when the 60° approximation is assumed and when the Boussinesq conditions are assumed.

8-10. A circular foundation 12 ft in diameter imposes a pressure of 8000 psf onto the soil. At the 12-ft depth, determine the vertical stress increase beneath the center and the edge of the loaded area, assuming

(a) the Westergaard conditions apply.

(b) the 60-degree approximation.

8-11. A 30-foot-diameter storage tank is supported on the ground surface at a site where a 15-foot-thick layer of dense sand overlies a very thick clay layer. The modulus of elasticity for the upper layer is ten times the modulus for the lower layer. The tank imposes a pressure of 3 ksf.

(a) Determine the increase in vertical stress below the center of the tank and at a depth of 30 ft.

(b) Determine the stress increase at the 30-ft depth if subsurface conditions were homogeneous (assume Boussinesq) and compare the result with (a).

8-12. For a construction project, the ground surface at a building location is lowered 5 ft. A 4-foot-square footing (4 ft by 4 ft) carrying a loading of 4000 psf is then constructed at the level of the new surface. What net stress increase results in the soil mass 4 ft below the center of the foundation? Assume that the soil unit weight is 120 pcf.

8-13. For a construction project, 10 ft of compacted earth fill is placed in preparation for erecting a building. At one of the building's interior locations a machine foundation 20 ft square will be installed at floor level to support equipment weighing 2000 kips. What net stress increase results below the center of the machine in the original soil mass, 5 ft under the natural ground surface? Assume a unit weight of 125 pcf for the compacted fill.

chapter *9*

Settlement
Soil Volume Change and Consolidation

The weight of any structure supported on the earth will result in stresses being imposed on the soils below the level of the base or foundation of the structure. The deformations in the soil occurring with these stresses cause volume changes in the soil, with the result that the structure undergoes settlement. The amount of settlement that will actually occur is related to the pressures (stresses) imposed on the soils, and the stress–strain properties of the soil.

For the typical situation, loadings imposed by a structure at foundation level act in a downward vertical direction. The resulting stresses developed within the soil mass beneath the structure act vertically but in other directions as well. For the generally occurring situation, however, where the stresses that are developed are well below the ultimate strength of the soil, most of the settlement of a structure results because of the stresses acting in the vertical direction. Reasonable accuracy in predicting settlements can be obtained by simply considering only the effect of vertical stresses.

Settlement is caused both by soil compression (or vertical squeezing together of soil particles) and lateral yielding of the soils located under the loaded area. The settlement factor that is most significant for cohesive soils is different from the factor that is most significant for cohesionless soils. In cohesive soils, compression is the cause of most of the settlement. For homogeneous cohesionless soils, lateral yielding is the more significant cause.

In practice, determination of the settlement characteristics of a soil is frequently attempted by one of several methods:

1. Working backwards from observations of the behavior of structures in the area near the planned building site.
2. Prior to construction, performing large-scale field-load tests at the actual building site.
3. Performing laboratory compression tests on soil samples obtained from borings or test pits made at the proposed construction site.
4. Estimating compressibility or volume change characteristics on the basis of index property tests performed on samples from borings or test pits. (Such tests typically include classification, moisture density determinations, liquid limit and plastic limit determination, and relative density determinations.)
5. Performing in situ tests in the field (in drilled boreholes) that relate to soil compressibility or expected settlement for a planned foundation.

Methods 1 and 2 have inherent shortcomings. With method 1, it can be difficult to accurately ascertain the actual amount of settlement that an existing structure has experienced, and, perhaps more important, soil conditions may not be identical at the different building sites. However, checking the behavior or performance of existing buildings in an area is good practice, provided that the procedures discussed hereafter are also followed. For method 2, field load tests seldom truly represent the loading conditions that will be developed by a structure, and the resulting settlement or compression data may be seriously misleading. Data from field load tests may be grossly in error when cohesive soil strata underlie the test area. Further, full-scale load tests are relatively expensive to perform.

Evaluation of a soil's compressibility or volume change characteristics is more accurately determined from laboratory tests. With the requirement for making soil borings or another form of subsurface investigation an accepted necessity for construction projects, it becomes relatively simple and economical also to obtain soil samples for purposes of performing laboratory tests. Compression tests provide accurate information (method 3), but index property tests can frequently provide reliable information, and are quicker and less costly to perform.

In situ field testing procedures to determine the volume change characteristics of a soil zone, such as accomplished with the *pressuremeter* apparatus (discussed in Chapter 14) and flat blade dilatometer (Chapter 11), show promise. However, such procedures are still in their infancy, with refinement necessary for reliable widescale application.

COMPRESSIBILITY

Compressibility is the term applied to one-dimensional volume changes that occur in cohesive soils that are subjected to compressive loading. This property of a fine-grained soil can be determined directly by performing a laboratory compression test, frequently called a *consolidation test*. In this test, an undisturbed sample is fit into a ring or cylinder so that the sample is confined against lateral displacement, and compressive loading is imposed to the soil (Fig. 9-1). For known magnitudes of load, the amount of compression and the time required for compression to occur are recorded. The test is usually performed by imposing a series of increasing compressive loadings and determining time rate-of-compression data for each increment of loading. The entire body of data permits the stress–strain characteristics of the soil to be determined, as discussed more fully in later sections of this chapter.

In soil compression, volume decreases are due principally to decreases in void spaces between soil particles as the particles rearrange so as to develop resistance to the new external loading. Practically, there is no decrease in the actual volume of soil particles.

The speed or rate of time that is required for volume changes to occur differs significantly for the coarse (cohesionless) soils and the fine-grained (cohesive) soils. The cohesionless soils experience compression relatively quickly—frequently in-

(a)

(b)

Figure 9-1 (a) Schematic representation of conventional types of laboratory consolidometers; (b) typical laboratory consolidation equipment.

stantaneously—after a loading is imposed. Conversely, the fully saturated and almost fully saturated clay soils (a common condition for many naturally occurring clay deposits) generally require a significant period before full compression under an applied loading results. Relating compression with the *time period* necessary for the compression to occur (time rate of compression) is consolidation. The effects of this are discussed in a later section of the chapter.

Laboratory compression tests are seldom performed on cohesionless soils. Part of the reason for this is the practical difficulty associated with obtaining suitably undisturbed samples of granular soil from a construction site. Also, because the rate of settlement for these soils is rapid, they do not cause the problems of postconstruction settlement that cohesive soils do. When information on the volume change or settlement characteristics of a granular soil is needed, it is most frequently obtained indirectly, from an in-place density determination, relative density tests, or other correlations.

Presentation and Analysis of Laboratory Compression Test Data

Compression test data are presented in any of several ways, usually depending on the preferences and experiences of the individual using the data. Because compression is due to changes in the void spaces in the soil, methods in common use frequently indicate compression as a change in the void ratio. Using arithmetic coordinates, a typical test result for change in void ratio versus the increase in loading pressure is as shown in Figure 9-2. The slope of the curve at any point is a_v, the *coefficient of compressibility*. Mathematically, $a_v = de/d\bar{\sigma}_v$ and the dimensional units for a_v are square feet per pound (or kip or ton) or square meter per kilonewton. Because of the constantly changing slope of the curve, it is somewhat difficult to use a_v in a mathematical analysis, as is desired in order to make settlement calculations. When semilog coordinates are used and the void ratio is plotted versus the logarithm of pressure, the data will plot approximately as a straight line (or, as described later, a series of straight lines) (see Fig. 9-3). In this form, the test data are more adaptable to analytical use. For all plots, the imposed compressive test pressure is the intergranular or effective pressure (stress), $\bar{\sigma}_v$.

Another method of presentation shows unit change in sample thickness (or

Imposed test pressure $\bar{\sigma}_v$ (tsf, ksf, kN/m^2, etc.) (arithmetic scale)

Figure 9-2 Presentation of compression test data on arithmetic coordinates.

Imposed test pressure $\overline{\sigma}_v$ (tsf, ksf, kN/m², etc.)
(log scale)

Figure 9-3 Presentation of compression test data on semilog coordinates.

strain) versus the logarithm of pressure (Fig. 9-4). This method gives essentially the same results as the method of Figure 9-3, but it has the advantage of minimizing the amount of work associated with reducing the test data. It may also make for simpler scttlement calculations. With this method, no conversion to void ratio is necessary. The compression data for the sample are converted to strain by dividing total compression by the original sample thickness, and strain is then plotted against the logarithm of pressure.

If, during the compression test, the pressures on a sample are increased to a certain magnitude, unloaded to a lesser value, and then reloaded and increased to magnitudes greater than previously, results like those shown in Figure 9-5 are obtained. Note that the soil does not expand to its original volume when pressure is removed. Some of the volume change due to external loading is permanent. Soil, therefore, is not an elastic material. Upon reloading, the resulting slope of the compression curve is less steep than the original slope. These factors of soil behavior have significant effect on the settlement of structures.

Consider a soil sample obtained from a site where conditions are as shown in Figure 9-6a. The ground surface overlying the sample has never been above the existing surface, and there never was extra external loading acting on the area. For this condition, the maximum vertical pressure ever imposed on the sample being considered is the current weight of overlying soil, $\overline{\sigma}_{v_0}$. The result of a compression test performed on the sample is as shown in Figure 9-6b. For laboratory loading less than $\overline{\sigma}_{v_0}$, the slope of the compression curve is less steep than it is for loads

Imposed test pressure, $\overline{\sigma}_v$ (tsf, ksf, kN/m², etc.)
(log scale)

Figure 9-4 Method of indicating soil compression as strain instead of void ratio.

Figure 9-5 Results of loading–unloading–reloading cycle applied to a soil.

greater than σ_{v_0} since, to the soil, values less than σ_{v_0} are in the "reloading range." The slope of the curve at loading greater than σ_{v_0} is termed the *virgin compression curve*, and the slope of the curve is the *compression index* C_c. The slope of the curve at values less than $\bar{\sigma}_{v_0}$ is the recompression slope C_r. Mathematically, the slope of the curve, for either C_c or C_r, is $\Delta e/\Delta \log \bar{\sigma}_v$. C_c and C_r are terms without dimensional units (that is, they will be indicated as numerical values that have no dimensional units).

From examination of Figures 9-5 and 9-6, it should be concluded that a change in the slope of the compression curve results when the previous maximum pressure ever imposed onto the soil is exceeded. If the ground surface had at some time in past history been above the existing surface and eroded away, or if the weight of a glacier had been imposed on the area at some time in history, $\bar{\sigma}_{v_0}$ (the existing overburden) is not the maximum pressure that has been imposed on the soil sample. The greatest pressure that previously existed on the soil is $\bar{\sigma}_{v_{\max}}$, which would be the total pressure that developed from the existing soil overburden *and* the weight of the eroded soil or glacier. Compression test results for this occurrence would be as shown in Figure 9-7.

Figure 9-6 Description of conditions applying to compression test sample: (a) location of soil sample obtained for compression test; (b) result of compression test.

Compressibility

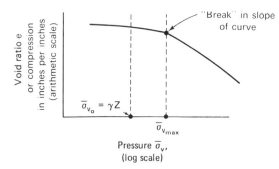

Figure 9-7 Compression test results where past pressure on soil has exceeded existing overburden pressure.

The effect of this soil property on the settlement of structures is shown by a comparison of conditions from Figures 9-6b and 9-7. Assume that the weight of the structure would cause an additional stress equal to $\Delta\bar{\sigma}_v$ to act on the sample being studied. The total soil compression that will occur within the soil deposit, and therefore the settlement that the structure experiences, is related to the compression occurring in the test sample. Comparative results are shown by Figures 9-8a and b. It is seen that, for the same magnitude of structural loading, soil conditions of Figure 9-8a cause more compression and, therefore, more building settlement than do the conditions of Figure 9-8b. This indicates that the stress history of a soil may be more significant than other soil properties insofar as settlement of structures is concerned.

Soil deposits whose condition is represented by Figures 9-6b and 9-8a are termed *normally loaded* or *normally consolidated*, meaning that the present overburden pressure is the greatest pressure that has been imposed on the soil. Soil whose condition is represented by Figures 9-7 and 9-8b are termed *precompressed, preconsolidated,* or *overconsolidated,* meaning that at some time in past history there were imposed pressures greater than those that currently exist.

If the virgin curve of a laboratory compression test begins at a loading less than $\bar{\sigma}_{v_0}$, the soil is termed *underconsolidated,* which means that the soil has not fully adjusted or stabilized under the current overburden pressures. (This would represent a "new" soil deposit.)

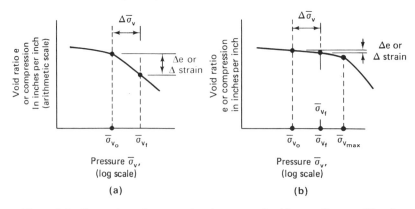

Figure 9-8 Comparison of compression that occurs for (a) normally consolidated and (b) overconsolidated soils at loading above the overburden pressure.

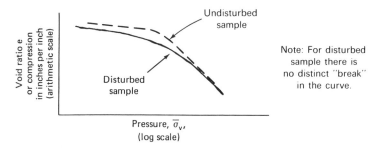

Figure 9-9 Typical compression test curve shapes for disturbed and undisturbed test samples.

For reliable results, undisturbed soil samples are required for the compression test. If the soil sample to be tested is disturbed because of the soil boring techniques used to obtain the sample or during transportation and handling, the test data may be in error. Typical test results occurring from disturbed samples are shown in Figure 9-9.

Estimating Compressibility from Index Properties Laboratory compression tests on fine-grained soils normally require days to complete (about 2 weeks in the period conventionally used). It is frequently necessary to obtain information about the compressibility of a soil in as short a time as possible. Or, in the interest of job economy, it may be desirable to limit the number of compression tests but still to evaluate the compressibility characteristics of many soil-boring samples. For these situations, it is possible to use correlations that have been established between compression properties and some more easily or more quickly determined properties of soils. These correlations, which permit *estimates* of the compressibility of silts and clays to be made, are

$$C_c = 0.54(e_0 - 0.35) \tag{9-1a}$$

where e_0 is the in-place void ratio,

$$C_c = 0.0054(2.6w - 35) \tag{9-1b}$$

where w is the in-place water content,

$$C_c = 0.009(\text{LL} - 10) \tag{9-1c}$$

where LL is the liquid limit. Equation 9-1c should be applied only for normally consolidated clays. In a normally consolidated clay, the natural water content is about at the liquid limit. If a clay has its natural water content significantly less than the liquid limit, it is preconsolidated.

The shear strength of a clay soil can also be used to indicate if the soil is normally consolidated or overconsolidated. The magnitude of the maximum pressure imposed on a soil is from three to four times its shear strength. By determining the shear strength and then $\overline{\sigma}_{v_{max}}$, the magnitude of $\overline{\sigma}_{v_{max}}$ can be compared with the overburden pressure that acted on the sample. Close agreement would indicate a normally consolidated soil.

Compressibility

(a)   (b)

Figure 9-10 Description of conditions applying to compression test sample: (a) subsurface profile indicating source of compression test sample; (b) compression test results.

Settlement Due to Soil Compression Assume that a building is to be constructed at a location where soil conditions are as indicated by the sketch of Figure 9-10a. The results of a laboratory compression test performed on a sample obtained from the center of the clay stratum is shown in Figure 9-10b. The value of $\overline{\sigma}_{v_0}$, the overburden pressure, is equal to $y\gamma_{\text{sand}} + (H_0/2)\gamma_{\text{clay}}$, where γ_{sand} and γ_{clay} are the unit weights (in pcf or kN/m³) of the sand and clay soils, respectively, and the y and H distances are in units (ft, m) compatible with the soil unit weight values.

The foundation load imposed by the new structure results in an additional pressure, $\Delta\sigma_v$, acting on the clay. Figure 9-11 uses the phase diagram method to illustrate changes that the clay sample experiences under the increased loading. The change in volume is equal to the change in void ratio. The relation of the change to the original volume is

$$\frac{\Delta V}{V_T} \quad \text{or} \quad \frac{\Delta e}{1 + e_0}$$

If the clay sample represents the *average* volume change that occurs throughout the clay stratum of Figure 9-10a, the following proportion will apply:

$$\frac{\Delta H}{H_0} = \frac{\Delta e}{1 + e_0}$$

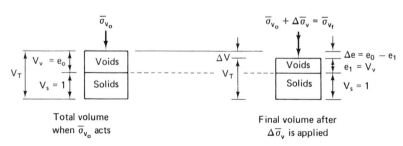

Figure 9-11 Phase diagram illustrating change in soil volume that occurs with increase in loading.

H_o is the original thickness of the clay layer and ΔH is the compression that this layer will experience. The settlement of foundations supported above the clay layer will be equal to the compression that occurs, or

$$\text{Settlement} = \Delta H = H_o\left(\frac{\Delta e}{1 + e_0}\right) \qquad (9\text{-}2)$$

As previously noted, the slope of the curve from the compression test for loadings greater than the overburden pressure is C_c, where

$$C_c = \frac{\Delta e}{\Delta \log \bar{\sigma}_v}$$

Rearranging gives

$$\Delta e = C_c[\Delta \log \bar{\sigma}_v]$$

Substituting in the equation for settlement gives

$$\Delta H = \frac{H_o}{1 + e_0} C_c(\Delta \log \bar{\sigma}_v) \qquad (9\text{-}3a)$$

or
$$\Delta H = \frac{H_o}{1 + e_0} C_c(\log \bar{\sigma}_{v_f} - \log \bar{\sigma}_{v_0}) \qquad (9\text{-}3b)$$

In this equation, $\bar{\sigma}_{v_0}$ is the overburden soil pressure, and $\bar{\sigma}_{v_f}$ is the sum of the overburden soil pressure σ_{v_0} and the pressure caused by the weight of the structure $\Delta\bar{\sigma}_v$.

If the compression test data are presented in the form shown by Figure 9-4, the settlement equation is

$$\Delta H = H_o \times \text{(change in percentage of compression for the load change } \Delta\bar{\sigma}_v)$$

or
$$\Delta H = H_o C_c' (\log \bar{\sigma}_{v_f} - \log \bar{\sigma}_{v_0}) \qquad (9\text{-}4)$$

where C_c' is the slope of the compression versus log σ_v plot (see Fig. 9-4).

ILLUSTRATION 9-1.   (a) Problem worked in U.S. customary units: Referring to the conditions shown by Figure 9-12, assume that y is 12 ft, H_o is 8

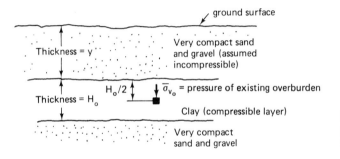

Figure 9-12 Soil conditions for problem of settlement due to compression in a buried clay layer.

Compressibility

ft, and γ_{sand} and γ_{clay} are 135 pcf and 100 pcf, respectively. For the clay, e_0 is 1.20 and the compression index C_c is 0.20 (both dimensionless values). The weight of the structure causes a stress of 600 psf at midheight of the clay layer. (Therefore, $\Delta\bar{\sigma}_v = 600$ psf.) (*Note:* Values of stress increase, $\Delta\bar{\sigma}_v$, are computed by using methods described in Chapter 8.)

The settlement would be

$$\Delta H = \frac{H_o}{1 + e_0} C_c(\log)\, \bar{\sigma}_{v_f} - \log \bar{\sigma}_{v_0})$$

where $\quad \bar{\sigma}_{v_0} = (12 \text{ ft} \times 135 \text{ pcf}) + (4 \text{ ft} \times 110 \text{ pcf}) = 2060 \text{ psf}$

and $\quad \bar{\sigma}_{v_f} = \bar{\sigma}_{v_0} + \Delta\bar{\sigma}_v = (2060 + 600) \text{ psf} = 2660 \text{ psf}$

$$\Delta H = \frac{8 \text{ ft}}{1 + 1.20} (0.20)(\log 2660 - \log 2060)$$

$$= \frac{(8 \text{ ft})(0.20)}{2.20} [3.426 - 3.315]^1 = 0.0806 \text{ ft} = 1 \text{ in. } (\pm)$$

If the groundwater table is at the soil surface, the effective soil overburden pressure $\bar{\sigma}_{v_0}$, is due to the submerged (or effective) weight of the soil. If the unit weights of 135 pcf and 110 pcf represent saturated unit weights, the submerged unit weights will be

For the sand:

$$\gamma_{sub} = \gamma_{sat} - \gamma_w = 135 \text{ pcf} - 62.4 \text{ pcf} = 72.6 \text{ pcf}$$

For the clay:

$$\gamma_{sub} = \gamma_{sat} - \gamma_w = 110 \text{ pcf} - 62.4 \text{ pcf} = 47.6 \text{ pcf}$$

If the soils are not fully saturated, it is generally sufficiently accurate to assume that a submerged effective soil weight is about half its weight when not submerged. Using the values calculated, the overburden pressure $\bar{\sigma}_{v_0}$ is then

$$\bar{\sigma}_{v_0} = (72.6 \text{ pcf} \times 12 \text{ ft}) + (47.6 \text{ pcf} \times 4 \text{ ft}) = 1062 \text{ psf}$$

and $\quad \bar{\sigma}_{v_f} = \bar{\sigma}_{v_0} + \Delta\bar{\sigma}_v = 1062 + 600 = 1662 \text{ psf}$

(Note that $\Delta\bar{\sigma}_v$ is not affected by the water table or submergence.)

$$\Delta H = \frac{H_o}{1 + e_0} C_c[\log \bar{\sigma}_{v_f} - \log \bar{\sigma}_{v_0}]$$

$$= \frac{(8 \text{ ft})(0.20)}{2.20} [3.222 - 3.028] = 0.14 \text{ ft} = 1.7 \text{ in. } (\pm)$$

---

[1] From mathematics, recall that the process of subtracting the logarithms of numerical values is actually accomplishing a division of those values. Hence, the *units* for the involved terms, such as psf or kN/m², will cancel, and the result of the logarithmic subtraction is dimensionless (without units).

Thus, the effect of a high water table is to cause more settlement.

(b) Problem worked in SI units:

For upper sand and gravel stratum, $y = 3.66\,\text{m}, \gamma = 21.2\,\text{kN/m}^3$

For compressible clay layer, $\qquad H_o = 2.44\,\text{m}, \gamma = 17.27\,\text{kN/m}^3$

$$C_c = 0.20, e_0 = 1.20, \Delta\bar{\sigma}_v = 28.8\,\text{kN/m}^2$$

$$\Delta H = \frac{H_o}{1 + e_0} C_c \left[\log\bar{\sigma}_{v_f} - \log\bar{\sigma}_{v_0} \right]$$

where

$$\bar{\sigma}_{v_0} = (3.66\,\text{m} \times 21.2\,\text{kN/m}^3) + \left(\frac{2.44\,\text{m}}{2} \times 17.27\,\frac{\text{kN}}{\text{m}^3}\right) = 98.9\,\frac{\text{kN}}{\text{m}^2}$$

and

$$\bar{\sigma}_{v_f} = \bar{\sigma}_{v_0} + \Delta\bar{\sigma}_v = (98.9 + 28.8)\frac{\text{kN}}{\text{m}^2} = 127.7\,\frac{\text{kN}}{\text{m}^2}$$

Therefore,

$$\Delta H = \frac{(2.44\,\text{m})}{(2.20)}(0.20)[\log 127.7 - \log 98.9] = .0246\,\text{m} = 2.46\,\text{cm}$$

$$(\text{recall } 1 \text{ inch} = 2.54\,\text{cm})$$

If the groundwater table is at the ground surface
(and using $\gamma_w = 9.81\,\text{kN/m}^3$),

$$\sigma_{v_0} = (3.66\,\text{m})\left(21.2\frac{\text{kN}}{\text{m}^3} - 9.81\frac{\text{kN}}{\text{m}^3}\right) + \left(\frac{2.44}{2}\,\text{m}\right)\left(17.27\frac{\text{kN}}{\text{m}^3} - 9.81\frac{\text{kN}}{\text{m}^3}\right)$$

$$= (41.69 + 9.10)\frac{\text{kN}}{\text{m}^2} = 50.79\frac{\text{kN}}{\text{m}^2}$$

$$\bar{\sigma}_{v_f} = \bar{\sigma}_{v_0} + \Delta\bar{\sigma}_v = (50.79 + 28.8)\text{kN/m}^2 = 79.59\,\text{kN/m}^2$$

and $\quad \Delta H = \dfrac{(2.44\,\text{m})}{(2.20)}(0.20)[\log 79.59 - \log 50.79] = 0.043\,\text{m} = 4.3\,\text{cm}$

If the soil is an overconsolidated soil, the equation for settlement calculations is modified to:

$$\Delta H = \frac{H_o}{1 + e_0} C_r(\log\bar{\sigma}_{v_f} - \log\bar{\sigma}_{v_0}) \qquad (9\text{-}5)$$

provided that $\bar{\sigma}_{v_{max}} > \bar{\sigma}_{v_f}$. (Note that $\sigma_{v_{max}}$ is the pressure where the slope of the compression test plot changes from C_r to C_c.[2]) For an overconsolidated soil where $\bar{\sigma}_{v_f}$ is greater than $\bar{\sigma}_{v_{max}}$, the settlement equation should be used as:

$$\Delta H = \frac{H}{1 + e_0} C_r (\log \bar{\sigma}_{v_{max}} - \log \bar{\sigma}_{v_0})$$

$$+ \frac{H_o}{1 + e_0} C_c (\log \bar{\sigma}_{v_f} - \log \bar{\sigma}_{v_{max}})$$

or

$$\Delta H = \frac{H_o}{1 + e_0} [C_r (\log \bar{\sigma}_{v_{max}} - \log \bar{\sigma}_{v_0}) + C_c (\log \bar{\sigma}_{v_f} - \log \bar{\sigma}_{v_{max}})] \qquad (9\text{-}6)$$

ILLUSTRATION 9-2. Assume that a buried stratum of clay 6 ft thick will be subjected to a stress increase of 700 psf at the center of the layer. The magnitude of the preconstruction soil overburden pressure is 1000 psf at the center of the layer. A laboratory compression test indicates that the clay is overconsolidated, with $\bar{\sigma}_{v_{max}}$ equal to 1500 psf. The value of C_c is 0.30, and the value of C_r is 0.05. What change in thickness results in the clay layer due to the stated conditions?

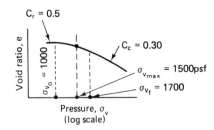

The change in thickness of the clay layer, from Equation 9-6 is

$$\Delta H = \frac{H_o}{1 + e_0} [C_r (\log \bar{\sigma}_{v_{max}} - \log \bar{\sigma}_{v_0}) + C_c (\log \bar{\sigma}_{v_f} - \log \bar{\sigma}_{v_{max}})]$$

$$= \frac{72 \text{ inches}}{2.50} [(0.05)(\log 1500 - \log 1000) + (0.30)(\log 1700 - \log 1500)]$$

$$= 0.73 \text{ in.}$$

If the thickness of the compressible soil layer is great, it should be divided into thinner layers for purposes of making the settlement calculations. The increment of settlement for each layer should be handled by using the methods discussed. The value of $\bar{\sigma}_{v_0}$ is the overburden pressure at mid-height of each layer, and $\Delta \bar{\sigma}_v$

[2]To obtain a value of C_r from the laboratory compression test for use in this equation, the recommended practice is as follows: Impose loading on the sample in increments to above the precompression stress, unload or rebound to at least the existing overburden; then reload the sample, and use the last recompression slope for determining C_r.

is the increase in pressure from the weight of the structure, also calculated for the midpoint of each layer. The total settlement will be the sum of increments occurring in all the layers. The depth of soil that is considered to be affected by foundation loading is limited to where $\Delta\bar{\sigma}_v$ is approximately one-tenth of the soil overburden pressure.

ILLUSTRATION 9-3. A settlement calculation is to be made for a structure that is planned for a site that is underlain by a thick deposit of normally consolidated clay soil. Soil properties are as indicated on the sketch. What building settlement is expected?

For this condition, the settlement calculation should be performed by dividing the thick clay deposit into sublayers, and calculating the compression that occurs in each sublayer. The overburden pressure is calculated for the center of each layer, and the stress increase due to the structure is also calculated for the center of each layer. Results of these computations are shown on the sketch. The related settlement calculations follow.

$$\Delta H_1 = \frac{48 \text{ inches}}{2.30}(0.20)(\log 1220 - \log 220) = 3.08 \text{ in.}$$

$$\Delta H_2 = \frac{48 \text{ inches}}{2.26}(0.20)(\log 1260 - \log 660) = 1.19 \text{ in.}$$

$$\Delta H_3 = \frac{72 \text{ inches}}{2.20}(0.20)(\log 1560 - \log 1210) = 0.78 \text{ in.}$$

$$\Delta H_4 = \frac{96 \text{ inches}}{2.16}(0.20)(\log 2160 - \log 1960) = \underline{0.55 \text{ in.}}$$

$$\text{Total settlement} = 5.41 \text{ in.}$$

VOLUME CHANGES IN SAND

In the illustrated problem of Figure 9-12, it was assumed for simplicity that the cohesionless soil layer overlying the clay was compact enough to be considered incompressible (i.e., compression of the sand layer would be negligible). This is not always a true condition. As stated earlier, the settlement of structures supported on cohesionless soil generally occurs immediately upon application of load. This settlement is primarily the result of volume changes caused by lateral yielding or shear strain that occurs in the soil. The exception is where the foundation or loaded area is large, in which case soil compression becomes more significant and should not be ignored.

In many practical situations, building loads developed gradually during the construction period will produce settlement whose effects can be absorbed by the structure without causing distress. However, building settlement caused by post-construction conditions such as live loads could result in distressing occurrences such as wall cracks, uneven floors, and ruptured buried utility lines.

In uniform cohesionless soil deposits, the soil rigidity (or modulus of elasticity) increases with depth because the overburden pressure and confining pressure, which affect the rigidity, increase with depth. For the condition where the increase in rigidity is uniform with depth, the following expression can be used to estimate settlements, provided that the *depth* of the foundation below the ground surface is less than the width of the foundation, and that the foundation width is not greater than 20 ft:

$$\Delta H = \frac{4qB^2}{K_v(B + 1)^2} \tag{9-7}$$

where B = width of the foundation in feet or meters.
q = pressure imposed by the foundation in kips/ft^2 or kN/m^2.
K_v = modulus of vertical subgrade reaction for one-foot-square (0.3-meter square) plate bearing on the ground surface, kips/ft^3 or kN/m^3.

The modulus of vertical subgrade reaction K_v can be determined directly from a plate-bearing test performed in the field at the planned location for the structure. In this test, loads are applied to the plate in increments, and the plate settlement is recorded for each load. The results are plotted as shown in Figure 9-13.

The tangent to the initial straight line portion of the plot is K_v, the modulus of vertical subgrade reaction. Mathematically,

$$K_v = \frac{\text{Pressure}}{\text{Settlement}} = \frac{\text{kips}}{\text{ft}^3} \text{ or } \frac{\text{kN}}{\text{m}^3}$$

Figure 9-13 Plot of load settlement data from a plate-bearing test, to determine modulus of vertical subgrade reaction.

Settlement   Chap. 9

TABLE 9-1   TYPICAL VALUES[a] OF K_v FOR DIFFERING SAND DENSITIES

| Condition | Relative density, % | Representative values of dry unit weight | | Values of K_v | |
		pcf	kN/m³	kips/ft³	kN/m³
Loose	<35	<90	<14	100	15×10^3
Medium dense	35–65	90–110	14–17	150–300	$(25–50) \times 10^3$
Dense	65–85	110–130	17–20	350–550	$(55–85) \times 10^3$
Very dense	>85	>130	>20	600–700	$(95–110) \times 10^3$

[a]For the condition where the groundwater table is at a depth greater than 1.5B. If the water table is at the base of the foundation, use $\frac{1}{2}K_v$. Interpolate for intermediate locations of the water table.

Field plate-bearing tests are time consuming and costly. For purposes of estimating settlements, representative values of K_v that have been correlated with other soil properties can be used; see Table 9-1.

If the subsurface conditions consist of a cohesionless soil stratum underlain by a cohesive layer, it may be necessary to calculate the settlement of the granular layer and the clay layer separately, and then sum these separate values to obtain the total expected settlement.

ILLUSTRATION 9-4.   A footing is to support a total column loading of 280,000 lb. Half of this will be live load. The building site is underlain by a thick layer of sand. Laboratory tests on samples from soil borings indicate that the dry density of the sand varies between 115 and 120 pcf. The design calls for the footing to be located 2 ft below the ground floor level of the building, and for an allowable soil-bearing pressure of 8000 psf to be used. Estimate the foundation settlement.

The footing area required is 280,000 lb/(8000 lb/ft²) = 35 ft². If a square footing is used, the width $B = \sqrt{35}$ = 5.9 ft → use 6 ft. For soil densities of 115–120 pcf, estimate a K_v value as 400 kips/ft³ from Table 9-1.

Estimated settlement:

$$\Delta H = \frac{4qB^2}{k_v(B + 1)^2} = \frac{(4)(8 \text{ kips/ft}^2)(6 \text{ ft} \times 6 \text{ ft})}{(400 \text{ kips/ft}^3)(6 + 1)(6 + 1)\text{ft}^2}$$

$$\approx 0.06 \text{ ft} = 0.75 \text{ in. } (\pm)$$

The postconstruction settlement (settlement due to live loading only) would be in the ratio of the live load to the total load. Since half of the total load is live load, the postconstruction settlement will be about $\frac{1}{2}$(0.8 in.) = 0.4 in., or less than $\frac{1}{2}$ in.

Volume Changes in Sand

SETTLEMENT RESULTING FROM EARTH FILL

It has been indicated that volume changes in subsurface soils should be expected as a result of any new loading imposed on the soil. Filling of construction sites with compacted earth so as to raise the grade of a low area or make an uneven site level is now a relatively common undertaking in the construction industry. Areal settlements due to fills should always be considered. And where structures are to be supported on the compacted earth fill, it should be recognized that the total settlement for the structure could well be the sum of the volume changes occurring in the natural soil from the weight of the fill plus the volume changes in the fill and natural soil caused by the weight of the structure itself. Only if the completed fill is left in place a sufficient time so that full compression of the natural soils occurs before the structure is built can the effect of settlement due to fill be neglected. Settlement of granular soils will still, of course, occur almost instantaneously. However, compression of fine-grained soil does usually require a time period.

Areal settlement due to the placement of fill can be computed by using methods already presented. However, the increase in stress $\Delta\sigma_v$ caused by the weight of the fill is assumed to remain constant throughout the full depth of the natural or original soil. This is in contrast to the condition that occurs beneath a foundation area, where the value of $\Delta\sigma_v$ decreases with increasing depth below the foundation.

The settlement of fill can be assumed to result from *compression* that occurs in the original soils underlying the fill. For cohesive soils, the necessary value of C_c or C_r is determined or estimated from laboratory tests. For granular soils, the expression for soil compression is also used. Appropriate values of C_c can be estimated from index properties, or from the following:

For loose uniform sands (D_R from 25 to 40%),

$$C_c = 0.05 \text{ to } 0.06 \tag{9-8a}$$

For dense or compact sands (D_R from 60 to 80%),

$$C_c = 0.02 \text{ to } 0.03 \tag{9-8b}$$

CONSOLIDATION

The compression of clay deposits usually occurs gradually when new loading is applied. The causes for this are related to the low permeability of these fine-grained soils and the condition of their usual occurrence in nature. Many clay deposits were formed under water, an exception being clays in residual soil deposits. In the underwater deposit, all void spaces were occupied with water. Even with the passage of time, these sedimentary materials remained fully or almost fully saturated. In soil, volume decreases are due to decreases in the void spaces between the soil particles as the particles rearrange in order to support the additional pressure caused by external loadings. For compression to occur in a saturated soil, water in the voids must first be expelled in order for the decrease in void spaces to occur. This behavior may be pictured as similar to that of a saturated sponge having the water squeezed out of it by a press.

When external load is applied to a saturated clay, the water in the voids, or pores, becomes subject to an immediate and equal increase of pressure. This is the same principle that is in effect for any hydraulic loading system, where an external force results in pressure developing in the fluid throughout the system. The trapped water starts to flow toward areas of lesser pressure, away from the area where loading is occurring. But because of the low permeability of fine-grained soil, the movement or escape of this pore water takes place slowly. Only as water escapes can soil particle rearrangement and decrease in void spaces take place. The result is that, for saturated clay soils, compression is a gradual occurrence. As water escapes, the pressure caused by the external loading is transferred from this water to the soil particles. The process of load transfer to the soil as pore water escapes is the *consolidation* process.

The rate of consolidation for a stratum of clay soil is affected by several factors, including:

1. The permeability of the soil
2. The extent or thicknesss of the compressible soil, and the distance that pore water in the soil must travel to escape from the zone where pressures due to foundation loading exist
3. The in-place void ratio of the compressible soil
4. The ratio of new loading to the original loading
5. The compression properties of the soil

The consolidation properties of a soil (not the soil stratum) are dependent on items 1, 3, 4, and 5. The effect of these factors can be grouped together to obtain a property termed the *coefficient of consolidation* c_v, which indicates how rapidly or slowly the process of consolidation takes place. The coefficient of consolidation is

$$c_v = \frac{k(1 + e)}{a_v \gamma_w} \qquad \left(\textit{Note: Units for } c_v \text{ are } \frac{\text{Length}^2}{\text{Time}} \right)$$

where e = void ratio (dimensionless value).
     k = coefficient of permeability (cm/sec, ft/min, ft/day, etc.).
     a_v = coefficient of compressibility (ft²/lb or m²/kN).
     γ_w = unit weight of water (lb/ft³, or Kn/m³).

Values for k, e, and a_v can be determined separately and substituted into the equation to determine c_v. It is common practice, however, to determine c_v directly from a laboratory consolidation test. The consolidation test is a compression test, but with the added provision that time readings (amount of compression versus time, for each applied loading) also are obtained.

As previously indicated, the consolidation process requires two interrelated

Consolidation   **197**

occurrences. One, the soil particles will be adjusting to a denser condition so that the soil mass can become strong enough to support the imposed loading. Simultaneously, pore water in the void spaces is escaping so that the required decrease in void ratio just referred to can occur. Referring to Figure 9-14, note that initially the stress increase due to structural loading $\Delta\sigma_v$ is imposed fully on the trapped pore water. This means that, at first, none of the new loading is imposed to the soil. Only after water is squeezed from the voids does the load start transferring to the soil.

The end of the consolidation process has been reached when the water pressure in the voids drops to the hydrostatic pressure normal for the location and no more water is being squeezed out. Full consolidation (100%), or a condition of equilibrium, is assumed to have occurred when the full loading of the structure is carried by the soil particles (no excess pressure in the pore water) and the total expected compression has taken place. Values of consolidation less than 100 percent indicate that, for the applied loading, compression (and settlement) is still occurring. Strictly speaking, however, compression resulting because trapped pore water

Hydrostatic pressure in clay layer
when foundation loading is first applied

Hydrostatic pressure in clay layer
when 100% consolidation has occurred

Figure 9-14 Change in pore water pressure occurring as clay soil consolidates: (a) hydrostatic pressure in clay layer when foundation loading is first applied; (b) hydrostatic pressure in clay layer when 100% consolidation has occurred.

Figure 9-15 "Double drainage" conditions in consolidation theory.

under pressure has escaped is primary consolidation. Percentage of primary consolidation is expressed by the term U percent. Some additional long-term compression from what is termed secondary consolidation also takes place as soil particles continue to adjust under the applied loading. For most inorganic soil deposits, however, the effects of secondary consolidation are small and can be neglected.

For given field conditions, where the distance that trapped pore water must travel to escape from the compressible layer (H_{dr} in Fig. 9-15) and c_v are known, the time period t required for a given percentage of consolidation to occur is

$$t = \frac{T_v H_{dr}^2}{c_v} \tag{9-10}$$

where T_v = time factor for consolidation due to vertical drainage.
$\quad H_{dr}$ = drainage distance for escaping pore water.
$\quad c_v$ = coefficient of consolidation.

The value T_v is a time factor that is a constant for a given percentage of consolidation and for a given type of subsurface condition. T_v is dimensionless. For the conditions indicated in Figure 9-15, referred to as "double drainage" because pore water can move downward and upward to escape, the values of T_v for a given percentage of consolidation ($U\%$) can be determined from the curve of Figure 9-16.

Figure 9-16 Variation of time factor T_v with percentage of consolidation U.

Consolidation

ILLUSTRATION 9-5. Referring to Illustration 9-1 and Figure 9-12, assume that laboratory consolidation test data for the clay indicates that, for the range of loading applied to the soil, c_v is 0.2 ft² per month. (Recall the settlement computed in Illustration 9-1 is one inch ±.)

(a) How long will it take for half of the estimated settlement to occur?

Half of the estimated settlement is a U of 50 percent. Referring to Figure 9-16, for U equals 50 percent, obtain the value $T_v = 0.20$.

$$t = \frac{T_v H_{dr}^2}{c_v} = \frac{(0.20)(8/2 \text{ ft})^2}{0.2 \text{ ft}^2/\text{month}} = 16 \text{ months}$$

[Note that for this type of problem, H_{dr} is one-half the total thickness of the clay layer.]

(b) How much settlement will occur in one year?

$$t = 1 \text{ year} = 12 \text{ months}$$

$$T_v = \frac{tc_v}{H_{dr}^2} = \frac{(12 \text{ months})(0.2 \text{ ft}^2/\text{month})}{(8/2 \text{ ft})^2} = 0.15$$

From Figure 9-16, for $T_v = 0.15$, obtain $U = 43$ percent, and therefore

Settlement, $\Delta H = 43\%$ of 1 inch (from Illustration 9-1)

$$= 0.43 \text{ in.}$$

SURCHARGING

The situation may exist where, because of compressible or weak subsoils, a proposed structure would undergo settlements that would exceed tolerable limits. Alternatively, stresses resulting in the weak soil from the weight of the structure could cause a weak soil to fail. If the site is to be used, the problem soil somehow must be circumvented (by removing it if possible, or by using pile foundations penetrating to below the poor soil) or improved so that the strength is adequate and the compressibility reduced. For construction projects extending over large areas, such as highways, improvement of poor subsoils is always given consideration because of possible cost savings.

The improvement of poor soils may possibly be accomplished by using a surcharge program. Surcharging of a soil, in its simplest intent, merely involves imposing an external loading for a long enough duration to cause desirable changes in the soil before the structure planned for the area is erected and supported on the soil.

Under the weight of a surcharge load, a poor soil will compress and increase in strength. The surcharge is made to the desired weight or loading and continued for a sufficient period to achieve results satisfactory for the need of the planned structure. Generally, this might include having the surcharge cause the magnitude of soil compression (settlement) that the planned structure would have caused, so that after the surcharge is removed and the structure is built, its settlement will be negligible, or, having the surcharge cause a sufficient increase in the strength of the poor soil so that it can safely support the weight of the planned structure.

Any material that will impose pressure onto the subsoils that require improvement can be used for the surcharge loading. Most conventionally, the material used is soil (borrow or fill). Soil is used because of its general availability and low cost, its ease of handling, and the absence of problems about deterioration.

Surcharging for improvement is most commonly applied for cohesive and organic soils—soil types that require a time period for compression (consolidation) and strength gain to occur. Surcharging programs *are* applicable for improving loose, granular soil deposits, but other methods, frequently quicker and more economical, can be used for these soils (methods that do not have application with cohesive soils).[3]

Surcharges for improving the strength of weak soils have to be applied slowly or in increments so that the weak soils are not overstressed (failed) *before* they have time to improve. With cohesive soils, the compression-consolidation process involves a readjustment of soil particles as water is squeezed from the voids of the soil. A gain in strength occurs because of the consolidation, but the strength gain results only as rapidly as water is squeezed from the soil (an implication from the strength curve shown in Figure 9-17). Consequently, a properly performed surcharge program requires field monitoring to establish a safe rate for increasing the surcharge and to determine how long it should remain in place. Monitoring normally includes instruments such as piezometers to measure excess pore water pressures developed within the weak soil, to learn of the rate at which consolidation is occurring, and to indicate when additional increments of the surcharge can be safely added. Settlement plates located in or on the surface of the original soil are used to monitor the rate and amount of settlement caused by a surcharge. For accurate records, any reference bench mark to measure settlement must be located outside of the area that is settling.

In some cases, the structure itself can be used to apply a surcharge load in increments. An example of this is with ground level storage tanks, such as those used to hold petroleum or other fluids. For many situations, the tolerable settlement of storage tanks is relatively large, provided that large *differential* settlements that

Shear strength increases as consolidation (compression and reduction in water content) occurs

Figure 9-17 Change in soil strength and water content as consolidation under surcharge occurs.

[3]See vibro-compaction and dynamic compaction methods discussed in Chapter 12.

Surcharging

might cause the tank to rupture do not occur. A fluid, possibly the material to be stored but more frequently water, is used to partially fill the tank. The tank is left partially filled until the subsoil achieves the necessary increase in strength. Then additional liquid is pumped in, and the next waiting period is allowed to elapse. This procedure continues until the subsoils supporting the tank reach the desired degree of stability. The tank can then be put into permanent use. Permanent piping connections should not be made until all, or most of, the settlement has occurred.

With this method, a laboratory test program should be performed before field operations are begun to ensure that the weak subsurface soils will be able to reach the strength required to support the tank and to obtain an estimate of the time required to complete the consolidation process. A laboratory program involves consolidating samples of the weak subsoil under the same vertical pressures that the tank will impose onto the soil, and then performing shear tests to determine if adequate shear strength (Chapter 10) is being obtained.

Acceleration of the Soil Improvement Process   Use of a surcharge program requires that the surcharge be applied and left in place for long enough to obtain the desired compression or strength gain. Depending on the properties and thickness of the poor soils, a surcharge may remain in place for months or longer before it accomplishes its purpose and can be removed. Construction cannot begin until the surcharge is removed, of course. If time is an important factor, means of accelerating the consolidation period can be undertaken.

One method to reduce the time for a desired amount of compression (or settlement) to result is to use an excessive surcharge, provided that the subsurface soils have sufficient strength. A given amount of settlement will occur more quickly under a heavy surcharge than under a light surcharge.

ILLUSTRATION 9-6.   Assume that an area is underlain by a stratum of compressible soil 16 ft thick. The weight of the proposed structure, say an earth embankment for a new highway, will result in an increase of 600 psf pressure to the compressible soil. The settlement under this loading would be 12 in. The compressible layer is doubly drained, and the soil has a c_v value of 3 ft²/month. Calculations indicate that it would take approximately 22 months for the settlement to occur under the weight of the proposed embankment. How long would be required for a surcharge imposing a pressure of 1200 psf to cause the 12 in. of settlement.

The first step of the solution requires that the total settlement to be expected from the 1200-psf surcharge be computed. Using Equation 9-3, we find that the settlement would be 20 inches. To obtain but 12 inches of settlement, 60 percent consolidation (12 in./20 in. × 100%) must occur. The T_v value for 60 percent consolidation is 0.3, and the time required is

$$t = \frac{T_v H_{dr}^2}{c_v} = \frac{(0.3)(8 \text{ ft} \times 8 \text{ ft})}{3.0 \text{ ft}^2/\text{month}} \cong 6\tfrac{1}{2} \text{ months}$$

Sand Drains, Wick Drains When a surcharge is used, another method for accelerating the consolidation process is to shorten the length of the drainage path for the pore water escaping from the consolidating soil. This can be accomplished by providing vertical drains or drain wells at spacings closer than the drainage distance for vertical flow. Frequently, too, the horizontal coefficient of permeability for cohesive soil deposits is many times greater than the coefficient of permeability for the vertical direction, which further increases the speed of consolidation.

Sand drains. Vertical drain wells can be holes that are drilled into the compressible soil and filled with sand (frequently called *sand drains*). Since the sand is very permeable material, pore water under pressure because of the surcharge will flow to the drain wells and be forced upward (or downward, too, if the well extends to a deeper permeable stratum underlying the compressible soil). After flowing upward to the surface, the water is carried away from the surcharge area (see Fig. 9-18a).

If the drain wells are located as indicated in Figure 9-18b, the zone of drainage can be assumed to be circular. The expression for the time period necessary to achieve consolidation when this condition exists is

$$t = \frac{T_h(\gamma_w a_v)}{k_h(1 + e_0)} = \frac{T_h d_d^2}{c_h} \tag{9-11}$$

(a) Cross-section of installed drain-wells and surcharge

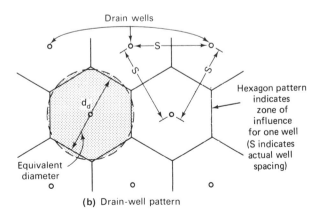

(b) Drain-well pattern

Figure 9-18 Cross-section and plan of typical sand drain installation: (a) cross-section of installed drain wells and surcharge; (b) drain well pattern [000].

Surcharging

203

Figure 9-19 Variation of time factor T_h with percentage of consolidation U for sand drain installations [000].

where t = elapsed time.

T_h = time factor for horizontal drainage (dimensionless).

c_h = horizontal coefficient of consolidation (*Note:* units are length²/time).

d_d = diameter of the zone drainage to a drain well, (ft or m).

The value of T_h varies according to the ratio of the draining area to the escape (drain well) area. If d_d is the diameter of the draining area, and d_w is the drain well diameter, n can be the ratio of d_d to d_w. Curves of T_h, similar to those for T_v used for vertical consolidation, are available for different ratios of n (see Fig. 9-19).

The drain well spacing affects the time for consolidation more than the drain well size. Quicker results will be obtained by using a small drain well spacing. However, there is the practical problem of constructing the wells close together without collapsing or otherwise damaging them. There is also the potential problem that the sand drains may shear along their length if the compressible soils experience large settlement or lateral movement during compression. The result is that water flowing from the consolidating soils to the drain well cannot escape to the surface, thus invalidating the drain well system. Because of the specialized techniques and equipment required for a sand drain installation, it is generally not economical to use the method for improving small projects.

ILLUSTRATION 9-7. The settlement problem of Illustration 9-6 examined the effects of using a surcharge to improve the subsurface soils for a planned highway embankment. The surcharge program involves the placement and removal of an amount of soil greater than that required for the embankment, with a related expense. It is desired also to study the effect of using a sand drain installation, on the possibility that it may be less costly than surcharging (because less surcharge is required) and faster results may be provided.

Laboratory testing of samples indicates that the coefficient of permeability for horizontal flow ranges from 5 to 15 times the coefficient for vertical flow; the coefficient of consolidation for horizontal drainage would be similarly effected. For a preliminary analysis, use a value of c_h that is 7 times the value of c_v. Since c_v was 3 ft^2/month, c_h will become about 20 ft^2/month.

It is planned to install sand drains that are 2 ft in diameter and on a center-to-center spacing of 10 ft, as indicated in Figure 9-18b.

Settlement calculations indicate that an 800-psf surcharge would cause a settlement of 13.5 in. This is 12/13.5, or 90 percent of the settlement expected from the necessary embankment fill.

The ratio of d_d to d_w is 10/2, or 5. With reference to Figure 9-19, the value of T_h for 90 percent consolidation and n equal to 5 gives a time factor of 0.28. Substitution of appropriate values into Equation 9-11 gives

$$t = \frac{T_h(d_d)^2}{c_h} = \frac{(0.28)(10 \text{ ft} \times 10 \text{ ft})}{20 \text{ ft}^2/\text{month}} \cong 1.5 \text{ months}$$

Wick drains.   A practical development of the 1970s was the prefabricated band drain consisting of synthetic fabrics and including a permeable core. The typical band drain has a small cross-section (e.g., 4 in. wide by 0.25 in. thick, or 100 mm by 7 mm), is extremely flexible, and can be used on a job site while being unwound from a storage or dispensing reel. The fabric drain can be rapidly installed with mobile crane or mast-equipped rigs by using a needle-punching technique (a nondrilling, soil displacement procedure; see Fig. 9-20). A long, thin mandrel (shaft) on the installation rig is vibrated or hydraulicly pushed into the soil to be drained. The fabric drain, attached at the tip of the mandrel, is pulled into the earth as the mandrel advances. At the desired penetration, the drain is disengaged from the mandrel and also cut from the band reel at the ground surface. The mandrel is withdrawn, but the fabric drain remains in place. This vertical drain or *wick* provides the escape path for excess pore water in the penetrated soil. The rate of drain installation can be on the order of 3 feet or 1 m per sec. Installation depths up to about 100 ft or 30 m have been used. In the typical application, the wick drains are installed at closely spaced intervals (e.g., on the order of 5 ft or 1.5 m or less). A surcharge material is applied to the area after the drains have been installed to create an increase in subsurface stress and pore water pressure, as for the sand drain installation. As with sand drains, a granular soil layer is placed on the site surface under or as part of the surcharge, to provide a drainage pad for water wicked upward. The close spacing of drains is conducive to rapid consolidation because of the small lateral distance that squeezed pore water must travel to reach a drain. The fabric drains offer some distinct advantages over sand drains, such as lower materials cost, easier and more rapid installation, and less danger of damage to the drain as the treated soil consolidates and settles. The theory previously outlined for sand drains can be applied where analytical studies involving wick drains are necessary.

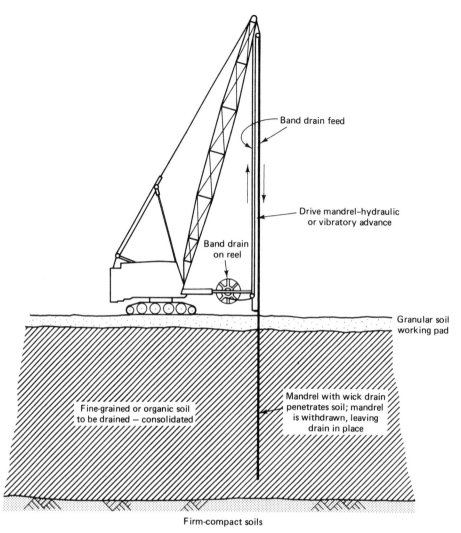

Band drain feed

Drive mandrel–hydraulic
or vibratory advance

Band drain
on reel

Granular soil
working pad

Fine-grained or organic soil
to be drained — consolidated

Mandrel with wick drain
penetrates soil; mandrel
is withdrawn, leaving
drain in place

Firm-compact soils

Figure 9-20 Typical wick drain installation equipment and procedure.

Whether or not the use of drains is more economical than a surcharge program without drains (where a heavier surcharge or longer time period would be involved) depends on the relative cost of the drain installation and price of embankment fill. Factors to make a drain installation more attractive would include the possibility for the surcharge to be adequately compacted during placement so that it can be left in place as the structural embankment when the desired settlement has been reached.

PROBLEMS

9-1. Provide reasons why field plate-loading tests performed at a planned construction site may give erroneous settlement information if the area is underlain by cohesive soils.

(*Hint:* Field loading tests are frequently performed with bearing plates smaller in area than the foundation footings will be. Also, consider the effects of consolidation.)

9-2. Indicate advantages related to performing laboratory compression tests on samples obtained from strata underlying a building site for determining soil compression data.

9-3. Briefly review the manner in which laboratory compression tests are conventionally performed so as to obtain load deformation data for a soil.

9-4. For soils undergoing compression, what is one-dimensional volume change?

9-5. In conventional laboratory compression testing, what is the cause of soil volume decrease?

9-6. In a laboratory compression test, the void ratio of the test sample changes from 1.55 to 1.36 as the loading increases from 2000 to 4000 psf.
(a) What is the value of the coefficient of compressibility for these conditions?
(b) What is the compression index for this loading range?

9-7. Referring to occurrences observed in a typical field or laboratory compression test, explain why a soil mass does not expand to its original volume when loading is released.

9-8. Briefly indicate the difference between a normally consolidated and an overconsolidated soil deposit.

9-9. A cohesive soil sample obtained from a known normally consolidated clay deposit is found to have a liquid limit of 80 percent. Approximately, what would the compression index for this soil be?

9-10. A 7-ft layer of clay is buried beneath a 10-foot stratum of very compact granular soil. Compact sand underlies the clay. The layer of granular soil is composed of material having a unit weight of 130 pcf. The clay weighs 105 pcf. A laboratory compression test on a sample of the clay indicates a compression index of 0.40 and a natural void ratio of 1.30. A planned building loading will cause a 550-psf stress increase at the middle of the clay layer.
(a) What amount of compression occurs in the clay layer from the indicated conditions?
(b) How much compression of the clay layer would result if the groundwater table were at the ground surface (all other conditions remain the same)?
(c) How much clay layer compression would occur if the clay were an overconsolidated material, the past maximum pressure were 2000 psf, and the C_r value were 0.10? Assume a deep water table.

9-11. A planned construction site is underlain by a thick deposit of normally consolidated clay soil. A building foundation 6 ft square will be located on the ground surface and carry a total loading of 180,000 lb. Determine the foundation settlement by analyzing the volume changes in layers that are 2, 4, and 6 ft thick, respectively, from the foundation level downward. For simplification, assume a soil unit weight of 115 pcf constant with depth, and an in-place void ratio of 1.05 and a compression index of 0.35 for each layer analyzed.

9-12. A plate-bearing test is performed on soil near the surface of a granular stratum in order to determine the modulus of vertical subgrade reaction. The load versus settlement information appears as a straight line on a graphical plot. At a point where the load is 5 tons/ft², the indicated settlement is 0.5 in. What is the value for the modulus of vertical subgrade reaction?

9-13. A 5-foot-square footing (5 ft by 5 ft) supported on a sandy stratum is to carry a column loading of 250,000 lb. The unit weight of the sands underlying the footing location vary between 120 and 125 pcf. Estimate what foundation settlement would be expected. (Neglect the weight of the footing.)

9-14. Describe the events that take place when a clay soil undergoes consolidation.

9-15. What is the physical meaning of the coefficient of consolidation c_v?

9-16. A buried clay layer 10 ft thick is sandwiched between strata of free-draining granular soil so that double drainage during consolidation can occur. Calculations indicate that, because of a planned building loading, an ultimate settlement of 2 in. is expected as a result of compression in the clay layer. The coefficient of consolidation for the clay is 0.01 ft²/day.

(a) How long will it take for 90 percent of the estimated settlement to take place?

(b) How much settlement will occur in one year?

(c) How long will it take for one inch of settlement to take place?

9-17. A sand drain installation is proposed for an airport project to accelerate the consolidation of a thick deposit of fine-grained soil underlying the construction area. It is planned to install sand drains 1.5 ft in diameter at a staggered spacing so that each sand drain will handle a plan area 15 ft in diameter. Laboratory tests indicate the coefficient of consolidation for horizontal drainage of the soil is 0.5 ft²/day. Computations indicate that the surcharge load will cause an eventual settlement of 12 inches. How long a period will be required for 90 percent of this settlement to take place?

chapter 10

Shear Strength Theory

The ability of a soil mass to support an imposed loading or for a soil mass to support itself is governed by the shear strength of the soil. As a result, the shearing strength of the soil becomes of primary importance in foundation design, highway and airfield design, slope stability problems, and lateral earth pressure problems that deal with forces exerted on underground walls, retaining walls, bulkheads, and excavation bracing.[1]

In the study of the shear strength of soils, it is common to consider the two major categories of soil types—cohesionless and cohesive—separately. Overall, the factors that can affect the shearing strength of both soil types are the same. Practically, however, the factors that have the *most* influence on the shear strength that is or will be developed by each soil type are different.

The shearing strength and related deformations (or stress–strain relationship) of a foundation or construction soil is conventionally studied in the laboratory by testing soil samples obtained from the construction site and using established testing procedures. Additionally, field test methods have also been developed for determining the shear strength of soil in its natural location, for reasons of expediency and economy and sometimes necessity, if samples for testing cannot be obtained.

[1]The shearing strength of soil deposits (which we recognize as consisting of an accumulation of discrete particles, possibly with some degree of interparticle bonding present) almost always refers to the resistance along a plane that passes between or along particle surfaces (but not through the particle). The mineral compositions of soil particles produce materials that have relatively high resistance to compressive and shear forces, and that rarely are fractured or sheared when a soil mass "shears." A plane of resistance passing between or along particle surfaces is weaker than a plane of resistance through the solid particles.

(a)

(b)

Figure 10-1 (a) Schematic diagram of direct shear apparatus; (b) laboratory direct shear equipment (manually operated). (Courtesy of Soiltest, Inc.)

Typically, field determinations of shear strength are quick procedures, so that many soil samples (from different borings or test pits and different depths) can be checked easily and economically. Commonly with field tests, strength values only (no deformation data) are generally obtained.

LABORATORY TESTS

The most widely used laboratory tests for studying the shear strength and related deformations of soils include the direct shear test (single and double shear), the triaxial compression test, and the unconfined compression test. For cohesive soils, vane shear tests can be used in the laboratory and the field to determine the cohesive strength, or cohesion, of soils (cohesion is related to shear strength).

Currently, the most preferred type of strength test is the triaxial test. The unconfined compression test is a type of triaxial test that can be used only for cohesive soils. The use of the direct shear test has decreased since the development of the triaxial test, but it still represents the basic approach for studying the stress–strain characteristics of a soil during shearing and possesses much merit as a learning tool.

Direct Shear The direct shear apparatus for performing single shear is essentially a rectangular or circular box having separated lower and upper halves (see Fig. 10-1a). After the sample to be tested is placed in the apparatus, a normal (compressive) loading is applied to compress the soil. The upper half of the apparatus is then moved laterally by a recorded shearing force, forcing the sample to shear across the plane between the two halves of the apparatus. The normal force is kept constant during the test. The shearing force starts at zero and increases until the sample fails (is sheared). Usually, a record of the magnitude of the shearing force and the resulting lateral movement is kept so that shearing resistance stress versus shearing displacement can be computed and plotted graphically. Changes in sample thickness that occur during the shearing process are also recorded so that volume change versus shearing stress or shearing strain can be studied. Typically, results of shearing stress versus shearing strain are as shown in Figure 10-2. The initial portion of the diagram is curvilinear (constantly changing slope), which continues until the maximum shear is reached, after which continuing de-

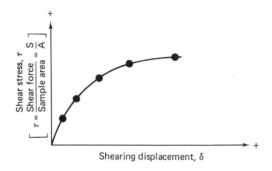

Figure 10-2 Typical plotted representation of shearing stress versus shearing displacement data.

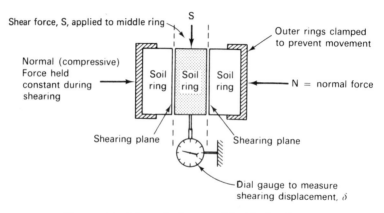

Figure 10-3 Schematic diagram of double-ring shear.

formation occurs with no increase in loading—that is, no increase in resistance. Failure is considered to have occurred at the maximum shearing value.

In direct shear testing, shearing can be accomplished by either controlling the rate of strain or the rate of stress. For the *strain-controlled* test, the shearing deformation (lateral movement) occurs at a controlled rate, usually continuously and at a constant speed. With this type of test, the shearing force necessary to overcome the resistance within the soil is automatically developed.

In the *stress-controlled* test, the magnitude of the shearing force is the controlled variable. The stress is increased at either a uniform rate or in established increments. For each increment of shearing force, it is applied and held constant until the shearing deformation ceases.

The strain-controlled shear test appears to be the most widely used of the two methods, probably because a mechanically operated strain-controlled apparatus is the simplest to devise.

Double shear testing is similar to the single shear test, except that two parallel surfaces are sheared. This type of test is usually performed on soil samples obtained from test borings that have utilized special tube equipment designed to fit directly into a shearing apparatus, so that a minimum of sample handling is required. As an illustration of one method, the soil-sampling apparatus used to extract samples from test borings is such that the soil is obtained in a tube whose interior lining consists of a series of rings. In the laboratory, three rings of soil are taken for the shear test. The shearing takes place as indicated in Figure 10-3. The stress–strain data from the double shear test are similar to the data from the single shear test.

A variation of the direct shear test is a torsional test, where one section of the tested sample is twisted relative to the other. The torsional resistance developed on the failure plane is related to the shear strength of the soil. This test is not in common use. Similarly, some past studies have been made of using an extrusion-type test for cohesive soils, but such tests are not in common use.

Triaxial Compression Test The triaxial test is currently the most popular test for determining the shearing strength of soils. Though not as simple a test as

Loading piston for
applying vertical force

To pressure gauge

Pressure supply
(air or water)

Air or fluid
in chamber,
under pressure

Top loading plate

Porous stone

Tie rod

Soil
sample

Rubber membrane
around soil sample

Cylinder (lucite, or
metal for high
pressure testing)

Porous stone

(a)

Triaxial chamber
for soil sample

Motor and mechanism
for applying axial load

Control panel for confining
pressure and soil pore water
pressure determinations

(b)

Figure 10-4 (a) Schematic diagram of triaxial compression test apparatus; (b) laboratory triaxial equipment (dual-chamber, motorized). (Courtesy of Soiltest, Inc.)

Laboratory Tests

the direct shear test, it has several advantages that are of practical importance: (1) the loading conditions in the triaxial test can be made to simulate more accurately the loading conditions that the soil was (or will be) subjected to in its natural state; (2) failure is not forced to occur across a predetermined plane, as occurs for the direct shear test.

In the triaxial test, a cylindrical soil sample (as conventionally obtained in soil borings) is wrapped in a rubber membrane for protection and placed in a chamber where an all-around, or confining, pressure can be applied. The confining pressure is usually applied through water or air introduced into the sealed chamber. The sample sits on a fixed pedestal, and a cap attached to a vertical piston rests on the top of the sample. In testing, the confining pressure is applied all around and to the top of the sample and, usually, held constant. An axial (vertical) load is subsequently applied to the sample through the piston, which passes through the top of the chamber. The axial load is steadily increased until failure of the sample occurs. Figure 10-4a shows the triaxial testing arrangement schematically.

Analysis of a three-dimensional element within the tested triaxial specimen shows that a lateral normal stress equal to the confining pressure p_c acts on orthogonal vertical planes, and a vertical stress acts on the horizontal plane. The vertical stress is equal to the sum of the confining pressure p_c plus that pressure increase resulting from the axial loading, Δp (see Fig. 10-5).

In practical problems, the confining pressure is frequently selected to be equal to the confining or lateral pressure that acted on the soil in its natural location within the soil mass, and the axial pressure that eventually causes the sample to fail is assumed to be representative of the maximum vertical pressure that can be imposed on the soil at the depth at which the confining pressure acts. By relating test pressures to subsurface stresses, the confining pressure represents σ_3, the minor principal stress, while the *total* axial stress represents σ_1, the major principal stress.

In the triaxial test setup, porous discs or stones are placed at the top surface and bottom surface of the sample so that pore water in the sample can be drained, if and when desired. The pedestal and loading cap are provided with drainage tubes for the water to escape and from which the pore water pressure can be determined. If the problem under study requires, water can also be introduced into the sample to determine the effect of increased water content on the strength.

The numerical difference between the total axial pressure σ_1 and the confining pressure σ_3 in the triaxial test is termed the *deviator stress*. When stress–strain data

Figure 10-5 Stress combination acting on incremental element of soil subjected to triaxial testing.

(a)

(b)

E_i = tangent modulus of elasticity (initial)

E_t = tangent modules (general)

E_s = secant modulus (general)

(c)

Figure 10-6 Representative triaxial test data: (a) typical result for loose sands and normally consolidated clays; (b) typical result for dense sands and overconsolidated clays; (c) indication of common terms used to relate stress and strain.

are graphed, it is the deviator stress that is conventionally plotted against strain. Typical qualitative results are shown in Figure 10-6.

For axially loaded test specimens, the related slope of the stress–strain curve is the modulus of elasticity E. The modulus of elasticity is an indication of the stiffness or resistance to deformation of the material; the higher the value of E, the stiffer or stronger the material. A *tangent modulus* is the slope of a line drawn tangent to a point on the curve. A *secant modulus* is the slope of a line connecting any two points on the stress–strain curve. By reference to Figure 10-6, it should be clear that a tangent modulus or a secant modulus will not be constant for all

Axial stress = $\dfrac{\text{Axial load}}{\text{Sample area}} = \dfrac{P}{A}$

Lateral stress = 0

$P = 0$ $P = 0$

Axial stress = $\dfrac{P}{A}$

(a)

(b)

Figure 10-7 Representation of unconfined compression test: (a) test arrangement; (b) stresses acting on incremental element.

Laboratory Tests

Figure 10-8 Vane of vane-shear apparatus, for determining in-place shear or cohesive strength (also refer to Figure 11-43).

Figure 10-9 Torvane for determining shear or cohesion of soil in field or laboratory.

parts of the curve. Both the tangent modulus and secant modulus are used in problem analysis.

Unconfined Compression Test   The unconfined compression test (Fig. 10-7) is a triaxial compression test, but a type where the all-around confining pressure is zero. The axial force represents the only source of external pressure imposed onto the soil. Because it is necessary that the soil sample under test be capable of standing in the testing apparatus under its own internal strength, the test is limited to use for soils possessing cohesion. Test results are generally similar to conventional triaxial test results.

Vane Shear Tests   Vane shear tests are coming into wider use for determining the in situ strength of cohesive soils. The vane shear apparatus consists of thin-bladed vanes that can be pushed into the soil with a minimum of disturbance. A torque applied to rotate the vanes is related to the shear strength of the soil. A vane shear apparatus, as pictured in Figure 10-8, can be attached to a long vertical rod and inserted into borings, so that the in-place strength of the soil can be determined without removing the soil from its natural state in the ground. Similar equipment is also used in the laboratory. It is specifically useful for determining the cohesive strength of soft or sensitive clays that could possibly be affected by the handling that the conventional laboratory shear tests require.

   An adaptation of the vane shear apparatus is the torvane (Fig. 10-9), used for determining the cohesive strength of samples in the field or laboratory.

SHEAR TEST RESULTS PLOTTED ON MOHR'S CIRCLE COORDINATES

Results of the direct shear and triaxial tests can be plotted graphically (or semi-graphically) on a shear stress versus normal stress coordinate system. They are the

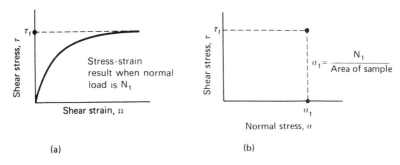

Figure 10-10   Direct shear results for one test: (a) stress–strain plot; (b) result of test on normal stress–shear coordinates.

same coordinates used for Mohr's circle plots (Chapter 7). The stress combination that represents the condition at the maximum shearing strength or the ultimate shearing strength (at failure) is generally used for making the plot.

For the direct shear test (Fig. 10-10a), the results of *each* test would plot as a point, as indicated in Figure 10-10b.

With triaxial test results, the values of σ_3 and σ_1, the principal stresses, are known, and plotting these points permits the Mohr's circle for these stress conditions to be drawn (see Fig. 10-11b).

If identical homogeneous soil samples were tested under identical conditions in a direct shear test *and* a triaxial test, the same strength information, for practical purposes, would be obtained. Where the results from a direct shear test are superimposed on the results from a triaxial test, the plotted point of τ versus σ appears as shown in Figure 10-12a or b.

Strength or Failure Envelope   If a series of direct shear tests were performed on different samples of homogeneous soil and the normal loading were different for each test, the results plotted on τ_f versus σ coordinates could be as shown in Figure 10-13. A curve passing through the plotted points establishes what is referred to as the *strength* or *failure envelope curve*. This envelope indicates the limiting

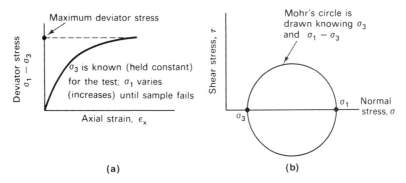

Figure 10-11   Triaxial results for one test: (a) stress–strain plot; (b) result of test on normal stress–shear stress coordinates.

Shear Test Results Plotted on Mohr's Circle Coordinates

Figure 10-12 Result of direct shear and triaxial test plotted on same coordinates: (a) general location of [tau] versus [sigma] point from direct shear test on cohesionless soil; (b) general location of [tau] versus [sigma] point from direct shear test on cohesive soil.

shear strength that a material will develop for a given normal stress. Since the strength or failure envelope is a boundary established from test results, it should be evident that it is physically impossible to achieve a stress combination whose coordinates plot above the boundary.

The same information can be obtained from a series of triaxial tests performed on a homogeneous soil. In each test the confining pressure σ_3 is different. This consequently effects the maximum axial stress σ_1 that develops at failure. The Mohr's circle test results would be as shown in Figure 10-14.

A curve that is tangent to all the Mohr's circles establishes the strength or failure envelope curve. The *point of tangency* to each circle establishes the combination of shear and normal stresses that act on the failure plane in the tested soil sample. These should be the same combinations of shear and normal stresses obtained from direct shear tests.

From reference to the Mohr's circle plot, it should be understood that the plane of failure does not necessarily occur on the plane where the shear stress is a maximum. Rather, it is the *combination* of shear and normal stress developing within the material that is critical. The combination that *is* critical relates to the slope or angle of the failure envelope curve. If the strength (failure) envelope is horizontal (parallel to the normal stress axis), the *maximum* shear stress indicated by the Mohr's circle is the shear stress on the failure plane. Where the envelope

$$\left[\sigma = \frac{\text{Normal loading during test}}{\text{Area of sample}} \right]$$

Figure 10-13 Results of direct shear tests on samples of a homogeneous soil.

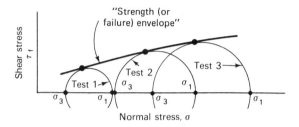

Figure 10-14 Results of triaxial test on samples of a homogeneous soil.

curve makes an angle with the horizontal axis, the shear stress on the failure plane is *less* than the maximum shear stress represented by a Mohr's circle. In soils, the condition of both the horizontal and the sloped strength-failure envelope exists. This is discussed further under the heading "Shearing Strength" later in this chapter.

Quite frequently in soil analysis, the Mohr's circle plot requires use of only the upper half of the circle, the lower half being considered redundant because it is a mirror image of the upper half. However, the entire circle is best shown when strength-failure envelopes are discussed so as to establish clearly the concept of boundaries for the nonfail and fail combination of stresses (see Fig. 10-15).

For strength conditions indicated by the Mohr's circle of Figure 10-15, it should be seen that an incipient failure situation develops on two different planes simultaneously. But when it is desired only to learn the combination of principal stresses that will cause failure or the magnitude of shear and normal stresses acting on the failure planes, as is usual, using only half of the Mohr's circle is sufficient.

SHEARING STRENGTH

Basic understanding of the shearing strength of cohesive and cohesionless soils can be obtained by reference to the results from triaxial or direct shear tests. A discussion relating to the more simple direct shear test is easiest to follow, and is presented first. The behavior described, and the explanation of the factors affecting the behavior, apply to triaxial conditions as well as to direct shear conditions. A discussion of triaxial testing and related results is presented later in this chapter.

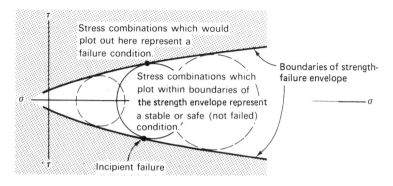

Figure 10-15 Concept of strength-failure envelope showing combination of stress representing failure and stable conditions.

Shearing Strength

Shearing Strength of Cohesionless Soil The results of a direct shear test performed on a dry cohesionless soil (e.g., a dry sand), where the normal load is held constant during the shearing process, are presented on stress–strain coordinates. Typical results are indicated in Figure 10-2.

The actual configuration of the stress–strain curve will be affected by the size and shape of the soil particles and by the density of the sample at the beginning of the test, as well as by the magnitude of the normal loading. A sample that is initially loose will develop a stress–strain curve as indicated in Figure 10-16a, whereas an initially dense sample will present a curve as shown in Figure 10-16b. The ultimate strength for samples whose only difference is the initial density will be the same. The difference in the behavior is explained by the factors that contribute to the shearing strength of dry cohesionless soil. Resistance to movement across the failure plane, and hence the shearing *strength,* is developed from friction that occurs between particles under the applied normal loading and to interlocking between particles. The extra shearing resistance for the initially dense sample (difference between peak strength and ultimate strength shown in Fig. 10-16b) is attributed to a greater degree of interlocking. This greater interlocking is overcome as shearing displacements increase, indicating that the initially dense sample loosens during shearing. This is verified by recording the thickness (or volume) of the sample during testing and observing that a thickness increase occurs. In other words, the void ratio of the initially dense sample increases during shearing. Conversely, the thickness of the initially loose sample decreases during testing, indicating a decrease in the void ratio. At the ultimate strength, after shearing movement, the final void ratio will be similar for the initially dense and loose materials, regardless of the initial void ratio. This final void ratio is referred to as the *critical void ratio.* Soils whose natural void ratios are above the critical void ratio will attempt to decrease in volume during shearing, whereas the reverse is true for soils whose natural void ratio is below the critical ratio (see Fig. 10-17).

If a series of shearing tests is performed on identical samples, but the normal loading that acts during shearing is different, the ultimate shearing resistances (and peak resistances if the soil is initially dense) will also be different. Greater shearing

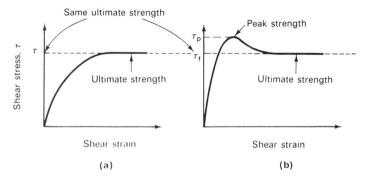

Figure 10-16 Comparison of shear test results as affected by soil density: (a) cohesionless soil, sample initially loose; (b) cohesionless soil, sample initially dense.

Figure 10-17 Effect of initial density on change in void ratio during shearing.

resistances, or shearing strengths, are obtained at higher normal loadings (see Fig. 10-18).

If the results of the series of direct shear tests are plotted on shear stress versus normal stress coordinates, as for a Mohr's circle analysis, a strength-failure envelope curve for the soil is obtained (see Fig. 10-19).

Through the range of normal stresses usually encountered in foundation problems, the plotted points of τ versus σ establish what is basically a straight line. The angle that the strength-failure envelope creates with a horizontal line is indicated as ϕ, the *angle of internal friction* for the soil. For dry cohesionless soils, the strength-failure envelope obtained from ultimate shear strength values is assumed

Figure 10-18 Effect of normal loading on shear strength of cohesionless soil.

Figure 10-19 Summary representing maximum shear strength versus applied normal stress for cohesionless soil.

Shearing Strength

TABLE 10-1 REPRESENTATIVE VALUES OF φ FOR COHESIONLESS SOILS

Soil type	Angle φ (degrees)	
	Ultimate	Peak
Sand and gravel mixture	33–36	40–50
Well-graded sand	32–35	40–50
Fine to medium sand	29–32	32–35
Silty sand	27–32	30–33
Silt (nonplastic)	26–30	30–35

to pass through the origin of coordinates. Thus, the relation of shearing strength to normal stress can be calculated from

$$\tan \phi = \frac{\tau}{\sigma}$$

or

$$\tau = \sigma \tan \phi \tag{10-1a}$$

If the peak values of shear strength are plotted, values of φ somewhat greater than obtained from the ultimate shear strength values will be obtained. Representative values for φ are presented in Table 10-1.

The value of φ (ultimate or peak) selected for use in practical soil or foundation problems should be related to the soil strains that are expected. If soil deformation will be limited, using the peak value for φ would be justified. Where deformations might be relatively great, ultimate values of φ should be used.

ILLUSTRATION 10-1. A sample of dry sand is tested in direct shear. A normal load equivalent to 2 ksf is imposed for the test. The shearing force applied to fail the sample is increased until shearing does occur. The shear stress at failure is 1350 psf. What is the angle of internal friction φ for the sand?

$$\tan \phi = \frac{1350 \text{ psf}}{2000 \text{ psf}} = 0.675$$

$$\phi = 34 \text{ deg} \pm$$

ILLUSTRATION 10-2.   A dry cohesionless soil is tested in a triaxial test to determine the angle of internal friction φ. A confining pressure equal to 1000 psf is used. The sample fails when the axial load causes a stress of 3200 psf. What is the value of φ?

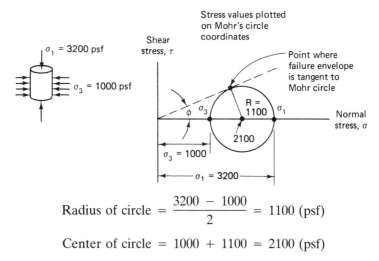

$$\text{Radius of circle} = \frac{3200 - 1000}{2} = 1100 \text{ (psf)}$$

$$\text{Center of circle} = 1000 + 1100 = 2100 \text{ (psf)}$$

From the Mohr's circle plot,

$$\sin \phi = \frac{1100 \text{ psf}}{2100 \text{ psf}} = 0.525$$

$$\phi = 31.5° \pm$$

If moisture is present in the soil samples during shearing, the subsequent plotting of ultimate shearing strength versus the applied normal stress does not present a failure envelope curve that passes through the origin. Rather, at zero normal stress, the failure envelope intersects the shear stress coordinate, as shown in Figure 10-20. This indicated "no load" shearing strength is referred to as *apparent cohesion,* a shear strength value attributed to factors other than friction developed from the normal stress. With damp cohesionless soils, the extra strength is due to compressive forces exerted on soil particles as a result of surface tensions where water menisci have formed between soil particles (as in capillary water). The extra shearing strength exists as long as the soil retains some moisture. The extra strength would be lost if the soil were to dry out or to become saturated or submerged. For

Figure 10-20   Results of shear tests on moist cohesionless soils indicate an "apparent cohesion" value.

saturated and submerged case, all voids are filled with water, and all water menisci are lost. For these reasons, the extra shear strength attributed to apparent cohesion generally is neglected in foundation studies.

Values of ϕ are not significantly affected when the soil is below a groundwater table or otherwise submerged. However, any hydrostatic pressure u that acts on a plane under analysis reduces the intergranular compressive stress (and will affect the soil shear strength). The resulting *effective stress* $\bar{\sigma}$(equal to $\sigma_t - u$; see Eq. 8-4) is utilized to obtain a preferred *general* expression for the shear strength of a cohesionless soil, whereby

$$\tau = (\sigma_t - u) \tan \phi = \bar{\sigma} \tan \phi \qquad (10\text{-}1b)$$

where σ_t is the total stress acting at a point. When u is zero, $\bar{\sigma}$ equals σ_t and Equation 10-1a, derived for the case of a dry cohesionless soil, results.

ILLUSTRATION 10-3. (a) Samples taken from a uniform deposit of granular soil are found to have a unit weight of 19.6 kN/m³ and an angle of internal friction of 35°. What is the shearing strength of the soil on a horizontal plane at a point 4 m below the ground surface?

At a depth of 4 m, the soil overburden pressure, or normal stress, is

$$(19.6 \text{ kN/m}^3) \ (4\text{m}) = 78.4 \text{ kN/m}^2 = \sigma \text{ on horizontal plane}$$

The shearing resistance that can be developed is

$$\tau = \sigma \tan \phi = (78.4 \text{ kN/m}^2)(\tan 35°)$$

$$= 54.9 \text{ kN/m}^2$$

(b) A proposed structure will cause the vertical stress to increase by 60 kN/m² at the 4-m depth. Assume that the weight of the structure also causes the shearing stress to increase to 52 kN/m² on a horizontal plane at this depth. Does this shearing stress exceed the shearing strength of the soil?

The total vertical pressure due to the structure and soil overburden is

$$60 \text{ kN/m}^2 + 78.4 \text{ kN/m}^2 \text{ overburden pressure} = 138.4 \text{ kN/m}^2$$

The shearing strength that can be developed by the soil at this depth is

$$\tau = (138.4 \text{ kN/m}^2)(\tan 35°) = 96.9 \text{ kN/m}^2$$

This would indicate that the shear strength of the soil is greater than the developed shear stress; therefore, a shear failure does not occur (96.9 kN/m² > 52 kN/m²).

If the water table rose to the ground surface, the effective soil overburden pressure would be reduced to about

$$(\tfrac{1}{2} \times 19.6 \text{ kN/m}^3)(4\text{m}) = 39.2 \text{ kN/m}^2$$

[This value represents the effective vertical stress, i.e., $\bar{\sigma} = \sigma_t - u = \gamma_{sub}Z = (\gamma_t - \gamma_w)Z$.]

The total vertical stress would be

$$39.2 \text{ kN/m}^2 + 60 \text{ kN/m}^2 = 99.2 \text{ kN/m}^2$$

The shear strength available is

$$\tau = (99.2 \text{ kN/m}^2)(\tan 35°) = 69.46 \text{ kN/m}^2$$

This is still greater than the shear stress resulting from the loading conditions i.e., $69.46 \text{ kN/m}^2 > 52 \text{ kN/m}^2$.

The preceding discussion has indicated that the shearing strength that can develop is directly proportional to the effective normal stress that acts on the plane under analysis. For most practical problems, the effective stress in cohesionless soil is calculated by using the effective overburden weight plus any stress increase created by structural loading. However, if the soil is saturated, or nearly so, there is the possibility that the stress resulting from loads newly applied onto the soil mass will not result in a related increase to the effective stress acting within the soil. This is the situation of an excess hydrostatic pressure condition developing (pore water in the soil voids becomes subject to a pressure greater than the normal hydrostatic, as discussed in the explanation of the consolidation process, Chapter 9). With this situation, there is the potential danger that the shearing stress resulting from the external loading may increase faster than the shearing strength (which is controlled by the effective stress), and a shear failure may occur. Fortunately, cohesionless soils have relatively high rates of permeability that under most conditions permit rapid drainage of pore water when new loadings and stresses are imposed onto the soil mass. The danger of excess hydrostatic, or excess pore pressure, conditions in cohesionless soils and possible shear failures are generally limited to the situation where loose saturated material is exposed to vibratory, instantaneous, or shock loading, such as from explosives, earthquakes, and traveling trains. The occurrence of loss of strength under these conditions is called *liquefaction*, for the soil momentarily liquifies and tends to behave as a dense fluid. Generally, for sandy soils, the number of vibrations or shock waves required for liquefaction to occur increases as the soil density increases, but the presence of fine-grained material decreases the susceptibility to liquefaction. The soils found most susceptible to liquefaction are the saturated and loose fine to medium sands having a uniform particle-size range.

Approximating Values of φ from Boring Data   Soil borings for subsurface investigations are frequently sized so that soil samples can be obtained with a "standard" two-inch-diameter split spoon soil sampler. Soil-boring and sampling procedures are discussed in Chapter 11. With the split spoon sampler, the blow-count required to drive the sampler into undisturbed soil is recorded for all samples obtained. The samples recovered with this equipment are considered to be disturbed and are unsuitable for performing strength tests. Obtaining undisturbed samples of cohesionless soil is generally difficult under many existing subsurface conditions and may require the use of large-diameter borings and special soil samplers. Because of the widespread usage of the two-inch sampler (partially because of the relative

TABLE 10-2 APPROXIMATE RELATION BETWEEN N^* AND ϕ FOR COHESIONLESS SOIL

Value of N^*	Relative condition of soil	Approximate value of ϕ
10	Loose	30° ±
20	Medium dense	32° ±
30	Medium dense to dense	35° ±
40	Dense	38° ±
50	Dense to very dense	40° ±
60	Very dense	42° ±

*In the so-called standard penetration test, N is the number of blows required to drive a standard 2-in. outside diameter split barrel soil sampler 12 inches into undisturbed soil with a 140-lb. weight falling 30 inches. For further information on the standard penetration test, refer to Chapter 11.

economy) correlations between the blow-count N from the standard penetration test and the angle of internal friction have been developed. These correlations are presented in Table 10-2. Due to the generalized nature of the correlation, any application of such data to final foundation designs should be made with caution.

Shearing Strength of Clay Soils The shearing strength that a clay deposit possesses is related to the type of clay mineral and the water content but, very importantly, also to the effective stress or consolidation pressure to which the soil has been subjected in its past (the soil's stress history). The change that is possible in a clay's shear strength (such as if loading conditions change because of the weight of a new structure) is affected by these just-mentioned factors but also by the pore water drainage that can occur as shearing deformations tend to occur. Consideration of drainage is of practical importance, because many clays in their natural condition are close to full saturation, and the low permeability of these soils tends to inhibit changes in pore water content that try to occur during shearing.[2]

The significance of effective stress and drainage during shearing can be explained by reference to a series of shearing tests made on fully saturated clays. Practically, the discussion also applies to nearly saturated clays.

Assume that the soil for all the test samples is obtained from one location in a homogeneous, isotropic, normally consolidated clay deposit. All properties of all samples to be tested are identical (see Fig. 10-21). Samples are to be tested in direct shear.

In each series of direct shear tests, each test sample will have a different normal load applied during shearing to determine the effect. The normal loads are greater than the effective overburden (or consolidation) pressure.

---

[2]Strictly speaking, stress history and drainage factors can also affect the shearing properties of a cohesionless soil, although shape and size distribution of particles have very considerable influence. A granular soil that had been subjected to high effective stresses or high overburden pressures in its past would be dense and capable of developing a peak strength, as shown in Figure 10-16 (b). The prevention of pore water drainage during shearing of a saturated soil would lessen the shearing strength, but under most practical conditions there are no restrictions on drainage because of the relatively high permeability.

Ground surface

Uniform deposit of
clay soil, homogeneous
and isotropic.
Unit weight = γ

Depth = Z

This clay deposit is normally
consolidated. The existing
soil over-burden pressure
represents the maximum
pressure that the soil has
been subjected to in its
history.

Overburden pressure
on soil samples = γZ

Source of all
test samples.

Figure 10-21 Source of samples for analysis of shear strength of clay soils.

For the first series of tests, no drainage of pore water is permitted, either
when the normal load is applied or during shearing. This "no drainage" control
can be achieved by having the sample wrapped in a thin, tight, impermeable
membrane when it is placed in the shearing apparatus. The normal load is applied
just prior to beginning the shearing process. Shearing is then completed relatively
quickly. These test conditions are referred to as *unconsolidated–undrained* (U–U)
shear tests, because the samples are not permitted the time or the drainage necessary to consolidate to the pressure exerted by the normal loading and no drainage
or volume change is permitted during the shearing process. For this condition,
excess pore water pressures develop in the samples during shearing. Results for
this series of tests are shown in Figure 10-22. For the U–U conditions, the shearing
strengths for all samples are the same, since the effective stress within each sample
has not changed from the condition that existed when the soil was in the ground.
Even though different normal loads are applied during shearing, consolidation to
the normal load pressure can only occur if pore water is permitted to drain from
the sample. Since drainage and consolidation cannot occur, the internal effective

$N_c > N_b > N_a$ (S_c, S_b, S_a represent ultimate shearing forces)

Shear stress, τ
$\left[\tau = \dfrac{S}{A} \right]$

Shear intercept
is the value of
cohesion, c

Failure
envelope

Area, A, is cross-
sectional area of
sample upon which
the normal load, N, acts.

σ_a σ_b σ_c

Normal stress, σ
$\left[\sigma = \dfrac{N}{A} \right]$

Figure 10-22 Shear strength results for unconsolidated–undrained (U–U) tests.

Shearing Strength

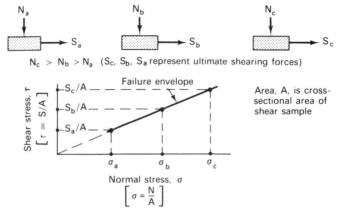

Figure 10-23   Shear strength results for consolidated–undrained (C–U) tests.

stresses are the same for each of the samples, and, therefore, the shearing strengths will remain the same.

For the second series of tests, different normal loads are applied to each test sample and full consolidation to the respective new normal load is permitted. After full consolidation has taken place so that the effective stress acting is equal to the applied normal loading, the samples are wrapped in the impermeable membrane (so that no further drainage or volume change can occur) and are placed in the shearing apparatus. Shearing is performed quickly. These test conditions are referred to as *consolidated–undrained* (C–U), indicating that the samples are consolidated to their respective normal load prior to shearing but that during shearing

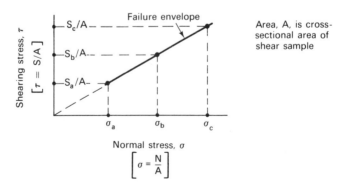

Figure 10-24   Shear strength results for consolidated–drained (C–D) tests.

Shear Strength Theory   Chap. 10

Figure 10-25 Qualitative comparison of shear strength results for U–U, C–U, and C–D tests.

no drainage or volume change is permitted. For this condition, excess pore water pressures develop in the sample during shearing, but they are not as great as those that occur in the U–U test. Results for such a series of tests are shown in Figure 10-23. The increase in shearing strength (compared to the U–U conditions) is the result of the increased effective pressure to which the test samples have been consolidated.

For the third series of tests, the samples are fully consolidated to the normal loads that will be applied during the shearing test. However, in this series, shearing will take place very slowly, and drainage and volume changes *are permitted* during the shearing process. These test conditions are referred to as *consolidated–drained* (C–D) conditions. No excess pore water pressures develop in the soil during shearing. Results for such a series of tests are shown in Figure 10-24.

The results from the three series of tests are presented together in Figure 10-25. A difference in the C–D and C–U curves results because of a normally consolidated soil's tendency to undergo volume decrease during shearing. If volume change is prevented, as in the undrained test, excess pore pressures are developed, with a subsequent reduction in the effective stress and shear strength.

As for tests on cohesionless soils, the slope of the τ versus σ curve is designated by the angle ϕ.

The stress represented by point A in Figure 10-25 is approximately the value of the effective stress σ_{v_c} that acted on the soil in its natural subsurface location. If the soil has been normally consolidated, σ_{v_c} is equal to the soil overburden pressure ($\sigma_{v_c} = \gamma Z$; see Fig. 10-21).

If C–U or C–D tests were performed and the applied normal loading was less than σ_{v_c}, the plotted shear strength values would fall close to the failure envelope curve obtained for the U–U test series.

The strength envelope curves of Figures 10-22, 10-23, 10-24, and 10-25 indicate the total stress condition existing on the shear failure plane (i.e., the total normal stress and related soil shearing resistance). Recall that the total normal stress represents the combined influence of effective stress $\bar{\sigma}$ and neutral stress u (the latter term indicating stress resulting from pore water pressure), or

$$\sigma_t = \bar{\sigma} + u \qquad \text{(from Eq. 8-4)}$$

A rearrangement gives

$$\bar{\sigma} = \sigma_t - u$$

Shearing Strength

(a)

(b)

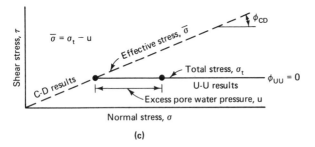

(c)

Figure 10-26 Relationship between effective stress, total stress, and pore water pressure: (a) C–D shear test results; (b) C–U shear test results; (c) U–U shear test results.

Values on the strength envelope from the consolidated–drained (C–D) test series indicate effective stress as well as total stress, since no excess pore water pressure existed during the shearing process. For any C–U or U–U–type test, the magnitude of excess pore water pressure existing in the soil at shear failure is indicated from the relationship between the C–D and C–U envelopes or the C–D and U–U envelopes; at points of similar shear strength, the difference in the normal pressures shown on the C–D and C–U curves, or the C–D and U–U curves, represents the excess pore water pressure (see Fig. 10-26).

ILLUSTRATION 10-4. To determine the strength properties of a clay soil, a series of consolidated–undrained direct shear tests is performed. For the first test, the normal pressure is 750 psf and the sample fails when the shear stress is 450 psf. The second sample is tested under a normal load of 1500 psf, and failure occurs when the shear stress is 500 psf. A third sample is tested under a normal loading of 2500 psf, and failure occurs when the shear stress is 800 psf. From these data, estimate the cohesion of the soil in the in situ condition and the value of ϕ_{CU}.

A problem of this type frequently is best solved graphically.

1. Locate test data on a scaled plot.
2. Draw a sloped failure envelope line to estimate ϕ_{CU}.
3. For a test having a low normal (compressive) pressure, assume that the pressure is less than σ_{v_c}, and draw a horizontal failure envelope line through it to obtain the value of in situ cohesion.
4. The intersection of sloped and horizontal failure envelope lines gives a normal pressure value that is approximately the value of σ_{v_c} (the maximum past overburden stress).

From the scaled plot, $c = 450$ psf, $\phi_{CU} = 17° \pm$

In many practical soils problems involving clays, applied structural loads result in excess pore pressures' being developed. Some drainage does occur, but it is restricted because of the low permeability of the soil. Consequently, the actual shearing conditions that are developed fall somewhere between the U–U and the C–D case. In many soil and foundation design problems, the U–U strength is used where the initial period of loading is critical, since it is realized that the shear strength will become greater (increase) and safer with time as excess pore water drainage occurs.

These shear test results also indicate that it is possible to improve the shear strength of clay soils by consolidation, provided that time is available for permitting the necessary pore water drainage to take place. In effect, consolidation results in decreasing the water content of the clay and obtaining a related increase in shear strength, as indicated by Figure 10-27.

Figure 10-27 Change in strength for a cohesive soil as water content changes.

Shearing Strength

Shear Strength of Clay Related to Triaxial Testing   Although the direct shear test is a convenient reference for introducing the factors affecting the shearing strength of clay soils, the triaxial compression test is the method most typically used in the laboratory for determining soil shearing strength properties. Recall from the early sections of this chapter that the triaxial compression test subjects the soil sample to a three-dimensional state of compression (i.e., compressive stresses act in the three orthogonal directions), thereby causing shear stresses to develop within the sample (see Fig. 10-28; also refer to Fig. 10-4).

   The following discussion relates to clay soil as defined by Figure 10-21; that is, the clay soil is fully saturated and the deposit from which the test sample is

Figure 10-28   Triaxial compression test representations: (a) schematic diagram of test apparatus; (b) state of stress on an incremental element in the soil sample.

Shear Strength Theory   Chap. 10

Note: $\sigma_{3c} > \sigma_{3b} > \sigma_{3a}$

Figure 10-29 Results of a series of triaxial tests performed on identical soil samples, as used for determining the strength envelope for the soil.

obtained is a *normally consolidated* deposit (i.e., the existing soil overburden and lateral pressures represent the maximum pressures the soil has been subjected to in its history as part of the deposit).

The strength (failure) envelope for a soil can be determined by performing the triaxial test on separate but identical samples; each test uses a different confining pressure (see Fig. 10-29). As explained in Chapter 7, it has been found adequate to work with only the σ_3 and σ_1 values on the Mohr's circle coordinates. In Figure 10-29, the value of σ_3 is the all-around confining pressure or stress acting on the soil sample at the start of the test, and σ_1 is the *measured* vertical (axial) stress that subsequently causes the soil sample to shear. If $\sigma_{3c} > \sigma_{3b} > \sigma_{3a}$, it will be found that $\sigma_{1c} > \sigma_{1b} > \sigma_{1a}$.

The typical triaxial equipment depicted by Figure 10-28a includes tubing lines connected to the porous stones positioned on the top and bottom of the soil sample; these lines can be utilized to drain pore (voids) water from the sample or to measure or control or vary the pore water pressure existing within the soil sample during the test procedure.

In the following descriptions, the magnitudes of the σ_3 and σ_1 test pressures are *greater* than the σ_3 and σ_1 stresses that acted on the soil sample in situ (in the ground).

For the consolidated–drained (C–D) test, the confining pressure is imposed onto the test sample and the porous stone drain lines are left open to enable soil pore water to escape from the soil as the confining pressure squeezes the sample (i.e., consolidates it). After the sample is fully consolidated by the confining pressure (identified as the condition when equilibrium for the imposed loading is reached, whereby no further pore water drains), the axial force is slowly applied. The drain

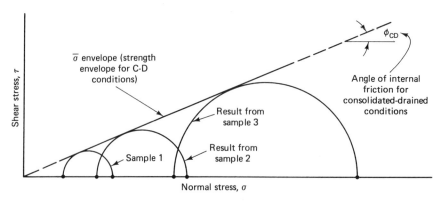

Figure 10-30 Triaxial results from consolidated–drained (C–D) tests and related strength envelope.

lines remain open as the axial force increases, permitting additional drainage of sample pore water to occur: since additional compression of the sample tends to occur because of the increasing (new) vertical stress, the continuous escape of pore water must be permitted if the fully consolidated (no excess pore water pressure) condition is to be satisfied. The axial and confining pressure acting when the soil sample shears provides the values to plot one Mohr's circle for the C–D case. A series of C–D triaxial tests on identical soil samples provides the data for determining the *effective stress*, $\bar{\sigma}$, envelope curve, as indicated in Figure 10-30.

In the consolidated–undrained (C–U) test, the soil sample in the triaxial apparatus is fully consolidated to the all-around confining pressure, σ_3, by permitting the pore pressure drain lines to remain open (as for the C–D test). Then the drain lines are closed and the axial load is imposed. Pressure gages on the drain lines permit measurements of the pore water pressure developing in the sample as the axial load is applied. The increasing axial force acting on the soil sample tends to cause sample compression (i.e., further consolidation), but since the pore water is now prevented from escaping because the drain lines are closed, an "excess pore water pressure" develops. The pore water pressure continues to increase in relation to the increase in axial loading. When the soil sample shears, the axial load, the internal pore water pressure, and the confining pressure are known (measured and recorded). The axial and confining pressures indicated by the triaxial gages represents the total axial and confining stresses acting on the soil sample. A total stress minus the measured pore water pressure provides the value of interparticle, or effective, stress acting within the soil sample at the time of failure[3]:

$$\bar{\sigma} = \sigma_t - u$$

[3]This equation helps clarify the phrase "excess pore water pressure." That term refers to the magnitude of pressure developed in the void space water that is above the magnitude of the interparticle pressure that acts. The occurrence is similar to the undergraduate strength of materials problem, where a structural member composed of two different materials carries a compressive load; the portion of the total load carried by each material relates to the stress–strain properties or rigidity of the material (the least deformable or more rigid material supports more than its share of the total load).

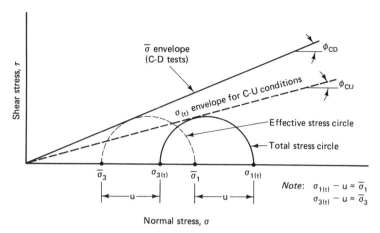

Figure 10-31 Results from consolidated–undrained (C–U) triaxial test and related strength envelope.

The test results are presented on the Mohr's circle coordinates, as shown by Figure 10-31. As for the C–D test, a series of tests performed on identical samples but at different confining pressures permits a strength envelope to be obtained.

In the performance of the unconsolidated–undrained (U–U) test, the soil sample is assembled in the triaxial apparatus and the pore water drain lines are closed. The confining pressure, σ_3, is applied and quickly followed by application of the axial load. The imposed pressures act to compress the soil sample (i.e., force the soil particles closer together), but because the pore water drains are closed, the trapped pore water prevents a decrease in sample volume from occurring. The trapped pore water has prevented the sample from consolidating. The pressure gages on the pore water drain lines will show increasing pore water pressure as the axial force increases. The values indicated by the triaxial gages for the confining pressure, σ_3, and axial stress, σ_1, represent the total pressure or stress internal to the soil sample. The effective stress, or intergranular pressure, when the sample shears is determined by deducting the pore water pressure from the total pressure (as for the C–U test), as shown in Figure 10-32a, or

$$\bar{\sigma} = \sigma_t - u$$

A series of tests on identical samples, but at differing confining pressures, σ_3, provides the data to obtain the strength envelope for the U–U case as shown in Figure 10-32b. Note that the Mohr's circles will be the same for all samples but will be positioned horizontally in accord with the σ_3 value used to perform the test. Even though the σ_3 and σ_1 values that cause the sample to shear are different for each of the tests, the internal *shear strength* of the soil remains the same because the internal conditions remained the same (the presence and quantity of pore water, the sample void ratio, and the particles spacing will not change when trapped pore water prevents a volume decrease).

Somewhat different occurrences result when the confining pressure applied in the triaxial test is *less than* the confining pressure that existed when the soil was

Shearing Strength

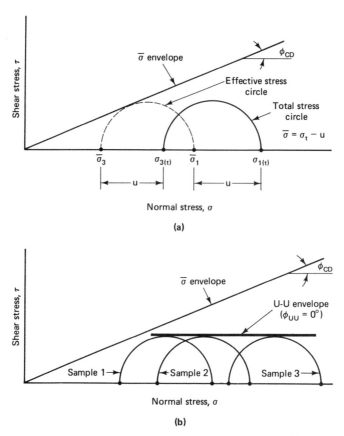

Figure 10-32 Unconsolidated-undrained (U–U) triaxial test data: (a) relationship between total stress, effective stress, and pore water pressure; (b) results of a series of tests on identical soil samples provides Mohr's circle of equal size but transposed laterally.

in situ (for this occurrence, the soil is considered overconsolidated in regard to the test conditions). When the test confining pressures *exceed* the in situ pressures, the sample volume tends to *reduce* during testing; conversely, the soil sample tends to *expand* during testing when the confining pressure is *less than* the in situ pressure. If an overconsolidated sample is prevented from taking in water during testing as the sample attempts to expand (the triaxial drain lines are closed), a negative pore water pressure develops in the soil void spaces (a condition similar to the effects of capillary tension) and the relationship between total and effective stress becomes

$$\overline{\sigma} = \sigma_t - (-u) = \sigma_t + u$$

The results plotted on the Mohr's circle coordinates are shown in Figure 10-33.

In the natural (in situ) condition, overconsolidated clay soils will tend to undergo expansion during some types of construction activity, such as excavation work, and negative pore water pressures will develop within the soil. A high soil shear strength results, as indicated by the Mohr's circle for the initial strength

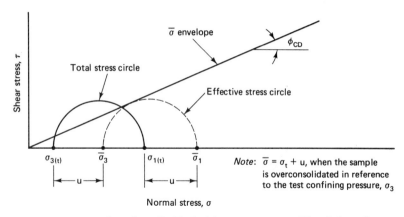

Figure 10-33 Data from U–U triaxial test on overconsolidated clay soil.

condition (Fig. 10-33). However, natural water, which is or becomes present, will tend to be drawn into the clay voids. Eventually, as the negative pore pressures vanish, the soil shear strength decreases toward the value indicated by the effective stress envelope (see Fig. 10-34).

Where the U–U strength is required to be known for analysis of a soil or foundation study, it is convenient to determine the shearing strength from unconfined compression tests. As explained earlier in this chapter, the unconfined compression test is a triaxial test where the confining pressure acting on the sample is zero. This test is quick and easy to perform. The axial stress required to fail the tested soil is designated q_u. The result of an unconfined compression test can be plotted on τ versus σ coordinates, as shown in Figure 10-35. The cohesion, or shear strength, is simply one-half the unconfined axial stress:

$$c = \tfrac{1}{2}q_u \qquad (10\text{-}2)$$

Some clay deposits have developed cracks or fissures (sometimes called *slickensides*). This condition may be the result of desiccation, seismic effects, or other factors. If tested in unconfined compression, shear failure along the slickensides

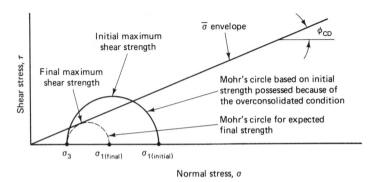

Figure 10-34 Mohr's circles illustrating expected change in strength for overconsolidated clay when soil water content increases.

Shearing Strength

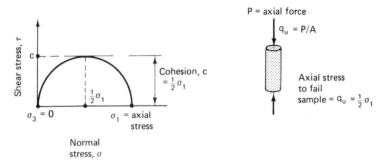

Figure 10-35 Unconfined compression test data used to determine cohesion c.

could give a low and misleading indication of the strength of soil confined in the natural deposit. For such material, a triaxial test is preferred.

Approximating Values of Cohesion from Boring Data Because of the widespread use of the standard penetration test for making soil borings, approximate relationships between values of cohesion and N have been developed. Values are presented in Table 10-3. Due to the approximate nature of the values, the data should be applied with caution.

TABLE 10-3 APPROXIMATE RELATION BETWEEN N^* AND COHESION OF CLAYS

Value of N^*	Relative condition of soil	Approximate value of cohesion, c	
		psf	kN/m²
2–4	Soft	250–500	12–24
4–8	Medium	500–1000	24–48
8–15	Stiff	1000–2000	48–96
15–30	Very stiff	2000–4000	96–190
above 30	Hard	above 4000	above 190

*N, the standard penetration test, is the number of blows required to drive a standard 2-in. outside diameter soil sampler 12 inches into undisturbed soil with a 140-pound weight falling 30 inches. For additional information on the standard penetration test, refer to Chapter 11.

Shear Strength of Mixed Soils Mixtures of clay and granular soils in nature are not unusual. Material that is predominantly clay, in which all granular particles are surrounded by clay materials, will behave essentially as a clay. Mixtures that are predominantly granular soil with limited clay will present a sloped failure envelope curve on a τ versus σ plot, but the intercept is on the τ axis, as shown in Figure 10-36. The relationship of shear strength to normal stress can be expressed as

$$\tau = c + \bar{\sigma} \tan \phi \qquad (10\text{-}3)$$

For such soils, the limitations on permeability and drainage should not be overlooked when considering new loadings that are applied to the soil mass. Excess

Figure 10-36 Typical plot of τ versus σ for mixed soils.

pore pressures may develop and only part of the newly applied stress may represent effective stress, with a subsequent lag in the development of shear strength.

Position of Failure Plane Related to Angle ϕ   Homogeneous soils stressed to failure during a triaxial test or unconfined compression test typically develop a distinct plane of failure, as indicated in Figure 10-37a. Applying the analysis for stress at a point (Fig. 10-37b and c), a practical relationship between the angle of internal friction, ϕ, and the position of the failure plane is obtained:

$$\phi + 90° + (180 - 2\theta) = 180°, \text{ the sum of the interior}$$

$$\text{angles in a triangle}$$

$$\phi + 90° = 2\theta \tag{10-4}$$

$$\theta = \frac{90° + \phi}{2}$$

$$\theta = \left(45 + \frac{\phi}{2}\right) \text{deg}$$

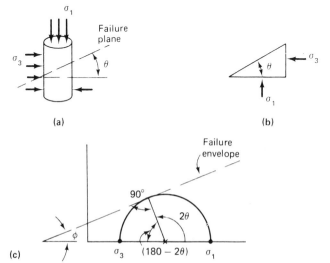

Figure 10-37 Mohr's circle analysis to relate ϕ and position of failure plane: (a) failure plane on tested sample; (b) incremental element at failure plane; (c) Mohr's circle.

Shearing Strength

PROBLEMS

10-1. A sample of dry sand is tested in direct shear. Under an applied normal stress of 5000 psf, the sample fails when the shear stress reaches 3000 psf. What is the angle of internal friction for this soil?

10-2. A sand sample is subjected to direct shear testing at its normal (in situ) water content. Two tests are performed. For one of the tests, the sample shears at a stress of 3000 psf when the normal stress is 4000 psf. In the second test, the sample shears at a stress of 4000 psf when the normal stress is 6000 psf. From these data, determine the value of the "apparent cohesion" and the corresponding angle of internal friction.

10-3. A sand sample in a triaxial test failed when the confining stress (minor principal stress) was 1000 psf and the axial stress (major principal stress) was 4000 psf. What is the angle of internal friction, ϕ, for this soil?

10-4. A sand is known to have an angle of internal friction, ϕ, equal to 35°. What is the maximum major principal stress that the soil can withstand when the minor principal stress is 20 psi?

10-5. The soil in a granular deposit has an angle of internal friction equal to 35°. At a point in the soil mass where the lateral pressure (minor principal stress) is 1000 psf, what maximum vertical pressure (major principal stress) can be applied?

10-6. Computations indicate that a planned building loading will cause the principal stresses in the soil at a point beneath the building to increase to total values of 4500 psf and 1500 psf (major and minor principal stresses, respectively). If the soil is a sand with an angle of internal friction equal to 35°, will the indicated stresses cause a shear failure at the point?

10-7. Samples of a dry sand are to be tested in a direct shear and a triaxial test. In the triaxial test, the sample fails when the major and minor principal stresses are 140 psi and 40 psi, respectively. What shear strength would be expected in the direct shear test when the normal loading is equal to a stress of 5000 psf?

10-8. A clay soil is subjected to a triaxial test under unconsolidated–undrained (U–U) conditions. At failure, the major and minor principal stresses are 3000 psf and 1000 psf, respectively.

   (a) What is the cohesion for this soil?

   (b) If this soil were subjected to an unconfined compression test, what axial load would result at failure?

10-9. A clay soil has a cohesion of 800 psf. How could the strength of this soil be increased?

10-10. A mixed soil is found to possess a unit cohesion of 500 psf and an angle of internal friction of 30°. What shear strength is expected at a point where the normal stress is 1500 psf?

10-11. A triaxial test is performed on a normally consolidated clay. The sample is further consolidated to the test all-around confining pressure prior to application of the axial load. The axial force is then applied very slowly. The equipment pore pressure lines remain open so that drainage of soil pore water can occur during the test. (The described conditions outline the procedure for a consolidated–drained type test.) The sample fails (shears) when the σ_3 pressure is 21 kN/m² and the σ_1 value is 61 kN/m². From the data, determine the angle of internal friction for the effective stress strength (failure) envelope (that is, determine ϕ_{CD}).

10-12. A normally consolidated clay sample is subject to a triaxial test where pore water pressure measurements are made. A consolidated–undrained type of test is performed. The sample fails (shears) when the total all-around confining pressure is 45 kN/m² and the total axial pressure is 97 kN/m². At failure, the recorded pore water pressure is 20 kN/m². Determine the angle of internal friction ϕ_{CD} for the effective stress strength envelope.

chapter *11*

Site Investigations
Purpose and Methods

Site investigation refers to the procedure of determining surface and subsurface conditions in an area of proposed construction. Surface and subsurface features may influence *what* can be built and will directly affect the design and construction procedures relating to *how* a structure is built.

Information on surface conditions is necessary for planning construction techniques. Surface topography may affect access to the site with necessary construction equipment, including the ability of equipment to work on and travel across the area. The thickness of vegetation, including the density and height of trees, affects the ease or difficulty associated with preparing a site for construction. Disposal of removed surface material may be a problem, particularly in urban areas. If a condition of surface water develops at times, its presence may hinder construction operations or affect the use of the site after construction. Other factors that could affect construction procedures or postconstruction use of an area include availability of water, availability of electrical power, the proximity to major transportation routes, and environmental protection regulations of various government agencies.

The land drainage pattern, a surface consideration but also partially a subsurface feature, is important, for it might affect construction. A finished grading pattern must be planned so that it does not harm the original areal pattern or cause other environmental changes.

Information on subsurface conditions existing at a site is a critical requirement. It is this information that is used to plan and design a structure's foundations and other below-ground work. Construction techniques are planned with the help of data on subsurface conditions. The possible need for dewatering will be revealed by the subsurface investigation. Information necessary to plan and design shoring or bracing of excavations for foundations and pipe trenches is obtained from such explorations. If the construction site is underlain by varying soil conditions, the explorations will be used to indicate "better" areas. For projects where there is flexibility in locating structures, considerable savings in foundation costs may be realized by constructing in the "better soil" areas.

In many locations, information about the area is frequently available in the form of maps showing surface topopgraphy and maps and literature that provide general information on subsurface soil or rock conditions. Aerial photographs can also offer useful data on subsurface conditions.

Though maps and aerial photographs of an area may provide much useful information about soil and rock conditions existing at a site, virtually all major construction projects will have on-site subsurface explorations performed in order to obtain the *detailed* information on soil types and properties necessary for designing foundations and for planning construction activities. Most typically, such information is obtained through the use of borings or test pits or by utilizing geophysical investigative methods. Properly used, these procedures are capable of giving a reliable definition of the type and extent of soil strata underlying an area. Where physical properties of the subsurface soil must be known, soil samples from appropriate depths can be obtained for laboratory testing. Alternatively, in-place testing of soil in its natural location is frequently possible.

These methods of subsurface investigation are also used in exploring for sources of soil fill and for checking material in borrow pit areas.

Frequently, the overall reliability of information obtained from a subsurface investigation is related to the extent of the work performed; the more borings and test pits, or the more geophysical lines run, the greater the detail. The availability of information reduces the need for interpolating between locations of known conditions.

Accurate preplanning of a subsurface exploration program can be difficult to do properly. The *depth* of borings or test pits considered necessary or adequate for design and planning should relate to the types and properties of earth materials revealed by the investigation as well as to the size and type of structure that is planned. The *number* of borings, test pits, or geophysical lines that will be necessary relates to the variation in conditions. A site underlain by uniform conditions normally requires a less extensive investigation than one underlain by highly variable conditions. It is not unusual to have to plan an exploration program as it progresses, with information as it becomes available determining the need for additional work.

MAPS AND AERIAL PHOTOGRAPHS AS SOURCES OF INFORMATION

Information on surface and subsurface conditions in an area is useful to the construction and engineering profession and is frequently present in the form of available maps. In the United States, such sources include U.S. Geological Survey topographic maps, U.S. Department of Agriculture soil conservation maps, and

Figure 11-1 U.S. Geological Survey topographic map (partial section of Cleveland-New York quadrangle). (Note: These maps are printed in color.)

state geologic (rock or soil) maps. Many other areas of the world have similar maps available.

Aerial photographs are also capable of providing considerable information about an area, particularly data on surface conditions and land forms that are not clarified on maps or detectable from ground observations. Aerial photographs frequently serve as the basis for topographic and soil maps. Available sources include the governmental agencies responsible for developing maps, other municipal governments or agencies that have aerial photographs from construction or tax-mapping projects, and private firms that take the aerial photographs and provide consulting services in photogrammetry.

U.S. Geological Survey Topographic Quadrangle Maps These maps provide information on surface features and topography. Included on these maps are elevation contours, bodies of water and water courses, indication of areas covered by forests or other vegetation, and man-made features such as buildings, roads, dams and reservoirs, railroads, power lines, airports, harbor development, military bases, and park preserves. Study of contour elevations and indicated land

Figure 11-2 U.S. Department of Agriculture soil conservation map showing coded soil categories (partial section from southern Herkimer County, N.Y.)

Maps and Aerial Photographs as Sources of Information

Figure 11-3 (a) U.S. Geological Survey geologic quadrangle map (section from Bloomsbury, New Jersey, quadrangle). (Note: These maps are printed in color.)

forms on these maps can relate the geology of subsoil formation and character. These maps are very useful for evaluating the effects that topography and drainage will have on an area. An illustration of a USGS map is shown in Figure 11-1.

U.S. Department of Agriculture Soil Conservation Maps
These maps provide information on surficial soils existing in an area. The information usually

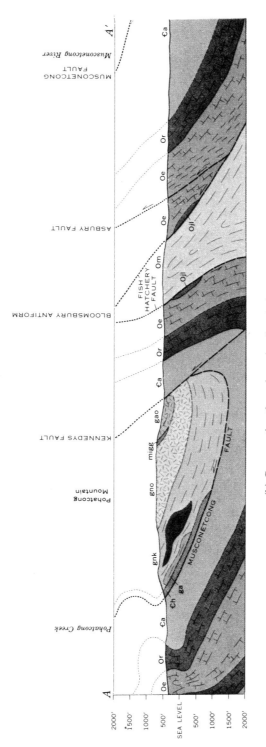

(b) Cross-section through section line A-A.

represents conditions to a depth of five or six feet (1.5–2 m). A coded typing is used to indicate different soil categories on the map. In literature accompanying the maps, various properties and possible uses of the soils are described. Included is the application for construction purposes; AASHTO and Unified Soil Classifications are given. General suitability of the various soils for embankment and highway base course materials, compaction characteristics, and permeabilities are also provided. An illustration of a soil conservation map is shown in Figure 11-2.

Geologic Maps   These maps indicate the rock types underlying an area. Frequently, geologic maps are accompanied by descriptive papers that complement the actual map. Information on the extent of soil cover overlying the rock and general physical properties of the soil cover and the rock, and data on natural resources such as oil, gas, and commercial minerals are usually included. Developers of geologic maps frequently include state-level governmental agencies. Figure 11-3 provides an illustration of a geologic map.

Aerial Photographs   Air-photo interpretation is the method of providing information on subsurface conditions by relating landform development and plant growth to geology. Applied to the building design and construction profession, air photos have particular value in their ability to provide detailed geologic information over a relatively large area and, as a result, can detect conditions that are difficult to observe or evaluate properly from a surface investigation. Illustrations of such special information include the observation of sinkhole cavities in areas underlain by limestone formations, occurrence of an area affected by landslides, past meanderings of existing rivers and probable new locations, presence and extent of glacially deposited landforms (such as drumlins, deltas, kettles), changes in beach areas and offshore deposits (such as sandbars), and land drainage patterns.

Not to be overlooked are the benefits of an aerial reconnaissance. A trained observer, or for that matter an experienced designer or constructor, should be capable of detecting items of land formation that can have an effect on design or construction from the view offered by a low and slow flight over a planned construction site. The disadvantage of a flight compared to aerial photographs is that no pictorial record remains for referral in future discussions. Figure 11-4 provides an example of information shown on aerial photographs.

BORINGS AND TEST PITS

Borings and test pits serve to provide a visual identification of soil strata underlying an area by literally penetrating into the earth. Subsurface materials are identified in place (test pits) or from samples that are taken at a known depth and brought to the surface for examination (borings). In both borings and test pits, soil samples can be obtained for laboratory testing and analysis.

Boring Methods   With borings, several different techniques are in use for obtaining information on soil conditions. The method utilized depends on the type and extent of information desired from the exploration, the general type of soil

(a)

(b)

Figure 11-4 (a) Aerial photograph showing urban development and surrounding land forms: (b) aerial photo showing landslide in Anchorage, Alaska, area resulting during 1964 earthquake.

Borings and Test Pits

conditions in the area being investigated, and the amount of money and time available.

Where only very basic data are necessary, as, for example, if depth to rock (thickness of soil cover) or the thickness of a soft surficial layer (e.g., a marsh deposit) is to be determined, probing by pushing or driving a metal rod until firm resistance or refusal is encountered is a frequently used and economic method. Penetration rods can be handled manually or with mechanical equipment. Usually, manual techniques are practical only where limited depths of probing are necessary.

Hand-operated auger methods (Fig. 11-5) are useful where it is desirable to obtain an indication of various soil types penetrated by the equipment or where it is desired to create an excavation that can give information on the depth to the groundwater table. Information on soil type at a particular depth is usually determined by noting the soil held on the auger. Continuous-flight augers are frequently used to ensure that soil cuttings are carried out of the boring, particularly for deeper borings. When only a limited section of auger is attached to the tip of the rods, the soil does not carry to the surface. Such an occurrence tends to bind the rods and auger in the hole.

Boring contractors and manufacturers have made various refinements to manual penetration and auger equipment that permit small samples of soil to be obtained from a desired depth and brought to the surface for examination or permit the measurement of resistance to penetration offered by the soil at a given depth (see Figs. 11-6 and 11-7).

Where the soil investigation is to extend to some depth, mechanical means of drilling borings are utilized. Two techniques are in wide use: the *auger method* and the *wash boring method*. The auger technique (Fig. 11-8) is basically similar to the hand auger method. Continuous-flight augers are used to drill into the earth, and soil cuttings are carried out of the hole by traveling up the flights of the rotating auger. The main difference between manual and mechanical augering is that drilling

Figure 11-5 Hand auger with recovered soil sample. (Courtesy of Acker Drill Company)

Figure 11-6 Retractable plug sampler, sequence of operation to recover samples: (1) casing driven with piston extended; (2) piston retracted and casing driven to recover sample; (3) sample recovered and casing withdrawn by hand jack (not shown). Brass sample liners (not shown) are used in bottom length of casing to facilitate recovery and preservation of sample. (Courtesy of Acker Drill Company)

machinery is utilized to rotate, and simultaneously mechanically to push downward, the auger sections. Because of the drilling machinery, larger diameter flights than those that are possible with manual methods are used, and the limits to depth are controlled only by the capacity of the equipment.

Subsurface soil types can be detected by noting the soil materials carried to the surface by the augers. In deep drilling, there is the disadvantage of not being able to correlate accurately soil type with depth. In order to better classify soil type with depth, auger samples are used. The procedure consists of augering to a desired depth, withdrawing the augers, inserting an auger sampler to obtain a soil specimen from the bottom of the hole, withdrawing the sampler after cutting the

(a) (b)

Figure 11-7 One type of manual penetrometer: (a) Acker geostick; (b) field use of geostick. (Courtesy of Acker Drill Company)

Borings and Test Pits

Figure 11-8 (a) Soil boring using auger method. (Courtesy of Acker Drill Company) (b) Truck-mounted rotary drill rig showing soil augers in use. (Courtesy of Central Mine Equipment Company)

(a)

(b)

POWER EARTH AUGER (TRUCK MTD)

CONTINUOUS FLIGHT AUGERS-IN SECTIONS

CUTTER HEAD (REPLACEABLE TEETH)

CUTTINGS CARRIED TO SURFACE

sample (Fig. 11-9), and then reinserting the augers to drill to the next sampling depth. Soil samples obtained with auger methods are disturbed samples suitable for classification and some laboratory tests (e.g., they are acceptable for grain-size and liquid and plastic limit determinations but not for strength or compressibility tests).

Wash boring refers to the method of making a boring by applying an up-and-down chopping and twisting motion to a drill bit (or chopping bit) attached at the end of drill rods while simultaneously having a stream of water under pressure directed through the bit to the soil (see Figs. 11-10 and 11-11). This combination of chopping plus wash water serves to loosen soil at the bottom of the boring and to flush the soil cuttings to the top of the hole. The method has long been popular for making borings because of the limited equipment necessary. Even small-sized engines for lifting drill rods coupled with small water pumps can be used to make deep borings. An advantage to this is that inexpensive but quite maneuverable and portable drilling equipment is possible. (Portability is a factor of importance in difficult-to-reach drilling sites.) Drilling rods are usually inserted into and lifted out of the boring by using a tripod or derrick mast to support a rope and pulley lift.

Borings advanced by wash boring methods through cohesionless soils or below water are subject to cave-in. To prevent this, it is typical to drive a protective casing around the boring. The casing consists of heavy wall pipe that is driven into the ground in sections with a drop hammer (drive weight) as the boring is advanced. The casing is withdrawn for reuse at the completion of the boring. A more recent alternate technique for preventing cave-ins consists of using a heavy liquid slurry ("drillers mud") in the boring as the hole is drilled. The slurry, typically a "bentonite" (a montmorillonite clay) and water mix, is dense enough to exert a lateral pressure adequate to keep the walls of the boring from collapsing inward. Soil cuttings are flushed up through the slurry. At the surface, the entire liquid mixture can be caught, filtered, and recirculated back into the boring. Some of the larger

Figure 11-9 Obtaining soil samples from auger cutting head. (Courtesy of Acker Drill Company)

Borings and Test Pits

and more sophisticated drilling rigs can make and force compressed air into the boring to prevent cave-ins, instead of using casing or a slurry.

Some information on soil type and changes in strata can be obtained by examining the soil cuttings washed to the surface. However, such soil is significantly disturbed, and there is the danger that mixing of different soil types can occur

(a)

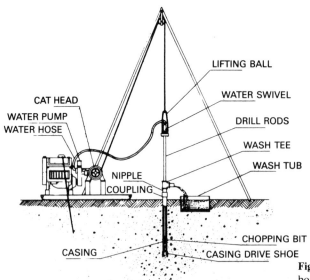

(b)

Figure 11-10 Typical setup for wash boring: (a) driving casing; (b) chopping and jetting. (Courtesy of Acker Drill Company)

Figure 11-11 Wash boring rig in operation in field. (Courtesy of Acker Drill Company)

before the cuttings reach the surface. Because of the significant soil disturbance and the difficulty in establishing boundaries between strata, the determination of subsurface conditions by using wash borings is no longer an acceptable method.

Soil Sampling   To develop information on subsurface conditions that is considered accurate, it is now established practice to obtain soil samples that are sufficiently undisturbed to permit accurate classification. Such soil samples are recovered from their natural location in the ground by the utilization of special techniques and sampling equipment. Typically, the boring and sampling procedure involves drilling a hole to a desired sampling depth by using wash boring or auger methods and then inserting a soil sampler into undisturbed earth to obtain a soil specimen.

A refinement of the auger method to advance a boring involves the use of hollow-stem augers. The soil sampler fits within the hollow stem of the auger and advances at the bottom of the boring without requiring removal of the augers. Use of this method can considerably speed up the boring and sampling operation.

To obtain a soil sample, the sampler is advanced by driving with a drop hammer (Fig. 11-12) or by pushing with a hydraulic piston or jack (Fig. 11-13). In its basic form, the soil sampler is a section of metal pipe or tube with a cutting edge at one end and attachments to hold the soil in the sampler as it is brought to the surface. Sampler lengths typically range between 18 inches and 3 ft (approximately 0.5 and 1 m). Samplers come in different diameters and with different wall thicknesses. The choice of sampler type selected relates to the type of soil being encountered and what needs to be done with the recovered specimen. Where in-place properties need to be determined (such as shear strength and compression-consolidation characteristics), "undisturbed" (or only slightly disturbed) samples are required. If samples are for classification or for performing remolded-type

DRIVE WEIGHT 140#

30" FREE FALL

DRILL ROD

DRIVE HEAD

DRIVE PIPE

DRIVE COUPLING

DRIVE SHOE

SPLIT TUBE SAMPLER
IN UNDISTURBED SOIL

Figure 11-12 Obtaining soil sample by driving with a drop weight. (Courtesy of Acker Drill Company)

laboratory tests (such as grain size and Atterberg limits), "disturbed" samples are permitted. Generally, "undisturbed" soils are obtained by using samplers having a thin wall and a large ratio of inside diameter to wall thickness. Thick-wall samplers and those having a low diameter-to-wall-thickness ratio are considered to provide "disturbed" samples.

One of the most widely known and used soil samplers is the *standard split spoon*. This sampler consists of a longitudinally split tube, or barrel, 2 inches (5.1 cm) in outside diameter and having a $1\frac{3}{8}$-inch (3.5-cm) inside diameter (see Fig. 11-14). The splitting aspect of the sampler permits it to be opened so that the soil specimen can easily be examined and then placed in a container for shipping. The wide use and acceptance of this sampler is due to its size (diameter about equal to typical drill rod diameter), its availability and use at the stage of development when investigators and designers started requiring samples for accurate classification, and the comparatively low cost of obtaining this type of sample. The standard split spoon sampler provides samples rated as "disturbed."

Split barrel samplers are also available in diameters larger than the 2-inch standard split spoon. The large-diameter samplers are considered to provide better samples for laboratory testing and for sampling soils that include gravel-sized particles. Split barrel samplers $3\frac{1}{2}$ inches in diameter for use in 4-inch-diameter borings are included in the typical stock equipment list of many soil-boring contractors.

CLAMP HOLDING
ACTUATING RODS
STATIONARY

HYDRAULIC DRILL SPINDLE
OR RAM PUSHES DRILL
RODS & SAMPLER DOWNWARD

ACTUATING ROD
DRILL ROD
CASING PIPE
STATIONARY PISTON
SAMPLER
PISTON IN PLACE
VIRGIN SOIL

Figure 11-13 Obtaining soil sample by hydraulic pushing. (Courtesy of Acker Drill Company)

(a)

HARDENED SHOE   BALL CHECK
SPLIT TUBE

(b)

Figure 11-14 Standard split spoon sampler: (a) diagram; (b) sampler opened to expose soil. (Courtesy of Acker Drill Company)

Borings and Test Pits

Borings of approximately 6-inch diameter, which permit even larger samples to be obtained, are sometimes used for projects requiring special soil testing or analysis. However, this size is not typical because of the greater expense involved with drilling borings of larger diameter.

Split barrel samplers can be provided with a *liner,* which is a thin metal or plastic tube fitted within the split barrel. The purpose of the liner is to help hold together and protect the sample during handling, shipping, and storage. The liner may consist of a solid length of tube or a series of rings.

The split barrel sampler is a heavy-wall sampler and generally is considered to provide disturbed samples (not suitable for shear and consolidation tests). However, in the large-diameter split barrel samplers, disturbance may be limited to just the peripheral zone of the sample.

Samplers for obtaining less disturbed ("undisturbed") specimens are commonly available. Most use a thin-wall tube as the sampler or as a sampler tip or extension (such as the Dames and Moore Sampler, Fig. 11-15). Methods to carefully advance the sampler into the natural soil are followed to avoid disturbance. When used by themselves, the thin-wall samplers are typically used only in fine-grained soils (silts and clays). Such samplers are generally not used in coarse-grained soils because of the danger of buckling or crimping the thin wall.

Three of the more widely used "undisturbed" samplers are the Shelby Tube, the Piston Sampler, and the Denison Sampler.

The thin-wall Shelby Tube sampler is a seamless metal tube having a limited wall thickness. To obtain the sample, the Shelby Tube is "pushed" (hydraulically pressed) into the earth to obtain the soil specimen. After recovery, the soil is left in the sampling tube for shipping or is hydraulically pushed out of the sampler and placed in an appropriate shipping container (see Fig. 11-16).

The Piston Sampler (Fig. 11-17) is an adaptation of the Shelby Tube sampling method. This sampler includes a piston device, which serves to push the thin-wall tube into undisturbed soil from the bottom of the boring.

The Denison Sampler, or Denison Core Barrel (Fig. 11-18), is a double-walled sampler that rotates or cores its way into undisturbed soil. The outer barrel rotates to cut into the soil. The sample is obtained with the inner barrel. Because of the coring feature, it has the advantage of being able to obtain samples in hard or cemented soils, where an otherwise pressed thin wall would be in danger of buckling.

Sample Spacing in Soil Borings   The accuracy of information obtained from a particular soil boring relates to the spacing between samples. Samples can be taken continuously; that is, samples will be obtained for virtually each foot of boring depth. However, it is more usual practice to take samples at selected intervals of depth. In the soil-boring industry it is common to sample at 5-ft (1.5 m) intervals (one sample for each 5-ft section of boring). Thus, if the sampler is driven 18 inches (0.5 m) to recover a sample, the actual distance between samples is $3\frac{1}{2}$ ft (about 1 m). Soil conditions between samples are determined by noting soil cuttings brought to the surface as the boring is made deeper and feeling resistance to the drilling

SOIL SAMPLER TYPE U
FOR SOILS DIFFICULT TO RETAIN IN SAMPLER

DRIVING OR PUSHING MECHANISM

COUPLING

WATER OUTLETS

NOTCHES FOR ENGAGING FISHING TOOL

NEOPRENE GASKET

HEAD

CHECK VALVES

VALVE CAGE

NOTE:
"HEAD EXTENSION" CAN BE INTRODUCED BETWEEN "HEAD" AND "SPLIT BARREL"

SPLIT BARREL
(TO FACILITATE REMOVAL OF CORE SAMPLE)

CORE-RETAINER RINGS
(2-1/2" O.D. BY 1" LONG)

BIT

CORE-RETAINING DEVICE
RETAINER RING
RETAINER PLATES
(INTERCHANGEABLE WITH OTHER TYPES)

ALTERNATE ATTACHMENTS

SPLIT BARREL

LOCKING RING

SPLIT FERRULE

THIN-WALLED SAMPLING TUBE
(INTERCHANGEABLE LENGTHS)

CORE-RETAINING DEVICE

Figure 11-15 Dames and Moore large-diameter split-barrel sampler. (Courtesy of Dames and Moore)

advance. Where it is detected that a change in soil conditions has been encountered, further drilling should cease and an extra soil sample should be taken.

The drilling of a soil boring, therefore, actually consists of a repetitive series of steps. The drilling equipment is used to make a hole to the depth where a sample is to be obtained. After sampling, the boring is then drilled to the next point where a sample is required. This procedure continues until a boring of the desired depth has been completed.

Boring Spacing and Depth The number of borings for a project, or the spacing between borings, is related to the type, size, and weight of structure planned,

Borings and Test Pits

Figure 11-16 Thin-wall sampler: (a) schematic diagram; (b) tube being removed from head; (c) sealing thin-wall tube with paraffin for shipping. (Courtesy of Acker Drill Company)

Figure 11-17 Stationary Piston Sampler. (Courtesy of Acker Drill Company)

Figure 11-18 Denison Core Barrel. (Courtesy of Acker Drill Company)

the extent of the variation in soil conditions that permits "safe" interpolation between borings, the funds available for the boring program, and possibly the demands of a local building code. Generally, these same considerations apply to the depth for borings. A primary purpose of borings is to establish the presence, location, and extent of "good" soil suitable for foundation support and to determine the possible existence and extent of "poor" soil that could have an adverse effect on foundation performance. Where poor soils are present, the type of foundation selected would be based on circumventing the location of poor material or would be designed to minimize the effect of its presence.

If an extensive thickness of poor material overlies good soil or rock, deep borings will be required. Where a sufficient thickness of good soil exists close to the ground surface, borings may not have to be deep. Even for this condition, however, it is wise to plan some deep borings to reveal conditions at the greater depths, for a deep material that could have an adverse effect on the structure might exist. Where deep borings are necessary to establish the depth at which good foundation soil can be found, soil sampling in the poor material can be minimized or omitted to help reduce drilling costs.

Because most building projects are unique to some degree, certainly with regard to location, no set of rules can be made for planning a boring program that ensures answering all of a designer's or construction contractor's questions. Where there is much uncertainty about subsurface conditions, a preliminary investigation can be made to obtain general information on the area. From this initial information, a more definite or final exploration program can be planned.

For projects extending over a long horizontal distance, such as a highway or a dam, borings for a preliminary investigation may be on 500- to 1000-ft (150- to 300-m) spacings. The final program may eventually require borings on a 100- or 200-ft (30- to 70-m) spacing. With building projects, borings for a preliminary investigation may be located near the planned boundaries of the building area, with a few borings being drilled at intermediate locations. A final program could include borings at building corners and at important interior locations, with spacings not to exceed 50 to 100 ft (15 to 30 m), depending on conditions encountered and building code requirements with regard to maximum spacing.

Penetration Resistance and the Standard Penetration Test (SPT)   In situations where soil samples from borings were obtained by using drive methods (the sampler is driven by use of a drop hammer), it became apparent that the number of blows required to advance the sampler (overcoming resistance) was capable of providing a qualitative indication of the in-place properties of the soil. In firm or dense soils, more blows would be required to advance the sampler than in soft or loose soil. Consequently, when samples are taken, it is now common practice to include the number of blows necessary to advance the sampler a distance of one foot (30 cm). For the blow-count information to be meaningful, the weight of the drive hammer used to advance the sampler must be indicated, since a heavy weight will drive a sampler with fewer blows than a light weight.

What has become known as the standard penetration test (SPT) is a soil-sampling procedure that is in wide use and is generally accepted as providing some correlation with in-place properties of a soil. The standard penetration test requires that a 2-inch split spoon sampler be used in conjunction with a 140-lb (63.6-kg) drive weight. The standard penetration test reports the number of blows N to drive the 2-inch (5.1 cm) sampler one foot (30 cm) into undisturbed soil by using a 140-lb weight falling 30 inches (0.76 m). In practice, it has become typical to obtain a sample by driving the sampler a distance of 18 inches. The blow count for each 6 inches of penetration is recorded separately, and the standard penetration test result is the number of blows required for the last 12 inches of driving. Detailed requirements for the taking and care of soil samples using the standard penetration test procedure are presented in ASTM Test Designation D-1586. A correlation between blow count and soil condition is shown in Table 11-1. Further correlations between the standard penetration test and soil properties are presented in Chapters 10 and 14.

Where the standard penetration test is to be related to soil parameters used for foundation design, the *field procedures* utilized for driving the soil sampler require consideration, because the driving energy transmitted to the sampler is affected by the type of drive weight, the dropping procedure, and other factors. In the United States, two types of drive hammers are in common use: the relatively long, thin safety hammer and a short, large-diameter donut hammer. The effective energy (or energy ratio) delivered by the safety hammer is about 60% of the theoretical simple energy (the value based on the product of hammer weight and the falling distance). The donut hammer has an energy ratio of about 45 percent. For the same soil, then, the donut hammer would require a greater blow count and thus would be indicating a higher resistance. In many other countries using equipment with a performance similar to the safety hammer, a proposed standard is to use the energy ratio of 60 percent as the international reference value (213). Soil parameters determined from penetration testing (empirical relationships) would be matched to the 60 percent energy ratio. For example, a field blow count using the donut hammer would be modified by a factor of 0.75 to be compared to results from the safety hammer and to relate to the 60 percent standard.

From investigations of cohesionless soil deposits, it is recognized that measured blow counts will be affected by the soil depth being sampled. For identical soils, the resistance to penetration at a deep location will be greater than the resistance value developed for a shallow location because of the influences of greater overburden and confining pressures and different driving energy losses in the drill

TABLE 11-1 CORRELATION BETWEEN SOIL CONDITIONS AND STANDARD PENETRATION TEST

Sampler ....2″ O.D. × $1\frac{3}{8}$″ I.D. (5.1 cm × 3.5 cm)
Hammer...140 lb., 30″ fall (63.64 kg, 0.76 m)

Soil	Designation	Blows/ft
Sand and silt	Loose	0–10
	Medium	11–30
	Dense	31–50
	Very dense	Over 50
Clay	Very soft	0–2
	Soft	3–5
	Medium	6–15
	Stiff	16–25
	Hard	Over 25

Source: Acker Drill Co.

rods. Field blow counts, N_{field}, can be corrected for the depth effect by applying a correction factor, C_N, with

$$C_N = 1/\sqrt{\overline{\sigma}_v}$$

when $\overline{\sigma}_v$ is the effective soil overburden pressure expressed in tons per square foot (146). Therefore,

$$N_{corrected} = C_N N_{field}$$

Sand deposits may experience liquefaction during an earthquake or other occurrence that creates seismic shock; liquefaction results in a temporary loss of soil shearing strength. Factors such as the ground acceleration created by shock waves, soil density, and depth are known to have an influence. The susceptibility to liquefaction has been related to the corrected N value (the N value that includes depth and energy ratio corrections). A relatively simple evaluation procedure for delineating sites prone to liquefaction during earthquake, developed from Chinese studies of earthquake-damaged areas, can serve as the basis for determining whether more detailed studies should be undertaken. Sites where the N values are less than $N_{critical}$ (as calculated from the following expression) are indicating susceptibility to liquefaction:

$$N_{critical} = \overline{N} [1 + 0.125 (Z_s - 3) - 0.05 (Z_W - 2) - 0.07 (\% \text{ clay})]$$

In this expression, use $\overline{N}$ equal to 6 for an earthquake intensity[1] of VII, 10 for an earthquake intensity of VIII, and 16 for an earthquake intensity of IX. The percent clay refers to the material finer than 0.002 mm. The terms Z_s and Z_w refer to the depth in meters to the sand layer under study and to the groundwater table, respectively.

Generally, corrected N values less than 20 are considered to indicate that the site has a high potential for earthquake damage. Sites where the corrected N values are between 20 and 30 are classified as having the potential for an intermediate degree of damage. Sites where N values are greater than 30 are considered locations where no significant damage from earthquake or seismic shock is expected.

Penetration Resistance and Cone Penetrometers (CPT) The cone penetrometer consists of a slender metal rod equipped with a cone-shaped tip. The penetrometer is either pushed or driven into the earth. When pushed, usually by hydraulic jack, the penetrometer is classified as a static cone penetrometer. If driven, usually by blows of a drop hammer, the equipment is referred to as a dynamic cone penetrometer. Electric penetrometers are also available. With this type, the cone tip is advanced by an electrical cell constructed within the penetro-

[1]Earthquakes are identified in terms of *intensity* and *magnitude*. Magnitude is an indication of the energy released by an earthquake at the source (the hypocenter). The Richter scale expresses the magnitude of an earthquake on a scale of 1 to 9 (actually, the scale has no upper limit, but no known earthquake has yet succeeded 9). Intensity is a measurement of the effects of an earthquake at the earth's surface, using factors such as different degrees of damage to structures. The modified Mercalli scale, ranging from I through XII, is in widespread use for indicating actual or potential damage for a particular area. Though an earthquake will have but a single magnitude value, the intensity value will vary, usually decreasing as distance from the earthquake source increases.

meter. In use, the penetrometer's resistance to advancing q_c is recorded. The cone penetration test (CPT) resistance is subsequently related to properties of the penetrated soil.

Cone penetrometers offer the advantage that a continuous resistance record is easily obtained for the full depth investigated. This is in contrast to the usual practice of taking standard penetration test samples or other samples at intervals. The method is applicable to cohesionless and cohesive soils. A main disadvantage with many penetrometers is that no soil samples are obtained.

In the past, cone penetrometers have received limited attention in the English-speaking countries. However, a variety of cone penetrometers have been widely used throughout the European countries, and considerable practical experience has been obtained. Consequently, interest has been developing rapidly in English-speaking areas, particularly for investigating sites underlain by cohesionless soils. With conventional boring and sampling methods, obtaining undisturbed samples of cohesionless soil below the water table is difficult and unreliable.

Of the various cone penetrometers in use, the Dutch (Delft) cone is one of the most widely known. For illustrative purposes, it is representative of many types of static cone penetrometers. The Dutch cone penetrometer consists of a conical point (Fig. 11-19) having a 1.4-inch (3.6-cm) diameter and a base area of 10 cm² attached to a rod that fits within a larger-diameter rod. For testing the soil at a particular depth, the outer rod (along with the cone and inner rod) is advanced to the desired elevation. Then the outer rod is locked in position and the cone is advanced a set distance, usually 5 cm, by applying a force to the inner rod. The force necessary to advance the cone is determined with a load cell or proving ring and recorded. Soil properties are correlated with the penetrating force.

The reaction of the force used to advance the cone penetrometer into the earth has to be resisted by the penetrometer rig. If the penetrometer equipment is truck-mounted (Fig. 11-20a), the weight of the vehicle is frequently sufficient to provide the necessary reaction. If lightweight field equipment is used, it is usually necessary to anchor the rig somehow to prevent it from being lifted when the cone is advanced (Fig. 11-20b).

A modification of the Dutch cone penetrometer is the friction cone (Fig.

(a)

(b)

Figure 11-19 Point of Dutch cone penetrometer: (a) position of cone for moving to new depth; (b) cone only advances to determine soil resistance or bearing capacity.

(a)

(b)

Figure 11-20 (a) Dutch cone penetrometer conversion unit fitted to conventional truck boring rig. (Courtesy of Soil Mechanics Equipment Company, Maryland) (b) Ten-ton trailer-mounted Dutch cone penetrometer. Sketch of helicoidal anchor indicates method used to anchor rig against lifting. (Courtesy of Soil Mechanics Equipment Company, Maryland)

11-21). A friction sleeve is provided above the cone point. Testing at a particular depth consists of first determining only a cone resistance value, then, also measuring the resistance to advancement of the cone plus friction sleeve acting together. The sleeve friction is used to help identify the soil type being penetrated.

For proper classification of soil, some calibration is generally required. This typically consists of comparison to a conventional boring where samples were recovered. Once calibration is established, the penetrometer boring normally progresses at a considerably faster rate than the conventional boring.

Dilatometer (DMT) and Pressuremeter (PMT) Tests Field procedures to investigate soil materials underlying an area and to provide or permit soil properties to be determined are of interest to designers, developers, and contractors because of the advantages of savings in time and, possibly, costs. Penetration tests have been correlated with soil strength and foundation bearing capacity, as discussed in previous sections. Other field procedures, such as those that measure a soil's resistance to deformation, theoretically are capable of yielding greater detail about soil properties. Two types of field test in this category are the dilatometer test (DMT) and the pressuremeter test (PMT).

The flat-blade *dilatometer* represents a type of penetration equipment that performs a dilation test, whereby resistance to lateral soil deformation is metered. The Marchetti flat-blade dilatometer diagrammed in Figure 11-22 consists of a

Borings and Test Pits

Figure 11-21 (a) Operation of the friction cone; (b) results from a friction cone surrounding [208].

266

Combination gas
and electrical line
(to ground surface
controls)

Threaded for connecting
to drill rod

Dilatometer
blade

Expandable
steel membrane

Figure 11-22 Sketch of Marchetti flat-blade dilatometer.

pointed stainless steel blade that has a thin flexible metal membrane centered on one side of the blade and flush with the surface. The blade is 94 mm wide and 15 mm thick (approximately 4 in. by $\frac{9}{16}$ in.) with a 10° vee-shaped cutting tip. In a field operation, the blade is advanced into the soil using conventional penetrometer methods (by jacking or driving, methods outlined in the sections describing the standard penetration test and the cone penetration test).

A combination gas and electrical line extends from the blade through the hollow drill rods to the dilatometer's ground surface controls. At the test depth, the equipment operator provides and records a gas pressure just to start membrane expansion or "lift-off" (a movement of approximately 0.05 mm is typical); then a second pressure to move the center of the membrane 1.0 mm farther is applied and recorded. An audio signal indicates when the desired membrane movement has occurred. The pair of pressure readings is typically obtained in less than 30 seconds. The gas pressure can then be carefully released so that a reading is obtained when the membrane is returned to the original position; that pressure indicates the in situ water pressure condition (simple hydrostatic or hydrostatic plus excess pore pressure). The blade is then advanced to the next test depth. Because of the speed in obtaining readings, a typical field procedure will test at depth increments of 0.15 to 0.30 m (6 to 12 in.).

There are some disadvantages or limitations to the use of dilatometer equipment; for example, it cannot be used in high-resistance soils and gravelly soils, and, no samples are obtained for visual examination or laboratory testing.

The resistance to membrane expansion (i.e., the results of the dilatometer test) relates to the total soil pressure against the blade and is used to indicate in situ soil stress, soil stiffness, and various strength and compressibility parameters. If the difference between an initial dilatometer pressure, p_o, and a final pressure p_1, is Δp (corrected by calibration factors such as membrane stiffness, etc.), the following dilatometer test indices apply:

Dilatometer modulus, $E_D = 35 (\Delta p) = E/(1 - \mu^2)$, where E is the soil modulus of elasticity and μ is the Poisson ratio.

Material index, $I_D = \Delta p/(p_o - u_o)$, where u_o is the pore water pressure at test depth.

Horizontal stress index, $K_D = (p_o - u_o)/\bar{\sigma}_v$, where $\bar{\sigma}_v$ is the vertical stress.

Borings and Test Pits

Empirical relationships using these indices to obtain soil properties important for design have evolved from the developers and users of the equipment. Generally, soil type is identified from the I_D value, lateral pressure coefficients and soil strength are related to K_D, and compressibility is related to E_D and K_D [152, 210].

The *pressure meter* is a device that includes a cylindrical probe that can be pressured and expanded. This equipment differs from the flat blade dilatometer in that a borehole must be provided before the pressuremeter probe can be inserted (the dilatometer can be advanced to test depth by driving or jacking). Probe pressures are increased in measured increments, and corresponding volume changes are recorded. Correlations between pressure and volume changes are related to soil parameters. Details about the pressuremeter equipment and related foundation design parameters are given in Chapter 14.

Test Pits   In their simplest form, test pits are excavations into the earth that permit visual inspection of the conditions exposed in the walls of the pit. The classification of soil type at various depths is possible, along with the opportunity to learn properties of the soil and determine stratum thicknesses. Where desired, soil specimens for testing can be cut from the walls or bottom of the test pit. Test pits can be made manually or with power equipment; backhoes are frequently utilized (see Fig. 11-23).

Test pits provide opportunity for studying subsurface features not possible with borings. Generally, more accurate information as to groundwater elevation is possible (if the pit is deep enough to penetrate to groundwater), as is better information on soil variations or unusual features such as presence of underground springs and fissures or cracks in the soil. When the soil deposit includes gravel or boulders, boring samples may not be large enough to recover and identify these

Figure 11-23 Test pit excavation with small backhoe.

items, but such material will be detected in a test pit. If the area under investigation represents a proposed borrow pit, bulk samples are easily obtained for laboratory compaction tests or other analysis.

Natural or man-made cuts in soil deposits offer the same advantage for information as a test pit.

Test pits can be a relatively economical way of obtaining information on subsurface conditions. Frequently, many test pit locations can be dug in one work day with a backhoe. The primary shortcoming of test pit exploration is the limited depth possible with commonly available equipment. Unless a large backhoe or similar equipment is obtainable, the test pits will not penetrate beyond depths of 12 to 15 ft (4–5 m). However, where shallow foundations can be used, the uppermost 15 feet or so of soil are very critical for foundation analysis, and test pits can provide a very useful complement to boring information. When explorations are made for foundation studies, test pits should not be dug at a foundation location, so that the soil eventually required to support the foundation remains undisturbed.

Rock Core Drilling   Rock core drilling relates to the procedure in which rock underlying an area is investigated by coring so as to obtain samples for classification and for determining those properties of rock important to that construction project.

In a structural design, the close presence of an underground rock surface may be desirable, provided that it does not interfere with construction, for the support capabilities of rock are almost always significantly greater than those of soil. The requirement for rock coring develops with the need to establish that an underground rock material encountered in a boring or test pit is actually bedrock and not a large boulder. Rock coring is commonly performed to determine the quality of rock and to check for possible detrimental properties such as cracks, fissures, and weathering or other deterioration that could affect the strength of the formation. Typically, rock cores are necessary to evaluate a rock's ability to support rock anchors, to determine porosity that could affect the flow of underground water or other liquids, or to obtain information for a subsurface rock profile and properties should it be necessary to excavate to depths below the top of the rock.

The method used for most rock drilling is similar to the method of rotary drilling in soil. Machinery used for drilling soil borings is frequently the same equipment as that used for drilling rock (Fig. 11-24). For rock work, special bits and core samplers are necessary, however. Cutting bits are hardened steel or steel alloys, or they are diamond chip bits (see Fig. 11-25).

To obtain rock core samples, hollow core barrels are used. Single- and double-tube core barrels (Fig. 11-26) are in wide use. Under rotary action, the core bit advances into the rock. Usually, a circulating supply of water is provided to the cutting edge to help flush rock cuttings and dissipate heat. "Core runs" are made to drill the hole in segments, usually up to 5 ft (1.5 m) in length. The length of core run is limited by the length of core barrel. At the completion of a core run, the barrel and rock sample are brought to the surface; the rock specimen is removed (Fig. 11-27), and the barrel is reinserted for additional drilling.

(b)

(a)

Figure 11-24 (a) Diamond core drill setup. (Courtesy of Acker Drill Company) (b) Skid-mounted rotary drill rig. This type is used in locations having difficult access. Machine shown has soil auger and rock core capabilities. (Courtesy of Central Mine Equipment Company)

Bit designation*	Nominal hole diameter (in.)	(mm)	Rock core diameter (in.)	(mm)
EWG, EWM	$1\frac{1}{2}$	38	$\frac{13}{16}$	21
AWG, AWM	$1\frac{7}{8}$	48	$1\frac{1}{16}$	30
BWG, BWM	$2\frac{3}{8}$	60	$1\frac{5}{8}$	41
NWG, NWM	3	76	$2\frac{1}{8}$	54
$2\frac{3}{4} \times 3\frac{7}{8}$	$3\frac{7}{8}$	99	$2\frac{11}{16}$	68
HWG	$3\frac{7}{8}$	99	3	76

*First letter is used to designate approximate size of hole obtained with the indicated size equipment; second letter indicates a group designation for compatible drill rods, casing, etc.; third letter designates type of core barrel for the bit. The W size is considered standard, while the M equipment is recommended for coring poor quality rock material. The letter W replaces the older X designation (but is synonymous).

Figure 11-25 Standard diamond core bit and summary of common core bit sizes.

Figure 11-26 Double-tube rock core barrel. (Courtesy of Acker Drill Company)

Borings and Test Pits

Figure 11-27 Rock core samples being placed in core box for shipping. (Courtesy of Acker Drill Company)

PRESENTATION OF BORING INFORMATION

Boring Logs Information on subsurface conditions obtained from the boring operation is typically presented in the form of a boring log (boring record). A continuous record of the various soil or rock strata found at the boring is developed. Description or classification of the various soil and rock types encountered and changes in strata and water level data are considered the minimum information that should constitute a log. Any additional information that helps to indicate or define the features of the subsurface material should also appear on the log. Items such as soil consistency and strength or compressibility can be included. "Field" logs typically consist of the minimum information—classification, stratum changes, and water level readings (see Fig. 11-28a). A more developed "office" or "lab" log might include laboratory test data presented alongside the boring sample actually tested, so all information pertaining to the various soil or rock types and properties found at a boring location is summarized (see Fig. 11-28b).

Where subsurface conditions are investigated through use of boring or test pits, the exploration program normally consists of making a number of borings or test pits at different locations. To assist in picturing and understanding underground conditions existing at a site, it has become common to use the boring or test pit series to develop a subsurface profile (Fig. 11-29). This profile helps to define the subsurface conditions more clearly, showing uniformity or variation, and can assist in delineating between good and poor areas. If a subsurface profile is developed as data become available (as the borings are completed), the information can be used for indicating the need and general location for additional borings or, conversely, for indicating that some originally planned borings can be omitted. When subsurface profiles are used, it is important to remember that conditions between borings have been estimated by interpolation, and that actual conditions are known only at boring and test pit locations.

Recognizing Limitations of Boring Data   It is accepted that borings are providing information on subsurface conditions only at the actual drilling location and that the standard practice of interpolating between borings to determine con-

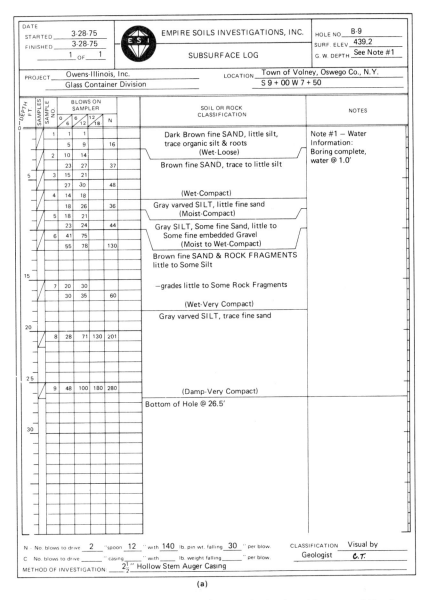

Figure 11-28   (a) Empire Soils Investigations boring log. (Courtesy of Empire Soils Investigations)

Presentation of Boring Information

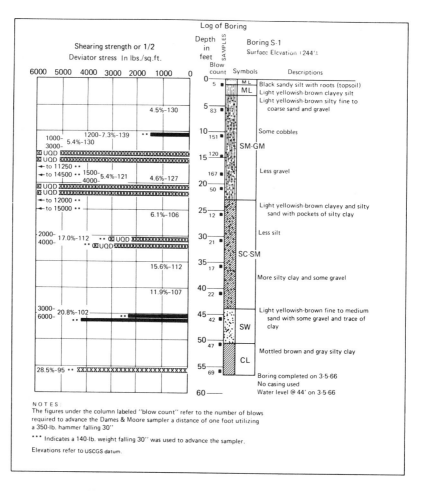

Figure 11-28 (b) Dames and Moore boring log. (Courtesy of Dames and Moore)

ditions does involve some degree of uncertainty. However, it is also important to recognize that there are limitations inherent to the information shown on the typical driller's log. Members of field crews employed by boring contractors are primarily drilling tradesmen. Such individuals typically have limited experience in detailed soil classification and have virtually no familiarity with the importance of subsurface conditions on the features of building design and construction. Important items of information can be innocently passed over by a driller whose major interest is in the rate of drilling progress, for borings typically are contracted for on a footage basis. Consequently, where an exploration is for a final design (and often for preliminary work as well), it is becoming increasingly common to have technically trained personnel assigned to the drilling crew in order to examine and classify recovered soil samples, to direct the depth at which samples should be taken, to select the sequence of drilling borings, and to document other factors relating to surface and subsurface conditions that could have an influence on design or con-

Direct shear and friction tests

Tests at
field moisture

Tests at artifically
changed moisture

— Test normal pressure in pounds per square foot.
— Per cent field moisture expressed as a percentage of the dry weight of soil
— Dry density expressed in pounds per cubic foot
— Per cent moisture when tested
expressed as a percentage of the dry weight of soil
2500 — 20.4% — 104   22.9% — 104 — 20.4%
— Shearing strength in pounds per square foot
— Friction of soil on steel in pounds per square foot
— Friction of soil on wood in pounds per square foot
— Friction of soil on concrete in pounds per square foot

Unconfined compression tests
— Per cent field moisture expressed as a percentage of the dry weight of soil
— Dry density expressed in pounds per cubic foot
20.4%   — 104
— Shearing strength in pounds per square foot
(from Mohr circle)

Triaxial compression tests
— TEST NORMAL PRESSURE IN POUNDS PER SQUARE FOOT (FROM MOHR CIRCLE)
— PER CENT FIELD MOISTURE EXPRESSED AS A PERCENTAGE OF THE DRY WEIGHT OF SOIL
— DRY DENSITY EXPRESSED IN POUNDS PER CUBIC FOOT
2500 — 20.4% — 104
— SHEARING STRENGTH IN POUNDS PER SQUARE FOOT
(FROM MOHR CIRCLE)

Rock compression tests
— Compressive strength in pounds per square inch

Key to test data

Indicte   ■ Indicates depth of undisturbed sample
           ⊠ Indicates depth of disturbed sample
           ☐ Indicates depth of sampling attempt with no recovery
           ◩ Indicates depth of split-spoon sample
           I Indicates depth and length of coring run

(b)   Key to samples

Figure 11-28   (b) Cont.

struction. Such an individual is typically from a designer's or foundation consultant's office. After the field work is completed, the individual remains an accessible resource person capable of answering questions if issues develop during the design period.

GEOPHYSICAL METHODS

The determination of subsurface materials through the use of borings and test pits can be time-consuming and expensive. Considerable interpolation between checked locations is normally required to arrive at an areawide indication of conditions. Geophysical methods involve the technique of determining underground materials by measuring some physical property of the material and, through correlations, using the obtained values for identification. Most geophysical methods determine conditions over a sizable distance. Frequently, this is an advantage over the "point" checking accomplished by borings and test pits. Most geophysical measurements can be rapidly obtained. Thus, the methods lend themselves well to the checking of large areas.

Geophysical Methods   **275**

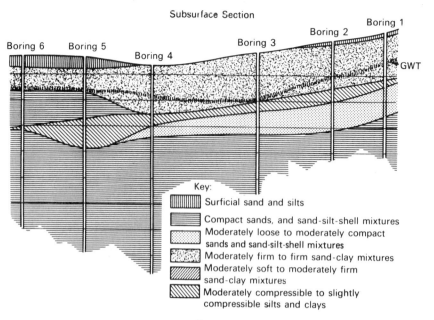

Figure 11-29 One method of presenting a subsurface profile to summarize boring results.

In the engineering-construction profession, two types of geophysical investigation have been found useful: the seismic refraction method and the electrical resistivity method. Though these methods have proven to be reliable, there are also certain limitations as to the data that can be obtained. Thus, at the present time, subsurface investigations can rely heavily on geophysical methods, but conditions should at least be spot-checked with borings or test pits. Typically, when a thorough investigation is made, a number of borings will be required in order to obtain test samples to make accurate determinations of soil properties such as strength and compressibility. It is these borings that can provide the detail required to check and complement the geophysical data.

Seismic Refraction   When a shock or impact is made at a point on or in the earth, the resulting seismic (shock or sound) waves travel through the surrounding soil and rock at speeds relating to the density and bonding characteristics of the material. In refraction seismology, the *velocity* of seismic waves passing through subsurface soil or rock materials is determined, and the magnitude of the velocity is then utilized to identify the material. A seismograph, the instrument used to make a seismic refraction study, consists of a shock- or impact-inducing mechanism, such as an impact hammer or small explosive, plus a receiver to indicate when the seismic wave reaches a point at a particular known distance from impact as well as a timing instrument for measuring the time for the wave to travel the distance from the point of impact to the point of measurement. In shallow refraction seismology, as used for determining subsurface conditions for construction purposes, the shock impact is created with a sledgehammer hitting a striking plate placed on

Figure 11-30 Seismic refraction study being performed in field. (Courtesy of Soiltest, Inc.)

the ground (Fig. 11-30). The seismic wave is then picked up by a sensitive geophone. (The geophone is actually a transducer, an electromechanical device that detects vibrations and converts them into electric signals that can be measured.)

The field survey involves obtaining a series of geophone readings at different distances along a straight line directed from the impact point. For geophone spacings close to the strike plate, the vibrations picked up by the geophone will be from those direct waves traveling through the upper layer of earth material (see Fig. 11-31). For direct waves traveling through the upper layer, the time to reach the geophone is proportional to the distance from the point of impact.

When the surficial layer is underlain by a harder layer, the seismic waves from the strike plate also progress downward and enter the harder layer. The seismic velocity will be greater in the harder material. Waves traveling through the upper portion of the harder layer transfer energy back into the upper layer through the surface of contact. This energy becomes a refracted wave. For large strike plate-to-geophone distances, the refracted wave will reach the geophone more quickly than the direct wave, even though the path of travel is longer. This occurs because part of the path is through the harder, high-velocity material (see Fig. 11-32).

Seismic velocities for the earth materials in the upper and lower strata would be obtained from plotting the measured values of geophone distance and time on a travel-time graph (both coordinate values use an arithmetic scale); see Figure 11-33. The slope of the first segment of the plot represents the seismic velocity for

Figure 11-31 Method of imparting sound waves into a soil.

Geophysical Methods

Figure 11-32 Travel of sound waves through different subsurface materials.

the material in the upper stratum. The slope of the second segment is the seismic velocity for the deeper layer. To obtain data that properly define the plotted segments, it is recommended that the maximum geophone distance be about five times the depth of investigation.

Figure 11-34a illustrates a soil layer–rock layer subsurface and indicates the type of seismic wave (direct or refracted) picked up at the various geophone positions. The resulting travel-time graph appears in Figure 11-34b.

Seismic velocity values representative of different earth materials and conditions are shown in Table 11-2.

Where a two-layer condition exists, the thickness or depth of the upper layer can be determined from

$$H_1 = \frac{X_1}{2} \sqrt{\frac{V_2 - V_1}{V_2 + V_1}} \qquad (11\text{-}1)$$

where H_1
    is the depth or thickness of the upper layer.

X_1 is the distance, taken from the travel-time graph, where the two plotted slopes intersect.

V_1, V_2 are seismic velocities in the upper and lower layer, respectively.

For the condition of three successively harder layers existing in an area, the travel-time graph will show three different slopes. The seismic velocity for each of the materials is the slope of the respective segment of the plot. The thickness of the upper layer can be calculated from Equation 11-1. The thickness of the inter-

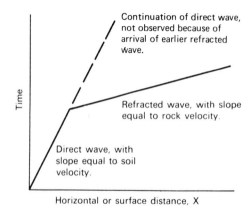

Figure 11-33 Typical travel-time graph for soil overlying rock.

Site Investigations   Chap. 11

(a)

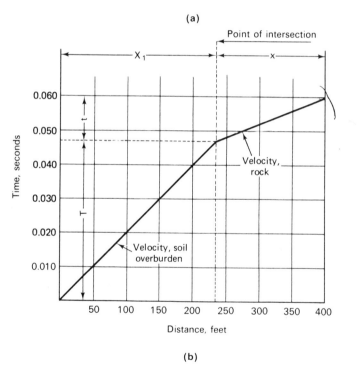

(b)

Figure 11-34 Seismic refraction conditions and data: (a) sursurface conditions showing direct and refracted sound waves; (b) travel-time plot for conditions in (a). (Courtesy of Acker Drill Company)

TABLE 11-2 REPRESENTATIVE SEISMIC VELOCITY VALUES (Velocity in ft/sec)

Soil—unconsolidated material		Rock—consolidated material	
Most unconsolidated materials	Below 3000	Most hard rocks	Above 8000
Soil—normal	800–1500	Shale—soft	4000–7000
—hard packed	1500–2000	—hard	6000–10,000
Water	5000	Sandstone—soft	5000–7000
Loose sand—above water table	800–2000	—hard	6000–10,000
—below water table	1500–4000	Limestone—weathered	As low as 4000
Loose mixed sand and gravel, wet	1500–3500	—hard	8000–18,000
Loose gravel, wet	1500–3000	Basalt	8000–13,000
Hard clay	2000–4000	Granite and unweathered gneiss	10,000–20,000
		Compacted glacial tills, hardpan, cemented gravels	4000–7000
		Frozen soil	4000–7000
		Pure ice	10,000–12,000

Note: Occasionally, formations may yield velocities that lie outside of these ranges. Source: Soiltest, Inc.

mediate layer, H_2, can be determined from

$$H_2 = 0.85\,H_1 + \frac{X_2}{2}\sqrt{\frac{V_3 - V_2}{V_3 + V_2}} \qquad (11\text{-}2)$$

where H_1

       is the thickness of the upper layer.

    X_2 is the distance from the travel-time graph, where plotted segments 2 and 3 intersect.

  V_2, V_3 are seismic velocities of layers 2 and 3 as determined from the travel-time graph.

There are certain significant limitations to the use of the seismic refraction method for determining subsurface conditions:

1. The method should not be used where a hard layer overlies a softer layer, because there will be no measurable refraction from a deeper soft layer. Refraction seismic test data from such an area would tend to give a single-slope line on the travel-time graph, indicating a deeper layer of uniform material.

2. The method should not be used on an area covered by concrete or asphalt pavement, because these materials will represent a condition of a hard surface over a softer stratum.

3. A frozen surface layer may give results similar to those obtained where a hard layer is over a soft layer because of the velocity increase resulting from the better wave transmission through the more "solid" frozen material.

Further, some topographic and underground features will give seismic data that are difficult to interpret fully and correctly. Such situations include the condition of an irregular or dipping underground rock surface, the condition where discontinuities such as rock faults or earth cuts or banks exist, the condition where layers having gradual changes in their velocity values occur, and the condition of thin layers of varying materials. Because of the possibility for misinterpretation of data with such occurrences, the seismic analysis should be performed by trained personnel, and, as a minimum, spot-checks should be made with borings or test pits.

Where rock exists at or close to the surface at a construction site, predetermining the methods necessary for removal (to lower the surface elevation) or for excavation becomes important for estimating, bidding, and scheduling purposes. Seismic velocity data have been used to determine when the rock material is capable of being ripped with dozer rippers (or other similar equipment) and when drilling and blasting are required. Such seismic rippability information, as developed by one major construction equipment manufacturer, is shown in Figure 11-35.

Electrical Resistivity   Resistivity is a property possessed by all materials. The electrical resistivity method for determining subsurface conditions utilizes the knowledge that in soil and rock materials, the resisitivity values differ sufficiently to permit that property to be used for identification purposes.

Geophysical Methods

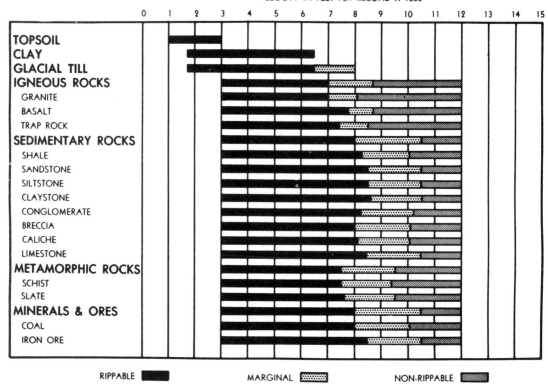

Figure 11-35 Seismic rippability chart developed by Caterpillar Tractor Company for D9 with mounted No. 9 ripper. (Courtesy of Soiltest, Inc.)

To determine resistivity at a site, electrical currents are induced into the ground through the use of electrodes. Soils or rock resisitivity can then be determined by measuring the change in electrical potential (voltage) between known horizontal distances within the electrical field created by the current electrodes (see Fig. 11-36).

A schematic diagram of equipment for resistivity testing, including electrode arrangements (the Wenner configuration), is shown in Figure 11-37. With four

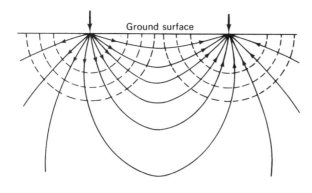

Figure 11-36 Path of current flow (solid lines) through a soil in the electrical resistivity study (dotted lines are equipotential surfaces).

Site Investigations   Chap. 11

Figure 11-37 Wenner configuration for arrangement of voltage and current electrodes.

electrodes equally spaced along a line, as indicated, the resistivity is calculated from

$$\beta = 2\pi S \left(\frac{V}{I}\right) \qquad (11\text{-}3)$$

where β

    is the resistivity of the earth material in ohm-feet.

    S is the electrode spacing.

    V is the difference in potential (volts) between the inner electrodes.

    I is the current flowing between the outer electrodes.

The calculated resistivity value is an apparent resistivity. This is a weighted average of all the earth material within the zone created by the electrodes' electric field. The depth of material included in the measurement (depth of penetration) is approximately the same as the spacing between electrodes.

Two different field procedures are in use for obtaining information on subsurface conditions. One method, *electrical profiling*, is well suited for establishing

Figure 11-38 Electrical resistivity field study being performed. (Courtesy of Soiltest, Inc.)

Geophysical Methods

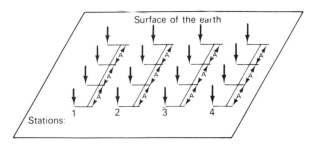

Figure 11-39 Electrode arrangement in a profiling survey.

boundaries between different underground materials and has practical application in prospecting for sand and gravel deposits or ore deposits. The second method, *sounding*, can provide information on the variation of subsurface conditions with depth and has practical application in indicating layered conditions and approximate thicknesses. It can also provide information on depth to a water table or water-bearing stratum. Figure 11-38 shows field work for an electrical resistivity study being performed.

In the *electrical profiling* method, an electrode spacing is selected, and this same spacing is used in running different "profile" lines across an area (see Fig. 11-39). The information obtained applies for the particular location of the line and is sometimes referred to as an "electrical trench," implying that the subsurface data revealed are similar to the information that would be obtained by examining an open-trench excavation.

The information resulting from a profile line can most simply be plotted on arithmetic coordinates, as shown in Figure 11-40. A change in the plotted curve indicates a change in the underground material. From the series of profile lines, boundaries of areas underlain by different materials can be established on a map of the area (areal map).

In the *electrical sounding* method, a center location for the electrodes is selected and a series of resistivity readings is obtained by systematically increasing the electrode spacing, as indicated by Figure 11-41. Since the *depth* of information recovered is directly related to electrode spacing, the series of resistivity data

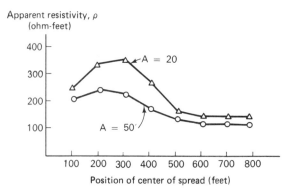

Figure 11-40 Apparent resistivity versus position of the center of electrode spread for two values of electrode separation A. (Source: Soiltest, Inc.)

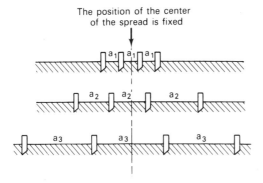

The position of the center
of the spread is fixed

Figure 11-41 Representative electrode
position during a sequence of sounding
measurements.

(a)

(b)

Figure 11-42 Illustration of two methods for graphing sounding data: (a) Cartesian
(arithmetic) coordinates; (b) logarithmic coordinates.

Geophysical Methods

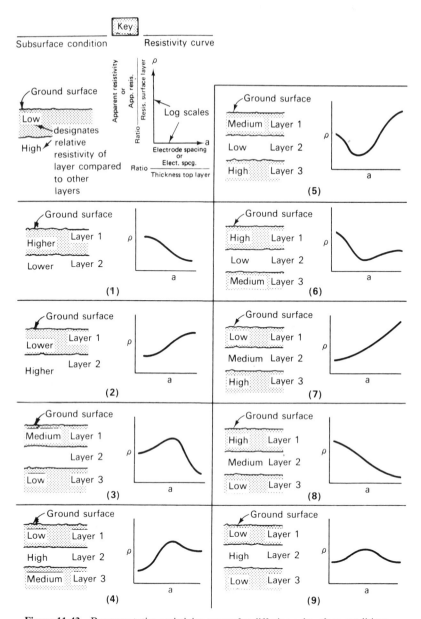

Figure 11-43 Representative resistivity curves for differing subsurface conditions.

obtained from successively increased electrode spacings will indicate changes of resistivity with depth and, hence, information on layering of materials. This method is capable of indicating subsurface variations where a hard layer underlies a soft layer and also the condition of a soft layer underlying a hard layer. Data can be presented on Cartesian (arithmetic scale) coordinates or logarithmic coordinates, as indicated in Figure 11-42. Logarithmic coordinates are the most popular.

TABLE 11-3 REPRESENTATIVE RESISTIVITY VALUES

Types of materials	Resistivity (ohm-ft)
Wet to moist clayey soils	5–10
Wet to moist silty clay and silty soils	10–50
Moist to dry silty and sandy soils	50–500
Well-fractured to slightly fractured bedrock with moist soil-filled cracks	500–1000
Sand and gravel with silt	1000
Slightly fractured bedrock with dry soil-filled cracks; sand and gravel with layers of silt	1000–8000
Massive bedded and hard bedrock; coarse dry sand and gravel deposits	8000 +

Source: Soiltest, Inc.

The spacing of electrodes is important. To obtain data that give a reliable indication of conditions, the closest electrode spacing should be no more than half the estimated thickness of the upper stratum. Three feet is the minimum recommended spacing, however. The largest spacing is between 5 and 10 times the total depth of interest. The number of intermediate spacings selected should be adequate to provide sufficient points to plot a well-defined curve.

Representative sounding curves for some typical subsurface conditions appear in Figure 11-43.

Correlation Between Resistivity and Earth Materials In earth materials, resistivity decreases with increasing water content and increasing salt concentration. Increasing degrees of water content and salinity make it easier for an electrical current to flow through the material. Consequently, nonporous materials (holding little water) will have high resistivity values. Such materials include most igneous and metamorphic rock plus some dense sedimentary rock, such as dense limestone and sandstone. In soil materials, clean gravel and sand have a relatively high resistivity value. Silts, clays, and coarse-grained–fine-grained soil mixtures have comparatively low resistivity values. Soil formations in nonglaciated areas typically have lower resistivity values than soils in glacial areas.

Representative values of resistivity for commonly occurring earth materials are presented in Table 11-3.

Thickness of Layers A method of obtaining a reliable and accurate determination of the depth to, or thickness of, soil layers by using resistivity data is currently not available. Approximation methods exist, but they are cumbersome to handle and not particularly suited for use in field work. With present knowledge, depth or thickness information is best obtained from borings or by seismic methods.

IN-PLACE TESTING

In-place testing, in the soil and foundation profession, refers to the procedure of determining soil properties or other subsurface conditions at the actual surface or subsurface location. In-place (in situ) testing includes shear strength determinations, permeability determinations, in-place density determinations, plate-bearing and settlement determinations, lateral movement determinations, and pore pressure determinations. In-place shear strengths are determined where undisturbed samples for laboratory testing cannot be obtained or where it is desired to eliminate the need to obtain samples. Field permeability determinations offer an advantage over laboratory tests, in that a larger volume of soil is being evaluated in its natural environment. Plate-bearing tests are used to simulate spread footing foundation loading and to obtain load-settlement information on soil that will be supporting shallow foundations or structural slabs (floors, pavements). Lateral movement determinations are of interest where the stability of earth masses and slopes or of embankments or retaining walls is being monitored or if there is a need to know about lateral soil movement caused by foundation or other loading. Underground lateral movements are measured with slope inclination indicator equipment. Methods for determining field permeability are described in Chapter 5. In-place densities are discussed in Chapters 4 and 12. Plate-bearing tests are discussed in Chapter 9. The pressure meter test (used to determine the volumetric stress–strain properties of a buried soil zone by inserting a probe into a borehole to obtain information directly applicable to foundation design) is discussed in Chapter 14. In-place shear testing, slope inclination equipment, and pore pressure devices are discussed below.

In-Place Shear Tests—Vane Shear   The vane shear test consists of inserting a vane (Fig. 11-44) into the soil and then rotating it by applying a torque. The torque is measured and, for a known-size vane, is easily related to the shearing strength of the soil. In field explorations, the vane testing is typically performed at different depths in a boring as it is being drilled. The soil to be tested should be undisturbed by the boring operation. The vane shear test can be performed on any soil, provided that the vane can be inserted into the soil without causing significant disturbance. Practically, then, the method is useful primarily for fine-grained soils. For typical field or laboratory conditions, where little or no overburden pressure exists, the shear value being determined is primarily cohesion.

Slope Inclination Indicators   Slope inclination equipment provides information by indicating the slope or variation from a vertical axis at desired depths in a special casing installed in the ground (see Fig. 11-45). A device to determine the variation from vertical runs in special grooves or tracks on the interior of the casing. The pendulum principle is normally used within the device to establish the vertical axis and for reference. The slope-versus-depth data are recorded. If data collected at different times show a change in slope, this would indicate that lateral movement is occurring. Knowing the slope at different points from top to bottom of the casing permits the lateral position at any depth to be calculated.

Pore Pressures and Piezometers   Pore pressure determinations refer to the procedure of measuring the water pressure values developed in the void or pore spaces of an underground soil mass. Usually, the interest is in the "excess" pore water pressure, or the magnitude of pressure greater than a normal hydrostatic pressure resulting from the elevation of a groundwater table (phreatic surface).

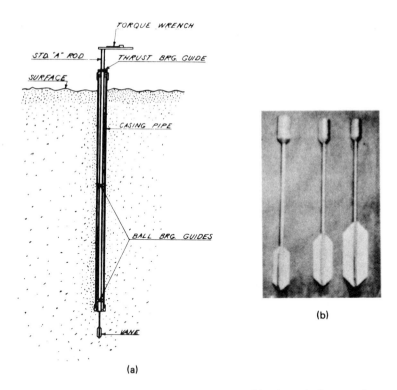

Figure 11-44 In-place vane shear test apparatus: (a) schematic diagram of vane shear test procedure; (b) vanes for vane shear testing. (Courtesy of Acker Drill Company)

Excess pore water pressures can develop in fine-grained soil strata when a new structural loading is placed on the earth above the fine-grained soil, as discussed under "Consolidation" in Chapter 9. Excess pore pressures provide information on the magnitude of stresses caused in the fine-grained soil by the new loading. On a typical construction project, pore pressure information is utilized to control

Figure 11-45 Slope indicator in use on a field project (equipment shown is a Soiltest slope meter probe). (Courtesy of Soiltest, Inc.)

In-Place Testing

the rate at which new loading occurs, to keep the stress resulting in the supporting soil from exceeding the strength of that soil.

The piezometer is a device to measure pore water pressure. In its simplest form, a piezometer would consist of an open tube or standpipe, with its tip inserted into the soil layer to be checked. Before construction, the water level observed would be the phreatic surface level. As construction loading results in increased underground stresses, the water level in the open standpipe rises. The rise in elevation multiplied by the unit weight of water gives the magnitude of excess pore pressure. As the stressed soil consolidates, the pore pressure decreases and the water level in the piezometer drops.

The simple piezometer just described would be limited to use for soil having a fairly high permeability. With fine-grained soil of low permeability, the time lag for changes in pore water pressures to be measured would be excessive. To indicate changes in pore pressures quickly, modifications (some extensive) have been made to the basic piezometer. The result is that some sophisticated types of equipment have evolved. Most types still include the piezometer unit, which has to be installed to the depth where readings are to apply, and pressure or gage lines, which are carried to a monitor located on the ground surface. Some piezometer types have special conditions for which they are best suited. With some complex units, in-

Figure 11-46 Illustrations of piezometer types: (a) open tube type for use in permeable soil; (b) pressure cell for use in impermeable soil.

stallation has to be accomplished by specially trained personnel. The diagrams in Figure 11-46 show some piezometer types.

PROBLEMS

11-1. What publicly available maps serve as good references for obtaining information about surface conditions in an area?

11-2. List and describe some of the advantages of learning about land surface features from aerial photographs.

11-3. Outline the general procedure used to drill soil borings and obtain soil samples for classification and testing.

11-4. In soil borings, what is the standard penetration test?

11-5. Compare advantages and disadvantages of test pits versus soil borings for obtaining information on subsurface conditions.

11-6. Make a comparison between the static cone penetrometer and standard penetration test methods for determining subsurface soil conditions.

11-7. Prepare a boring log from the following information, as obtained from a $2\frac{1}{2}$-inch boring where standard split spoon soil samples were taken.

Sample depth (ft)	Blow count N	Soil classification
$2-3\frac{1}{2}$	3-4-4	Brown fine to medium sand
$7-9\frac{1}{2}$	7-8-7	Brown fine to medium sand
$12-13\frac{1}{2}$	8-9-10	Brown fine to medium sand in upper part of sample
		Red-brown clay in lower part of sample
$17-18\frac{1}{2}$	9-12-11	Red-brown clay
$22-23\frac{1}{2}$	9-25-27	Gray fine to coarse sand, silt and clay, occasionally gravel (compact glacial till)
$27-28\frac{1}{2}$	29-35-39	Gray fine to coarse sand, silt, clay with gravel (compact glacial till)
$31-31\frac{1}{2}$	100	Refusal (no sample recovered)

Water level encountered at 21 ft.

11-8. (a) Briefly describe the principles on which seismic refraction studies for subsurface explorations are based.

(b) Briefly describe the principles on which electrical resistivity studies for subsurface explorations are based.

11-9. List and briefly describe the type of subsurface information that seismic refraction studies can provide and the limitations on information that can be obtained.

11-10. List and briefly describe the type of subsurface information that electrical resistivity studies can provide and the limitations to data that can be obtained.

11-11. A seismic refraction study made for an area provides the following field data:

Distance from impact point to geophone (ft)	Time to receive sound wave (sec)
50	0.025
100	0.05
200	0.10
300	0.11
400	0.12

(a) Graph the time-travel data and determine the seismic velocity for the surface layer and underlying layer.

(b) Determine the thickness of the upper layer.

(c) Using the seismic velocity information, give the probable earth materials in the two layers.

11-12. List and briefly discuss the major advantages and disadvantages of in-place shear tests, such as those performed by the in-place vane shear.

chapter **12**

Earth Moving, Compaction, and Stabilization

In the natural location and condition, soil provides the foundation support for many of man's structures. But soil is also extensively used as a basic material of construction, as witnessed by the existence of earth structures such as dams, dikes, and embankments for roads and airfields. For situations where the natural topography needs to be changed to make the area more suitable for building development, soil is the material most used for filling low locations. The desirability of utilizing soil as a building material stems from its general availability, its durability, and its comparatively low cost.

When soil is used for construction purposes, it is typical for it to be placed in layers to develop a final elevation and shape. Each layer is compacted before being covered with a subsequent layer. Properly placed and compacted, the resulting soil mass has strength and support capabilities that are as good as or better than many natural soil formations. In the case of earth structures such as dams, the compacted earth is capable of supporting itself and the forces to which it is subjected. With earth fills, it is possible to support buildings, highways, and parking areas on the compacted soil mass. Such soil is referred to as a *compacted earth fill* or a *structural earth fill*.

Whether soil is used as the foundation material to support buildings, roads, or other strucutres or is used to build the structure itself (e.g., an earth dam), it is desirable that the in-place material possess certain properties. The soil should have adequate strength, should be relatively incompressible so that future settlement is not significant, should be stable against volume change as water content or other factors vary, should be durable and safe against deterioration, and should possess proper permeability. These desirable features can be achieved with a compacted fill by proper selection of the fill soil type and by proper placement. The important properties of a fill could be checked independently, but the more desirable characteristics, such as high strength, low compressibility, and stability, are normally associated with high-density (or unit weight) values and hence will result from good compaction.

Virtually any type of soil can be used for structural fill, provided that it does not contain organic or foreign material that would decompose or otherwise undergo change after it is in place. Granular soils are considered the easiest to work with on a construction site. This material is capable of developing high strength, with little volume change expected after compaction. Permeabilities are high, which can be an advantage or a disadvantage. Generally, compacted silts are stable, are capable of developing fairly good strength, and have limited tendency for volume change. Silty soils can be difficult to compact if wet or if work is performed in wet periods. Permeability is low. Properly compacted clay soils will develop relatively high strengths. Their stability against shrinkage and expansion is related to the type of clay mineral; for example, the montmorillonite clays would have a greater tendency for volume change than the more stable kaolinite clays. Compacted clays have a very low permeability, a factor that can be used to advantage where movement of water needs to be restricted. Clay soils cannot be properly compacted when wet. Working with clay soil is difficult under wet conditions.

FIELD PROCEDURES—GENERAL CONSIDERATIONS, METHODS, AND TECHNIQUES

The field procedure for constructing a compacted fill is simple in principle. The fill soil is transported to the area being worked, where it is spread in relatively thin layers, and each layer is then compacted to a predetermined density (unit weight). However, proper accomplishment of these requirements involves consideration of the soil type, its water content, and the type of equipment used for the compacting operation.

On big projects, where the soil fill is obtained from an earth cut or borrow pit on or near the construction site, self-propelled scrapers (Fig. 12-1) can be considered for hauling and spreading the fill. Self-propelled scrapers are widely used because of their excavating and self-loading capabilities and the relatively fast haul speeds (see Figs. 12-2 and 12-3). With scraper operations, bulldozers or graders frequently work in the fill area to help keep newly placed uncompacted fill uniformly spread (Figs. 12-4 and 12-5). Compaction equipment follows the spreading equipment.

If the fill material is obtained from an off-site source, trucks are generally used for transportation (see Fig. 12-6). At the fill location, the soil is dumped and then spread with dozers and graders. Compaction follows the spreading operation.

Trucks are also commonly used for transporting the soil on cut-and-fill projects, particularly when the fill material is obtained from a cut or borrow pit area where excavation can be efficiently handled by power shovel equipment or when the hauling distance is great (see Figs. 12-7, 12-8, and 12-9).

Figure 12-1 Self-propelled scraper spreading soil for an earth fill project. (Courtesy of Caterpillar Tractor Company)

When the site being worked is of a limited area and fill is obtained from an on-site cut, bulldozers may be used to perform excavation and to push the soil to the fill area, where it is spread and compacted.

The thickness of layers that can be properly compacted is known to relate to the soil type and the method or equipment of compaction. Typically, granular soils can be adequately compacted in thicker layers than the fine-grained silt and clay soils. Generally, for a given soil type, heavy compaction equipment is capable of compacting thicker layers than light equipment.

The types of equipment commonly used for compaction include pneumatic or rubber tire rollers; drum-type rollers that have projecting feet or lugs, such as the sheep's-foot roller; vibratory compactors, which impart vibrations into the soil; and smooth drum rollers. All types are available in a variety of sizes and weight.

Figure 12-2 Scrapers self-loading in borrow pit. (Courtesy of Terex Division, General Motors Corporation)

Field Procedures—General Considerations, Methods, and Techniques   **295**

Figure 12-3 Scraper being loaded in borrow area with assistance of pushdozer, a procedure to reduce the time required for loading. (Courtesy of Terex Division, General Motors Corporation)

The vibratory compactors are most effective on cohesionless soils. The sheep's-foot and similar rollers that have feet or other projections should be limited to cohesive soils. Pneumatic tire rollers can be used effectively on all soil types. The smooth drum rollers have a very limited effective depth of compaction; hence, their use should be restricted to situations where only thin layers or a surface zone needs to be compacted.

Hand-operated tamping and vibratory compactors are available for working in limited spaces and for compacting soil close to structures, where care is required to prevent damage.

Figure 12-4 Bulldozer utilized to spread soil fill. (Courtesy of Terex Division, General Motors Corporation)

Figure 12-5 Grader of type used on fill projects to spread soil and construct drainage ditches. Photo shows grader working on a roadside ditch. (Courtesy of Galion Division of Dresser Industries, Inc.)

The water content of the fill soil has an effect on its ability to be well compacted with reasonable effort. The fine-grained silt and clay soils, and granular soils containing fine materials, are particularly affected by variations in water content. Soil that is too dry is difficult to compact. Material that is too wet may be difficult to spread properly and to compact. When the soil is too wet at its source, measures should be taken to dry it before compaction is attempted at the fill area. Drying can be accomplished by scarifying and aerating the soil at the borrow pit or cut area, by hauling it to an open area and loosely spreading it to permit aeration, or by letting it aerate after spreading across the fill area. These procedures presume

Figure 12-6 Front-end loader used in borrow area. Truck type shown is typically used for on-site or highway hauling. (Courtesy of Fiat-Allis Construction Machinery, Fiat-Allis Chalmers)

Field Procedures—General Considerations, Methods, and Techniques   **297**

Figure 12-7 Rear dump truck of type used for on-site hauling. (Courtesy of Caterpillar Tractor Company)

that space and time are available. When the fill soil is too dry, water should be added and mixed throughout. Wetting can be achieved by spraying water at either the cut or fill area with a water truck, followed by a mixing operation performed with the excavating or earth-moving equipment. If the dry soil is spread across the fill area before wetting, dozers and graders can frequently perform some mixing after spraying by "rolling" the earth on the front of their blades as they work to even out the layer thickness. Where the fill source is a large borrow area, ponds can be created and flooded. This procedure permits the water to percolate through the soil before it is excavated and transported. Fine-grained soils will require a longer ponding period than granular soil.

When an area is being filled, the ability of the first fill layers to be properly compacted will depend on the condition of the natural material being covered. If weak or compressible soil exists, it may be very difficult to compact the fill properly. If poor material is left in place and covered over, it may compress over a long

Figure 12-8 Bottom dump truck, typically utilized for on-site hauling. (Courtesy of Caterpillar Tractor Company)

Earth Moving, Compaction, and Stabilization   Chap. 12

Figure 12-9 Power shovel loading operation. (Courtesy of Terex Division, General Motors Corporation)

period under the weight of the earth fill, causing settlement cracks in the fill or in any structure supported by the fill. Consequently, where the postconstruction settlement and deformation of an earth fill has to be limited, it is common practice to require that poor soil and nonsoil materials (vegetation, garbage, other waste material) by removed before filling commences.

To determine whether the surface zone of the natural soil is adequate for supporting the compacted fill, the area can be "proofrolled." Proofrolling consists of utilizing a piece of heavy construction equipment (typically, heavy compaction equipment or hauling equipment) to roll across the fill site and watching for poor areas to be revealed. Poor areas will be indicated by the development of rutting or ground weaving. Where the height of a structural fill will be limited, even marginally poor soils should be removed. If the height of fill is to be great, marginal materials often can be left in place without future adverse effect.

Placement of a compacted fill may have to begin at an elevation that is below the water table. This requirement frequently develops where the excavation of poor material lowers the beginning working surface. Fill placed under water should consist of coarse, granular material. Fine-grained soil should not be used. The thickness of the initial fill layer may have to be considerably greater than the normal fill layer (several feet thick) in order to create a working pad capable of supporting equipment used for the subsequent placement and compaction of fill. A procedure that has been followed with success in situations where the disturbance to the in-place underwater soil must be minimized is to create a working base of very coarse material, such as cobble sizes. Clean sand and gravel materials are placed over this base. Close to and above the water surface, the granular material can be compacted with conventional equipment. Once above the water table, the placement and compaction of fill layers can proceed in the normal manner; such upper fill can consist of fine-grained soil as well as granular soil.

The working surface of earth fills made with fine-grained soils can deteriorate rapidly if exposed to accumulations of water from rain or other causes. These fills should be constructed so that rapid surface drainage can occur. This need can be satisfied by placing fill so as to achieve a cambered or turtle-backed surface. When the fill area is lower in elevation than the surrounding terrain, as is frequently the situation during early stages of construction, interceptor drainage ditches should be provided around the perimeter of the fill site. Accumulating surface water is normally not a problem in fills constructed of granular soils, because the material's high percolation rate permits rapid dispersing. The major detrimental effect of surface water on granular soil fills is the erosion possibility on slope areas.

Compaction of backfill in narrow trenches and against buildings normally cannot be accomplished by using the compaction equipment utilized for areal fills. Small or hand-operated equipment is required, and progress may be comparatively slow. Soil densification in such confined spaces may be attempted by using flowing water, such as from a hose. This method can be successful where the backfill consists of clean granular material and the material surrounding and underlying the fill is also a coarse soil, for the flowing water percolates rapidly through the soil and does not puddle. This rapid flow causes a rearrangement of soil particles, and densification results. The method should *not* be attempted where the backfill is a fine-grained soil or where the surrounding soils do not possess a high permeability. With such conditions, the water will not flow rapidly through the fill and will not densify the soil. The water may puddle in the excavation, causing a loose soil structure to remain after drying occurs. For fine-grained backfills, compaction should be achieved through the use of compaction equipment and by working with thin soil layers.

Alternate Methods of Transporting Earth Fill

Most transporting of soil for earthwork projects is achieved through the use of construction equipment and methods discussed in preceding sections. However, where large quantities of material are to be moved, alternate methods of transportation should also be considered because of possible savings in cost or time. Methods that fall into this category are belt-conveyor transportation and hydraulic transportation.

Belt-conveyor systems offer the possibility for economic advantage where large volumes of material are moved for distances of up to several miles. A belt-conveyor system is usually constructed to closely follow the terrain it crosses and typically consists of a series of completely individual belt flights. Normally, each flight has its own drive motor. The transported material passes from one flight to another in order to complete the trip.

The belts of a conveyor system are available in different widths; stock belts run to 5 ft wide. Conveyor speeds can vary, and rates of several hundred feet per minute are practical. When the wider belts are used, it is easily possible to transport several hundred cubic yards of material per hour.

On a compacted fill project, earth received at the deposit end of the conveyor is usually moved and spread by using conventional earth fill equipment and procedures.

A major disadvantage of a belt-conveyor system is the expense and time to construct it. Construction costs include the necessity for a maintenance road for servicing during operation as well as the expense for erection and dismantling. Advantages include more independence from the effects of weather, easy round-the-clock operation, and reduced labor operating costs.

Hydraulic transportation refers to the method of mixing the borrow soil with large quantities of water and pumping the resulting slurry through a pipeline to a desired location. The method is highly dependent on an adequate source of water being available. Waterfront and dam-reservoir construction typify those projects that have the advantage of an available and economical source of water. For practical ease of handling at both the supply and the deposit ends, cohesionless soil or soil possessing only slight cohesion is the most desirable, although all soil types can be transported hydraulically.

Where a sand supply is located below water (a popular situation for hydraulic transportation), suction dredging methods are used. The sand is sucked into a flexible pipe extending from a pump into the soil supply and then is passed into the transporting pipe. Underwater cohesive soils are cut into chunks by powered rotating cutters before entering the flexible pipe. The slurry passing through the pipe is usually 80 to 90 percent water and 10 to 20 percent solids.

Above the water table, the borrow soil can be excavated and washed into a ponding area by utilizing high-pressure streams of water, whence it is then piped to the desired location.

Landfills can be created with hydraulically transported soil. Such fill is referred to as *hydraulic fill.* At a free-flowing outlet, the coarse soil particles drop out close to the point of discharge, and the smaller particles are carried a farther distance by the fanning-out water. This is similar to the natural formation of a soil delta where a river enters a lake. If mixed soils are transported, periodic movement of the discharge end of the pipe to planned locations permits fill areas of the desirable soil type (coarse soil areas and fine soil areas) to be obtained.

The natural side slopes created by a flowing coarse soil slurry are usually in the range of between five and ten horizontal to one vertical. Hydraulically transported soft clay soils may develop slopes as shallow as fifty to one. If it is necessary to contain the area receiving fill, dikes are constructed or sheetpiling is installed to form a ponding area. Soil particles will settle out of the slurry in this area. The water accumulating in the surface zone of the pond is drawn off. Sizable land areas have been reclaimed or created and relatively large earth dams have been constructed by using hydraulic fill methods.

Sand deposited by hydraulic methods will be in a relatively loose condition. Usually it is necessary to densify the soil if it is intended to provide structural support. Normal compaction procedures can be followed, using rolling equipment (preferably vibratory) to compact the fill in layers. Silt and clay hydraulic fills are difficult to compact after placement. These soil types would not be a choice for a structural fill but are used on land reclamation projects if economical sources of coarse material are not available. Where time permits, such fill is left to consolidate and stabilize naturally. Major structures are supported by piles or other special foundations. If necessary, the more involved and costly methods of densification, such as by pile driving or use of sand drains, could be performed, but results are somewhat unreliable.

Field Procedures—General Considerations, Methods, and Techniques **301**

FIELD EQUIPMENT—SURFACE ZONE COMPACTION

The construction of a structural fill usually consists of two distinct operations—the placing and spreading in layers and then the compaction process. The speed of the compaction operation is typically the more critical of the two steps and often controls the rate of a job's progress. The use of adequate and proper compaction equipment becomes a matter of economic necessity for contractors on almost all earth fill projects. Because of this need, various types of special compaction equipment have been developed for the construction industry. Some equipment has been designed to be specially effective for a particular soil type, whereas other equipment is for general or all-purpose use.

Soil compaction or densification can be achieved by different means—by tamping action, by kneading action, by vibrating, or by impact. Compactors operating on the tamping, kneading, and impact principles are effective on cohesive soils. For cohesionless soils, equipment operating on the kneading, tamping, and vibratory principles are effective.

Surface Compaction Equipment The *sheep's-foot roller* and similar rollers that have projecting studs or feet are examples of equipment that compacts by a combination of tamping and kneading. Typically, these compactors consist of a steel drum manufactured with small projections (see Figs. 12-10 and 12-11). With most rollers, the drum can be filled with water or sand to increase the weight. As rolling occurs, most of the roller weight is imposed through the projecting feet. Contact pressures imposed by the projections can be fairly high. Pressures vary from about 100 psi (700 kN/m^2) for the lighter equipment to over 600 psi (4200 kN/m^2) for the heavier equipment in common use.

When a loose soil layer is initially rolled, the projections sink into the layer and compact the soil near the lowest portion of the layer. In subsequent passes with the roller, the zone being compacted continues to rise until the surface is reached. This continually rising effect experienced by the compactor is referred to as "walking-out" by the compactor. Such equipment is well suited for compacting

Figure 12-10 Sheep's-foot rollers in use on a cohesive soil fill, being pushed-pulled by crawler tractors. (Courtesy of Fiat-Allis Chalmers Construction Machinery, Fiat-Allis Chalmers)

Figure 12-11 Close-up of projecting feet on a sheep's-foot roller.

clay and silt–clay soil.[1] The depth of layer that can be well compacted relates to the length of the projecting feet and the compactor weight. It is conventionally assumed that the larger, heavy units will properly compact layers on the order of 12 inches thick in three to five passes. Small, light equipment is limited to working layers less than 6 inches thick where high soil densities are required.

Sheep's-foot-type compactors are available as both self-propelled units and as rollers only. A separate roller requires a tow tractor.

Pneumatic tire rollers compact primarily by kneading. This type of compaction equipment is available in a variety of designs, ranging from the conventional two-wheel-per-axle units to the multiwheel-per-axle unit (Fig. 12-12). Some equipment is provided with a "wobble-wheel" effect, a design in which a slightly weaving path is tracked by the traveling wheel. Another type is provided with an axle construction that permits individual wheels to follow the ground surface so that low spots are not skipped over.

Pneumatic tire compactors are usually outfitted with a weight box or ballast box so that the total compaction load can be easily varied. Ground contact pressure can also be controlled somewhat by varying air pressure in the tires.

Pneumatic tire rollers are available as self-propelled units (Fig. 12-12) and as towed units (Fig. 12-13). These compactors are available in a wide range of load sizes, the heaviest having a capacity of about 200 tons (1800 kN). However, the heaviest units in common use are in the 50-ton (450-kN) range.

The pneumatic tire rollers are effective for compacting both cohesive and cohesionless soils and are the best type of equipment for general compaction use. Light rollers (about 20 tons, or 20,000 kg) are generally considered to be capable of properly compacting layers on the order of 6 inches (15 cm) thick, with few passes. Equipment in the 40- to 50-ton (40,000- to 50,000-kg) category will usually compact layers on the order of 12 inches (30 cm) thick, with three to five passes. The very heavy equipment is presumed to compact layers up to about 1½ feet (45 cm) thick, with a limited number of passes.

---

[1]Projection-type rollers are not recommended for cohesionless soil, because the studs (feet) continuously loosen the fill surface.

Field Equipment—Surface Zone Compaction

Figure 12-12 Pneumatic roller being used to compact sand base for a highway. (Courtesy of Galion Division of Dresser Industries, Inc.)

The effectivness of pneumatic tire compaction is not limited to the specially made compaction equipment. Other heavy-tire equipment, such as trucks, graders, and scrapers, is capable of providing an effective job of compaction (Fig. 12-14). In emergencies, such equipment can be pressed into service.

Vibratory compactors are available as vibrating drum, vibrating pneumatic tire, and vibrating plate equipment. With the vibrating drum equipment, a separate motor drives an arrangement of eccentric weights so that a high-frequency, low-amplitude, up-and-down oscillation of the drum occurs. Smooth drums and sheep's-

Figure 12-13 Fifty-ton pneumatic tire compactor showing soil-filled weight box.

Figure 12-14 Scrapers being utilized to haul and spread fill for a dam project. Note compaction effect achieved by rubber tire in photo foreground. (Courtesy of Fiat-Allis Construction Machinery, Fiat-Allis Chalmers)

foot-type drums are available. On the pneumatic tire compactor, the separate vibrating unit is attached to the wheel axle. The ballast box is suspended separately from the axle so that it does not vibrate. The vibrating plate equipment typically consists of a number of small plates, each of which is operated by a separate vibrating unit. The drum and the pneumatic-type equipment are available as either self-propelled or towed models.

On some vibratory compactors, the vibrating frequency can be varied by the equipment operator. Frequencies usually range between 1500 and 2500 cycles per minute, values that are within the natural frequency of most soils. The natural frequency is that value at which the soil particles tend to oscillate in unison, giving maximum effect to the repeated impact imposed by the compactor, instead of having a random oscillation of particles occur, which would create a damping effect. Particles are thus "shaken" into a more dense arrangement. Usually, for granular soils, the most effective results are achieved when the compactor travels at a slow speed, on the order of 2 to 4 mph (or 3 to 6 km/hr).

Smooth-drum vibrators (Fig. 12-15) have proven very effective in compacting

Figure 12-15 Vibratory smooth-drum compactor, typically used for cohesionless soil fills.

Field Equipment—Surface Zone Compaction

Figure 12-16 Vibratory compactor with pads on drum, used where soil has cohesion. (Courtesy of Dynapak, Stanhope, New Jersey)

granular soils having little or no silt- and clay-sized material. Layers on the order of 3 feet (1 m) deep have been compacted to high densities (densities close to the maximum modified Proctor value). As the percentage of fine material increases, the thickness of layer that can be well compacted is reduced.

The *vibratory pneumatic tire* equipment also has been successful in compacting primarily granular soil. It is commonly presumed that at least 1-foot-thick (30-cm) layers of predominantly granular soil will be satisfactorily compacted by most vibratory smooth drum and pneumatic tire compactors after a few passes.

The effectiveness of vibratory equipment on cohesive soil (Fig. 12-16) is not nearly so pronounced as the results achieved on granular soils.

The *vibrating plate* compactors generally have a limited depth of effectiveness. Their use has been primarily in compacting granular base courses for highway and airfield pavements.

Figure 12-17 Smooth-drum roller compacting a base course for a roadway. (Courtesy of Galion Division of Dresser Industries, Inc.)

Figure 12-18 Hand-maneuvered vibratory compactor for working close to structures. (Courtesy of Dynapak, Stanhope, New Jersey)

Conventional smooth-drum rollers (Fig. 12-17) are not well suited for compacting earth fill. Because of the size of the drum and the large soil contact area, the resulting compaction pressures are relatively low. Smooth-drum rollers can be utilized for compacting limited thicknesses of material, such as granular base course on highway and airfield work. On earth-moving projects, the smooth-drum roller can be used advantageously to "seal" the surface of the fill at the end of each work day. Sealing provides a smooth surface so that rain water will quickly run off from the work area; the water is not given the opportunity to percolate into the upper fill, where it might subsequently create a soft working surface.

Table 12-1 provides a generalized summary that relates soil fill type and compaction characteristics with equipment types considered suitable for achieving compaction.

Most self-propelled and towed equipment is large and cannot maneuver adequately to properly compact soil in confined areas and against structures. When structures are adjacent to a fill area, there should be a concern that heavy equipment will exert forces that could damage the structure. Consequently, small, portable compaction equipment should be utilized for working in areas of limited space and locations close to structures. Small vibratory drum and vibrating plate equipment is available (see Fig. 12-18). Pneumatic tampers and piston-type tampers are also available. It should be realized that with this small equipment, the thickness of the layer that can be compacted to a high density is frequently less than 6 inches.

DEEP GROUND IMPROVEMENT TECHNIQUES

The surface compaction equipment and procedures discussed in the preceding sections have the capability to improve in-place soils only to shallow depths. Typ-

TABLE 12-1   SOIL COMPACTION CHARACTERISTICS AND RECOMMENDED COMPACTION EQUIPMENT

General soil description	Unified soil classification	Compaction characteristics	Recommended compaction equipment
Sand and sand–gravel mixtures (no silt or clay)	SW, SP, GW GP	Good	Vibratory drum roller, vibratory rubber tire or pneumatic tire equipment
Sand or sand–gravel with silt	SM, GM	Good	Vibratory drum roller, vibratory rubber tire or pneumatic tire equipment
Sand or sand–gravel with clay	SC, GC	Good to fair	Pneumatic tire, vibratory rubber tire, vibratory sheep's-foot
Silt	ML	Good to poor	Pneumatic tire, vibratory rubber tire, vibratory sheep's-foot
	MH	Fair to poor	Pneumatic tire, vibratory rubber tire, vibratory sheep's-foot, sheep's-foot-type
Clay	CL	Good to fair	Pneumatic tire, sheep's-foot, vibratory sheep's-foot and rubber tire
	CH	Fair to poor	
Organic soil	OL, OH, PT	Not recommended for structural earth fill	

ically, depths below a few feet, or a meter or two, undergo little or no increase in density. However, techniques have been developed that utilize other special equipment and procedures to accomplish in-place improvement of thick zones of soil materials. Certain of these techniques are capable of changing soil properties to considerable depths. These deep soil improvement techniques represent a relatively new specialty area in the geotechnical construction industry. Included within the growing family of deep ground treatment systems that improve soil materials in place are the vibrocompaction procedures, the vibroreplacement procedure, the dynamic deep compaction procedure, an accelerated consolidation procedure through application of wick-drain installations, and stabilization via several methods of in-place grouting (slurry grouting, compaction grouting, chemical grouting, jet grouting). Where deep or thick zones of problem soil or fill materials exist, the deep ground treatment techniques may offer practical, economical alternatives to the selection of deep foundations or soil-fill replacement for making the site suitable for use. For the purpose of determining or ensuring the extent of a thick or deep zone's improvement, the treated area can be monitored; commonly, a program of in situ testing for the site prior to and subsequent to treatment is undertaken via use of borings or probings (e.g., using the standard penetration test or cone penetration testing).

The vibrocompaction and vibroreplacement procedures, the dynamic compaction procedure, and soil stabilization are described in the following sections; wick drains are discussed in Chapter 9.

Vibrocompaction   The vibrocompaction methods are suited for compacting thick deposits of loose sandy soil. The vibrocompaction equipment operates from a site's ground surface, but it can densify the full depth of granular deposits that are as deep as about 75 feet (25 m). The procedures followed by the specialty contractors vary, but the vibroflotation and Terra-Probe described below are indicative of the general methodology.

The vibroflotation method, illustrated in Figures 12-19 and 12-20, first compacts deep zones of soil and then works its way toward the surface. A cylindrical vibrator, weighing about 2 tons (18 kN) and approximately 6 ft (2 m) long and 16 inches (40 cm) in diameter, called the *Vibroflot®*, is suspended from a crane and jetted to the depth where compaction is to begin. The jetting consists of a pressured stream of water directed from the tip of the Vibroflot into the earth. As the sand is displaced, the Vibroflot simultaneously sinks into the soil. Depths of about 40 ft (12 m) can be reached. At a desired depth, the vibrator is activated. The Vibroflot vibrates laterally, an action that tends to cause the soil to compact in the *horizontal* direction. Typically, the material from 4 to 5 ft (1.5 m) outward from the Vibroflot is densified. Vibration continues as the Vibroflot is slowly raised to the surface. As the vibrating process occurs, additional sand is continually dropped into the space around the Vibroflot to fill the created void. To improve an entire site, treatment locations at approximately 10-foot (3-m) spacings are usually necessary.

The *Terra-Probe®* (Fig. 12-21) essentially consists of a vibrodriver (similar to the unit that is used for vibratory pile driving) coupled to an open-ended steel tubular probe (such as a 30-inch- or 76-cm-diameter pipe section). Activated, the

Figure 12-19 Vibroflotation equipment and process. (Courtesy of Vibroflotation Foundation Company, Pittsburgh, Pennsylvania)

Earth Moving, Compaction, and Stabilization   Chap. 12

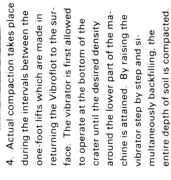

1. At start, lower jet is opened fully.

2. Water is introduced more rapidly than it can drain away. This creates a momentary "quick" condition ahead of the equipment, which permits the vibrating machine to settle of its own weight to the desired depth.

3. The water from the lower jet is transferred to the top jets and the pressure and volume are reduced just enough to carry the sand to the bottom of the hole.

4. Actual compaction takes place during the intervals between the one-foot lifts which are made in returning the Vibroflot to the surface. The vibrator is first allowed to operate at the bottom of the crater until the desired density around the lower part of the machine is attained. By raising the vibrator step by step and simultaneously backfilling, the entire depth of soil is compacted.

Figure 12-20 Details of vibroflotation: at the location to be compacted the Vibroflot is jetted into the soil. The compaction sequence has four basic steps, as shown. (Courtesy of Vibroflotation Foundation Company, Pittsburgh, Pennsylvania)

311

(a)   (b)

Figure 12-21 Terra-Probe® equipment (a) at a job site (note water-ponded surface to assist compaction); (b) close-up of vibrodriver and tubular probe. (Photos courtesy of L. B. Foster Company)

vibrodriver causes the probe to vibrate in the *vertical* direction. To achieve soil compaction, the probe is vibrated to the planned depth of penetration; then, with the vibrodriver continuing to operate, the probe is slowly drawn upward. The procedure densifies the soil within and closely surrounding the probe. Densification across a site is achieved by driving and extracting the probe at closely spaced intervals (e.g., spacings on the order of 5 ft, or 1.5 m, are frequently selected). The Terra-Probe operation works best if the groundwater table is within 5 to 10 ft (2–3 m) of the ground surface. For sites where the water table is deep, water jets can be incorporated onto the probe to assist the penetration and densification procedure, or the work area surface can be ponded or flooded to provide the desired water.

Some general comparisons of the vibroflotation and Terra-Probe methods are available. The lateral soil zone improved by each vibroflotation penetration is considerably larger than that with the Terra-Probe. To improve a given area uniformly, the Terra-Probe requires a more closely spaced penetration pattern than is necessary with vibroflotation. However, the Terra-Probe procedure is considerably faster than the vibroflotation procedure, and the greater number of probes that can be completed in a given time period compensates for the required closer spacing and greater number of probes. Though improvement in density is good with both procedures, the vibroflotation method apparently will achieve somewhat higher relative densities. Overall, in terms of time required to improve most sites equally (approximately), the vibroflotation and Terra-Probe methods are comparable. The Terra-Probe method does not require a sand fill and it can be used at offshore locations, important factors for some sites.

Vibroreplacement The vibroreplacement process uses the equipment and general techniques of the vibrocompaction methods, but crushed stone (or coarse gravel) material rather than sand is added and vibrated into the soil (see Fig. 12-22). The method is appropriate for improving sand deposits outside the range considered suitable for vibrocompaction (i.e., for sand deposits with more than 15 percent material finer than the #200 sieve) and for cohesive soils. The installed stone mixes with the in-place soil in the zone affected by the compactor probe; heavy concentration of stone at the immediate probe location results in a "stone column." Stone columns have been found capable of carrying loadings in the 10- to 40-ton range. The overall load-supporting capability of a treated area will be influenced by the spacing of the columns, typically in the 4- to 10-ft (1- to 3-m) range and the properties of the earth material underlying the improved soil zone.

Dynamic Deep Compaction Surface and near-surface zones of soil and fill material whose existing condition is considered marginal or inadequate for foundation support have been improved by a field procedure identified by various names, such as *dynamic compaction, pounding,* and *high-energy impact.* The method consists of dropping a heavy weight from a relatively great height; on projects to date, the weights have ranged from 2 tons to 50 tons, and drops have ranged from about 30 ft to 150 ft (10 to 45 m). For a given project, the weight and drop utilized relate to the crane equipment available and to the soil depth that requires improvement. Usually, a closely spaced grid pattern is selected for the pounding locations, and multiple poundings are provided at each drop location (typically, 5 to 10 drops). A repetitive series of pounding passes, at intervals of a day or more, may be required at some sites because of the character of the subsurface material. The process can densify loose cohesionless soils, fracture and densify buried building rubble such as that which exists at old building sites, consolidate fine-grained soils, and compact buried garbage fills. The pounding creates a depression at each drop location and also produces an areal settlement (see Fig. 12-23).

Realistically, the intent of the pounding process is to economically improve surficial zones of structurally marginal soil materials that exist at a site so as to obtain a foundation-supporting capacity that will be adequate for relatively light structures. When successful, the method precludes the need for the usual alternatives, such as expensive deep foundations or compacted earth fill that replaces the marginal material.

The depths that can be improved relate to the impact equipment and materials being treated. Because the method is relatively new, information available for prediction and design is general and approximate. Very compressible, cohesive, and energy-absorbent garbage and fill materials probably realize lesser depths of improvement than do uniform cohesionless soils. Generally, job experiences have

Figure 12-22 Depth vibrator for the vibrocompaction and vibroreplacement processes. Photo is from a vibroreplacement project. Note crushed rock for creating the stone column in the loader bucket. (Photo provided by GKN Hayward Baker Inc.)

indicated that the improvement depth for soil and rubble materials can be estimated from

$$D = \text{between } 0.3 \text{ and } 0.5 \text{ of } \sqrt{WH} \qquad (12\text{-}1)$$

where W = falling weight, tons.
    H = height of drop, meters.
    D = depth of zone receiving some improvement, meters.

The lower factor of 0.3 is suggested for landfill sites; the larger factors of 0.4 to 0.5 are suggested for soil sites.

The extent of improvement is greatest near the surface and diminishes with depth. The degree of improvement increases with the number of poundings, up to some limit that seems to be between five and ten drops for the typical conditions where the method is used. An increase in the number of poundings apparently does little to increase the depth of the soil zone being improved. Where saturated fine-grained soils are involved, a series of poundings, performed at intervals of one or several days to provide time for the dissipation of pore water pressures created by the previous sequence of poundings, may be required to achieve satisfactory results.

If the surface stratum is granular, it may remain or become loosened because of the nature of displacements caused by the poundings. In such a case, surface compaction can be achieved with conventional rolling equipment when the pounding procedure is completed.

Ground vibrations will carry horizontally from the pounding location, and there may be concern about damage when structures are located near an area being treated. On the basis of limited data, it appears that facilities farther than a distance L from the point of pounding will not experience damage, where

$$L \text{ in feet } = 5\sqrt{\text{impact energy in ft-lb}} \qquad (12\text{-}2)$$
(very approximately)

Compacting by Explosives Under proper conditions, explosives can be used to densify loose, sandy deposits. The shock wave and vibrations induced by the explosives' blast produce results similar to those achieved by vibratory compaction equipment. The method is most effective in dry cohesionless or completely saturated cohesionless soil. Where partial saturation exists, compressive stresses from the presence of air–water menisci act to prevent the soil-particle movement necessary for densification. With this method, the depth that can be effectively improved economically is usually limited. Loosest soils experience the most improvement. If variations exist in the original deposit, the blasting would tend to produce a more uniform deposit. Where explosives are used, it should be planned to compact the uppermost 3 feet or so by using conventional compaction methods, for little densification of this zone results from the blasting. Costwise, the technique compares well with other procedures for site improvement. However, the involvement of explosives and the concern of nuisance insurance claims limit the practical applications to remote areas.

SOIL STABILIZATION

Soil stabilization refers to the procedure in which a special soil, a cementing material, or some other chemical material is added to a natural soil material to improve one or more of its properties. One may achieve stabilization by mechanically mixing the natural soil and stabilizing material together so as to achieve a homogeneous

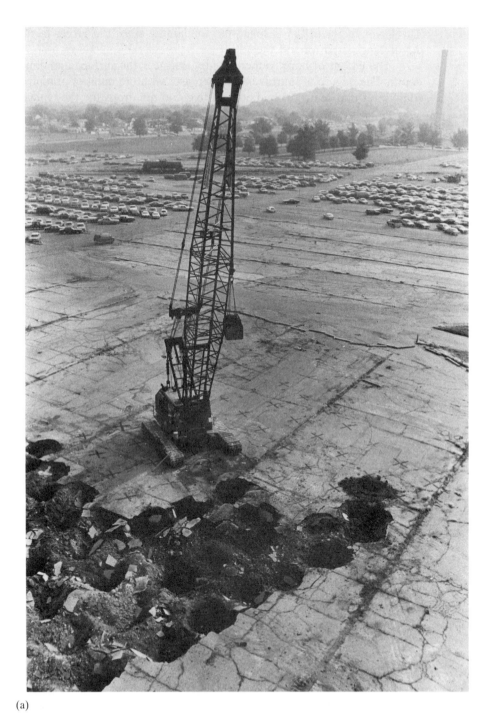

(a)

Figure 12-23 Dynamic deep compaction site: (a) photo indicating grid pattern for drop locations; (b) close-up of a drop location. (Photos provided by GKN Hayward Baker Inc.)

(b)

Figure 12-23 Continued.

mixture or by adding the stabilizing material to an undisturbed soil deposit and obtaining interaction by letting it permeate through the soil voids. Where the soil and the stabilizing agent are blended and worked together, the placement process usually includes compaction.

Many of the stabilization procedures of mixing and then compacting in place are for providing a limited thickness of treated material, such as in bases for road and airfield pavements and beneath floor slabs.

One of the more common methods of stabilization includes the blending of natural coarse aggregate and fine-grained soil to obtain a mixture that possesses some internal friction plus cohesion and provides a material that is workable during placement but will remain stable when in place and subject to a range of temperature and moisture changes. Improvement by the proportioning of coarse with fine soil is commonly referred to as *mechanical stabilization*. The proper combination of coarse- and fine-grained material (the latter is referred to as *binder*) is related to the size and shape of particles in the mixing materials. Generally, the best mixtures will include about one-quarter binder.

Sodium chloride and calcium chloride are additives noted for their water-holding properties. The presence of moisture in a soil creates capillary water in the voids, and the resulting compressive stresses imposed onto the soil particles increase the soil's internal shear strength. Spread on dirt roads, such materials help prevent dust. Calcium chloride is an especially preferable material on dirt roads, for it is capable of absorbing moisture from the air.

Portland cement and asphalt cement are additives intended to bond soil particles together. The result is a soil cement or asphalt-stabilized soil. In this respect, the cements are utilized as they are in the more familiar portland cement concrete and asphaltic concrete. In the stabilized soils, the range of soil aggregates is not as select as the materials used for the concretes. The strength of a stabilized soil will be less than that of the concretes. Mixing can be in place on-site or in a mixing plant. In the construction of a proper soil cement, the soil needs to be at a water content close to the optimum percentage necessary for maximum compaction. After the cement and soil have been mixed, the mixture is compacted in place. Typically, the quantity of cement required ranges from about 7 percent by weight for sandy soils to about 15 percent for clay soils. Requiring only a limited wearing surface, soil cements have been satisfactory as bases for roads carrying low to medium volumes of traffic, provided that wheel loads were not heavy.

Asphalt-stabilized soils are capable of serving as the combination base and wearing surface for low-volume roads not subject to heavy wheel loads or as a quality base material to support pavements of major roads.

Lime and calcium chloride have been used as additives to improve clay soils. A decrease in plasticity results as a base change, or exchanging of cations in the adsorbed water layers occurs. The resulting material is more friable than the original clay. The lime stabilization process requires mixing, then curing for a period of a few days, followed by remixing and compaction. The stabilized soil will possess strength similar to low-grade concrete. When mixed with expansive-type clays, volume changes are prevented. Lime has been successfully used to stabilize road materials in areas where expansive clays have been a problem.

Various combinations of commercial and natural chemicals have been successful in acting as sealing or cementing agents for soil. The general categories are the silicate chemicals, the polymers, and chrome-lignin. As an illustration, sodium silicate mixed with calcium chloride reacts quickly to form calcium silicate, a hard and impervious material. The polymers represent those materials resulting from combining chemically complex organic manomers with a second chemical that acts as a catalyst to cause polymerization, (joining together of molecules in the manomer). One of the most widely known soil stabilizers, AM-9, a polymer, has been found to possess hazardous characteristics, and the product AC-400 is being used as a replacement. Chrome-lignin is a slow-acting stabilizing gel formed from the reaction between the lignin in paper manufacture waste and sodium dichromate. The chemicals are typically water soluble and produce the reaction necessary to obtain a bonding of particles after being placed in the soil. With most chemical additives, the reaction does not include the soil particle. An advantageous feature of most chemical stabilizers is that their setting or curing time can be varied.

Grouting and injection stabilization are processes wherein a bonding material is forced into or through, or is mixed with a natural soil deposit in order to improve the strength, water resistance, or other properties. The method is utilized where it is necessary to improve soil that cannot be disturbed. Typically, this procedure is followed where treatment involves a considerable thickness or depth of earth or where the treated area is close to existing structures or other facilities that cannot be disturbed. Chemical stabilizers are the materials commonly used in the process. Many stabilizers are marketed under special trade names. Injection and grouting are usually handled by specialty contractors that have proper equipment and have developed familiarity with one or more stabilization procedures. The injection or grouting is done under pressure. The stabilizing material moves through the void spaces in the soil. Consequently, the more viscous stabilizers are limited to treating soils that have high coefficients of permeability. Some chemicals have viscosities comparable to water and can be used for finer soils, such as fine sand and silt deposits. At present, injection methods are not suitable for clay because of the very low permeability. With all injection-grouting methods, there is always some uncertainty in results obtained. The pressured stabilizer may follow paths through only the more permeable zones in a soil or along cracks and fissures and may not be distributed uniformly through the soil mass as desired. Figure 12-24 depicts the features of the general categories of grouting-injection stabilization.

A summary of methods and materials applicable for stabilizing in-place soil of different types is presented in Figure 12-25.

Fabrics of synthetic fibers (geofabrics, geotextiles) are being used to reinforce and stabilize soil masses. Fabric integrated with the earth fill behind retaining walls or in constructed embankments and areal fills acts as reinforcement (Fig. 12-26a, b, and c). In retaining walls and dams, the structure itself has been of earth and fabric construction (Fig. 12-26d).

Fabrics are widely used for erosion control on soil slopes and in areas exposed to flowing water. Fine-mesh fabrics are often utilized where the soil slope is also seeded; the soil surface is adequately protected against erosion from surface flow, while the mesh openings permit the vegetation to germinate and grow. The open

Soil Stabilization

(a) Slurry (intrusion) grouting: Pressurized grout material is forced into seams, joints, cavities of the earth material and through voids of the permeable materials.

(b) Compaction grouting: Low slump grout under high pressure forms a bulb whose volume displaces soil laterally and vertically, causing the soil to densify.

(c) Chemical grouting: Fluid grout under pressure permeates into the earth material; as the grout sets and solidifies, the included soil volume is strengthened.

(d) Jet grouting: High-energy erosive jets of water or air displace soil in the zone requiring treatment, while simultaneously a grout or cementing material is delivered into the created void; a grouted mass or, if mixing of soil and grout or cement is permitted, a cemented soil column results.

Figure 12-24 Features of general categories of grouting-injection stabilization. (After GKN Hayward Baker Inc. [271].)

texture allows water from within the slope to escape and not be trapped beneath the fabric. *Fabric mattresses* are receiving increasing usage where erosion protection against flowing water is required. Generally, mattresses consist of a double layer of fabric whose interior cell will subsequently be filled, usually with concrete or grout material. At the construction site, the "empty" mattresses are assembled to achieve the necessary area and placed on the slopes to be protected. Typically, concrete or grout is then pumped into the mattress to provide a slope protection covering that possesses strength and durability (Fig. 12-26e). Advantages to the mattress method include ease of installation on slopes and underwater surfaces without the need for forming or dewatering.

METHODS FOR ESTABLISHING REQUIRED SOIL DENSITY

On structural earth fill projects, job specifications will indicate the soil density (unit weight) or degree of compaction that must be achieved in order for the fill to be considered satisfactory. The job specification requirements are typically based

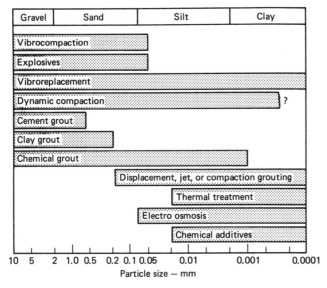

(a) Methods and particle-size range for in-place treatment of soils

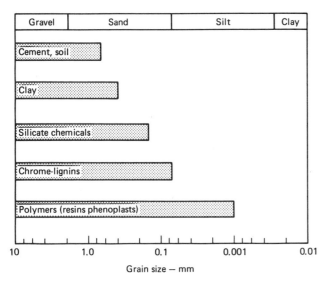

(b) Particle size ranges to which different grout materials apply

Figure 12-25 Summary of various methods for stabilizing in-place soils. (Modified from Mitchell [168])

on the results of laboratory compaction tests (more properly described as moisture-density tests) performed on representative samples of soil to be used in the filling operation. The laboratory test determines the maximum density (or unit weight) for the soil and the influence of moisture content on obtaining that density.

The most widely used procedure for moisture-density testing consists of compacting the soil in layers in a cylindrical mold by using a drop hammer (equipment

(a) Conventional retaining wall with fabric reinforced backfil (pervious fabrics)

(b) Constructed slopes or embankments provided with fabric reinforcing

(c) Ground reinforcement to help obtain support for light structural loading

(d) Retaining wall of fabric and soil construction

(e) Fabric mattress for slope protection of open channel

Figure 12-26 Use of fabrics to reinforce and stabilize soil masses, and to provide slope protection.
(a) Conventional retaining wall with fabric reinforced backfill (previous fabrics).
(b) Constructed slopes or embankments provided with fabric reinforcing.
(c) Ground reinforcement to help obtain support for light structural loading.
(d) Retaining wall of fabric and soil construction.
(e) Fabric mattress for slope protection of open channel.

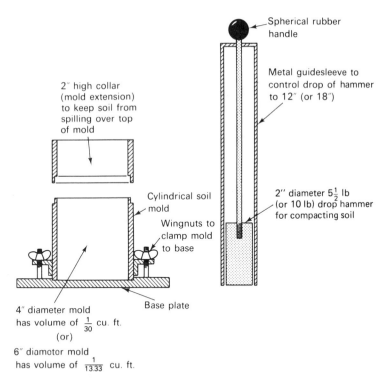

2" high collar
(mold extension)
to keep soil from
spilling over top
of mold

Cylindrical soil
mold

Wingnuts to
clamp mold
to base

4" diameter mold
has volume of $\frac{1}{30}$ cu. ft.
(or)
6" diameter mold
has volume of $\frac{1}{13.33}$ cu. ft.

Base plate

Spherical rubber
handle

Metal guidesleeve to
control drop of hammer
to 12" (or 18")

2" diameter $5\frac{1}{2}$ lb
(or 10 lb) drop hammer
for compacting soil

Figure 12-27 Widely used cylindrical mold and drop-hammer type of apparatus for performing moisture-density (compaction) test.

illustrated in Fig. 12-27). For a particular method, the mold will have set dimensions, and the number of layers used to fill the mold will be specified, as will the weight and drop of the compacting hammer. To establish the moisture-density relationship for a soil, separate samples are each compacted at a different water content. Each sample is compacted in the same manner (same volume, same number of layers, same compaction energy). The compacted dry density and water content for each trial is then determined by weighing and drying the soil.

A comparison of results obtained from all the samples will reveal that the dry densities are different. This is caused by the variation in water content present during the compaction process. If the results obtained from all samples are plotted on dry density versus water content coordinates, a curve as indicated in Figure 12-28 is developed. From such a plot, the maximum dry density is evident. The water content corresponding to the maximum density is termed the *optimum moisture content*. The optimum moisture is the best water content for achieving a high density for the given soil when a compaction energy corresponding to the particular laboratory test method is used.

With sands, the influence of moisture on the compacted density at low water contents is less well defined than for fine-grained soils (see Fig. 12-29). A scattering of dry density versus water content points is rather usual at moisture contents below the optimum. However, the information obtained from the overall test is still useful.

Methods for Establishing Required Soil Density   **323**

Figure 12-28 Typical moisture-density curve obtained from laboratory compaction test trials.

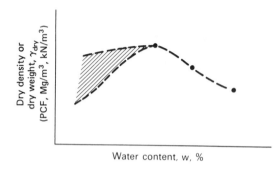

Figure 12-29 Representative moisture-density curve expected for sands, indicating indefinite location of curve at low water contents.

It should never be expected that compaction will result in a no-void space condition for the soil, primarily because of the irregular shapes and various sizes of soil particles. Reference to a moisture-density curve should reaffirm the necessity for the presence of water and void spaces.

In Figure 12-30, the curve representing a typical moisture-density relationship is shown, along with a curve showing the 100 percent saturation (or zero-air-voids) condition. The moisture-density curve approaches but does not overlap the zero-air-voids curve. This indicates that some air will always exist in void spaces during compaction.

The moisture-density curve for one method of compaction, as represented by Figure 12-28, shows the maximum dry density for that test. If the results of a second test, which imparts more compaction energy, are included on the same coordinates, the new curve will be located upward and to the left, indicating that a greater dry density is attained at a lower optimum moisture content (see Fig. 12-31). Typically, a greater compaction energy results in a greater dry density, coupled with a reduced dependency on water content in obtaining that maximum density.

The development of the aforementioned general method, which establishes the influence of water content on the ability of a soil to be compacted and provides a value of compacted density to use for field control, is credited to R. R. Proctor. Proctor developed the laboratory test procedure while working with compacted earth dam projects in the early 1930s. The laboratory procedure established by Proctor utilized a 4-inch-diameter mold having a volume of $\frac{1}{30}$ cubic foot and a 2-inch-diameter $5\frac{1}{2}$-lb hammer having a 1-foot drop, and indicated that three layers be used to fill the mold, with each layer receiving 25 blows of the drop hammer.[2]

[2]ASTM Test Designation D-698.

Figure 12-30 Zero-aid-voids curve related to moisture-density curve, indicating that soil does not become fully saturated by compaction.

Figure 12-31 Effect of compaction procedure on dry density. Curve 1 represents results from method using heavier compaction hammer and greater compaction energy than used to obtain curve 2.

This test is commonly referred to as the standard Proctor compaction test. The energy used to compact one cubic foot of soil is 12,400 ft-lb. This energy compared favorably with the compaction energy transmitted by construction equipment in use at the time the method was developed.

With subsequent technological advances came the development of heavier vehicles and airplanes that would have to be supported on compacted earth bases, plus the desire to construct larger earth structures and the intent to support heavy building structures on compacted earth. Larger and heavier earth-moving and soil-compaction equipment was created. Consequently, laboratory test procedures were developed that would use a greater compactive energy and obtain higher values of dry density than the standard Proctor test. What has become known as the modified Proctor compaction test utilizes a 4-inch-diameter mold having a volume of $\frac{1}{30}$ cubic foot, as before, but it requires a 10-lb hammer having a drop of 18 inches. Soil to fill the mold is compacted in five layers, with each layer receiving 25 blows.[3] The energy used to compact one cubic foot of soil in this test is 56,250 ft-lb, a value comparing favorably with that provided with current construction methods. The presentation of laboratory data and the resulting moisture-density (unit weight) curve for a soil compacted in accord with the modified Proctor requirements are shown in Figure 12-32.

If the compaction samples contain significant coarse material, a larger mold should be used, for the presence of coarse aggregates such as gravel in the $\frac{1}{30}$-cubic-foot mold can give dry densities that are too high to represent field conditions. A

[3]ASTM Test Designation D-1557.

Methods for Establishing Required Soil Density

Compaction method

1. — 1/30 cu. ft. mold, 5-1/2 lb hammer, 12" drops, 3 layers @ 25 blows/layer
2. — 0.075 cu. ft. mold, 5-1/2 lb hammer, 12" drop, 3 layers @ 56 blows/layer
3. — 1/30 cu. ft. mold, 10 lb hammer, 18" drop, 5 layers @ 25 blows/layer
4. — 0.075 cu. ft. mold, 10 lb hammer, 18" drop, 5 layers @ 50 blows/layer

Trial	1	2	3	4	5	6	7
Wet density determinations							
Weight of mold and wet soil	13.84	14.30	14.00	13.89			
Weight of mold	9.32	9.32	9.32	9.32			
Weight of wet soil (W_T)	4.52	4.98	4.68	4.57			
Wet unit weight	135.6	149.4	140.4	137.1			
Moisture determinations							
Cup identification	B-1	B-2	B-3	B-4			
Weight of cup plus wet soil	39.10	55.30	66.60	75.48			
Weight of cup plus dry soil	38.15	52.81	62.28	68.53			
Weight of cup	15.10	14.21	14.43	14.33			
Weight of dry soil	23.05	38.60	47.85	54.20			
Weight of water	0.95	2.49	4.32	6.95			
Water content — %	4.0	6.5	9.0	12.8			
Dry unit weight — PCF	130.3	140.3	129.0	121.5			
— Mg/m³	2.09	2.25	2.07	1.95			

Figure 12-32 Laboratory moisture-density test results.

6-inch-diameter mold having a volume of 0.075 cubic foot is commonly used in place of the smaller mold. Layers are compacted with 56 blows of the drop hammer.

Variations of the drop-hammer methods described above exist throughout the many organizations involved in developing earthwork specifications. Most commonly, the size of the drop hammer or mold is changed, or the number of layers or blows is varied as necessary to reflect local experiences or preferences. However, other types of laboratory test methods, such as those using kneading forces, have also been developed in attempts to reproduce more closely conditions resembling field compaction procedures. Their use has been limited because of the specialized techniques involved and the establishment of the method described previously. On a comparison basis, results obtained with other methods are not significantly different from the drop-hammer results.

A summary of the details for the laboratory compaction tests in common use is shown in Table 12-2.

Typical earthwork specifications for a structural fill project will require that the soil be compacted to a density equal to at least X percent of the maximum density obtainable with the (standard or modified) Proctor laboratory compaction test method. Currently, many compacted fills for buildings, roads, and dams use the modified Proctor as the reference test. For small dams, the standard Proctor may still be the reference. It is common to require that at least 95 percent of the maximum laboratory density be obtained by the field compaction (refer to Fig. 12-33). Other typical requirements are 90 percent and 92 percent. The percentage selected is usually determined by the project designer on the basis of the project's requirements (e.g., fill for a parking area or fill beneath a building area) and his experience with various soil types. Occasionally, a requirement of 100 percent or greater is found, particularly for granular soils. Unless the project is unusual, such a high percentage should not be required. Values of 100 percent compaction referred to the modified Proctor test will be close to the maximum relative density for many sands (relative density is described in Chap. 4).

When it is assumed that field compaction energy is similar to laboratory compaction energy, accepting a field compaction density less than the maximum laboratory density reduces the criticalness of water content in the fill soil. Reference to a moisture-density curve will reveal that it is possible to achieve a field density equal to, say, 95 percent compaction over a comparatively wide range of water content (Fig. 12-33).

Usually, the dry density of the soil being placed is the major item of concern on a compacted fill project. The water content of the compact soil is normally not specified and is left to the choice of the contractor. An exception is on deep fills and earth dam projects involving cohesive soils, where the water content during placement and compaction is limited to the optimum but preferably is slightly lower. If the water content is above optimum, excess pore water pressures may develop in the lower fill zones due to the weight of overlying material. Excess pore pressures interfere with the development of soil shear strength (see Eq. 10-3). Embankment failure due to inadequate shear strength may result.

Results of laboratory compaction tests are frequently included with the job specifications data assembled for a project. Experienced earth-moving contractors will pay close attention to the moisture-density curve(s) and the natural moisture content(s) of the fill soil, for a comparison will indicate if the fill requires wetting or drying before compaction. If laboratory compaction results are not available, the approximate ranges of optimum water contents from modified Proctor tests, presented in Table 12-3, can be used as a guide to evaluate the water content condition of a borrow soil (too wet or too dry).

Methods for Establishing Required Soil Density

TABLE 12-2 SUMMARY OF COMMON COMPACTION TEST EQUIPMENT AND PROCEDURES

ASTM designation	AASHTO designation	Mold size	Hammer weight and drop	Number of layers at blows per layer	Upper particle size limits (sieve size)
D-698 (A)*	T-99 (A)	4-in. dia, $\frac{1}{30}$ ft³	5.5 lb @ 12 in.	3 at 25	#4
(B)	(B)	6-in. dia, 0.075 ft³	5.5 lb @ 12 in.	3 at 56	#4
(C)	(C)	4-in. dia, $\frac{1}{30}$ ft³	5.5 lb @ 12 in.	3 at 25	$\frac{3}{4}$ in.
(D)	(D)	6-in. dia, 0.075 ft³	5.5 lb @ 12 in.	3 at 56	$\frac{3}{4}$ in.
D-1557 (A)†	T-180 (A)	4-in. dia, $\frac{1}{30}$ ft³	10 lb @ 18 in.	5 at 25	#4
(B)	(B)	6-in. dia, 0.075 ft³	10 lb @ 18 in.	5 at 56	#4
(C)	(C)	4-in. dia, $\frac{1}{30}$ ft³	10 lb @ 18 in.	5 at 25	$\frac{3}{4}$ in.
(D)	(D)	6-in. dia, 0.075 ft³	10 lb @ 18 in.	5 at 56	$\frac{3}{4}$ in.

*Standard Proctor compaction test.
†Modified Proctor compaction test.

Figure 12-33 Example of method to compute density for a specified percentage of compaction and related range of water content.

TABLE 12-3 APPROXIMATE RANGE OF OPTIMUM MOISTURE CONTENT VERSUS SOIL TYPE

Soil type	Probable value of optimum moisture, %, modified Proctor test
Sand	6–10
Sand–silt mixture	8–12
Silt	11–15
Clay	13–21

FIELD CONTROL AND FIELD DENSITY TESTS

Where soil fill is compacted for a project or deep compaction is performed, it is usual to obtain some type of check or verification of the improvement. Surface zones of soil commonly are checked using an in-place density test procedure. Deep zones commonly are checked by evaluating soil resistance using the standard penetration test (SPT) or the cone penetrometer test (CPT).

On compacted earth fill projects, it is usual practice to have in-place density tests performed on the compacted soil layers to ensure that the desired density is being achieved. Typically, each layer is tested at several random locations after it has been compacted. When tests indicate that satisfactory compaction has been obtained, the contractor can begin placement of the next layer. If the density tests indicate inadequate compaction, the contractor is notified and more compaction rolling is performed. Normally, the personnel doing in-place density testing are directly responsible to the project owner or designer and are independent of the earthwork contractor.

Several methods for determining or checking in-place density are in use. The simpler, more direct methods involve the "destructive testing" principle: A small hole is excavated in the compacted layer and its volume is determined. The wet soil obtained from the hole is weighed and the water content is determined; these values permit the dry soil weight to be calculated. Knowing the dry soil weight and the in-place volume permits the dry density or unit weight to be determined. The *sand-cone method* and the *rubber-balloon method* are the most widely utilized applications of this type of testing.

A "nondestructive" type of testing is provided with nuclear moisture-density-determining apparatus. With such equipment, a nuclear source emits gamma rays, which are passed into the soil and reflected back to a detector. The gamma photon energy received at the detector is calibrated to indicate the wet density of the soil material. The amount of moisture is determined by calibration to a "thermal neutron" count moving through the soil from a fast neutron source. Moisture readouts are expressed as weight or mass of water per unit of volume (i.e., pounds per cubic foot or grams per cubic centimeter).

Moisture-density determinations using the sand-cone and balloon methods are relatively time-consuming. The minimum time required to complete all steps necessary to obtain a dry density and moisture determination at one location could be on the order of one-half hour. This is a drawn-out period in which construction progress awaits answers. When a series of in-place density determinations are made for a large area—a usual procedure—the time to obtain results is even greater. The time required for the performance of such testing is frequently cited as a major drawback. In contrast, density and moisture determinations are rapid with a nuclear apparatus. Results for a test location are typically available in one to two minutes. At present, disadvantages associated with the use of nuclear moisture-density equipment include the relatively high purchase cost and the safety precautions necessary when one is dealing with a radioactive material.

On fill projects involving sufficient area, density testing can be planned to minimize interference with soil placement and compaction. If work operations are scheduled so that one area is receiving a fill layer while a different area is being compacted, the density testing is performed at locations that are believed to have received adequate passes of the compaction equipment. As soon as testing indicates that an area has been properly compacted, the compaction equipment moves over to begin work on a newly placed layer. Placement of a new layer begins in the area just checked.

When the source of a fill soil is from a natural deposit, it should be anticipated that the soil and its properties may vary within the deposit. Consequently, when density tests are performed, the tested soil type should be examined for correlation to the soil used to obtain the moisture-density curve. If a difference in soil exists, the laboratory-determined density value may not apply.

Field control of a compacted fill project should involve more than making in-place density tests. The thickness of newly placed soil layers should be watched to the greatest extent possible; proper depth and the possibility of undesirable soil's being mixed with the desirable soil should be checked. The behavior of the ground surface as earth hauling or compaction equipment moves over it should also be observed. Rutting, weaving, or other movement of the ground surface is typically an indication that poor soil exists at the surface or is buried below it. Where poor material is observed and it cannot be improved by additional compaction, it should be excavated and removed from the fill area. Restoring the area to grade involves placement and compaction of soil in layers, as is required at all other locations. With experience, field personnel will impose better control over a fill project by observing the performance of equipment travelling over fill areas than by continuously making in-place density tests. Density tests are performed frequently at the beginning of the project to establish a familiarity with the soil types and related moisture. As the project progresses, the amount of density testing can be reduced. The running of in-place density determinations should not be discontinued completely, however, for they represent one of the permanent written records relating to earthwork performed for the project.

Sand-Cone Method   Determinations of in-place density using the sand-cone method involve the use of a sand-cone apparatus for obtaining only the volume of a density test hole. Field density (really field unit weight) will be soil weight divided by total volume occupied. The soil weight is determined directly by using the actual soil removed from the test hold. The water content is calculated after obtaining the wet and dried weight of the soil.

The sand-cone apparatus derives its name from the shape of the cone funnel and sand jar, as shown in Figure 12-34. The volume of a test hole is determined by weighing the amount of sand originally in the jar that is necessary to fill the test hole. The sand utilized with this equipment is a dry, free-flowing, uniformly graded sand whose bulk density (unit weight) is known. Bulk density is the sand weight (voids included) per unit volume. Ottowa sand having a bulk density on the order of 100 pcf (16 kN/m³) is commonly used. If the weight of jar sand to fill the test hole is known, the volume of the hole is easily calculated. Test holes up to about 6 inches (15 cm) in diameter and 6 inches deep can be made with conventional equipment. Details of the sand-cone equipment and test procedure are presented in ASTM Test Designation D-1556.

Balloon Method   As with the sand cone, the balloon apparatus is actually limited to determining the volume of a density test hole. The weight of soil necessary

Figure 12-34   Sand-cone density test being performed at a construction project.

1. Position base plate on flat test surface and set Volumeasure in place. Open valve for inflation of balloon. Pump down until water level in cylinder reaches lowest level. Take the initial base reading. Reverse bulb for vacuum. Pump balloon up into cylinder.

2. Remove Volumeasure, leaving base plate in place as template for hole. Dig down through opening in base to make hole to desired depth. Keep all removed soil in tight can for weight measurement.

3. Set Volumeasure on base plate over hole. Insert inflation end of bulb into holder hole.

4. Pump balloon down into hole. Record lowest point reached by water on the cylinder scale.

5. Invert the inflation-vacuum bulb to put it in vacuum position and pump balloon back up into cylinder. To determine volume of hole, subtract initial base reading from final reading.

Figure 12-35 Five-step procedure for using balloon apparatus to determine in-place density. Equipment demonstrated is the Soiltest Volumeasure. (Courtesy of Soiltest, Inc.)

to complete a density calculation is determined by direct measurement of the material dug from the test hole.

The typical balloon apparatus (Fig. 12-35) consists of a water-filled vertical cylinder having a bottom opening over which a rubber membrane or balloon is stretched. The cylinder is constructed so that water levels in it are visible. Graduation marks indicating volumes are etched onto the sides of the cylinder. A small hand pump (bulb or piston type) is attached so that air can be forced into the top of the cylinder. When the apparatus is placed over a density hole, the pumped air forces the balloon and water into the hole. The volume is determined directly by noting the water level in the cylinder before and after the balloon is forced into the hole. The water and balloon are retracted from the test hole by reversing the air pump and evacuating air from the cylinder. Outside atmospheric pressure forces the water and balloon back into the cylinder. The apparatus is then ready for another test location.

Rubber-balloon equipment is available in a range of sizes. The smaller, more typical type is capable of measuring holes approximately 4 inches in diameter and 6 inches deep (10 cm and 15 cm). Larger equipment can measure larger holes. More information on the balloon-type apparatus and test method is presented in ASTM Test Procedure D-2167.

Nuclear Moisture-Density Method   Surface-type nuclear moisture-density equipment (Fig. 12-36) is coming into more prevalent use for performing density tests on compacted fill, replacing the sand-cone and rubber-balloon methods, primarily because of the rapid results that can be obtained.

Figure 12-36 Nuclear moisture-density apparatus in use. (Courtesy of Troxler Electronic Laboratories, Inc., North Carolina)

Field Control and Field Density Tests

The principal elements in a nuclear density apparatus are the nuclear source, which emits gamma rays, a detector to pick up the gamma rays or photons passing through the tested soil, and a counter or scaler for determining the rate at which the gamma rays reach the detector.

Commonly used nuclear sources include radium–beryllium and cesium–americium–beryllium combinations in equipment where moisture determinations as well as density information are to be provided. The detectors usually consist of gas-filled Geiger-Mueller tubes.

When the equipment is in use, the gamma rays penetrate into the soil, where some are absorbed, but some reach the detector by direct transmission or after reflecting off soil mineral electrons. The amount of gamma radiation reaching the detector is inversely proportional to the soil density. Densities (unit weights) are determined by obtaining a nuclear count rate received at the detector and relating such readings to calibration readings made on materials of known densities. Calibration curves are provided by the equipment manufacturer. The density determined by this method is a wet, or total, density.

Moisture determinations are obtained from a "thermal neutron" count. Alpha particles emitted from the americium or radium source bombard a beryllium target. This bombardment causes the beryllium to emit fast neutrons. These fast neutrons lose velocity if they strike the hydrogen atoms in water molecules. The resulting low-velocity neutrons are thermal neutrons. Moisture results are provided as weight or mass of water per unit of volume. Dry densities are obtained by subtracting the moisture determination from the wet density determination. With this method for determining moisture, significant error can result if the soil contains iron, boron, or cadmium.

Several field procedures for making the moisture-density determinations are available. The direct transmission mode, as indicated in Figure 12-37a, provides the most accurate results. In this method, the radioactive source is placed into the test material by utilizing a punched or drilled hole. Depths between 2 and 12 inches can be tested with conventional equipment.

The backscatter method operates by locating both the radioactive source and the detector on the surface of the test material (see Fig. 12-37b). The gamma rays are directed into the soil and some are reflected back to the detector. With this method, accuracy suffers if a gap exists anywhere between the bottom of the device and the soil surface.

A third procedure, the air-gap method, requires that the nuclear device sit a distance above the surface of the test material, as indicated in Figure 12-37c. The accuracy obtained with this method is related to attaining a proper gap height for the equipment.

The direct transmission method provides information on the soil volume surrounding the gamma rays' source, whereas the backscatter and air-gap methods provide data on the zone of soil nearest the surface at the test location. More detailed information for making moisture-density determinations by nuclear methods is presented in ASTM Test Procedure D-2922.

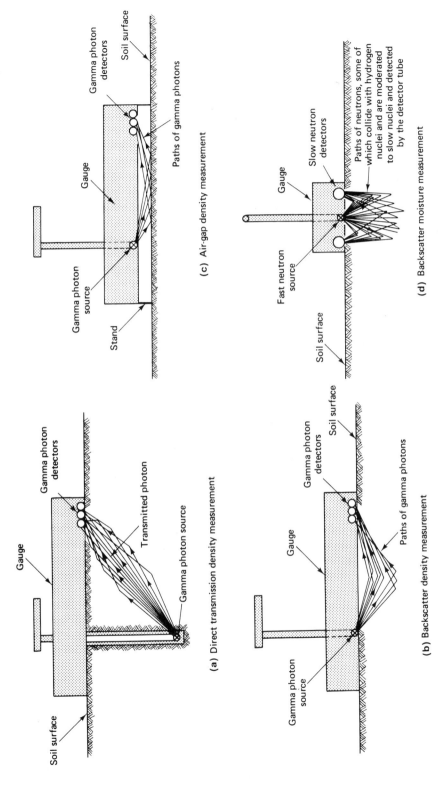

(a) Direct transmission density measurement

(c) Air-gap density measurement

(b) Backscatter density measurement

(d) Backscatter moisture measurement

Figure 12-37 Illustration of different modes for measuring soil density and moisture content by nuclear methods. (Courtesy of Troxler Electronic Laboratories, Inc., North Carolina)

PROBLEMS

12.1. Indicate the best type, and also other suitable types, of compaction equipment (such as sheep's-foot roller, vibratory roller) to use for easiest compaction of the following soil materials:
(a) Material A: well-graded fine to coarse sand.
(b) Material B: silty fine to coarse sand, trace clay.
(c) Material C: silt of low plasticity, trace clay and sand.
(d) Material D: silty clay of low plasticity.
(e) Material E: sand–silt–clay mixture, some gravel.

12-2. A contractor has bid on two different earth-moving–compacted fill projects. One project involves cohesionless soil, the other cohesive soil. The volume of soil to be excavated, transported, and compacted is similar for both projects. All working conditions are similar for both projects. The contractor's bid for compacted fill on the cohesive soil project is 50 percent greater than for compacted fill at the cohesionless soil project. Indicate whether the contractor's bidding practice is proper or not, and why.

12-3. For an earth-moving project, the contractor is required to assume the responsibility for locating a source of off-site borrow to use for compacted fill. Two possible sources are found; the cost of purchase and hauling from either will be comparable. At location A, the soil is a silt–clay material and is found to have a natural moisture content in the 10- to 20-percent range. At location B, the soil is also cohesive and is found to have a natural water content in the 30- to 40-percent range. The contractor selects location A. Indicate whether this represents a good choice, and why.

12-4. The following moisture-density data are results from laboratory compaction tests:

Water content, %	Dry unit weight, pcf
8	111
11	113
14	115
17	114
20	109

(a) Plot the moisture-density curve and indicate maximum density and optimum moisture content.
(b) What range of water content appears advisable in order to obtain 92 percent (or more) compaction?

12-5. A series of laboratory compaction tests on the same soil provides the moisture and density information shown. Plot the dry density-moisture curve and determine the maximum dry density and optimum moisture content.

Water content, %	Wet density, pcf
7.0	118
9.5	129
13.5	136
15.0	132

12-6. Laboratory compaction test results for a soil are tabulated below. Review the data and determine if there are errors.

Water content, %	Wet density, pcf	Dry density, pcf
9	122	112
12	129	117
15	137	119
18	107	109

12-7. Laboratory compaction tests have been performed on several different soils. The maximum dry density and optimum moisture content for each soil are as shown. Determine the probable type (classification) of soil for each test.

Soil	Max. dry density, pcf	Optimum moisture, %
A	119	9
B	124	18
C	114	14

12-8. Sand-cone equipment is used to perform a field density test on a compacted earth fill. Ottowa sand is used in the cone and is known to have a bulk density of 100 pcf.
(a) From the information given below, determine the in-place dry density of the tested soil and the water content.

Soil sample dug from test hole, wet weight	= 4.62 lb
Dried weight of soil sample	= 4.02 lb
Weight of Ottowa sand (san cone) to fill test hole	= 3.60 lb

(b) Determine the percentage of compaction of the tested soil if the laboratory moisture-density curve indicates a dry density of 115 pcf and an optimum moisture content of 13 percent.

12-9. A balloon-type apparatus is used to perform a field density test. The volume of the test hole determined by reading the water level gradations on the apparatus cylinder before and after digging the test hole is 0.025 ft³. The wet weight of soil obtained from the test hole is 3.10 lb. The water content is determined to be 14 percent by drying a small sample on a field stove.
(a) Determine the in-place dry density of the tested soil.
(b) Determine the percentage of compaction if the tested soil is a compacted fill whose maximum density (from laboratory compaction tests) is 118 pcf.

12-10. Indicate the general advantages and disadvantages associated with hydraulic fill placement methods.

12-11. It is proposed to stop groundwater from seeping through a building's basement walls by pressure-injecting a bentonite clay slurry into the soil against the exterior of the leaking walls to seal the walls on the outside. The soil type is silt–clay. Will the method work in the indicated soil conditions?

12-12. Asphalt, cement, and lime are commonly used to stabilize soil for road bases. Which of these seems most suitable for stabilizing the following?

(a) Sand.

(b) Sand–silt mixture.

(c) Silt with trace of sand and clay.

(d) Clay with silt.

chapter 13

Foundations
Introductory Concepts

For many of man's structures, it is the earth underlying the structure that provides the ultimate support. The soil at a building location automatically becomes a material of construction affecting the structure's stability. Typically, soil is a material weaker than the other common materials of construction, such as steel, concrete, and wood. To carry a given loading satisfactorily, a greater area or volume of soil is necessarily involved. In order for loads carried by steel, concrete, or wood structural members to be imparted to the soil, load transfer devices—the structural foundations—are required. The major purpose of the structural foundation is the proper transmission of building loading to the earth in such a way that the supporting soil is not overstressed and does not undergo deformations that would cause serious building settlement. The type of structural foundation utilized is closely related to the properties of the supporting soils. A structural foundation performs properly only if the supporting soil behaves properly. Consequently, it is important to recognize that building support is actually being provided by a soil–foundation system, a combination that cannot be separated. Designers and constructors are aware of this relationship, but it has become common practice to consider the structural foundation separately, primarily because it is a cost item that is built or installed, while the supporting soil is usually the natural earth that "is there."

Since the soil–foundation system is responsible for providing support for the lifetime of a structure, it is important that all forces that may act over that time period are considered. For a building to last, its foundations should be designed for the worst conditions that may develop. Typically, the foundation design always includes the effect of the structure's dead plus live loads. It is important also to consider load effects that may result from wind, ice, frost, heat, water, earthquake, and explosive blasts.

GENERAL TYPES OF FOUNDATIONS—FOUNDATION CATEGORIES

The various types of structural foundations can be grouped into two broad categories—shallow foundations and deep foundations. Generally, the classification indicates the depth of the foundation installation and the depth of the soil providing most of the support. Spread footing and mat (or raft) foundations usually fall within the shallow foundations category. Deep foundation types include piles, piers, and caissons. The floating foundation, a special category of foundation, is actually not a different type, but it does represent a special application of soil mechanics principles to a combination mat–caisson foundation.

Spread Footings Spread footing foundations are typically of plain concrete or reinforced concrete, although masonry and timber have also been used. The spread footing foundation is basically a pad used to "spread out" building column and wall loads over a sufficiently large soil area. Spread footings are constructed as close to the ground surface as the building design permits (considering requirements such as basements or the need to resist lateral forces) and as controlled by local conditions (considering factors such as frost penetration, soil shrinkage and expansion, the possibility of soil erosion, or building code stipulations). Footings for permanent structures are rarely located directly on the ground surface. To be classified as a spread footing, the foundation does not have to be at a shallow depth; spread footings will be located deep in the ground if soil conditions or the building design requires. Spread footing foundations for building columns, walls, and equipment bases commonly have the shapes of squares, rectangles, trapezoids, and long strips (see Fig. 13-1). Usually, the shape and dimensions for a footing result from having the structural loading positioned so that, theoretically, a *uniform* bearing pressure on the soil beneath the foundation is achieved. For the support of walls and single columns, the loading is usually centered on the footing. For foundations supporting two or more column loads, or machinery, the positioning of the loading or weight often makes a rectangular or trapezoidal shape necessary.

Mat (or Raft) Foundations The mat (or raft) foundation can be considered a large footing extending over a great area, frequently an entire building area (Fig. 13-2). All vertical structural loadings from columns and walls are supported on the common foundation. Typically, the mat is utilized for conditions where individual column footings, if used, would tend to be close together or would tend to overlap. The mat is frequently utilized as a method to reduce or distribute building loads in order to reduce differential setlement between adjacent areas. To function properly, the mat structure will be more rigid and thicker than the individual spread footing.

Figure 13-1 Types of shallow spread footing foundations: (a) square spread footing to support column loading; (b)long (strip) footing to support wall loading; (c) rectangular footing for two columns (combined footing) or machine base; (d) trapezoidal footing for two columns (combined footing) or machine base.

Pile and Pier Foundations   Piles and piers are foundation types intended to transmit structural loads through upper zones of poor soil to a depth where the earth is capable of providing the desired support (Fig. 13-3a and b). In this respect, where loadings developed at one level are transmitted to a lower level, piles and piers are similar to structural columns. Though typically considered as long, slender structural members, such foundations obtain adequate lateral support from the embedding soil along their length so that there is no concern about buckling under axial load, as with conventional columns. These deep foundation types are also utilized in situations where it is necessary to provide resistance to uplift or where there is concern about possible loss of ground or erosion due to flowing water or other causes.

In years past, the pile or pier category was indicative of the method used to install the foundation or of its size. Piles were slender foundation units, usually

Figure 13-2 Mat foundation—for soils having low bearing capacity or where soil conditions are variable and erratic—used to obtain low bearing pressure and reduce differential settlement. The mat foundation may also consist of a grid arrangement of closely spaced and interconnected grade beams capped with a floor slab.

General Types of Foundations—Foundation Categories   **341**

Figure 13-3 Representative types of deep foundations: (a) slender driven, drilled, or cast-in-place pile; (b) drilled or cast-in-place pier with enlarged base; (c) pile-type open caisson; (d) box-type open caisson; (e) pneumatic caisson.

driven into place. Piers, typically larger in area than piles, were units formed in place by excavating an opening to the desired depth and pouring concrete. Often, such foundations were large enough to permit a man to enter and inspect the exposed earth. Currently, a clear distinction between pile- and pier-type foundations is not always present because of changes and innovations in construction or installation techniques. For example, some types of cast-in-place piles are constructed by using the basic methods historically attributed to pier foundations. As a result, the developing practice is to classify all deep, slender foundation units simply as pile-type foundations, with terms such as *driven, bored,* or *drilled* and *precast* or *cast-in-place* to indicate the method of installation and construction.

Caissons A caisson is a structural box or chamber that is sunk in place or built in place by systematically excavating below the bottom of the unit, which thereby

Figure 13-4 Rigid box caisson foundation utilizing floating foundation concept.

descends to the final depth. Open caissons may be box-type or pile-type. Usually, the top and bottom are open during installation. When in place, the bottom may be sealed with concrete if necessary to keep out water, or the bottom may be socketed into rock to obtain a high bearing capacity. Pneumatic caissons have the top and sides sealed and use compressed air to keep soil and water from entering the lower working chamber, where excavation to advance the caisson is occurring. Representative types of caissons are illustrated in Figure 13-3c, d, and e.

Floating Foundations　The floating foundation is a special type of foundation construction that is useful under proper conditions. Particularly, it has application in locations where deep deposits of compressible cohesive soils exist and the use of piles is impractical. The floating foundation concept requires that a building's substructure (the below-ground structure) be assembled as a combination mat and caisson to create a rigid box, as shown in Figure 13-4. This foundation is installed at a depth so selected that the total weight of the soil excavated for the rigid box equals the total weight of the planned building. In theory, the soil below the structure is therefore not subjected to any change in loading. For such an occurrence, there would be no settlement. Usually, however, some settlement does occur because the soil at the bottom of the excavation expands after excavation and recompresses during and following construction.

PILE FOUNDATION TYPES AND INSTALLATION PROCEDURES

Pile Drivers for Driven Piles　Driven piles are installed from the ground surface by hammering a ready-made unit or hollow shell, usually with special pile-driving equipment (see Fig. 13-5). Most driving is done with an impact type of hammer; a moving weight falls or is forced against the top of the pile. General categories of modern-day pile hammers include the single- and double-acting units (steam, compressed air, or hydraulic) and diesel hammers, illustrated in Figure 13-6. The term *hammer* refers to the entire driving unit; usually, the moving weight that strikes the pile is the *ram*.

Single-acting hammers use steam or compressed air to raise the hammer ram

Pile Foundation Types and Installation Procedures　　**343**

Figure 13-5 Typical pile-driving equipment. (Courtesy of Raymond International, Inc.)

Figure 13-6 Schematic diagram of ram-type pile-driving hammers [181].

to a ready-for-driving position. The ram is then released to enable it to drop on the top of the pile. A *double-acting hammer* uses steam or compressed air to raise the ram to a ready-for-driving position and also to accelerate the ram's downward thrust. *Differential-acting hammers*, another category, are similar in operation to the double-acting hammers. Double-acting hammers actuated by hydraulic pressures are also available.

Diesel hammers are self-contained, self-activated units. The ram is located within an enclosed cylinder. Initially, the ram is mechanically raised to the top of the cylinder and released for its fall. A fuel mixture injected into the cylinder ahead of the falling ram is compressed due to the piston effect. Near the bottom of the stroke, the fuel is detonated and the force of the resulting explosion and the ram impact is delivered to the pile, driving it. Within the cylinder, the force of the explosion raises the ram up to the top of the cylinder, where it is ready to begin another cycle.

Single-acting hammers need to rely on the weight of a heavy ram for driving piles. Double-acting and diesel hammers can develop high driving energy that is equal to or greater than the energy of the falling ram in a single-acting hammer, but they achieve this through greater impact velocity. One advantage of the double-acting and diesel hammers over the single-acting hammer is the greater operating speed; a greater number of blows will be delivered per unit of time. When long or heavy piles are driven, a hammer that has a heavy ram should be used. For effective driving, the weight of the hammer ram needs to be approximately the same weight as the pile or greater. Equipment manufacturers provide data on the important characteristics of their hammers, including the weight of the ram and the stroke, hammer efficiency, driving energy per hammer blow, and number of blows per minute (see Table 13-1).

Vibratory drivers rely on a principle different from the conventional hammers for installing a pile. Vibratory units are typically more contained and compact than the falling-ram type of hammer. Basically, the vibratory driver (Fig. 13-7) consists

TABLE 13-1   DATA ON REPRESENTATIVE PILE-DRIVING HAMMERS

Hammer		Weight: ram, piston, or moving parts		Blows per minute	Rated energy per blow	
Make	Model (type)	Kips	kN		k-ft	kN-m
Vulcan[a]	08 (single-acting)	8	35.6	50	26	35.3
	040 (single-acting)	40	177.9	60	120	162.7
	060 (single-acting)	60	266.9	62	180	244.1
	3100 (single-acting)	100	448.8	58	300	406.8
	140 C (differential-acting)	14	62.3	103	36	48.8
	200 C (differential-acting)	20	89	98	50.2	68.1
	400 C (differential-acting)	40	178	100	40	177.9
	N-33 (diesel)	3	13.3	50–60	24.6	33.4
MKT[b]	S-8 (single-acting)	8	35.6	55	26	35.3
	S-20 (single-acting)	20	89	60	60	81.4
	C-5 (double-acting)	5	22.2	110	16	21.7
	DE-20 (diesel)	2	8.9	40–50	To 18	To 24
	DE-70B (diesel)	7	31	40–50	To 63	To 85
Raymond[c]	8/0 (single-acting)	25	111	35	81	110
	150 C (differential)	15	66.7	95–105	48	66
Link Belt[d]	520 (diesel)	5.07	22.6	80–84	26.3	35.7
	440 (diesel)	4.0	17.8	86–90	18.2	24.7
Kobe[e]	K-25 (diesel)	5.51	24.5	40–60	50.7	68.8
	K150 (diesel)	33.1	147.2	45–60	280	380
Mitsubishi[f]	M-145 (diesel)	2.97	13.2	42–60	12–26	16–35
	MB70 (diesel)	15.84	70.5	38–60	63–141	86–191

[a]Vulcan Iron Works, Florida.

[b]McKiernan-Terry, New Jersey.

[c]Raymond International, Texas.

[d]Link Belt, Iowa.

[e]Kobe Diesel, Japan.

[f]Mitsubishi International, Japan.

(b)

Figure 13-7 (a) Schematic diagram of vibratory pile driver; (b) vibratory hammer utilized to install steel-casing cast-in-place concrete piles for a ship channel. Photo shows concrete being tremied into a casing. The vibratory hammer is shown hanging from the crane boom.

(a)

Crane cable

Suspension system with vibration suppressor

Main chassis

Drive chain

Direction of rotation

Eccentric weights

Amplitude of vibration

Center of rotation

Radius of gyration

Side cabinet

Driving head with hydraulic clamp

Pile

Center of gravity of eccentric weight

Shaft

Motor

Eccentric weight

Figure 13-8 Piles being provided with protective points. (Courtesy of Associated Pile and Fitting Corporation)

of a pair of counter-rotating weights that are synchronized so that the lateral components of thrust always counteract, or cancel, each other's effects. The vertical components of thrust are additive, however, and create up-and-down pulsations, or vibrations. For an installation, the driver is clamped to the pile. The pile is then vibrated into the earth under its own weight. Vibratory drivers may be low-frequency type (operating range between about 10 and 30 Hz or cps) or resonant type (capable of an operating frequency up to about 150 Hz or cps). The intent of a resonant driver is to create a condition of resonance between the driver, pile, and zone of affected soil so that penetration occurs very rapidly. Vibratory drivers are considered to be most effective when installing piles in sand and silty-sand soils.

An item of importance in pile installation is the factor of stresses created in the pile by the driving. For wood piles and concrete piles, excessive driving when high resistance is met (a high number of blows per inch of penetration) may result in structural damage or breakage in the pile. It is helpful for the foundation designer to impose an *upper limit* to the number of blows that can be safely imposed, for reference by field personnel. Breakage while driving can be difficult to detect but is often indicated by a drop in blow count following a high blow count. Metal tips or end covers can be installed on piles to help protect them in hard driving and to aid penetration, as shown in Figure 13-8.

Pile Types and Materials The common types of pile that are *installed by driving* include *timber piles, steel H* (see Fig. 13-9) *or pipe, reinforced concrete,* and *prestressed concrete.* Generally, with these types, the pile unit is complete and ready to be installed when it is delivered to the job site.

The *driven steel shell* (Fig. 13-10) is a different category of pile installed by driving. Often, with this type, a hollow steel shell is installed to the desired depth by driving on a steel mandrel or steel core that fits inside the shell (Fig. 13-11). Much of the force of driving thus acts at the tip of the pile, so, in effect, the pile is partially being pulled into the ground. At the desired penetration, the mandrel or core is withdrawn and plain or reinforced concrete is placed in the shell. Corrugated or fluted steel is conventionally used for the shell so that it will possess adequate strength to withstand the stresses of driving. This type of pile is usually considered a cast-in-place unit.

Timber piles (Fig. 13-12) can be treated or untreated. "Treated" refers to the procedure by which the wood has been impregnated with a protective material or preservative, such as creosote. Creosoting is a typical treatment for piles that are to be exposed to moisture but not permanently submerged in water. Untreated wood permanently below water will not decay and is considered to have unlimited life unless threatened by other effects. Preservative-protection treatment is required to protect wood piles from marine borers (if for a marine environment), from wood-infesting insects such as termites, or from decay (wet rot) if the pile is embedded in soil above the water table.

Cast-in-place piles include the *steel-shell and concrete type*, described previously; the *shell-less type*, which is formed by excavating to a desired depth and then filling the opening with concrete; and the type in which *a concrete unit is formed in the ground without prior excavation.*

Where pre-excavation is performed for a *shell-less pile* before the concrete is placed, the excavation may be unlined or may be provided with a temporary lining, such as a steel shell, whose purpose is to keep soil from caving into the open excavation and to seal off water from the soil walls. Excavation for this type of pile is typically performed by augering or by applying a wash boring technique similar to that utilized when borings are drilled (Chapter 11). With either of these methods, a bentonite clay slurry may be used in the excavation while it is being drilled (Chapter 11) instead of a temporary steel lining to keep the soil walls from caving in. The bentonite slurry is a heavy liquid whose purpose is to exert a lateral

(a)   (b)

Figure 13-9 (a) H-piles being driven. Photo shows battered piles. (Courtesy of Associated Pile and Fitting Corporation) (b) Installation of pipe piles. (Courtesy of MKT Corporation)

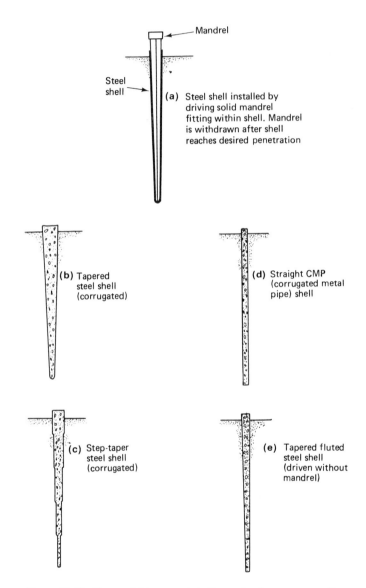

Figure 13-10 Types of driven steel-shell, cast-in-place concrete piles.

Figure 13-11 Installation of step-taper steel-shell cast-in-place concrete piles. (Courtesy of Raymond International, Inc.)

pressure sufficient to hold the soil walls in place. Concrete for the foundation unit is tremied (placed under water through a large-diameter flexible hose or tube in order to prevent contamination) to the bottom of the excavation. The pile is formed from the base up, and the slurry is displaced from the excavation. The shell-less, cast-in-place pile is often referred to as a bored-pile or drilled-shaft foundation. Representative types are illustrated in Figure 13-13.

In cohesive soils, the base of the excavation may be enlarged to provide a greater bearing area. The excavation for the shaft section and the belled or underreamed base is often performed by special auger-type drilling equipment, but can be accomplished manually. This type of foundation is often referred to as a drilled (drilled and belled) pier, drilled (drilled and belled) caisson, or drilled-shaft foundation (Fig. 13-14).

A different type of cast-in-place pile is constructed by *augering into the earth without removing soil*, then pumping concrete to the bottom of the drilled zone through a hollow stem in the auger and forming the pile from the bottom up as the auger withdraws and removes soil (Fig. 13-15).

Still another category of cast-in-place foundation is the *bulb-type uncased concrete pile* (Fig. 13-16). To construct this type, a mass of very dry concrete is placed in a steel casing standing on the ground surface and formed into a plug by

Figure 13-12 Timber piles being installed with single-acting hammer. (Courtesy of Associated Pile and Fitting Corporation)

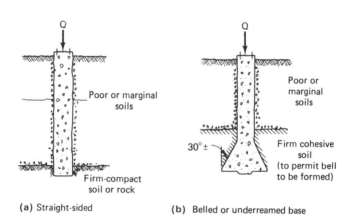

(a) Straight-sided

(b) Belled or underreamed base

Figure 13-13 Typical drilled-shaft foundations: (a) straight-sided; (b) belled or underreamed base.

(a)   (b)

Figure 13-14 (a) Truck-mounted rig for constructing drilled-shaft foundations. (Courtesy of Association of Drilled Shaft Contractors, Inc.) (b) Crane-mounted equipment for constructing drilled-shaft foundations. Photo shows underream tool for forming enlarged base. (Courtesy of Association of Drilled Shaft Contractors, Inc.)

a falling heavy ram. High friction develops between the concrete and inside casing wall, and continued blows of the ram force the concrete plug and casing into the ground. At the depth where it is desired to form a base for the pile, the casing is locked to the driving rig, and continued blows of the ram force the concrete plug from the bottom of the casing into the earth. An enlarged base forms as the driven

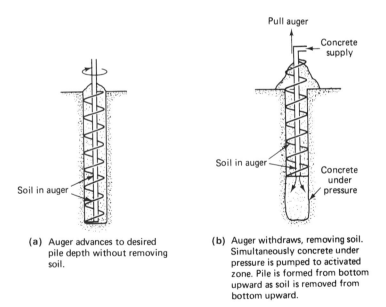

(a) Auger advances to desired pile depth without removing soil.

(b) Auger withdraws, removing soil. Simultaneously concrete under pressure is pumped to activated zone. Pile is formed from bottom upward as soil is removed from bottom upward.

Figure 13-15 Augered cast-in-place pile.

Pile Foundation Types and Installation Procedures

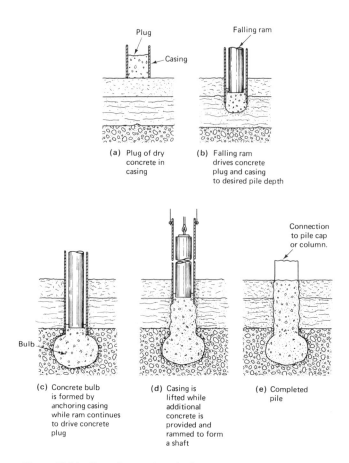

(a) Plug of dry concrete in casing

(b) Falling ram drives concrete plug and casing to desired pile depth

Bulb

(c) Concrete bulb is formed by anchoring casing while ram continues to drive concrete plug

(d) Casing is lifted while additional concrete is provided and rammed to form a shaft

Connection to pile cap or column.

(e) Completed pile

Figure 13-16 Procedure to form bulb-type uncased concrete pile.

concrete plug compacts the soil around this level. Additional dry concrete is then added and rammed while the casing is slowly lifted. A continuous pile shaft is formed as the rammed concrete continues to be driven from the bottom of the withdrawing casing.

The term *composite piles* usually refers to piles that have different materials for their different sections of length. The most typical combinations include timber or steel H pile or pipe pile for the lower section and cased cast-in-place concrete for the upper section (see Fig. 13-17). Composite piles are normally used for reasons of economy (timber is less costly than steel or concrete) or to take advantage of certain structural features that one material possesses (steel will fare better than timber or concrete in hard driving, or timber or cast-in-place concrete piles may not be available in the required length). Where composite piles are utilized, the splice joint between sections should be as strong as the pile materials, particularly if the pile will be subject to uplift forces. *Composite pile* is also the term applied

Figure 13-17 Composite pile showing splice connections: (a) typical makeup of composite pile; (b) typical splice connections.

to a pile cross section of more than one material, such as a concrete-filled pipe pile.

Representative Pile Load Capacities and Available Lengths The pile type and cross section to be selected for a project will be influenced by soil conditions, required pile length, required structural capability of the pile, and consideration of the pile installation method. Information on the maximum lengths generally available for the various pile types is summarized in Table 13-2. Representative structural load ranges for various pile types are shown in Table 13-3.

Methods to Aid Pile Installation The installation of driven piles can be aided by the use of spudding or predrilling. These techniques are frequently utilized in situations where obstacles that could damage the driven pile are buried in the soil to be penetrated, where compact or hard soil must be penetrated, or where driving vibrations may affect nearby structures. Another form of installation assistance is jetting, a procedure that eliminates some driving and hastens pile penetration.

Spudding refers to the procedure of driving a steel H or similar section into the earth to break up obstacles before installing the pile. Beyond the depth where the obstacles exist, the spud is withdrawn. The pile is then installed in the hole and driven to its final depth.

Predrilling consists of drilling a hole, approximately the diameter of the pile, through very hard soils to eliminate the danger of pile damage that might result if driving were attempted (Fig. 13-18). Predrilling is frequently utilized on projects

TABLE 13-2 AVAILABLE LENGTHS OF VARIOUS PILE TYPES

Pile type	Comment, available maximum length
Timber	Depends on wood (tree) type. Lengths in the 50- to 60-ft range (15 to 18 m) are usually available in most areas; lengths to about 75 ft (25 m) are available but in limited quantity; lengths up to the 100-ft range (30 m) are available, but supply is very limited.
Steel H and pipe	Unlimited length; "short" sections are driven and additional sections are field-welded to obtain a desired total length.
Steel shell, cast-in-place	Typically to between 100 and 125 ft (30 to 40 m), depending on shell type and manufacturer-contractor.
Precast concrete	Solid, small cross-section piles usually extend into the 50–60-ft length (15 to 18 m), depending on cross-section shape, dimensions, and manufacturer. Large-diameter cylinder piles can extend to about 200 ft long (60 m).
Drilled-shaft, cast-in-place concrete	Usually in the 50–75-ft range (15 to 25 m), depending on contractor equipment.
Bulb-type, cast-in-place concrete	Up to about 100 ft (30 m).
Composite	Related to available lengths of material in the different sections. If steel and thin-shell cast-in-place concrete are used, the length can be unlimited; if timber and thin-shell cast-in-place concrete are used, lengths can be on the order of 150 ft (45 m).

TABLE 13-3 TYPICAL CAPACITIES FOR VARIOUS PILE TYPES

Pile type	Typical design load range	
	Tons	kN
Wood	15–30	100–300
Concrete, cast-in-place, steel shell and uncased	30–75	250–700
Concrete, reinforced or prestressed (lower range for smaller cross sections, upper range for larger cross sections)	30–200	250–2,000
Concrete, bulb-type	75–1,000	600–9,000
Composite: wood and concrete	30–60	250–600
Steel pipe (lower range for small diameter and wall thickness, upper range for larger diameter and heavy wall thickness)	30–100	250–1,000
Steel HP (lower range for light sections, upper range for heavier sections)	40–200	400–1,500

Figure 13-18 Predrilling equipment for installing steel-shell piles in clay soils. (Courtesy of Raymond International, Inc.)

where driving effects must be minimized, as protection against possible damage from driving vibrations to nearby facilities. The procedure is also utilized when piles are installed in clay soils to prevent ground heave, which can result from pile driving. If ground heave occurs, previously driven piles may also heave up and have to be reseated.

Jetting is the technique of using a powerful stream of water directed below the tip of a long pile penetrating sandy soil to wash ahead of the pile to assist it in advancing through the sand. The jetting nozzle may be temporarily attached directly to the pile. As sand is flushed from below the pile tip, the pile settles into the created void or is easily driven if the driving hammer is activated. Jetting causes the sand that eventually surrounds the pile to be loose. Typically, the jetting is stopped and the pile is driven for the last segment of the desired penetration to develop high end friction and tip bearing. For short piles, jetting is also used to wash a hole at a pile location, before driving, to make installation easier.

Other Installation Considerations Pile foundations may be required to resist lateral forces instead of or in addition to vertical loads. Driven piles and some types of formed-in-place piles can be installed at an angle to the vertical to develop high resistance to lateral forces. Such piles are referred to as *batter piles*. Most vertical piles are capable of resisting lateral forces also, but usually of only small magnitude.

Deep foundations may be required at locations where available headroom is limited. Driven and formed-in-place piles can be installed where space is limited,

Figure 13-19 Pipe pile installation in area of limited headroom. Short leads are utilized along with short pile sections. (Courtesy of Associated Pile and Fitting Corporation, and George W. Rogers Construction Corporation)

but special equipment is necessary, as illustrated in Figure 13-19. If headroom is very limited, driven-type piles can be installed by working with very short sections and jacking. Sections are jacked and added to until the desired penetration is reached.

The augered-excavation cast-in-place piles can offer the advantage of relatively quiet, vibration-free installation compared to driven piles. Such factors may be important if construction is in a highly developed area where there is concern about noise or the effect of driving vibrations on nearby structures.

Comparative installed costs for different foundation types will vary, depending on soil conditions to be penetrated, required pile length, desired load capacity, geographic area and labor costs, availability of pile materials, site accessibility and site conditions, and contractor availability. Although drilled-shaft or cast-in-place piles are often considered more economical than driven piles where short lengths are required, and vice versa, each project should be considered unique and costs should be determined accordingly.

RELATING SOIL CONDITIONS AND FOUNDATION TYPES

A structural foundation serves as the intermediary element to transmit forces from a building's superstructure to the supporting soil. It is necessary to know soil conditions and soil properties underlying an area as well as the magnitude and type of building loading before selection of a proper foundation type can be made. After an appropriate foundation has been decided upon, each unit is sized for proper carrying capacity. Individual foundations should be analyzed, as is any other structural member, to ensure that the element itself possesses adequate internal strength.

As a guide for developing an understanding of the intereffect of soil conditions and a required type of foundation, illustrations of different subsurface conditions and related foundation considerations are presented in Table 13-4. For the design comments, it was assumed that a multistory commercial structure, such as an office building, was to be supported.

TABLE 13-4

ILLUSTRATIONS RELATING SOIL CONDITIONS AND APPROPRIATE
FOUNDATION TYPES

Soil conditions	Appropriate foundation type and location	Design comments

(1) El.0′, ground surface

Compact sand, (deposit to great depth)

Installation below frost depth or where erosion might occur

Spread footings most appropriate for conventional foundation needs. A deep foundation such as piles could be required if uplift or other unusual forces were to act.

(2) El.0′

Firm clay or firm silt and clay (to great depth)

Installation depth below frost depth, or below zone where shrinkage and expansion due to change in water content could occur

Spread footings most appropriate for conventional foundation needs. Also see comment for (1) above.

(3) El.0′

Firm clay

El. −10′

Soft clay (to great depth)

Comments as for (2) above

Spread footing would be appropriate for low to medium range of loads, if not installed too close to soft clay. If heavy loads are to be carried, deep foundations might be required.

(4) El.0′

Loose sand (to great depth)

Depth greater than frost or erosion depth

(or)

Spread footing may settle excessively or require use of very low bearing pressures. Consider mat foundation, or consider compacting sand by vibroflotation or other method then use spread footings. Driven piles could be used and would densify the sand. Also consider augered cast-in-place piles.

(5) El.0′

(soft) Soft clay, but firmness increasing with depth (to very great depth)

El. −25′

(med. firm)

El. −50′

(firmer)

(or)

Spread footings probably not appropriate. Friction piles or piers would be satisfactory if some settlement could be tolerated. Long piles would reduce settlement problems. Should also consider mat foundation or floating foundation.

Pile Foundation Types and Installation Procedures

359

Table 13-4 continued

Soil Conditions	Appropriate Foundation Type and Location	Design Comments

(6) El. 0' / Soft clay / El. −65' / Rock

Deep foundation — <u>piles</u>, <u>piers</u>, <u>caissons</u> — bearing directly on/in the rock.

(7) El. 0' / El. −8' Compact sand / El. −20' Med. soft clay / Hard clay (extending deep)

Spread footings in upper sand layer would probably experience large settlement because of underlying soft clay layer. Consider <u>drilled piers</u> with a bell formed in hard clay layer, or other <u>pile foundation</u>.

(8) El. 0' / Soft clay / El. −20' / Med. dense sand (extending deep)

Auger pile   Bulb type pile

Deep foundation best — <u>cast-in-place piles</u> such as <u>auger piles</u> or <u>bulb piles</u> into sand layer appear most appropriate.

(9) El. 0' / Miscellaneous fill (soil, non-soil) El.-10' / Loose sand, soft clay, organic mat'l El.-16' / Med. dense sand El.-22' / Compact glacial till / El.-60' / Rock

(or)

Deep foundation types extending into medium dense sand, or more preferably, into compact glacial till. <u>Strong possibility</u> for <u>drilled pier</u> with <u>bell</u> constructed in till. Also consider <u>cast-in-place</u> and <u>driven concrete pile</u>, <u>wood pile, pipe pile</u>.

(10) El. 0' / Miscellaneous Fill (poor) El.-8' / Med. dense sand / New compacted sand fill / El.-40' / Med. firm clay / El.-100' / Rock

(or)

Deep foundations penetrating through fill are appropriate. With <u>piles</u> or <u>piers</u>, consider stopping in upper zone of sand layer so to limit compression of clay layer. Also consider replacing poor fill with a <u>compacted fill</u> and then using <u>spread footings</u> in the new fill.

360

Table 13-4 continued

Soil conditions	Appropriate foundation type and location	Design comments

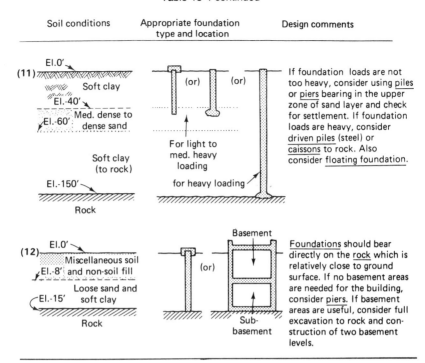

(11) El.0'

Soft clay

El.-40'

Med. dense to dense sand

El.-60'

Soft clay (to rock)

El.-150'

Rock

(or) (or)

For light to med. heavy loading

for heavy loading

If foundation loads are not too heavy, consider using piles or piers bearing in the upper zone of sand layer and check for settlement. If foundation loads are heavy, consider driven piles (steel) or caissons to rock. Also consider floating foundation.

(12) El.0'

Miscellaneous soil and non-soil fill

El.-8'

Loose sand and soft clay

El.-15'

Rock

Basement

(or)

Sub-basement

Foundations should bear directly on the rock which is relatively close to ground surface. If no basement areas are needed for the building, consider piers. If basement areas are useful, consider full excavation to rock and construction of two basement levels.

PROBLEMS

13-1. Why are foundations, as a distinct structural element, required for buildings?

13-2. Typically, a foundation design will be most influenced by the properties of the supporting soil and the magnitude of structural loading to be carried. Of these two factors, soil properties represent the primary concern. Explain.

13-3. (a) What factors determine whether a foundation type is in the shallow or deep foundation category?
(b) Piles and piers are considered deep foundation units. Why are deep foundation units typically long, slender members?

13-4. Generally, shallow foundations, such as poured concrete spread footings, offer definite cost advantages over deep foundation types, such as piles. Assume that you are making a presentation to a nontechnical audience; outline reasons for the usually significant cost differential between shallow and deep foundations.

13-5. Why are site factors such as a high water table or the potential for frost heave or soil shrinkage and swelling considerations important to the design of shallow foundations?

13-6. A multistory building with a plan area of 200 ft by 100 ft will impose an estimated total loading of 20,000 kips onto the supporting earth. If the floating foundation concept is to be utilized for this structure and the average unit weight of soil underlying the site is 120 pcf, what volume of soil excavation (and subsurface structure) is required?

13-7. Structural designers frequently mention that steel piles arc a good choice for sites where long piles are required and the depth to bearing will be variable and somewhat unpredictable. What are the probable reasons for this belief?

13-8. Soil conditions at a proposed construction site make it necessary for a driven pile foundation system to be utilized to support a planned building. The designer has the following design-cost estimate data:

(a) Wood piles, 25-ton capacity, required length 35 ft, $12 per lineal foot in place.

(b) Steel-shell, cast-in-place concrete piles, 50-ton capacity, required length 45 ft, $18 per lineal foot in place.

(c) Steel HP piles, 95-ton capacity, required length 75 ft, $22 per lineal foot in place.

Of these types of piles, which appears to be the most economical for supporting the typical column loadings of 350 tons and 550 tons?

chapter *14*

Foundations
Design Considerations and Methods

Building foundations need to be capable of carrying an imposed loading without undergoing movement that causes structural damage or affects the facility's planned usage. These considerations require that the soil responsible for supporting a foundation not be stressed beyond its strength limits. Simultaneously, the deformations resulting within this soil because of loading and action of natural forces cannot be excessive. The pressure that a foundation unit can impose onto the supporting earth mass without causing overstressing (or shear failure) is the soil's *bearing capacity*. Deformations occurring because of foundation loading usually cause settlement, but lateral movements may also be of concern. It is important also to consider the possibility of foundation movements due to natural phenomena, such as soil expansion and shrinkage if moisture changes or freezing occurs. The magnitude and type of loading (static, live, or repetitive), the foundation performance requirements (how much settlement is permissible), and properties of the supporting soil all have influence on the type and size of foundation that will be necessary and its resulting behavior.

Methods in widespread use for determining a soil's bearing capacity include the application of bearing capacity equations, the utilization of penetration resistance data obtained during soil explorations, and the practice of relating the soil type to a presumptive bearing capacity recommended by building codes. Permissible bearing capacities determined by the equation method or from building code tables typically do not consider effects of soil compressibility and the possible influence of poorer soil layers underlying the bearing layer. Consequently, settlement determinations and other results of soil deformations must be analyzed separately (e.g., by using the methods discussed in Chapter 9). Foundation design criteria developed from boring–penetration resistance data often relate a foundation bearing pressure to settlement. Design data in this form are convenient to use, but the methods available do not cover all foundation and soil types and are felt to be less precise than the analytical methods for determining bearing capacity and settlement.

An additional method in use for determining the permissible or safe design loading, applied primarily for pile foundations, is the field load test performed on an in-place foundation unit. Load tests relate carrying capacity and settlement together, which is an advantage. Disadvantages include the cost and time involved. Further, test results require care in their evaluation, for it is known that a load test on a small shallow foundation may not be representative of the behavior of a large shallow foundation. With piles, the load test results on a single unit may not be indicative of the behavior of a loaded pile group.

Of the common procedures for foundation design, the analytical method using soil mechanics principles (e.g., the use of bearing capacity equations with settlement analysis) and the use of penetration resistance data are preferred. Properly applied, these methods consider the effects of foundation type and size as well as the properties of soil to the depth that will have significant effect on the foundation performance. Load test data will provide reliable design information if properly related to the results of a subsurface exploration and a final foundation design. The use of presumptive bearing capacities is discouraged because of the heavy reliance on the soil-type description, with little correlation to the soil's actual physical properties and no consideration of the possible existence of poor soil strata underlying the foundation bearing level.

The procedures for foundation design that follow represent currently accepted methods. These methods generally have a history of being conservative. As in the past, foundation design procedures are subject to improvement for greater precision as new techniques are developed to better determine soil properties and behavior or as new analytical tools evolve.[1] The foundations profession is still considered a "state of the art" profession. Scientific methods and principles are utilized, but exact answers are not always expected. Final decisions concerning best foundation type, design criteria, expected behavior, and methods for construction and field control are greatly influenced by experience and intuition.

SHALLOW FOUNDATIONS

Bearing Capacity Equations

Basic Concepts–Long Footings. The ultimate soil-bearing capacity for foundations (the loading that will cause a shear failure in the supporting soils) is related to the properties of the soil, including the past stress history and the proximity of the groundwater table; it is also affected by the characteristics of the

---

[1]For example, the pressure meter method discussed later in this chapter represents a procedure that is new to most of the world's building designers but that offers the promise of applying field-determined pressure-resistance data directly to foundation design and behavior.

foundation, including size, depth, shape, and the method of construction or installation.

For the case of an increasing load being imposed onto a shallow, horizontal strip footing resting on a homogeneous soil, a characteristic load-settlement curve is shown in Figure 14-1. Information important for predicting foundation behavior and for developing criteria appropriate for foundation design has resulted from studies in which influential soil characteristics have been correlated with the settlement data (e.g., the soil descriptions have identified the materials as dense or firm, exhibiting brittle-type stress–strain behavior, or as loose or soft, exhibiting plastic properties). The soil zones involved in developing resistance to foundation loading (therefore, the soil zones responsible for bearing capacity) have been identified in a qualitative manner. The three principal modes of soil failure, established by the patterns of the shearing zones, are defined as *general shear failure*, *local shear failure*, and *punching shear failure*. Figure 14-2 illustrates the differences in the three modes and the foundation load-settlement curve typical to each mode.

The *general shear failure* (Fig. 14-2a), expected for soils possessing brittle-type stress–strain characteristics, is identified by a well-defined wedge beneath the foundation and slip surfaces extending diagonally from the side edges of the footing downward through the soil, then upward to the ground surface. The ground surface adjacent to the footing bulges upward. Soil displacement is accompanied by tilting of the foundation (unless the foundation is restrained). The load-settlement curve for the general shear case indicates that failure is abrupt.

The *punching shear failure* (Fig. 14-2c), occurring in soil possessing the stress–strain characteristics of a very plastic material, involves poorly defined shearing planes. Significant compression of a wedge-shaped soil zone beneath the foundation is accompanied by the occurrence of vertical shear beneath the edges of the foundation. The soil zones beyond the edges of the foundation are little affected, and no significant degree of surface bulging occurs. Aside from large settlement, failure is not clearly recognized.

The *local shear failure* condition (Fig. 14-2b) involves some of the characteristics of both the general shear and the punching shear failure modes. As for general shear, the well-defined wedge and slip surfaces are formed *beneath* the foundation, but the slip surfaces fade into the soil mass beyond the edges of the foundation and do not carry upward to the ground surface. Slight bulging of the ground surface adjacent to the foundation does occur. As with punching shear, significant vertical compression of soil directly beneath the foundation takes place. The local shear condition represents a transitional mode between the general shear

Figure 14-1 Typical load-settlement relation for shallow foundations.

Shallow Foundations

(a) General shear

(b) Local shear

(c) Punching shear

Figure 14-2 Conditions for ultimate soil-bearing capacity; involved soil zones and related foundation settlements [267].

and the punching shear failures and is expected for soils possessing somewhat plastic stress–strain characteristics.

The load-settlement curves of Figure 14-2 are qualitative in nature. Investigators of the bearing capacity problem have found that relatively large settlements are required in order to have foundations reach the "failure" load (viz., 3 to 15 % of the foundation width for very shallow installations and up to 25% of the foundation width for deeper installations).

For application to shallow foundation design, it is commonly considered that the general shear case applies to dense granular soil and to firmer saturated cohesive soils subject to undrained loading (the U–U and C–U shearing conditions apply). The punching shear case is considered appropriate for compressible soil, such as sands having a low to medium relatively density, and for cohesive soils subject to slow loading (the C–D shearing conditions apply).

Historically, over the past one hundred years, a number of investigators have undertaken studies relating to foundation bearing capacity, typically applying the classical theories of elasticity and plasticity to soil behavior to develop equations appropriate for foundation design.[2] Behavior described by the classical theory of plasticity has been widely used to obtain a solution for the case of a general shear failure. The original theoretical concepts for analyzing conditions considered applicable to foundation performance using the theory of plasticity are credited to Prandtl [190] and Reissner [197]. Prandtl studied the effect of a long, narrow metal tool bearing against the surface of a smooth metal mass that possessed cohesion

---

[2]Jumikis (1962) [121] provides a summary of the works of early investigators.

and internal friction but no weight. The results of Prandtl's work were extended by Reissner to include the condition where the bearing area is located below the surface of the resisting material and a surcharge weight acts on a plane that is level with the bearing area. Terzaghi [249] applied the developments of Prandtl and Reissner to soil foundation problems, extending the theory to consider rough foundation surfaces bearing on materials that possess weight.

Conditions for relating the classical theory of plasticity to the case of a general shear failure are indicated by Figure 14-3. The arrangement shown establishes criteria for developing the ultimate bearing capacity for a long strip foundation; because of the infinite foundation length, the analysis proceeds as for a two-dimensional or plane-strain problem. The theory assumes that the (soil) material in Zones I, II and III possesses the stress–strain characteristics of a rigid plastic

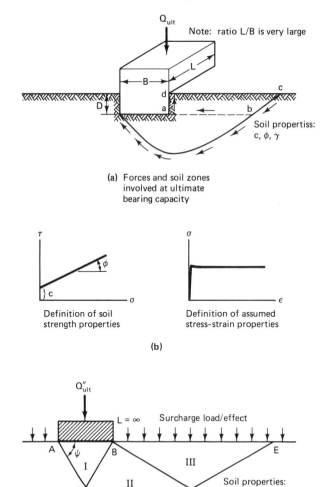

(a) Forces and soil zones involved at ultimate bearing capacity

Note: ratio L/B is very large

Soil propertiss: c, ϕ, γ

Definition of soil strength properties

Definition of assumed stress–strain properties

(b)

(c) Assumption of forces and soil failure zones

Figure 14-3 Definition of conditions for developing the ultimate bearing capacity equation.

Shallow Foundations

body (viz., the material shows an infinite initial modulus of elasticity extending to the point of shear failure, followed by a zero modulus (see Fig. 14-3b). Applied to the soil mass providing support for the foundation, the theory assumes that no deformations occur prior to the point of shear failure but that plastic flow occurs at constant stress after shearing failure. It is also assumed that the plastic deformations are small, and the geometric shapes of the failure zones remain essentially constant. The use of an equivalent surcharge to substitute for the soil mass above the level of the foundation, along with some estimations, simplifies the analysis, but the effect is to provide conservative results. When subject to a foundation loading near to the ultimate, Zone I behaves as an active zone that pushes the radial Zone II sideways and the passive Zone III laterally upwards. Boundaries AC and DE shown on Figure 14-3c are straight lines; the shape of section CD varies from circular (when the soil angle of internal friction ϕ is zero) to a curve intermediate between a logarithmic spiral and a circle (when ϕ is greater than zero degrees).

Terzaghi developed a general bearing capacity equation for strip footings that combined the effects of soil cohesion and internal friction, foundation size, soil weight, and surcharge effects in order to simplify the calculations necessary for foundation design. His equation utilized the concept of dimensionless bearing capacity factors whose values are a function of the shear possessed by the supporting soils. Through ensuing years, the ultimate bearing capacity for shallow and deep foundations has continued to be studied in the quest for refined definition of foundation-soil behavior and a generalized bearing capacity equation which agrees well with failure conditions occurring in model and large-scale foundation tests.[3] Modifications to early concepts have emerged from such studies, but the general form of the Terzaghi bearing capacity equation has been retained because of its practicality.

The ultimate bearing capacity equation, shown as Equation 14-1a and developed from the conditions outlined in Figure 14-3c for long footings, has been found to provide good agreement with ultimate loads observed for model and large-scale foundations. This equation shows the Terzaghi format, but the current dimensionless bearing capacity factors reflect the result of better definition of the soil failure zones:

$$\frac{Q_{\text{ult}}}{(B \times L)} \approx \frac{Q''_{\text{ult}}}{(B \times 1)} = q_{\text{ult}} = cN_c + \frac{1}{2}B\gamma_1 N_\gamma + \gamma_2 D_f N_q \qquad (14\text{-}1a)$$

where
Q_{ult} = total loading acting at the base of the strip foundation whose width is B and length is L (kips, kN, etc.).

Q''_{ult} = load acting at base of foundation for unit length in L-direction (k/ft, kN/m, etc.).

q_{ult} = ultimate gross bearing capacity or soil bearing pressure (ksf, kN/m^2, etc.).

c = cohesion of the soil below foundation level (ksf, kN/m^2, etc.).

---

[3]Meyerhof [157], Hansen [99], Vesic [267], DeBeer [60].

D_f = depth of footing below lowest adjacent soil surface (ft, m, etc.).

γ_1 = effective unit weight of soil below foundation level (pcf, kcf, kN/m³, etc.).

γ_2 = effective unit weight of soil above foundation level (pcf, kcf, kN/m³, etc.).

N_c, N_γ, N_q = soil-bearing capacity factors, dimensionless terms, whose values relate to the angle of internal friction, ϕ, whereby

$$N_q = \tan^2 (45 + \phi/2)^{\pi\tan\phi}$$

$$N_c = (N_q - 1)\cot\phi \qquad (\text{for } \phi > 0°)$$
$$= 5.14 \qquad\qquad (\text{for } \phi = 0°)^4$$

$$N_\gamma = 2(N_q + 1)\tan\phi$$

The relationship between the bearing capacity factors N_q, N_c, and N_γ and the angle of internal friction is presented in Figure 14-4.

The first and third terms in this equation represent the Prandtl–Reissner solution for the condition of a weightless soil. The second term represents the separate solution to a determination of the ultimate bearing capacity for a cohesionless soil with weight but no overburden effects (a necessary consideration because the Prandtl–Reissner terms do not include a shearing resistance from the effect of soil weight and internal friction, ϕ, in the failure zones). This superposition (i.e., a simple combination of three terms) to produce Equation 14-1a is not a theoretically correct procedure, but errors are on the safe side and small for most practical applications.

Equation 14-1a implies that the bearing capacity for foundations on soil possessing internal friction, ϕ, increases indefinitely with increases in foundation width, as indicated by the solid lines of Figure 14-5. However, physical studies have indicated that the rate of increase for bearing capacity decreases somewhat as foundation width increases, and there may be an upper limit to a soil's bearing capacity (see dashed lines of Fig. 14-5). Foundation widths beyond the value that develops the upper limit would not contribute to the bearing capacity. Fortunately, the width corresponding to such an upper limit on bearing capacity apparently is relatively large; as a result, the condition is not a serious restriction for commonly used sizes of shallow foundations. This "size effect" can be compensated for during design by using the ϕ value from soil testing appropriate to the general range of the bearing capacity pressure and by applying the rigidity index reduction factors discussed in the following paragraphs. Nevertheless, the effect of using higher bearing pressures on larger foundations requires careful consideration where settlement is important. Because of the manner in which stresses from foundation loadings are transferred into the earth (Chapter 8), a large foundation tends to settle more than a small foundation when both impose the same intensity of bearing pressure, because the loaded area and *total load Q* is greater. Using a greater

---

[4]A rigorous mathematical solution for the value of N_c when ϕ equals zero is presented by Jumikis [122], pgs. 626–27.

Figure 14-4   Bearing capacity factors for the bearing capacity equation.

ϕ	N_c	N_q	N_γ
0	5.14	1.0	0.0
5	6.5	1.6	0.5
10	8.3	2.5	1.2
15	14.0	3.9	2.6
20	14.8	6.4	5.4
25	20.7	10.7	10.8
30	30.1	18.4	22.4
32	35.5	23.2	30.2
34	42.2	29.4	41.1
36	50.6	37.7	56.3
38	61.4	48.9	78.0
40	75.3	64.2	109.4
42	93.7	85.4	155.6
44	118.4	115.3	224.6
46	152.1	158.5	330.4
48	199.3	222.3	496.0
50	266.9	319.1	762.9

In figure:
$$N_q = e^{\pi \tan \phi} \tan^2 (45 + \phi/2)$$
$$N_c = (N_q - 1) \cot \phi$$
$$N_\gamma = 2(N_q + 1) \tan \phi$$

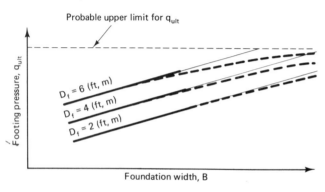

Figure 14-5   Implications of the general bearing capacity equation: Allowable pressures increase with increases in footing width and depth (solid lines). Note that the actual rate of bearing capacity increase *decreases* as width becomes greater (dashed lines).

bearing pressure for a large footing further increases the tendency for greater settlement. Consequently, if lightly loaded and heavily loaded foundations for a structure are designed only on the basis of allowable bearing capacity, there is a strong possibility of differential settlement between the large and small footings.

The assumption that the soil responsible for developing a foundation bearing capacity behaves as a rigid material is satisfied for the case of general shear but is not appropriate for punching shear and local shear. Comparison of the relative load-settlement curves of Figure 14-2 indicates that, for the punching and local shear cases, the ultimate load is less and the settlement is greater than for the condition of the general shear failure. Methods applied in the past to compensate for lower bearing capacity design values where a foundation was to be supported on soil that is compressible and that would undergo significant volumetric changes (i.e., where the local or punching shear condition was expected) typically utilized reduced values for the angle of internal friction, ϕ, and the cohesion, c, in the general bearing equation. Results could be overly conservative, however. Vesic [267] has proposed the use of a rigidity index, I_r, which provides a relative measure of soil deformability, whereby

$$I_r = \frac{G}{c + \overline{\sigma}_v \tan \phi} = \frac{E}{2(1 + v)(c + \overline{\sigma}_v \tan \phi)} \qquad (14\text{-}2)$$

where G = soil shearing modulus.
   c, ϕ = soil cohesion and angle of internal friction.
   $\overline{\sigma}_v$ = effective soil overburden pressure at a depth corresponding to $B/2$ below the foundation base.
   v = Poisson's ratio for the bearing soil (see Table 14-1).
   E = soil modulus of elasticity[5] = $\dfrac{1}{m_v}\left[\dfrac{(1 + v)(1 - 2v)}{(1 - v)}\right]$ (also see Table 14-1).
   $\dfrac{1}{m_v}$ = constrained modulus.
   $m_v = \dfrac{\Delta \varepsilon_v}{\Delta \overline{\sigma}_v} = \dfrac{a_v}{1 + e_0} = \dfrac{0.435\, C_c}{(1 + e_0)\overline{\sigma}_{va}}$ where $\overline{\sigma}_{va}$ is the average of the initial and final stress, determined at a depth of $B/2$.

(Note: Values of E and m_v determined from field and laboratory tests are considered to include the effects of elastic and plastic deformations.)

Using a critical value of rigidity index $I_{r\text{critical}}$ as a reference value, the actual rigidity index for a site is compared to the critical index:

$$I_{r\text{critical}} = \frac{1}{2} \exp\left[\left(3.30 - 0.45\,\frac{B}{L}\right)\cot\left(45 - \frac{\phi}{2}\right)\right] \qquad (14\text{-}3)[6]$$

[5]Soil modulus of elasticity can also be obtained as the slope of the deviator stress versus strain curve, as taken from the triaxial test.
[6]Note: e^x can also be written as $\exp(x)$; that is, $e^x = \exp(x)$

TABLE 14-1 RANGE OF VALUES: MODULUS OF
ELASTICITY AND POISSON'S RATIO

Soil type	Modulus of elasticity, E	
	ksf	kN/m²
Sand, loose	200–500	9,000–25,000
Sand, dense	1,000–1,700	45,000–80,000
Sand, silty	150–450	7,000–21,000
Sand and gravel, loose	1,000–3,000	45,000–145,000
Sand and gravel, dense	2,000–4,000	90,000–180,000
Silt	50–400	2,400–20,000
Loess	300–1,100	15,000–50,000
Clay, soft	10–100	500–5,000
Clay, medium	100–200	4,000–10,000
Clay, firm	150–400	7,000–20,000
Clay, sandy	550–850	25,000–40,000

Soil type	Poisson's ratio, v
Sand, loose	0.10–0.30
Sand, dense	0.30–0.40
Silt	0.30–0.40
Loess	0.20–0.40
Clay, saturated	0.40–0.50
Clay, partially saturated	0.30–0.40
Clay, with sand and silt	0.20–0.40

Note: Values for Poisson's ratio lie within a narrow range and for
analytical studies usually are estimated. The modulus of elasticity
varies widely, being affected by stress history, water content, density, and grain-size distribution; with a given soil, values will vary
according to the applied load range.

Values of the critical rigidity index, $I_{r_{\text{critical}}}$, appropriate for a strip foundation and
a square foundation are presented in Figure 14-6. Values for rectangular shapes
(for $0 < B/L < 1$) can be interpolated between the two limit curves or calculated
from Equation 14-3.

Where the actual index is *greater than* the critical index, the general shear
failure mode applies and Equation 14-1a is suitable. Where the actual rigidity index
is *less than* the critical index, the local or punching shear failure mode applies and
the ultimate bearing capacity will be less than indicated by Equation 14-1a. For
this case, reduction factors r_c, r_γ, and r_q are applied to modify the bearing capacity
factors N_c, N_γ, and N_q, resulting in Equation 14-1b. Reduction factors are obtained
from Figure 14-7.

$$q_{\text{ult}} = c(N_c r_c) + \tfrac{1}{2}B \, \gamma_1(N_\gamma r_\gamma) + \gamma_2 D_f(N_q r_q) \qquad (14\text{-}1b)$$

*Equations 14-1a and 14-1b should not be used directly for foundation design. These
equations serve as the basis for designs but require modification because of the effect*

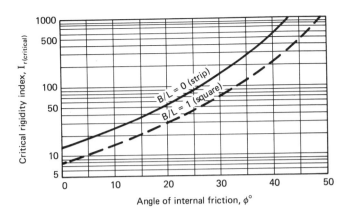

Figure 14-6 Relationship of Critical Rigidity Index, $I_{rcritical}$ and soil angle of internal friction, ϕ.

of various practical factors. Such factors and the form of the equations suited to foundation design are discussed in the following sections.

Additional Considerations, Bearing Capacity Equation

The ultimate bearing capacity of a long strip footing (Eq. 14-1b) indicates the gross or total bearing pressure that can be imposed at the level of the base of the footing. For the usual condition of a foundation installed below the ground surface, the gross bearing pressure includes the pressure developed from the foundation loading *and* the weight of the buried footing and soil backfill directly above the footing. For practical design purposes, the net bearing pressure q_{net}, then becomes

$$q_{net} = q_{ult} - \gamma_2 D_f \tag{14-4}$$
$$= cN_c r_c + \tfrac{1}{2}B\gamma_1 N_\gamma r_\gamma + \gamma_2 D_f (N_q - 1) r_q$$

where $\gamma_2 D_f$ is the pressure of the soil overburden adjacent to the level of the foundation base. Where the overburden is not of constant height, the lesser value should be used (see Fig. 14-8).

The values for soil unit weight to be used in the bearing capacity equation (γ_1 and γ_2) are effective unit weights. When the soil in the yield zone is below the water table, the submerged unit weight must be used. For the condition where the water table is at the base of a footing, the submerged (or buoyant) soil unit weight applies for the γ_1 term. Since the depth of the failure zone is considered to be approximately equal to the width of the footing, the full unit weight of the soil (not the submerged unit weight) is used when groundwater is lower than a distance B below the footing. For in-between depths of the water table, an interpolated value of effective soil unit weight (between $\gamma_{wet\ soil}$ and γ_{sub}) can be used. Continuing, if the water table extends above footing level, a submerged soil unit weight should also be used for the γ_2 value.

A high water table results in a lowered bearing capacity because of the requirement to use a reduced effective soil weight (the submerged weight) to determine the safe capacity. Further, situations arise in which a high water table forces additional factors to be taken into account. In the case where a building's basement will be below the level of an expected groundwater table, unequal pressures acting

Shallow Foundations

373

(a) r_q and r_γ values

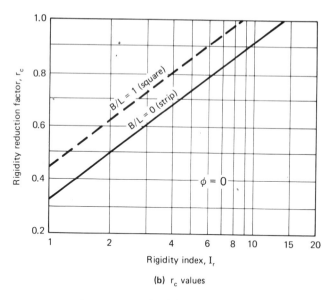

(b) r_c values

Figure 14-7 Rigidity reduction factors when soil rigidity index is less than $I_{rcritical}$.

on the structure's sidewalls and floor as a result of this groundwater need to be considered in the design (Fig. 14-9). The possible requirement for dewatering during construction (Chapter 6) should also be studied.

Equations 14-1a, 14-1b, and 14-4 provide ultimate values of bearing capacity. Designers conservatively assume that some variation in soil conditions will exist over an area to be occupied by construction or could develop because of environ-

Figure 14-8 Illustration of unequal surcharges encountered in foundation design.

(a) Unequal pressure condition (inside compared to outside of basement) due to ground water

(b) Groundwater level rises over foundation but no unequal water pressure acts on foundation base

Figure 14-9 Effects of high groundwater on foundation and basement design.

mental factors, such as a fluctuating water table or drying, and they apply the results of soil properties determined from explored locations with some caution. Also, as discussed earlier, ultimate loadings result in foundation settlements that are large and typically greater than desired or tolerable. As a result, when the bearing capacity equation is used for foundation design, it is conventional practice to apply a factor of safety of 2.5 or 3 to the value of q_{net} (Equation 14-4) to obtain q_{design}:

$$q_{design} = \frac{q_{net}}{2.5} \quad or \quad \frac{q_{net}}{3} \qquad (14\text{-}5$$

The illustrations that follow demonstrate application of the theory that has been developed to this point.

ILLUSTRATION 14-1. A strip footing 4 feet wide is supported in soil that has the properties indicated by the sketch. What design loading can be imposed onto the foundation per foot of length. Use a factor of safety equal to 3 with the extended general bearing capacity equation.

Shallow Foundations

Allowable wall loading = ?

γ_2 = 125 pcf

D_f = 5 ft.

wta

B = 4 ft $\gamma_1 = \gamma_{sub}$ = 125/5 pcf

Soil properties:
c_d = 300 psf
ϕ_d = 28°
I_r = 220

From bearing capacity factor chart, obtain $N_c = 26$, $N_\gamma = 16$, $N_q = 15$.
  From Figure 14-6, $I_{rcritical} \cong 140$ for $B/L = 0$ and $\phi = 28°$.
  Since $I_r > I_{rcritical}$, $r_c = r_\gamma = r_q = 1$. Therefore,

$$q_{net} = cN_c(1) + \frac{1}{2}B\gamma_1 N_\gamma(1) + \gamma_2 D_f(N_q - 1)(1)$$

$$= (0.3\ \text{ksf})(26) + \frac{1}{2}(4\ \text{ft})\left(\frac{.125}{2}\ \text{kcf}\right)(16)$$

$$+ (.125\ \text{kcf})(5\ \text{ft})(15 - 1) = 18.55\ \text{ksf}$$

$$q_{design} = \frac{18.55\ \text{ksf}}{3} = 6.2\ \text{ksf}$$

Allowable wall loading = (6.2 ksf)(4 ft wide)(1 ft long) = 24.8 k per foot of wall
length.

ILLUSTRATION 14-2.   A strip foundation similar to that used in Illustration 14-1
is located in an area where medium-soft clay soil exists. Properties are indicated
on the sketch. Using the extended general bearing capacity equation, with a factor
of safety equal to 3, calculate the wall load that can be carried by the footing.

Allowable wall loading = ?

γ_{fill} = 110 pcf

D_f = 5 ft

wta

B = 4 ft γ_1 = 125 pcf

Soil properties:
c_d = 150 psf
ϕ_d = 22°
E (from triaxial test) = 750 psi = 108 ksf
Poisson's ratio = 0.35 (estimated on basis of soil type)

Bearing capacity factors: $N_c = 17$, $N_\gamma = 7$, $N_q = 8$. Compute

$$I_r = \frac{E}{(2)(1 + \nu)(c + \bar{\sigma}_v \tan\phi)} = \frac{108 \text{ ksf}}{(2)(1 + .35)(.150 + .675 \tan 22°)\text{ksf}} = 48$$

where $\bar{\sigma}_v$ at depth of $B/2$ beneath footing $= (.110 \text{ ksf} \times 5 \text{ ft}) + \left(\frac{.125}{2} \text{ ksf} \times 2 \text{ ft} \right)$.

From Figure 14-6, obtain $I_{r\text{critical}} \cong 60$, and since $I_r < I_{r\text{critical}}$, use rigidity reduction factors from Figure 14-7. For $I_r = 48$, obtain $r_q, = r_\gamma = 0.92$, $r_c = 1.00$.

Calculate $\quad q_{net} = cN_c r_c + \frac{1}{2}B\gamma_1 N_\gamma r_\gamma + \gamma_2 D_f(N_q - 1)r_\gamma$

$$= (.15 \text{ ksf})(17)(1.00) + \frac{1}{2}(4 \text{ ft})\left(\frac{.125}{2} \text{ kcf} \right)(7)(0.92)$$

$$+ (.125 \text{ kcf})(5 \text{ ft})(0.92) = 3.93 \text{ ksf}$$

$$q_{design} = \frac{q_{ult}}{\text{FS}} = \frac{3.93 \text{ ksf}}{3} = 1.31 \text{ ksf}$$

Allowable wall loading $= (1.31 \text{ ksf})(4 \text{ ft wide} \times 1 \text{ ft long}) = 5.2 \text{ k/ft of wall length.}$

ILLUSTRATION 14-3. A wall footing is to be constructed on a clay soil, as indicated by the sketch. The footing is to support a wall that imposes a loading of 135 kN per meter of wall length. What footing width should be provided to have a factor of safety of 3 for a bearing pressure computed from the general bearing capacity equation.

Load: 135 kN/m (on footing)

0.5 m

1 meter length

B = ?

Soil properties:
$\gamma = 17.3 \text{ kN/m}^3$
$c_u = 72 \text{ kN/m}^2 \ (\phi = 0°)$
$E = 5500 \text{ kN/m}^2$
$\nu = 0.35$
$I_r = 28$

From Figure 14-6, $I_{r\text{critical}} = 13$ for $\phi = 0°$ and $B/L = 0$. Since $I_r > I_{r\text{critical}}$, we have $r_c = 1$. For $\phi = 0°$, $N_c = 5.14$; N_γ and N_q are negligible:

Shallow Foundations

Calculate $\quad q_{ult} = cN_c r_c = (72 \text{ kN/m}^2)(5.14)(1.0) = 370 \text{ kN/m}^2$

$$q_{design} = (370 \text{ kN/m}^2)(\tfrac{1}{3}) = 123 \text{ kN/m}^2$$

Allowable footing load $= (123 \text{ kN/m}^2)(B \text{ meters}) = 123B \text{ kN/m of wall length.}$

Required footing width, $B = \dfrac{135 \text{ kN/m}}{123 \text{ Kn/m}^2} = 1.1 \text{ m.}$

Application for Design—The Extended Bearing Capacity Equation.
Equations 14-1a, 14-1b and 14-4 apply for the condition of an infinitely long strip foundation with the base horizontal, with a vertical load centrically applied, where the ground surface surrounding the foundation is horizontal; also recall that the shearing strength of the soil above the plane level with the foundation base is neglected. In practice, these conditions are not always present: Foundations have finite dimensions (the commonly used shapes include square, rectangular, and circular as well as the long strip); the soil above the level of the footing may have significant shear strength; the loading on a horizontal foundation may be inclined or eccentrically positioned; the foundation base may be inclined; or the soil surface may be sloped.

The general bearing capacity equation developed for the infinite strip can be extended to consider variations from the basic assumptions by applying modification factors that account for the effect of each variation. The *extended bearing capacity equation* [99] becomes

$$q_{net} = cN_c(r_c s_c d_c i_c b_c) + \tfrac{1}{2}B\gamma_1 N_\gamma(r_\gamma s_\gamma d_\gamma i_\gamma b_\gamma) \\ + \gamma_2 D_f(N_q - 1)(r_q s_q d_q i_q b_q) \tag{14-6}$$

where r_c, r_γ, r_q = reduction factors to compensate for the punching–local shear condition.

s_c, s_γ, s_q = shape factors for square, rectangular, and circular foundations.

d_c, d_γ, d_q = depth factors.

i_c, i_γ, i_q = load inclination factors.

b_c, b_γ, b_q = base tilt factors.

Suitable modification factors to use with Equation 14-6 are presented in the following sections. Where a modification factor does not apply for the foundation condition under study, its value for Equation 14-6 is considered to be unity (that is, neglected; reduction factors that do not apply simply drop out).

In summary, Equation 14-6 should be utilized for calculating the value of q_{net} that is substituted into Equation 14-5 to obtain q_{design}.

Modification Factors for Square, Rectangular, and Circular Footings
For practical use, the yield zones occurring in the soil beneath an infinitely long footing can be adequately analyzed in a two-dimensional study. Where foundations of a finite length are involved, such as with square, rectangular, and circular shapes, the yield zones are three-dimensional and Equations 14-1a, 14-1b, and 14-4 do not

Foundations   Chap. 14

directly apply. Mathematical solutions have been managed for the case of a circular footing, and use of a shape factor permits the format of the general bearing capacity equation to be used. Mathematical solutions have not yet been obtained for square and rectangular shapes because of the complexity of the problem, but shape factors are available, as developed from empirical data, to include with the general bearing capacity equation. The shape factors appropriate for square, rectangular, and circular foundations are as follows:

$$s_c = 1 + (B/L)(N_q/N_c) \qquad (14\text{-}7a)$$

$$s_\gamma = 1 - 0.4(B/L) \qquad (14\text{-}7b)$$

$$s_q = 1 + (B/L)\tan\phi \qquad (14\text{-}7c)$$

For the square and circular foundation shapes, the B/L ratio equals unity. Note that for a strip foundation, the B/L value approaches zero and the shape factors become 1.

ILLUSTRATION 14-4. A square foundation for a column is to carry a loading of 200 kips. Determine the footing dimensions if it bears on the surface of a sand having properties indicated on the sketch. Use a factor safety of 3 for the general bearing capacity equation.

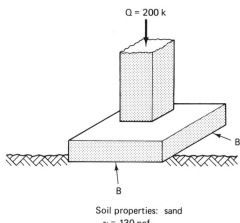

Soil properties: sand
$\gamma = 130$ pcf
$\phi_d = 36°$ (C = 0)
$N_\gamma = 50$
$I_r = 450$, $I_{r(critical)} = 150$

For a square foundation on the surface of sand:

$$q_{net} = \tfrac{1}{2}B\gamma_1 N_\gamma r_\gamma s_\gamma$$

where $s_\gamma = 1 - 0.4(B/L) = 0.6$. Since $I_r > I_{r critical}$, $r_\gamma = 1$. Obtain

$$q_{net} = \tfrac{1}{2}(B)(.130 \text{ kcf})(50)(1.0)(0.6) = 1.95B \text{ ksf}$$

$$q_{design} = (1.95B \text{ ksf})(\tfrac{1}{3}) = 0.65B \text{ ksf}$$

Shallow Foundations

Since $Q_{design} = 200$ k

$$q_{design} = \frac{Q}{A} = \frac{200k}{B^2}$$

$$0.65B = 200/B^2$$

$$B^3 = 308 \text{ ft}^3$$

$$B = 6.75 \text{ ft}$$

ILLUSTRATION 14-5. In an industrial building, two columns are close together and will be supported on a common rectangular foundation. The soil is a clay having a cohesion of 1700 psf. For the conditions indicated by the sketch, what footing dimensions should be provided? Use a factor of safety of 3.

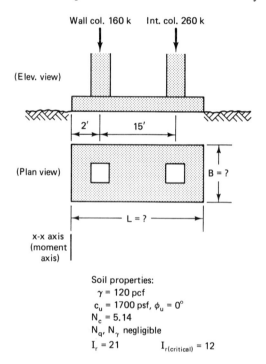

For the rectangular foundation on clay, $q_{net} = cN_c r_c s_c$. Assume $L/B \simeq 5$; therefore, $s_c = 1 + (B/L)(N_q/N_c) = 1 + (.2)(.2) = 1.04$. Since $I_r > I_{r\text{critical}}$, get $r_c = 1.0$.

$$q_{net} = (1.7 \text{ ksf})(5.14)(1.0)(1.04) = 9.09 \text{ ksf}$$

$$q_{design} = (9.09 \text{ ksf})(\tfrac{1}{3}) = 3.03 \text{ ksf}$$

but use 3.0 ksf. Two unknowns require two independent equations; use

$$\text{(i) } \Sigma F_v = 0 \qquad \text{(ii) } \Sigma M_{xx} = 0$$

For $\Sigma F_v = 0$: downward column loading = upward reaction on foundation base

$$(160 + 260) \text{ k} = (3 \text{ ksf})(BL)\text{sf} \qquad \text{(weight of foundation is neglected)}$$

$$BL = 140$$

$$B = 140/L$$

For $\Sigma M_{xx} = 0$: Moment due to column loading = moment of soil reaction on foundation

$$(160 \text{ k})(2 \text{ ft}) + (260 \text{ k})(17 \text{ ft}) = (3 \text{ ksf})(BL \text{ sf})(L/2 \text{ ft})$$

$$BL^2 = 3150 \text{ ft}^3$$

Since $B = 140/L$, get $BL^2 = (140/L)(L^2) = 3150 \text{ ft}^3$.
Obtain $L = 22.5$ ft and $B = 6.25$ ft.

Modification Factors for Footing Depth The development of the general bearing capacity for a long strip foundation does not consider the shearing resistance of the failure plane passing through the soil zone above the level of the foundation base. If the soil in this zone is weak or compressible or consists of a poorly placed backfill, the omission is considered proper. However, if this upper soil zone possesses significant shearing strength, because of natural conditions or from compaction, the ultimate value for bearing capacity would be increased. For this case, depth factors (d_c, d_γ, d_q) can be applied to the extended bearing capacity equation, whereby

$$d_\gamma = 1 \tag{14-8a}$$

$$d_q = 1 + 2 \tan \phi (1 - \sin\phi)^2 \, \frac{\tan^{-1}(D/B)}{57.3} \tag{14-8b}$$

$$d_c = d_q - \frac{1 - d_q}{N_c \tan \phi} \quad \text{(when } \phi > 0°\text{)} \tag{14-8c}$$

$$= 1 + \frac{\tan^{-1}(D/B)}{(3)(57.3)} \quad \text{(when } \phi = 0°\text{)} \tag{14-8d}$$

Modification Factors for Eccentric and Inclined Loads If the loading imposed onto a horizontal foundation does not act at the center, or if the loading is not vertical, the pattern of the soil yield zone beneath the foundation is different from the pattern that develops beneath a level footing carrying a vertical load.

For a design, eccentricity should be limited to one-sixth of the foundation dimension to prevent the condition of theoretical uplift occurring under part of the foundation (a condition that causes rapidly increasing and potentially dangerous changes in bearing imposed onto the soil beneath the loaded side of the foundation). The effect of eccentric placement of foundation loading can be conveniently and conservatively considered by substitution of a reduced foundation width (B') or length (L') in the bearing capacity equation, using

Shallow Foundations

$$B' = B - 2e_B \qquad (14\text{-}9a)$$

or

$$L' = L - 2e_L \qquad (14\text{-}9b)$$

where e_B and e_L are the eccentricity distances with reference to the center of the foundation area (see Fig. 14-10).

The inclined loading can be handled by the inclusion of inclination factors (i_c, i_γ, i_q) with the extended bearing capacity equation, whereby

$$i_q = \left[1 - \frac{Q_h}{Q + BLc \cot \phi} \right]^m \qquad (14\text{-}10a)$$

$$i_r = \left[1 - \frac{Q_h}{Q + BLc \cot \phi} \right]^{m+1} \qquad (14\text{-}10b)$$

$$i_c = i_q - \left(\frac{1 - i_q}{N_c \tan \phi} \right) \quad (\text{when } \phi > 0°) \qquad (14\text{-}10c)$$

$$= 1 - \frac{mQ_h}{cN_cBL} \quad (\text{when } \phi = 0°) \qquad (14\text{-}10d)$$

Recommended values of m are

$$m_L = (2 + L/B)/(1 + L/B) \qquad \text{if the angle of} \qquad (14\text{-}10e)$$
inclination is in the
plane of the L-axis

Inclined and eccentric loading

Figure 14-10 Definition of conditions for eccentric and inclined loading.

Foundations   Chap. 14

$$m_B = (2 + B/L)/(1 + B/L) \qquad \text{if the angle of} \qquad \text{(14-10f)}$$
$$\text{inclination is in the}$$
$$\text{plane of the } B\text{-axis}$$

Should the inclined load act in a plane that makes an angle θ with the L-axis of the foundation, the value for m becomes

$$m_\theta = m_L \cos^2\theta + m_B \sin^2\theta \qquad \text{(14-10g)}$$

When an inclined loading is also eccentric, the modified values B' and L' should be used in Equations 14-10a, b, c, and d. The actual values of B and L are still used to determine the m factors, however.

The horizontal component of an inclined load acts to slide the foundation laterally. If the shearing or frictional resistance developed under the base is not adequate, sliding occurs. The maximum horizontal force that can be resisted along the base of the footing is

$$Q_{h(\max)} = Q_v \tan \delta + A'c_a \qquad \text{(14-11)}$$

where A' is the effective bearing area of the footing ($B'L'$), δ is the angle of friction between the foundation material and soil, and c_a is the adhesion between the foundation and soil (for clay, a value related to the undrained shear strength).

Inclined Foundation Base   Where the base of a foundation is inclined or tilted from the horizontal and an applied load acts normal to the base, the pattern of the soil yield zone beneath the foundation is different from the pattern that develops beneath the level footing carrying a vertical load. For this condition, base tilt factors, b_c, b_γ, and b_q, developed originally for the strip footing foundation but considered also appropriate for other foundation shapes, can be applied to the general bearing capacity equation:

$$b_\gamma = \left(1 - \frac{\alpha}{57.3} \tan \phi\right)^2 \qquad \text{(14-12a)}$$

$$b_q = b_\gamma \qquad \text{(14-12b)}$$

$$b_c = b_q - \frac{(1 - b_q)}{N_c \tan \phi} \quad \text{(for } \phi > 0°) \qquad \text{(14-12c)}$$

$$= 1 - .0067\,\alpha \quad \text{(for } \phi = 0°) \qquad \text{(14-12d)}$$

In these expressions, α represents the angle of the base inclination, in degrees, with respect to the horizontal.

Footings on Slopes   The bearing capacity for footings on slopes is less than that for footings on level ground. The subsurface soil zones that provide resistance to foundation loading on the downhill side of the slope are smaller than they are where the ground is level. The safe loading is related to the soil failure zone involved. For footings of limited size, the soil failure zone is usually confined to the region near the vicinity of the foundation (regarding footings on level ground,

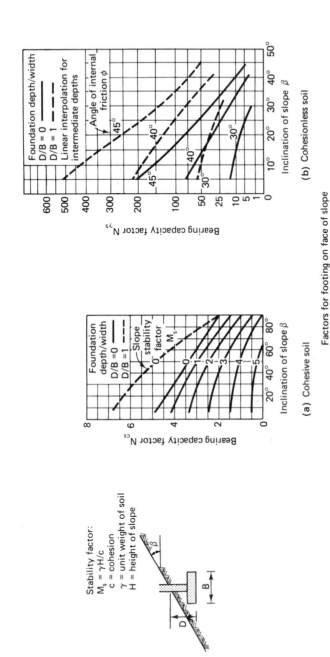

Figure 14-11 Bearing capacity factors for long footings on face of slope [161]: (a) cohesive soil, (b) cohesionless soil. Bearing capacity factors for footings on top of slope: (c) cohesive soil, (d) cohesionless soil.

Stability factor:
$M_s = \gamma H/c$
c = cohesion
γ = unit weight of soil
H = height of slope

(a) Cohesive soil

Bearing capacity factor N_{cs}

Foundation
depth/width
$D/B = 0$
$D/B = 1$
Slope
stability
factor
M_s

Inclination of slope β

Factors for footing on face of slope

(b) Cohesionless soil

Bearing capacity factor $N_{\gamma s}$

Foundation depth/width
$D/B = 0$
$D/B = 1$
Linear interpolation for intermediate depths
Angle of internal friction ϕ

Inclination of slope β

Inclination of slope β

Foundation depth/width
D/B = 0 ——————
D/B = 1 ——————
Linear interpolation
for intermediate depths
Angle of internal
friction φ

Bearing capacity factor $N_{\gamma s}$

Distance of foundation from edge of slope b/B

(d) Cohesionless soil

Inclination of slope β

Foundation depth/width
D/B = 0 ——————   D/B = 1 ——————
Slope stability factor M_s
$M_s = 0$

Bearing capacity factor N_{cs}

Distance of foundation from edge of slope
b/B (for $M_s = 0$) or b/H (for $M_s > 0$)

(c) Cohesive soil

Factors for footing on top of slope

Note: 1. To obtain a value
of N_{cs} for footings where
B < H, use the curves for
$M_s = 0$. When necessary,
interpolate for values of D/B
between 0 and 1.
2. To obtain the value of
N_{cs} when B ≥ H, use the
curve for the calculated
stability factor M_s.

Figure 14-11 (cont.)

385

see Fig. 14-2). For large footings, the failure zone may include all or most of the slope.

For continuous strip footings, the ultimate bearing capacity is evaluated from

$$q_{ult} = cN_{cs} + \tfrac{1}{2}\gamma BN_{\gamma s} \tag{14-13}$$

where N_{cs}, $N_{\gamma s}$ = bearing capacity factors for footings on slopes. Values for the bearing capacity factors are shown in Figure 14-11. For cohesive soil, N_{cs} is related to a slope stability factor, M_s, as defined in Fig. 14-11. The bearing capacity factor curves can also be used to indicate the footing setback distance where the slope inclination is no longer influential. For an adequate setback, the bearing capacity factors for level ground are used.

ILLUSTRATION 14-6. A bearing wall for a warehouse building is to be located close to a slope, as indicated by the sketch. For the given conditions, what size strip footing should be provided?

The allowable bearing pressure relates to the footing setback and the resulting b/B ratio, as well as the M_s factor. A trial-and-error procedure can be undertaken; it is initially assumed that $D_f/B = 0.5$ and $b/B = 1$. Since B is less than H, refer to the curves for $M_s = 0$. From Figure 14-11c, for $M_s = 0$, $b/B = 1$, $\beta = 60$ deg, get $N_{cs} = 4.9$. Therefore,

$$q_{ult} = cN_{cs} = 4.9c = 4.9(1000 \text{ psf}) = 4900 \text{ psf}$$

$$q_{design} = \frac{4900 \text{ psf}}{FS} = \frac{4900 \text{ psf}}{3 \text{ (assumed)}} \cong 1600 \text{ psf}$$

Required footing width,

$$B = \frac{Q}{(q_{design})(1 \text{ ft length})}$$

$$= \frac{4500 \text{ lb}}{(1600 \text{ psf})(1 \text{ ft})} \cong 2.8 \text{ ft}$$

Use $B = 3$ ft (conservative).

Spread Footing Design Using Penetration Resistance Data Obtaining foundation design criteria directly from the soil borings or soundings normally performed to explore conditions underlying a site is desirable from the view of cost and time savings. At locations where it is difficult to recover soil samples suitable for determining soil properties (a requirement when an analytical study for a foundation design is to be performed), obtaining foundation design criteria based directly on exploration data may be a necessity.

Typically, it is not a great problem to recover samples of soil possessing cohesion from borings, although care is required to minimize disturbance. On the other hand, obtaining undisturbed samples of cohesionless soil can be difficult, particularly when explorations extend below the groundwater table. Partly because of necessity, empirical relationships between the standard penetration test (SPT, Chapter 11) and performance of spread footings supported on sands have evolved. Relationships have also been developed for the cone penetrometer (Chapter 11) and foundations on sand.

Designing Spread Footings on Sand by Using the Standard Penetration Test Early information relating standard penetration test results (the blow count *N*) in sand to spread footing size, bearing pressure, and settlement was presented by Terzaghi and Peck in 1948[7] and has been widely referred to for foundation design. This empirically determined design method was intended to provide foundations whose maximum settlement would not exceed one inch, with the expectation that the greatest differential settlement between different footings would not exceed one-half to three-fourths inch (1.3 to 1.7 cm), a tolerable range for most structures. These early recommendations were based on limited data and were deliberately conservative.

Subsequent studies, which included performance evaluations of foundations designed in accord with the original recommendations, have indicated that modification of the original design criteria is necessary. Greater allowable bearing pressures can be permitted. Importantly, the value of *N* was found to be related to the soil overburden pressure (or depth) where the soil sample and blow count was taken. For a given soil density, the blow count is higher at deeper sampling depths because of the greater confinement and lateral pressure existing at deep, compared to shallow, locations. In contrast, blow count values obtained close to the ground surface are lower than should be indicated because of lack of overburden pressure and confinement. Thus, when SPT values are used for foundation design, the field blow counts need to be corrected to reflect the effect of sample depth on actual soil properties (see Fig. 14-12). The stress history of a sand deposit, including effects of compaction rolling or the presence of a high water table, also will affect a footing's performance, and these factors become a design consideration.

Empirically developed foundation design methods are typically based on the averaged or representative performance of case studies, but they will be conservative. Practically, deviations will always exist between individual cases and the

---

[7]Also in their subsequent publications through 1968, including [252].

SPT correction factor C_N

Effective overburden stress $\bar{\sigma}_v$, TSF

Effective overburden stress, $\bar{\sigma}_v$, KSF

$$C_N = \sqrt{1/\bar{\sigma}_v}$$
($\bar{\sigma}_v$ in TSF)

Figure 14-12 Correction factor for field SPT values [146].

design recommendations that evolve. Often, empirical design methods are recommended only for preliminary studies. Realistically, designers frequently need also to apply the procedures to final designs because of lack of further information or methods. When such methods are applied to future designs, it is necessary to expect a range in the predicted performance accuracy (e.g., an expected maximum settlement of one inch could end up being somewhat lesser or greater). Figure 14-13 presents design criteria for spread footings located at the shallow installation

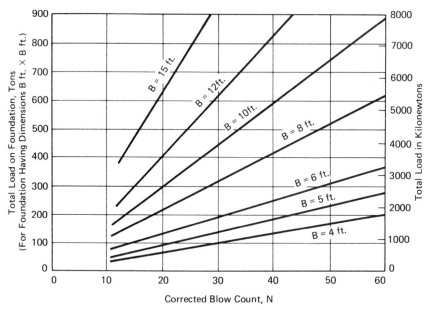

Total Load on Foundation, Tons (For Foundation Having Dimensions B ft. × B ft.)

Total Load in Kilonewtons

B = 15 ft.
B = 12ft.
B = 10ft.
B = 8 ft.
B = 6 ft.
B = 5 ft.
B = 4 ft.

Corrected Blow Count, N

Figure 14-13 Chart for spread footings on sand. Corrected standard penetration test results related to foundation size and loading for approximately one-inch settlement. Water table more than depth *B* below footing. (Data presentation after F. H. Collopy)

depths normally associated with basementless buildings (3 to 5 feet below grade). The bearing pressures are intended to be values that produce a maximum settlement on the order of one inch. The maximum differential settlement that results between all foundation units on the site is expected to be less than three-fourths inch.

The N values in Figure 14-13 used for design are corrected values, which consider effects of depth or overburden pressure on the field SPT value of N. Figure 14-12 provides a factor C_N that should be applied to the field blow count in order to arrive at a modified N value (i.e., $N_{corr} = C_N N_{field}$).

The N values in Figure 14-13 apply for dry or saturated sands. Where a condition of partial saturation exists, the sands possess some "apparent cohesion" because of the presence and effects of the air–water meniscus. Typically, this creates a greater strength. If the meniscus effect could disappear at some future time (through evaporation or submergence), a slight reduction should be applied to the N value used for design.

The procedure for designing foundations from Figure 14-13 involves working initially with the most heavily loaded units. For each boring location, the average corrected N value (see Illustration 14-7) is determined for the soil that lies within the zone between the bottom of the footing and a depth of about $1.5B$. A value for B is based upon approximating a bearing pressure value from the design curves of Figure 14-13. Since soil conditions are expected to vary somewhat at most construction sites, the N value selected for design is the lowest N_{avg}.

ILLUSTRATION 14-7. Standard penetration test results from a soil boring located adjacent to a planned foundation for a proposed warehouse are shown below. If it is assumed that little site grading will be performed, and if spread footings for the project are to be founded 4 ft below surface grade, what foundation size should be provided to support a 400-kip column load? Assume that a one-inch settlement is tolerable.

SPT sample depth, feet	Boring log summary	
	Blow count, N_{field}	Soil classification
1	9	Fine to medium sand, trace silt
4	10	Fine to medium sand
8	15	Fine to medium sand
12	22	Fine to coarse sand
16	19	Fine to medium sand
20	29	Fine to coarse sand
25	33	Fine to coarse sand
30	27	Fine to coarse sand

Drillers' Note Water table encountered at 25 ft.

A solution requires, first, that the field SPT values be corrected. A tabular arrangement, as shown below, is practical. Correction factors are from Figure 14-12.

SPT depth	N_{field}	Correction factor	N_{corr}	N_{avg} to depth shown
1 ft	9	2.5	22	—
4 ft	10	2.04	20	21
8 ft	15	1.44	21	21
12 ft	22	1.18	26	22
16 ft	19	1.02	19	21
20 ft	29	0.91	26	22
25 ft	33	0.82	27	23
30 ft	27	0.78	21	23

For a foundation to support 200 tons (400 kips) when the corrected $N_{average}$ value (to a depth between about 10 and 15 ft) is between 21 and 22 blows, Figure 14-13 indicates that a footing approximately 7.5 feet square (7 $\frac{1}{2}$ by 7 $\frac{1}{2}$ ft) is required.

The design bearing pressures shown in Figure 14-13 presume the water table to be greater than a depth B below the bottom of the footing. If the water table is within the zone close to the bottom of the footing, a bearing pressure value obtained from the design curves should be reduced to keep settlement from exceeding the one-inch limit. For the condition where the water table is at the base of the foundation, a one-third reduction in the bearing pressure value should be applied. A linear interpolation can be assumed for water table depths intermediate between the foundation level and a distance B below it.

A modification to the blow count value obtained in the field should also be applied to the condition where fine sands and silty fine sands are submerged. This modification can be applied before correcting for the effects of overburden pressure. Letting N' be the modified field value, the following relationship is recommended:

$$N' = 0.6N_{field} \quad \text{(for submerged fine sand and silty sand)} \quad (14\text{-}14)$$

The bearing pressure–settlement values indicated by Figure 14-13 do not apply to narrow foundations. Where narrow footings are installed on cohesionless soil, bearing capacity values on the basis of shear failure of the supporting soil will control design. Angles of internal friction for the sand to permit analytical design can be estimated from the SPT blow count (Chapter 10).

Sites showing a blow count value of less than 10 are indicating loose sand. The data of Figure 14-13 should not be applied to such conditions. Consideration should be given to improving the density of the sands by vibratory compaction, vibroflotation or Terra-probe, blasting, or other methods before construction. Where an entire area is improved, foundation design and performance will benefit, but other aspects of construction, such as building slabs, roads, parking areas, and buried utilities, are also affected. Foundation design should be made on the basis of the improved soil properties.

Different foundations usually carry different magnitudes of loading (e.g., interior column foundations generally are more heavily loaded than wall column footings). Foundations carrying different loads can have their allowable bearing pressures determined individually from the curves in Figure 14-13, using the lowest corrected N_{avg} or an N value more appropriate for the actual footing area. Frequently, however, a bearing pressure is selected for the worst condition (lowest N value and heaviest foundation loading), and this pressure is used for proportioning all footing units. Although it is usually a safe procedure, this method tends to increase the range of differential settlement that results between light and heavily loaded foundations.

On building sites underlain by sand, many designers take the precaution of having the surface of the finish-graded area compacted by vibratory equipment to increase the density of the upper zone of soil and achieve a better degree of uniformity across the site before foundation construction takes place. Where sand fill projects are concerned, vibratory compactors are typically selected because of their effectiveness and efficiency. Densifying sand with vibratory methods causes high lateral pressures to develop in the compacted zone, a condition that produces high resistance to further volume changes and settlement. For the condition where the soil zone providing the foundation support has been compacted by vibratory methods, an increase in the bearing pressure values obtained from Figure 14-13 can be made. Limited indications are that a one-fourth increase will be conservative.

Figure 14-13 is intended to apply only to sand. Where a subsoil contains gravel, the SPT blow count can be erroneously high. For gravelly soils, a large-diameter soil sampler should be used to recover samples for examination. Better, test pits can be excavated and the compactness of soil that will lie beneath footing level can be checked visually or with density testing equipment. Where deep soil zones need their density known, nuclear density meters capable of extending to deep depths can be used in the borings.

If a maximum settlement greater than one inch can be tolerated, or if it is desired to restrict the maximum settlement to less than one inch, bearing pressure values presented in Figure 14-13 can be increased or reduced in the proportion of the final settlement desired, within reasonable limits (e.g., for half of one-inch settlement, assume half the bearing pressure).

The information of Figure 14-13 can also be utilized for designing mat foundations. Although mat foundations typically impose comparatively low bearing pressures in accord with the purpose of their design, allowable pressures from the design can be doubled without expecting differential settlement of the mat to exceed three-fourths inch.

The Standard Penetration Test and Cohesive Soil
Shallow foundations supported on clay are not designed directly from standard penetration test blow count data. A major reason for this situation has been the difficulty in relating blow count values to a cohesive soil's stress history accurately enough to permit reliable foundation settlement predictions. Since practical procedures exist for separately determining the properties of a clay (vane shear tests can be performed in borings on the in-place soil, or laboratory strength and compressibility tests can be performed on undisturbed samples recovered from borings), some of the usual reasons for converting boring results directly into foundation design data do not apply. However, blow counts from the standard penetration test are useful for estimating the value of cohesion, c (the unconfined shear strength):

$$c = \frac{N}{4} \text{ ksf} \quad \text{(for clay)} \tag{14-15a}$$

$$c = \frac{N}{5} \text{ ksf} \quad \text{(for silty clay)} \tag{14-15b}$$

The value of cohesion, c, can then be substituted into Equation 14-6 to estimate the ultimate bearing capacity for the clay.

Designing Spread Footings on Sand by Using the Static Cone Penetrometer

Static cone penetrometers are used extensively throughout Europe in the performance of investigations to determine subsoil stratification and related soil properties. In recent times, investigations utilizing penetrometer methods have received considerable attention in virtually all areas of the world. Interest has been generated by the developing awareness that direct relationships between penetrometer results and foundation design have been formulated.

For studying the relationship between static cone penetration results and foundation performance, much attention has been directed to the Delft (Dutch) cone penetrometer. This apparatus has a 60-deg cone point with a base area of 10 cm^2. Many other static penetrometers in use have similar cone dimensions. To evaluate the soil in a boring or sounding, the cone is advanced a short distance to determine the point resistance q_c (kg/cm^2 or tons per square foot) of the undisturbed soil. European experience indicates that for spread footing foundations located at shallow depths (on the order of 3 ft or 1 m), the allowable bearing pressure, q_{allow}, is about one-tenth of the point resistance obtained with the Dutch cone, or

$$q_{\text{allow}} = \frac{q_c}{10} \quad \text{(in } \text{kg/cm}^2 \text{ or ton/ft}^2\text{)} \tag{14-16}$$

More detailed design information, reflecting the effect of footing width and depth, has been developed, as shown in Figure 14-14.

Easily usable, refined relationships between static cone penetration, foundation size, bearing pressure and *settlement* have not been developed, athough the issue continues to receive attention. For *order-of-magnitude information*, it is prac-

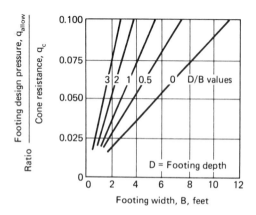

Figure 14-14 Relationship among static cone resistance, footing size and depth, and allowable bearing pressure [206].

tical to use correlations between cone penetration resistance and the standard penetration test (SPT). For clean sands and sands with little silt or gravel, the ratio of q_c to N usually ranges between 3.5 and 5. A reasonable, practical approximation is

$$q_c = 4N \quad \text{(approximately)} \tag{14-17}$$

where q_c is in kg/cm^2 or ton/ft^2 and N is the blow count from the SPT.

With this value, the information of Figure 14-13 relating shallow foundation design to settlement (an anticipated maximum settlement of one inch) has been replotted in terms of the static cone resistance q_c (see Fig. 14-15). In practical terms, the positioning of the bearing pressure curves are not highly sensitive to slight variations in the q_c-to-N ratio. Hence, the approximations of Figure 14-15 are applicable for the sand categories indicated earlier. The conditions assumed for developing Figure 14-13 would also apply to Figure 14-15 (i.e., the foundation embedment is on the order of 3 to 5 feet [1 to 1.5 m] below grade, the value of q_c is representative of the soil zone below the base of the footing to a depth extending approximately 1.5B further, and the water table is deep). Reductions in bearing pressures recommended for the case of a high water table also apply to Figure 14-15.

Static Cone Resistance and Cohesive Soil   In practical terms, good relationships have been established between q_c values and the cohesion and stress history of clay. The bearing capacity for the clay is subsequently calculated from the theoretical bearing capacity equations (Eq. [14-6]). For the Delft (Dutch) cone:

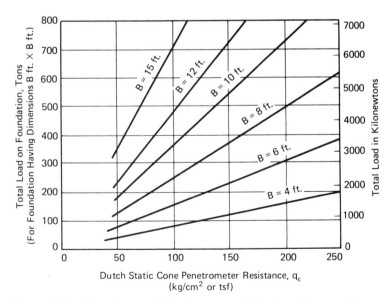

Figure 14-15 Chart for spread footings on sand. Dutch static cone resistance related to foundation size and loading for approximately one-inch settlement. Water table more than depth B below footing. (Data presentation after F. H. Collopy)

Shallow Foundations

$$c = \text{between } \frac{q_c}{15} \text{ and } \frac{q_c}{18} \qquad (14\text{-}18\text{a})$$

(for normally consolidated clay, $q_c < 20$)

$$c = \text{between } \frac{q_c}{10} \text{ and } \frac{q_c}{14} \qquad (14\text{-}18\text{b})$$

(for soft clays where a local shear failure is expected)

$$c = \text{between } \frac{q_c}{22} \text{ and } \frac{q_c}{26} \qquad (14\text{-}18\text{c})$$

(for overconsolidated clays, $q_c > 25$)

Settlement estimates can be obtained by using the methods described in Chapter 9. The value for C_c, the compression index, to apply when Equation 9-3b (repeated below) is used can be determined from Table 14-2.

$$\Delta H = \frac{H_0}{1 + e_0} C_c (\log \overline{\sigma}_{v_f} - \log \overline{\sigma}_{v_0}) \qquad (9\text{-}3\text{b})$$

If soil samples are not recovered from borings or test pits, an appropriate value of e_0 can be obtained by estimating the water content from data in Table 14-2 while assuming full saturation and selecting a representative value for G_s.

If the coefficient of volume compressibility, m_v, is defined as

$$m_v = \frac{\Delta e}{\Delta \sigma_v (1 + e_0)} \qquad (14\text{-}19)$$

then Equation 9-3b can be rewritten as

$$\Delta H = H_0 (\Delta \sigma_v)(m_v) = \frac{H_0}{\eta q_c} \qquad (14\text{-}20)$$

where $\Delta \sigma_v$ represents the stress increase in the clay layer, as for Equation 9-3b, and η is obtained from Table 14-3.

TABLE 14-2 CORRELATION OF CONE RESISTANCE, COMPRESSIBILITY INDEX, AND WATER CONTENT

Point resistance, q_c (tsf, kg/cm²)	Water content, w (%)	Compression index, C_c
$q_c > 12$	$w < 30$	$C_c < 0.2$
$q_c < 12$	$w < 25$	$C_c < 0.2$
	$25 < w < 40$	$0.2 < C_c < 0.3$
	$40 < w < 100$	$0.3 < C_c < 0.7$
$q_c < 7$	$100 < w < 130$	$0.7 < C_c < 1$
	$w > 130$	$C_c > 1$

Source: [202].

TABLE 14-3 VALUES OF THE η COEFFICIENT FOR CLAY AND SILT SOILS

	(q_c in tsf or kg/cm²) ·	
CL—low-plasticity clay	$q_c < 7$	$3 < \eta < 8$
	$7 < q_c < 20$	$2 < \eta < 5$
	$q_c > 20$	$1 < \eta < 2.5$
ML—low-plasticity silt	$q_c < 20$	$3 < \eta < 6$
	$q_c > 20$	$1 < \eta < 2$
CH—very plastic clay	$q_c < 20$	$2 < \eta < 6$
MH–OH—very plastic clay	$q_c > 20$	$1 < \eta < 2$

Source: [204].

Pressuremeter The pressuremeter is a device developed to determine in situ properties of earth materials. As used for evaluating soil deposits, the pressuremeter is simply a cylindrical apparatus whose volume can be increased by expanding in the lateral direction only. To test a soil zone, the pressuremeter cylinder, identified as the *probe*, is lowered to the desired position in a boring hole (borehole), and an internal pressure is applied that causes the probe to expand laterally into the surrounding soil. Pressure is increased in measured increments, and related changes in volumes are recorded. The test continues until the soil is considered to be failed, a condition that is assumed where large increases in volume (indicative of large volumetric strain) occur under small increments of pressure.

Credit for the concept and development of the pressuremeter types that are presently in use to obtain information applicable to foundation design is given to Louis Menard of France. In the mid-1950s, Menard conceived the idea that the pressure required to expand a balloonlike device that had been inserted into a soil mass would also be indicating that material's resistance to load-carrying elements such as structural foundations. To date, usage of the pressuremeter has, for the most part, been limited to France, but interest and usage has been increasing in the English-speaking countries and other parts of the world as knowledge of the equipment and the related foundation design procedure spreads.

The major component of Menard's prototype pressuremeter apparatus was an in-line three-cell probe that, positioned in the earth, would provide pressure-related, soil-volume-change information. The center cell was the test or measuring cell; the end cells were guard cells. During the test, each cell would be independently inflated to the same pressure. This arrangement protects the center cell from end effects that would develop in a single-cell device and also permits the test cell to expand only radially outward from the probe's longitudinal axis. Though refinements and modifications have been made to the original design, present pressuremeters retain the feature of a protected center test cell. The effect on the soil zone surrounding the expanding center cell is that of a probe having an infinite length, where compression of the soil can be attributed to deformations resulting from plane strain.[8] This latter condition permits available solutions to the heretofore

---

[8]All displacements that result from deformation are parallel to the same plane.

theoretical problem of expansion of a cylindrical cavity in an infinite medium to be applied to the pressuremeter.

The Menard-type pressuremeter consists of the probe, which is inserted into a borehole, a surface-stationed control unit that controls and monitors the probe's pressure and volume changes, and tubing that connects the control unit and probe (see Fig. 14-16). Water typically is used in the test cell to measure the volume changes that occur as pressure increases. Containerized compressed gas is used to pressurize the test and guard cells.

To provide visualization of equipment size, one of the most widely used probes, described as the BX probe, has a diameter of 58 mm, a length of 42 cm, and a test cell volume, V_c, of 535 cm^3. The BX designation is taken from the diameter of a borehole made with a 60-mm, or BX-size, diamond bit.

The field test procedure consists of inserting the probe into a drilled borehole to the depth to be tested. Pressures are applied in increments until the soil "fails." Usually, failure is considered to have been reached when the total expanded volume of the test zone reaches twice the volume of the original cavity. Each increment of pressure is held for a period, typically one minute, and the related volume-change readings are noted. Subsequently, a plot of pressure versus volume (or

(a) Basic components of pressuremeter

(b) Schematic indication of method to pressurize probe

Figure 14-16 Illustration of Menard-type pressuremeter.

change in volume) is made to obtain parameters necessary for foundation design. A typical pressuremeter curve is shown in Figure 14-17.

The limit pressure, p_l, indicated by the pressuremeter curve of Figure 14-17b, is taken as the cell pressure that has caused the volume of the tested borehole cavity to be doubled. The ultimate bearing capacity, q_{ult} for the soil zone supporting a shallow foundation, based on theoretical considerations with empirically determined modifications, has been related to the limit pressure as follows:

$$q_{ult} = \bar{\sigma}_v + k_{bc}(p_l - \sigma_h) \tag{14-21}$$

where q_{ult} = ultimate bearing capacity of the soil, in kN/m².
$\quad\quad \bar{\sigma}_v$ = effective vertical stress at the planned foundation depth, in kN/m².
$\quad\quad \sigma_h$ = at-rest horizontal soil pressure at the planned foundation depth, or $K\bar{\sigma}_v$, in kN/m².
$\quad\quad k_{bc}$ = bearing capacity factor for the proposed foundation shape and embedment and soil type (see Table 14-4).
$\quad\quad p_l$ = limit pressure (see Fig. 14-17b).

The settlement, ΔH, of a shallow foundation situated in homogeneous soil can be estimated from

$$\Delta H = \frac{q_{des}}{9E_m} \left[2B_0 \left(\lambda_d \frac{B}{B_0} \right)^\alpha + \alpha \lambda_c B \right] F_d \tag{14-22}$$

(a) Uncorrected test result

Note:
1. p_o is pressure required for probe to push sides of boring back to original position (soil position before boring was made), point v_o represents the corrected initial size of cavity.
2. p_o also represents the at-rest pressure, σ_h.
3. Volume of liquid in probe cell prior to test is V_c.

(b) Corrected test result

Figure 14-17 Pressuremeter test results.

Shallow Foundations

TABLE 14-4 VALUES OF k_{bc} FOR PRESSUREMETER BEARING CAPACITY EQUATION

Soil Type →		Values of k_{bc}, Strip Foundations								
		Sand			Silt			Clay		
p_l (kN/m²)	D/B ratio →	0	2	4	0	2	4	0	2	4
500		0.8	1.5	1.8	0.8	1.4	1.6	0.8	1.3	1.5
1000		0.8	1.7	2.2	0.8	1.45	1.75	0.8	1.4	1.7
3000		0.8	2.0	2.6	0.8	1.65	2.0	0.8	1.5	1.8
6000		0.8	2.3	3.0						
		Values of k_{bc}, Square and Round Foundations								
500		0.8	2.2	3.0	0.8	2.1	2.45	0.8	1.9	
1000		0.8	3.0	4.0	0.8	2.25	2.75	0.8	2.2	2.5
3000		0.8	3.7	4.8	0.8	2.45	3.1	0.8	2.4	2.9
6000		0.8	3.9	5.4						

where q_{des} = foundation design bearing pressure minus the vertical pressure of the soil overburden adjacent to the foundation base.

B_0 = a reference dimension, equal to 0.6 m or 2 ft.

B = width or diameter of the foundation, provided that B is equal to or greater than B_0.

α = rheological or creep deformation factor, which depends on the soil type and the ratio $E_m/(p_l - \sigma_h)$ (see Table 14-5).

λ_c, λ_d = shape factors that are based on length-to-width ratio of the foundation (see Table 14-6).

E_m = Menard pressuremeter modulus, equal to 2.66 G_m, where G_m is the Menard shear modulus for the pressuremeter curve between v_0 and v_f; i.e., $G_m = \left(V_c + \dfrac{v_0 + v_f}{2} \right) \dfrac{\Delta p}{\Delta V}$,

or, also:

$E_m = 2.66 \left[V_c + \dfrac{v_0 + v_f}{2} \right] \left(\dfrac{p_f - p_0}{v_f - v_0} \right)$, where the respective pressure and volume values are obtained from the pressuremeter curve (refer to Fig. 14-17; units of E_m are kN/m²).

F_d = depth factor, equal to 1 if the foundation depth is greater than B, equal to 1.20 for a foundation at the ground surface, equal to 1.10 for a foundation depth equal to one-half B.

Presumptive Bearing Pressures   Allowable foundation bearing values that are related to the visual classification of a site's bearing soil, a type of design information that conventionally appears as part of the building codes in effect for cities and suburban areas, are termed *presumptive bearing pressures* (i.e., assumed safe bearing pressures). Figure 14-18 illustrates a table of presumptive bearing values.

TABLE 14-5 PRESSUREMETER SETTLEMENT EQUATION, α FACTORS

Soil type	$E_m/(p_l - \sigma_h)$	α
Clay, normally consolidated	9 to 16	2/3
Clay, overconsolidated	greater than 16	1
Silt, normally consolidated	8 to 14	1/2
Silt, overconsolidated	greater than 14	2/3
Sand	7 to 12	1/3
Sand, compact	greater than 12	1/2

TABLE 14-6 PRESSUREMETER SETTLEMENT EQUATION, λ SHAPE FACTORS

L/B ratio:	Circular	Square	2	5	20
λ_c	1	1.10	1.20	1.40	1.50
λ_d	1	1.12	1.53	2.14	2.65

Presumptive bearing pressures predate the development of soil mechanics. Their origin lies in the experiences accumulated by the early builders in an area. Information of this type easily became part of the early building codes, for the developing cities needed reference criteria for new construction that presumably would ensure safe design.

Presumptive bearing pressures can be appropriate for design when utilized in the area for which the values were developed and for the type of construction that provided the original experience data. Unfortunately, presumptive bearing pressures frequently no longer reflect local geologic conditions and experiences but are values extracted from other codes or references. Importantly, methods and materials of construction that affect the behavior of commercial-industrial buildings likely have changed significantly since the origin of the presumptive bearing values for places such as older cities; for example, compared to the older style of low masonry construction, modern structures are taller, with steel frame construction, and the performance demands of foundations have been changed correspondingly. Since presumptive bearing pressures do not consider the important influence of factors such as foundation size and embedment, position of the groundwater table, soil density or consistency, and soil stress history, unsafe or uneconomical foundation designs can occur. Though building codes must be followed in the area of their jurisdiction, it is fortunate that many modern codes also permit foundation designs made on the basis of engineering studies that include a site investigation and soil testing to supersede the presumptive values.

DEEP FOUNDATIONS

The load-carrying capacity of deep foundations such as piles and piers is typically evaluated by analytical methods, by in-place field load tests on an installed unit, or through the application of pile-driving formulae.

Class	Material	Allowable bearing value, tons per square foot[1]
1	Massive crystalline bed rocks, such as granite, gneiss, trap rock, etc.; in sound condition . .	100
2	Foliated rocks, such as schist and slate, in sound condition	40
3	Sedimentary rocks, such as hard shales, silt-stones, or sandstones, in sound condition . . .	15
4	Exceptionally compacted gravels or sands . . .	10
5	Gravel; sand-gravel mixtures; compact.	6
6	Gravel, loose; coarse sand, compact	4
7	Coarse sand, loose; sand-gravel mixtures, loose; fine sand, compact; coarse sand, wet (confined)	3
8	Fine sand, loose; fine sand, wet (confined). . .	2
9	Stiff clay	4
10	Medium stiff clay	2
11	Soft clay	1
12	Fill, organic material, or silt.	(²)

[1]Presumptive bearing values apply to loading at the surface or where permanent lateral support for the bearing soil is not provided.

²Except where, in the opinion of the enforcement officer, the bearing value is adequate for light frame structures, fill material, organic material, and silt shall be deemed to be without presumptive bearing value. The bearing value of such material may be fixed on the basis of tests or other satisfactory evidence.

Figure 14-18 Illustrative Table of Presumptive Bearing. (From New York State Building Construction Code, 1977).

The analytical method applies the principles of soil mechanics and requires a knowledge of subsurface conditions and soil properties as well as information on pile type, dimensions, and installation method. Field load tests consist of imposing loadings in increments onto the in-place pile or pier and obtaining settlement data for each increment. The foundation design capacity is frequently taken where a predetermined tolerable settlement is reached or where the load–settlement plot is no longer proportional. Pile-driving formulae typically relate the dynamic energy imparted by the pile-driving hammer to the pile capacity. Most of the driving formulae in common use are not appropriate for determining the true capacity of a driven pile. Their lack of accuracy notwithstanding, driving formulae unfortunately are still in wide use as the only field control for pile installations. However, application of the driving formula for field control used in conjunction with load test results is a recommended procedure, for the driving record serves to relate each installed pile to the tested pile.

Statical Analysis For a pile or pier having adequate structural strength to carry an intended loading, the total downward capacity, Q_{total}, will be based on soil conditions (Fig. 14-19). The ultimate capacity of a pile is due to soil resistance

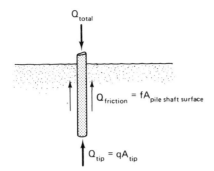

Figure 14-19 Basic concepts—pile capacity related to soil support.

developed by friction or adhesion between the soil and pile shaft, $Q_{friction}$, and the end bearing at the tip of the pile, Q_{tip}:

$$Q_{total} = Q_{friction} + Q_{tip} \tag{14-23a}$$

$$Q_{total} = fA_{surface} + q_{tip}A_{tip} \tag{14-23b}$$

where $A_{surface}$ = effective surface area of pile in contact with soil along the embedded shaft length.

f = average unit skin friction or adhesion between soil and pile surface.

q_{tip} = bearing pressure of soil at pile tip.

A_{tip} = pile tip bearing area.

Methods in use to compute $Q_{friction}$ and Q_{tip} relate to the type of soil penetrated. The analyses differ for clay soil and for sand soil, as detailed below. Where strata of soil possessing different properties are penetrated or the pile cross section and surface area vary along its length, the skin friction can be calculated by using segments of pile length and the appropriate soil value and pile area.

Statical Method—Driven Piles in Sand The ultimate capacity of a single pile driven in sand is the sum of the point resistance and the skin friction acting along the shaft of the pile:

$$Q_{total} = fA_{surface} + q_{tip}A_{tip} \tag{14-23b}$$

The unit skin friction for a straight-sided pile is a function of the soil pressure acting normal to the pile surface and the coefficient of friction between the soil and pile material (Fig. 14-20). Thus skin friction on a pile shaft is determined in the manner used in engineering mechanics to compute frictional resistance developing between two solid materials with movement impending.

Soil pressure acting normal to a vertical pile surface is assumed to be directly related to an effective vertical soil pressure (overburden pressure) and a lateral pressure coefficient K.

$$\overline{\sigma}_h = K\overline{\sigma}_v \tag{8-5}$$

where $\overline{\sigma}_h$ = horizontal soil pressure acting at any depth Z in a soil mass.

Deep Foundations

Direction of pile movement under loading of Q_{total}

Pile

Soil surrounding pile

Representative soil particle against pile

$N =$ Unit force of soil acting normal to pile surface

δ

$f =$ friction   Resultant of N and F

$$\tan \delta = \frac{\text{Friction, } f}{N}$$
or, $f = N \tan \delta$

Figure 14-20 Solid-to-solid friction developing against pile shaft.

$\bar{\sigma}_v$ = effective vertical pressure (overburden) acting at same depth Z within a soil mass.

K = lateral pressure coefficient expressing the ratio of $\bar{\sigma}_h$ to $\bar{\sigma}_v$.

The unit value of skin friction f acting at any depth in a sand mass theoretically becomes

$$f_{sand} = \bar{\sigma}_h \tan \delta = K\bar{\sigma}_v \tan \delta \qquad (14\text{-}24)$$

where $\tan \delta$ = coefficient of friction between sand and the pile surface.

Representative values for the coefficient of friction between silica sand and the pile materials are shown in Table 14-7. The total skin friction acting along the embedded length of pile is then

$$Q_{friction} = f_{sand}A_{surface} = (K\bar{\sigma}_v \tan \delta)A_{surface} \qquad (14\text{-}25)$$

In cohesionless deposits, the vertical (overburden) stress, σ_v, is conventionally assumed to increase with depth, according to Equation 8-1;

$$\sigma_v = \gamma_{soil} Z \qquad (8\text{-}1)$$

where γ_{soil} = unit weight of soil.

Z = depth below ground surface.

TABLE 14-7 REPRESENTATIVE VALUES FOR COEFFICIENT OF FRICTION BETWEEN SAND AND PILE MATERIALS

Material	Tan δ
Concrete	0.45
Wood	0.4
Steel (smooth)	0.2
Steel (rough, rusted)	0.4
Steel (corrugated)	Use tan ϕ of sand

Note: Ref. 51 suggests δ equal to 0.8 times the peak soil friction angle, ϕ_{peak}.

However, in evaluating skin friction that develops *with driven piles*, evidence indicates that the *influence* of the effective overburden stress of soil adjacent to the pile does *not* continue to increase without limit, as implied by Equations 8-1 and 14-24. Adjacent to a pile, the effective vertical stress of influence, $\bar{\bar{\sigma}}_v$, increases only until a certain distance of penetration, termed the critical depth D_c, is reached. Below this depth, the influential effective vertical pressure remains essentially constant, or increases at a low rate. (Evidence indicates that driving a pile in sand results in a thin zone of loose sand around the pile wall, which is encircled by a zone of densified sand. By arching, the cylindrical zone of loose and dense sand prevents the development of high lateral earth pressure against the pile [51].) The point where the critical depth is reached is influenced by the initial condition of the sand (loose or compact) and the dimension of the pile. Field and model tests suggest that the critical depth ranges from about ten pile diameters for loose sands to about twenty pile diameters for dense, compact sand. Figure 14-21 provides information on critical depth for different conditions that can be conservatively used for pile design: The indicated depths refer to soil above the water table; for submerged deposits, the critical depth is 1.6 times greater.

The value of K that acts at a particular depth in a soil mass after the pile has been driven is affected by the initial condition of the sand (such as relative density), the shape and size of the pile, and the method of installation. Piles are driven into undisturbed ground or installed in predrilled holes or with the assistance of jetting. The latter two procedures are commonly utilized where it is anticipated that a pile cannot be driven to a desired depth without damage because of the presence of hard material or hazardous objects in upper zones of soil. Figure 14-22 relates installation conditions with values of K that are commonly assumed in pile capacity analysis.

Driven piles causing large soil displacement (e.g., cylindrical piles) develop greater unit skin friction than piles with small volume displacement (e.g., H-piles). This is the effect of a greater K value resulting from the pile installation. Similarly,

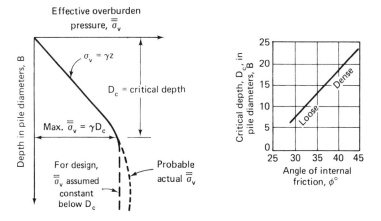

Figure 14-21 Variation of influential effective overburden stress in sands adjacent to driven straight-sided piles [165, 263, 265, 51].

Deep Foundations

Before installation $\sigma_h = 0$ $K = 0$

Before installation $\sigma_h = 0$ $K = 0$

Before installation $\sigma_h = K\sigma_v$ $K = 0.3$ to 0.6

After installation — Soil movement $K = 0.1$ to 0.4

After installation — Soil movement $K = 0.4$ to 0.75

After installation — Soil movement $K = 0.75$ to 4

(a) Pile driven in oversize hole

(b) Pile driven in undersize hole

(c) Pile driven in undisturbed sand

Figure 14-22 Values of lateral pressure coefficient K used for design of piles in sand.

tapered piles develop greater capacity along the shaft than do straight piles because of the greater change in properties of the soil surrounding the pile and the greater inclination in the angle of the soil force resultant acting against the pile shaft.

Where information on soil conditions and properties as well as on the type and shape of the pile to be driven is available, the previously detailed methods should be applied to compute the skin friction. Because the condition of the sand surrounding the pile has significant influence on the skin friction that develops, it is possible to establish a probable range of skin friction values acting along the shaft of a pile based on the relative density of the sand. Such information is shown in Figure 14-23 for driven piles having straight sides and limited diameter. Such data can be used to obtain *preliminary estimates* of skin friction during the absence of detailed information.

For computing the skin friction that develops along the shaft of an embedded pile, it is convenient to work with a diagram indicating the variation of $\bar{\bar{\sigma}}_v$ with depth (see Illustration 14-8). Multiplying the area of this diagram by K and $\tan \delta$ provides the total skin friction acting on an incremental strip along the embedded length of pile. The product of this increment of skin friction and the pile perimeter (circumference of the pile cross section) completes the numerical integration that gives the total skin friction.

The end bearing pressure, q_{tip}, at a pile tip can be computed from the bearing capacity equation for deep foundations in cohesionless soil:

$$q_{tip} = 0.4\gamma\, BN_\gamma + \bar{\bar{\sigma}}_v N_q \qquad (14\text{-}26a)$$

where N_γ, N_q = bearing capacity factors for deep foundations.
$\bar{\bar{\sigma}}_v$ = effective vertical pressure of influence acting at pile tip depth.
B = pile tip diameter or width.
γ = unit weight of soil in zone of pile tip.

This bearing capacity equation has the same form as the bearing capacity for shallow

Unit skin friction (ksf)

Depth in pile diameters, B
$\left(\text{ratio}, \dfrac{\text{actual depth, D}}{\text{pile diameter, B}}\right)$

Loose

Medium dense

Dense-very dense

(kN/m²)

Figure 14-23 Range of values: Skin friction versus depth for straight-sided piles driven in sand. (After Coyle and Castello [51])

foundations. With most driven piles, the first term of the equation is small compared to the second term because of the limited B dimension. Thus, for many design problems,

$$q_{\text{tip}} = \bar{\bar{\sigma}}_v N_q \qquad (14\text{-}26b)$$

and the total end bearing becomes, for practical purposes,

$$Q_{\text{tip}} = (\bar{\bar{\sigma}}_v N_q) A_{\text{tip}} \qquad (14\text{-}26c)$$

If the pile is a large-diameter pile, the tip dimension will be significant and the end bearing should be determined from Equation (14-26a).

The value of the bearing capacity factor, N_q, is related to the angle of internal friction of the sand in the vicinity of the pile tip (several pile diameters above and below the tip) and the ratio of pile depth to pile width. Determining the value of N_q from field studies is not easily accomplished because of the difficulty of separating it from other influential factors. Values of N_q presented by various investigators have been developed primarily from theoretical analysis. Results range widely (Fig. 14-24) because of the assumptions made in defining the shear zones near the pile tip. Values of N_q obtained from the zone between the Berezontzev and Terzaghi curves (Fig. 14-24) are believed to be most applicable for commonly encountered soil conditions. The magnitude of effective vertical pressure, $\bar{\bar{\sigma}}_v$, that develops at the pile tip is limited below the critical depth. For preliminary design purposes, it can be conservatively assumed that the value of $\bar{\bar{\sigma}}_v$ in Equation 14-26 is equal to the effective overburden existing at the critical depth (see Fig. 14-21).

Deep Foundations

Figure 14-24(a) Bearing capacity factor N_q for piles penetrating into sand [156, 178, 51].

Figure 14-24(b) Ultimate unit tip resistance for piles driven in sand. (After Coyle and Castillo [51])

The angle of internal friction for soil in the zone of the pile tip is determined from laboratory tests on recovered samples or from correlations with penetration resistance in borings (e.g., SPT test) or from soundings. If Dutch cone data are available, the end bearing for a pile is directly related to the cone resistance, q_c:

$$Q_{tip} = \frac{q_c}{2} A_{tip} \qquad (14\text{-}27)$$

Figure 14-24b presents direct values for unit tip resistance, q_{tip}. The curves have been developed from regression analysis on a number of pile load test results [51] and at this time should be considered tentative. Direct values for q_{tip} are highly practical and improve the designer's ability to predict a safe pile loading; the term combines the influence of $\bar{\bar{\sigma}}_v$ and sand density ϕ or the N_q factor on the driven pile, values difficult to determine with accuracy.

If the pile analysis requires use of Equation 14-26a, the value of N_γ for a deep foundation can be conservatively taken as twice the N_γ value used for shallow foundations.

Values of N_q shown in Figure 14-24a assume that the soil above the pile tip is comparative to the soil below the pile tip. If the pile penetrates a compact layer only slightly and loose material exists above the compact soil, an N_q value for a shallow foundation will be more appropriate than a value from Figure 14-24a.

ILLUSTRATION 14-8. Prestressed concrete piles are planned for use as the foundation for a waterfront structure. Soil conditions are as indicated by the sketch. What is the approximate axial capacity for a single 12-inch-square pile driven to a depth of 30 ft?

Total skin friction = (area of $\bar{\bar{\sigma}}_v$ diagram)$(K)(\tan \delta) \times$ (pile circumference)

$$= \left[\left(1250 \text{ psf} \times \frac{10 \text{ ft}}{2} \right) + \left(\frac{1900 \text{ psf} + 1250 \text{ psf}}{2} \right) (10 \text{ ft}) \right.$$

$$\left. + (1900 \text{ psf} \times 10 \text{ ft}) \right] (3 \times 0.45 \times 4 \text{ ft})$$

$$= 220,000 \text{ lb} = 220 \text{ k}$$

Deep Foundations

$$\text{End bearing} = \bar{\sigma}_v N_q A_{\text{tip}} = (1900\ \text{psf})(80)(1\ \text{sf}) = 152{,}000\ \text{lb}$$

$$= 152\ \text{k}$$

$$Q_{\text{total}} = 220\ \text{k} + 152\ \text{k} = 372\ \text{k}; \qquad \text{then}$$

$$Q_{\text{design}} = \frac{372\ \text{k}}{FS}$$

Statical Method—Driven Piles in Clay   The ultimate supporting capacity of a driven pile in clay is

$$Q_{\text{total}} = Q_{\text{friction}} + Q_{\text{tip}} \qquad (14\text{-}23a)$$

As driven piles penetrate into a saturated clay, the soil in the vicinity of the pile is remolded because of displacement and disturbance. The remolded strength of a clay is almost always less than the original strength (cohesion), but typically the strength improves with time (thixotropy). The rate of strength gain will be related to the consolidation characteristics of the clay, for dissipation of excess pore water pressures developed because of the pile installation must occur.

The skin friction or adhesion, f, that develops between the soil and pile shaft has been related to the undisturbed cohesive strength of the clay.

$$f_{\text{clay}} = \alpha c \qquad (14\text{-}28a)$$

where f_{clay} = unit adhesion or skin friction developed between clay and pile shaft.
$\quad\quad\ c$ = cohesive strength of undisturbed clay.
$\quad\quad\ \alpha$ = factor that relates adhesion to cohesion (or the friction ratio).

For *normally consolidated* clays in the soft-to-firm range (cohesion less than one ksf), the value of α can be taken as unity; therefore,

$$f = c \quad \text{(for normally consolidated clays with } c \leqq 1.0\ \text{ksf)} \qquad (14\text{-}28b)$$

Equation 14-28b may also be valid for normally consolidated clays having cohesive strengths greater than one ksf, but current data are too limited for confirmation.

Various investigators have reported values of α for clays that are *overconsolidated*. Results vary, but fall within the band shown in Figure 14-25.

The magnitude of Q_{friction} for clay to use in Equation 14-23 then becomes

$$Q_{\text{friction}} = f A_{\text{surface}} = \alpha c A_{\text{surface}} \qquad (14\text{-}29)$$

It is recognized that the lateral pressure existing in the remolded soil adjacent to the pile shaft has an influence on the dissipation of excess pore water pressures in this zone. If sufficient pore water drainage can occur, the final strength of the clay conceivably may be greater than the undisturbed strength. Because of the phenomenon of strength gain with time, load tests on piles in clay should be performed some weeks after installation to obtain a reliable indication of actual capacity.

Figure 14-25 Correlation of friction factor α and clay cohesion c_u.

c_u, kN/m²

Friction ratio, α ($\alpha = f/c_u$)

c_u, ksf

Undrained shear strength

– – – Recommended for design

ILLUSTRATION 14-9. A 14-inch-square prestressed concrete pile is to be driven at a site where soil conditions are as indicated by the sketch. If a penetration of 40 ft is assumed, approximately what total skin friction is expected to develop along the embedded length of the pile?

For depth from 0 ft to 25 ft: $\alpha = 1$; therefore, adhesion = skin friction = 600 psf.

For depth from 25 ft to 40 ft: $\alpha = 0.5\pm$ and adhesion = αc; therefore,

$$\text{adhesion} = (0.50)(2000 \text{ psf}) = 1000 \text{ psf}$$

$$Q_{\text{friction}} = (600 \text{ psf})\left(\frac{14 \text{ in}}{12 \text{ in/ft}} \times 4 \text{ sides}\right)(25 \text{ ft})$$

$$+ (1000 \text{ psf})(\tfrac{14}{12} \text{ ft}) \times (4)(15 \text{ ft})$$

$$= 70{,}000 \text{ lb} + 70{,}000 \text{ lb} = 140{,}000 \text{ lb} = 140 \text{ k}$$

Note: A value of Q_{total} would include Q_{tip} but then would be reduced by the factor of safety to yield Q_{design}.

Calculating the value of skin friction developing along the shaft of a pile by use of the method in Illustration 14-9 has proved to be fairly reliable, though not

Deep Foundations

precise, for piles, provided that the embedded length has not been too great (less than about 75 ft or 25 m). For very long piles, the method has been found to be too conservative in the prediction of the frictional capacity. Reasons for the discrepancy are not yet clear. Disturbance and remolding may not be as severe at deep depths as at shallower depths, with the result that the α factors are too low. Or, as recent evidences imply, the manner in which skin friction in clay occurs may be basically similar to the development of friction in sands, where resistance is related to an effective lateral pressure.

In recognition of the probable relationship between effective overburden pressures and skin friction, an empirical method for determining the frictional capacity of long cylindrical steel piles in normally consolidated clay had been proposed (the lambda method [268]). The method has been extended to other pile types [132]. The method considers the theoretical maximum passive pressures that would act in the soil zone adjacent to the pile, $\overline{\sigma}_v + 2c$ (see Fig. 14-26), and applies a variable lambda factor λ to account for a limit to the influence of the effective overburden $\overline{\sigma}_v$ and the adhesion between the pile shaft and surrounding soil. The unit skin friction is taken as

$$f = \lambda(\overline{\sigma}_v + 2c_u) \tag{14-30a}$$

where λ = a coefficient that evaluates the effect of soil-pile adhesion plus the influence of the soil overburden.
c_u = undrained shear strength (cohesion) of the clay.

The total friction capacity for a pile is then

$$Q_{\text{friction}} = \lambda(\overline{\sigma}_{vm} + 2c_m)A_{\text{surface}} \tag{14-30b}$$

where $\overline{\sigma}_{vm}$ = mean effective vertical pressure for the embedded length.
c_m = mean undrained shear strength for depth of pile (Fig. 14-27).
A_{surface} = surface area of pile shaft.

The curves relating design values for λ to normally consolidated soil deposits and overconsolidated soils (Fig. 14-28) have resulted from regression analysis on a number of pile load test results. The curves are considered appropriate for all driven pile types.

Figure 14-26 Mohr's circle presentation indicating relation between vertical pressure and maximum horizontal pressure.

Foundations   Chap. 14

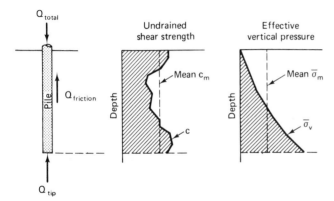

Figure 14-27 Mean vertical pressure and mean shear strength used in designing long piles in clay [155, 268].

Note: Use normally consolidated curve for $c_m / \bar{\sigma}_{v_m} < 0.4$

Use overconsolidated curve for $c_m / \bar{\sigma}_{v_m} > 0.4$

Figure 14-28 Relation between λ coefficient and pile length for normally consolidated clays. (After Kraft, Focht, and Amerasinghe [132])

ILLUSTRATION 14-10. A pipe pile with an outside diameter of 18 in. and a flat end plate is driven 200 ft into a normally consolidated clay deposit having the properties shown. The water level is above the ground surface. Applying the lambda (λ) method, calculate the skin friction expected to develop along the shaft of the pile.

Deep Foundations

Note: γ_{soil} is effective
(submerged) unit weight
of soil

Note: Effective vertical pressure =
weight of soil overburden =
$\Sigma \, (\gamma_{soil} \times depth)$

Depth (feet)	Cohesion, c (psf)	Sub. unit wt. (pcf)
0 to 30	600	52
30 to 70	1000	58
70 to 90	1200	58
90 to 130	1600	55
130 to 200	3000	60

$$c_m = \frac{\text{area of } c_u \text{ diagram}}{\text{pile depth}}$$

$$= \frac{\left[\begin{array}{c} (0.60 \text{ ksf} \times 30 \text{ ft}) + (1.0 \text{ ksf} \times 40 \text{ ft}) + (1.20 \text{ ksf} \times 20 \text{ ft}) \\ + \ (1.60 \text{ ksf} \times 40 \text{ ft}) + (3.00 \text{ ksf} \times 70 \text{ ft}) \end{array} \right]}{200 \text{ ft}}$$

$$= \frac{356 \text{ k/ft}}{200 \text{ ft}} = 1.78 \text{ ksf}$$

$$\bar{\sigma}_{v_m} = \frac{\text{area of } \bar{\sigma} \text{ diagram}}{\text{pile depth}} = \frac{1120 \text{ k/ft}}{200 \text{ ft}} = 5.6 \text{ ksf}$$

$$Q_{\text{friction}} = \lambda(\bar{\sigma}_{v_m} + 2c_m)A_{\text{shaft}}$$

$$= (0.12)[5.6 \text{ ksf} + (2)(1.78 \text{ ksf})] \times (200 \text{ ft} \times 3.14 \times \tfrac{18}{12} \text{ ft})$$

$$= 1035 \text{ kips}$$

The values of *end bearing* for a pile in clay can be computed from

$$q_{\text{tip}} = cN_c \tag{14-31}$$

where c = cohesion of the clay in the zone surrounding the pile tip.

N_c = bearing capacity factor for deep foundations, ranging between 6 and 10, depending on the stiffness of the clay. A value of 9 is conventionally used.

The foregoing equation assumes that the lower section of pile penetrates at least five diameters into the clay whose cohesion is c.

If the subsurface investigation includes Dutch cone data, the end bearing for a pile can be directly related to the cone resistance, q_c in kg/cm^2 or tons per square foot. For homogeneous conditions, where the pile penetrates at least eight diameters into the clay whose q_c is used in the design computation and no soft soil underlies the pile tip, the end bearing can be taken as

$$Q_{tip} = A_{tip}q_{design} = A_{tip}\frac{(q_c)}{1.5} \tag{14-32}$$

Factor of Safety   The value of Q_{total} obtained by using the analytical procedures discussed for piles in sand and clay represents an estimate of the maximum load that can be applied to a pile. Whenever possible, predicted capacities should be verified by a field load test before a final design loading is selected. Where load tests have not been performed, it is usual practice to apply a factor of safety of 2 during the analysis to determine the downward design load:

$$Q_{design} = \frac{Q_{total}}{2} \quad \text{(for downward loading)} \tag{14-33a}$$

Piles subject to uplift develop resistance to pullout only from the skin friction developed along the embedded length. End bearing does not apply, but the weight of the pile can be included in uplift resistance. For design purposes, it is common to apply a factor of safety of *at least* 2. If nonhomogeneous conditions exist or soil properties are not accurately known, a larger theoretical factor of safety is warranted. Tapered piles are commonly assigned a larger factor of safety than are straight-sided piles. Generally, a larger safety factor is applied to a design uplift capacity than to the downward capacity. The reason frequently stated is that an overrated capacity for downward loading probably results only in a greater-than-estimated settlement, whereas a pile whose uplift is overrated may experience significant upward movement with serious effects to the supported structure. The strength of the pile-to-pile cap connection becomes critical where uplift forces are imposed, for tensile failure at this location will negate any potential pullout resistance that a pile possesses.

$$Q_{design} = \frac{Q_{friction} + W_{pile}}{FS} \quad \text{(for uplift)} \tag{14-33b}$$

where W_{pile} = weight of pile.
    FS = factor of safety, 2 or greater.

Negative Skin Friction   When the properties of the soil through which a pile penetrates are evaluated, it is important to watch for and recognize the condition

Deep Foundations

that will create *negative friction*, or *downdrag*. The phenomenon occurs when a soil layer surrounding a portion of the pile shaft settles more than the pile. This condition can develop where a soft or loose soil stratum located anywhere above the pile tip is subjected to new compressive loading. As an illustration, new loading to existing soil results when fill is placed on a construction site to raise the area. If the soft or loose layer settles after the pile has been installed, the skin friction-adhesion developing in this zone is in the direction of the soil pulling downward on the pile (see Fig. 14-29). Extra loading is thus imposed onto the pile. It is necessary to subtract negative skin friction values from the total load that the pile can support in order to know what building load can be carried. Values of negative skin friction are computed in the same manner as those of positive skin friction.

Where it is anticipated that an upper zone of soil would impose undesirable or intolerable downdrag on a pile, a common practice is to provide the pile with a protective sleeve or coating for the section that is embedded in the settling soil. Skin friction for this section of pile is eliminated, and downdrag is prevented.

Other Design Considerations   The development of skin friction along the shaft of a pile does require some shear strain in the soil adjacent to the pile. If the tip and end section of a pile are embedded in a very firm or compact material, high end bearing can be developed with relatively little downward movement of the pile. Only limited deformation may occur in the upper zone of soil surrounding the pile shaft, and the maximum skin friction may not develop. The percentage of reduction in skin friction that should be attributed to comparatively soft or loose strata in contact with the pile shaft is generally a judgment factor, influenced by a comparison of relative values of cohesion or density in the various soil zones. Conversely, if a pile should penetrate through firm or dense soils and terminate in a soft or loose material, the maximum computed tip resistance may not be able to develop unless significant downward movement occurs.

Statical Method—Bored Piers and Piles   Bored piers and piles refer to the type of deep foundations that are constructed by drilling into the earth and subsequently placing concrete in the excavation, usually directly against the soil,

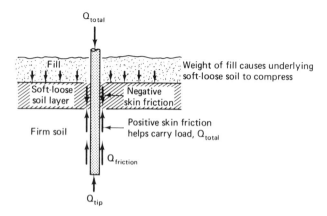

Figure 14-29   Action of negative skin friction on pile shaft.

to form the foundation unit. The concrete is often reinforced with steel. This type of foundation can be straight-sided for its full depth, or it may be constructed with a belled or underreamed base if in cohesive soil, in order to increase the tip bearing. Bored foundations have gone under a variety of names in the past, such as drilled piers, piles, or caissons, and cast-in-place or cast-in-situ piles. When provided with an enlarged base, the foundation may be referred to as a drilled-and-belled type. The designation currently receiving general acceptance is *drilled-shaft foundation*.

Drilled-shaft foundations are constructed by utilizing mechanical auger drill equipment to excavate the hole in the earth. When subsurface conditions permit, such as a sufficiently strong cohesive soil and no groundwater, the hole can be drilled dry, after which the cast-in-place concrete comes in direct contact with the soil forming the walls of the excavation. If cohesionless soils are penetrated or the water table is encountered, a bentonite slurry may be circulated into the hole as it is being drilled to prevent soil cave-in and to assist in flushing soil cuttings to the surface. (This method is similar to the procedure used for drilling uncased soil borings.) Reusable protective casing may also be utilized with the bentonite slurry if a particularly bad groundwater condition is encountered. Concrete for the finished foundation is placed at the bottom of the excavation and worked upward in a continuous pour so as to force displacement of the bentonite slurry. If a casing has been used, it is pulled as the concrete is poured, but in such a manner as to prevent the soil walls from falling into the excavation and mixing with the concrete. This is accomplished by pouring high-slump concrete inside the casing and keeping the height of concrete above the bottom of the withdrawing casing at all times. The earlier presence of a bentonite slurry leaves a film on the soil surrounding the excavation, an effect that will reduce the skin friction between the soil and hardened concrete.

Design criteria for *drilled-shaft foundations in clay* have evolved from instrumented studies performed on full-scale foundations. For foundations embedded in relatively homogeneous clay, the ultimate capacity is due to the resistance provided from the end bearing and skin friction. In calculating the foundation depth that effectively provides skin friction, the lower 5-ft section and the belled section (if provided) are neglected because of disturbance and loss of strength caused by construction. There is also a strong possibility of disturbance and loss of strength occurring in the surface zone of soil. Skin friction should be neglected in such a zone. A depth of 5 ft can be assumed unless more accurate information is available.

$$Q_{\text{total}} = Q_{\text{base}} + Q_{\text{friction}} \qquad (14\text{-}23\text{a})$$

becomes
$$Q_{\text{total}} = cN_cA_{\text{base}} + fA'_{\text{shaft}} \qquad (14\text{-}34\text{a})$$
(for drilled shaft foundations)

where c = cohesion of the soil at base of foundation.
$\quad N_c$ = bearing capacity factor.
$\quad A_{\text{base}}$ = bearing area of foundation base.
$\quad f$ = unit skin friction developing between clay and concrete shaft.
$\quad A'_{\text{shaft}}$ = surface area of shaft that is effective in developing skin friction.

TABLE 14-8 SKIN FRICTION VALUES FOR DRILLED SHAFT FOUNDATIONS IN CLAY
[194, 195]

Foundation type and drilling method utilized	Skin friction, f	Upper limit on skin friction, ksf*
Straight shaft, excavation drilled dry	$0.5c$	1.8
Straight shaft, drilled with slurry	$0.3c$	0.8
Belled, drilled dry	$0.3c$	0.8
Belled, drilled with slurry	$0.15c$	0.5

Note: c is soil cohesion determined from triaxial testing, not in situ vane shear tests.
*1 ksf = 48 kN/m².

The skin friction that develops along the shaft is related to the cohesion of the surrounding clay and the field procedure for drilling the foundation. Values appropriate for design are shown in Table 14-8.

If the base of the foundation is in very firm clay but the shaft is not, the supporting capacity of the unit is due primarily to end bearing. If the movement of the foundation base is very limited, the soil adjacent to the shaft does not experience the shear strain necessary for significant skin friction to develop; thus,

$$Q_{\text{total}} = Q_{\text{base}} = cN_cA_{\text{base}} \qquad (14\text{-}34\text{b})$$

(for drilled shaft foundations bearing on very firm clay)

An N_c value of 9 is assigned for all the conditions described previously.

When the methods presented above are applied to a foundation design, it is recommended that a factor of safety of 3 be applied to the bearing capacity of the base of the unit. Thus,

$$Q_{\text{design}} = \tfrac{1}{3}cN_cA_{\text{base}} + fA_s' = 3cA_{\text{base}} + fA_{\text{shaft}}' \qquad (14\text{-}35)$$
(for drilled shaft foundations)

ILLUSTRATION 14-11. A 3-foot-diameter drilled-shaft foundation is constructed with a 6-foot-diameter base in soil conditions shown by the sketch. The excavation is drilled dry. For the foundation length shown, what maximum axial load (design load) should be planned?

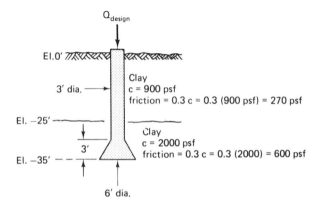

$$Q_{\text{tip}} = 9cA_{\text{tip}} = (9)(2000 \text{ psf})\left(\frac{\pi}{4} \times 6 \text{ ft} \times 6 \text{ ft}\right)$$

$$= 510{,}000 \text{ lb} = 510 \text{ k}$$

$$Q_{\text{skin friction}} = fA'_{\text{shaft}} = (270 \text{ psf})(\pi \times 3 \text{ ft})(25 \text{ ft} - 5 \text{ ft}) +$$

$$(600 \text{ psf})(\pi \times 3 \text{ ft}) \times (10 \text{ ft} - 3 \text{ ft} - 5 \text{ ft})$$

$$= 51{,}000 \text{ lb} + 11{,}300 \text{ lb} = 62 \text{ k}$$

$$Q_{\text{design}} = \tfrac{1}{3}Q_{\text{tip}} + Q_{\text{friction}} = \tfrac{510}{3} \text{ kips} + 62 \text{ kips} = 232 \text{ kips}$$

The capacity of *drilled-shaft foundations in sand* can be analyzed by applying the procedures discussed for driven piles in sand:

$$
\begin{aligned}
Q_{\text{total}} &= Q_{\text{tip}} + Q_{\text{friction}} \\
&= \bar{\bar{\sigma}}_v N_q A_{\text{tip}} + \Sigma\,(K\bar{\bar{\sigma}}_v \tan \delta)(\Delta A_{\text{shaft}}) \quad\quad (14\text{-}23a) \\
&= (\text{area of } K\bar{\bar{\sigma}}_v \tan \delta \text{ diagram})(\text{shaft circumference})
\end{aligned}
$$

where $\bar{\bar{\sigma}}_v$ = effective vertical pressure considering the limits imposed by the concept of critical depth.

$\tan \delta$ = coefficient of friction between sand and concrete.

K = lateral pressure coefficient for a drilled foundation in sand.

The value of K for drilled-shaft or bored foundations ranges between about 0.3 for loose sand and 0.75 for compact sand. The value of $\tan \delta$ can be taken as equal to $\tan \phi$ for the sand when the excavation has been drilled dry, because of the roughness of concrete against soil. If a slurry has been used when drilling the excavation, some reduction should be applied. The design load should include a factor of safety at least equal to that for driven piles.

Arrangement for Piles in a Group   Pile analysis discussed previously refers to the capacity of an individual unit. When used for foundation support, driven piles will almost always be used in a grouping. This requirement results from the desire to ensure that the imposed structural load (e.g., column or wall load) falls within the support area provided by the foundation. Usually, driven piles are not used singularly beneath a column or wall because of the tendency for the pile to wander laterally during driving. If a single pile were to be used as the foundation, a designer could not be certain that the pile would be centered beneath the foundation. If an unplanned eccentric loading results, the connection between pile and column may be inadequate, or the pile may fail structurally because of bending stresses created within it. As a result, piles for walls are commonly installed in a arrangement staggered to both sides of the wall centerline. For a column or isolated load, a minimum of three piles is used in a triangular pattern, even for light loads. Where more than three piles are required in order to obtain adequate capacity, the pile arrangement is symmetrical about the point or area of load application.

Deep Foundations

(a) For wall (b) 3-Pile group (c) 4-pile group (d) 5-pile group

Note: Pile spacings for groups typically range between $2\frac{1}{2}$ and 4 pile diameters, center to center.

Figure 14-30 Representative pile patterns for wall and column foundations.

Representative patterns are illustrated in Figure 14-30. Column and wall loads are usually transferred to the pile group through a pile cap. The pile cap is typically a reinforced concrete slab structurally tied to the pile butts (top) to help the group act as a unit (Fig. 14-31).

The requirement for group arrangement of driven piles does not necessarily apply to bored piles (drilled-shaft foundations). Drilled shafts can be located and installed quite accurately. For building construction, it is common to use a single, large-diameter, drilled-shaft foundation to support a column. For light loads, a single unit can usually be more properly matched with soil conditions to provide necessary capacity than can a driven pile foundation, where the three-pile minimum usually provides excessive carrying capacity. Economy can result. Additional cost savings will be realized with a single-pile foundation where the need for a pile cap is eliminated.

Group Capacity   The capacity of a pile group is not necessarily the capacity of the individual pile multiplied by the number of piles in the group. Soil disturbance because of pile installation, and overlap of stresses between adjacent piles, may cause the group capacity to be less than the sum of individual capacities. Conversely, soil between individual piles may become "locked-in" because of strong adhesion or densification from driving, and the group may tend to behave as an equivalent single large pile. Densification and improvement of soil surrounding the group can also occur. These latter factors tend to provide a group capacity greater than the sum of the individual piles. The capacity of the equivalent large pile is analyzed by determining the skin friction around the embedded perimeter of the group and calculating the end bearing by assuming a tip area formed by this same perimeter (see Fig. 14-32).

Plan   Section

Figure 14-31 Pile cap of type provided for reinforced concrete column.

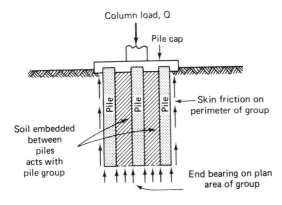

Column load, Q

Pile cap

Skin friction on
perimeter of group

Pile

Soil embedded
between
piles
acts with
pile group

End bearing on plan
area of group

Figure 14-32 Skin friction and end bearing acting on the single equivalent pile formed by a pile group.

To determine the *design load* for a pile group, compare the sum of the individual pile capacities with the capacity of the single large equivalent (group) pile. With a proper factor of safety, the least capacity will be the design load. The capacity of the equivalent (group) pile is affected by soil type and properties and pile spacing. Generally, there is a greater tendency for the group to act as a large single unit when pile spacings are close and the soil is firm or compact.

For driven piles embedded in cohesionless soil, the capacity of the large equivalent (group) pile will almost always be greater than the sum of the individual pile capacities. This is an indication that the soil in the immediate proximity of each individual pile controls the group capacity. Consequently, for design, the group capacity is typically based on the single-pile load and the number of piles in the group.

For bored piles in sand, the group capacity will be less than the sum of the individual pile capacities, in part because of limited densification of the soil zone surrounding the pile group (compared to the driven pile group) and because of the overlapping of stresses between adjacent units. The capacity of a bored-pile group is typically about two-thirds the capacity of the sum of the individual pile capacities.

The capacity of closely spaced piles embedded in clay is often limited by the behavior of the group acting as a single large unit. In determining the capacity of the single equivalent large pile, the skin friction and end bearing are calculated by using the general methods discussed for the individual pile. The unit value of perimeter skin friction is intermediate between adhesion or remolded shear strength and the undrained shear strength. For pile spacings greater than about three diameters, the group capacity is, for practical purposes, equal to the capacity of the piles acting individually. The capacity should be reduced by one-third if the pile cap for the group does not rest on the ground; this modification accounts for the condition that group load is controlled by the capacity of individual piles as influenced by stress overlap between adjacent units.

ILLUSTRATION 14-12. A nine-pile group composed of 12-inch-diameter pipe piles is embedded 50 ft deep in soil conditions indicated by the sketch. A $2\frac{1}{2}$-diameter spacing is used. What design capacity should be estimated for the group?

Deep Foundations   **419**

Note:
group perimeter = 6′ × 4 sides
= 24 ft

Capacity, Piles Act Individually

$$Q_{\text{friction}} = (0.85 \times 900 \text{ psf})(3.14 \times 20 \text{ ft}) + (0.75 \times 1200 \text{ psf})$$

$$\times (3.14 \times 20 \text{ ft}) + (0.50 \times 2000 \text{ psf})(3.14 \times 10 \text{ ft})$$

$$= 136{,}000 \text{ lb}$$

$$Q_{\text{tip}} = 9cA_{\text{tip}} = (9 \times 2000 \text{ psf})\left(\frac{\pi}{4} \times 1 \text{ ft}^2\right) = 14{,}000 \text{ lb}$$

$$Q_{\text{total}} = 136 \text{ k} + 14 \text{ k} = 150 \text{ k/pile}$$

Group total = 150 k/pile × 9 piles = 1350 k

Capacity, Group Action

$$Q_{\text{friction}} = \left(\frac{900 \text{ psf} + 760 \text{ psf}}{2}\right) (24 \text{ ft} \times 20 \text{ ft})$$

$$+ \left(\frac{1200 \text{ psf} + 900 \text{ psf}}{2}\right) (24 \text{ ft} \times 20 \text{ ft})$$

$$+ \left(\frac{2000 \text{ psf} + 1000 \text{ psf}}{2}\right) (24 \text{ ft} \times 10 \text{ ft}) = 1{,}260{,}000 \text{ lb}$$

$$= 1260 \text{ k}$$

$$Q_{\text{tip}} = 9cA_{\text{tip}} = (9)(2 \text{ ksf})(6 \text{ ft} \times 6 \text{ ft}) = 650 \text{ k}$$

Group total = 1260 k + 650 k = 1910 k

Use least group total for design. Therefore,

$$Q_{\text{design}} = \frac{1350 \text{ k}}{FS = 2} = 675 \text{ k}$$

Pile Group Settlement   The vertical movement that occurs at the pile cap level is the result of compressive shortening within the pile from the loading plus the settlement occurring in the soil supporting the pile. Analytical methods available to predict the settlement of pile groups provide only approximations. A widely used procedure assumes that the pile group acts as a single large, deep foundation, such as a pier or mat. Where the piles are embedded in a uniform soil (friction plus end bearing piles), the total load is assumed to act at a depth equal to two-thirds the pile length. Conventional settlement analysis procedures assuming the Boussinesq or Westergaard stress distribution are then applied to compute compression of the soil beneath the pile tip. If the piles have their tip section embedded in a stratum firmer or more compact than the overlying soil (end bearing piles), the total load is assumed to act at a depth corresponding to pile tip elevation (see Fig. 14-33).

Compressive properties of soil below the pile tip are determined from laboratory tests on recovered soil samples (typical for cohesive soils) or from empirical correlations developed from soil exploration penetration tests (typical for cohesionless soil). For piles embedded in sand, the following expressions for approximating settlement can be applied:

$$\Delta H = \frac{q\sqrt{B}}{N} \quad \text{(approximately)} \tag{14-36a}$$

where ΔH = settlement, in inches
q = net foundation bearing pressure, in tons/ft^2.
B = width of pile group, in feet.
N = blow count from standard penetration test corrected for depth.

The N value applies to the sand in the zone most subject to compression by the pile load. A distance of one group width (or B feet) is recommended. If static cone penetration data (e.g., Dutch cone) is available for the soil below pile tip level, the settlement can be approximated from

$$\Delta H = \frac{qB}{q_c} \quad \text{(approximately)} \tag{14-36b}$$

where q_c = static cone resistance, in same units as q (the foundation load) and B (the pile group width).

If load testing is performed on a single pile, caution is in order when one is extrapolating settlement results to a group. Group settlements typically range from two to more than ten times the settlement of the single pile. The greater settlement ratio (i.e., group settlement to single-pile settlement) occurs with the larger pile groups.

Figure 14-33 Assumed conditions for estimating settlement of pile groups.

Deep Foundations

Pile Load Tests

Applied to construction projects, on-site load tests are performed on test piles installed during the design stage to check estimated capacities (as predetermined by analytical or other methods) and to help develop criteria for the foundation installation contract, or as a check on contract piles installed by the builder to verify the carrying capacity (proof testing).

Both cohesive and cohesionless soils will have their properties altered by the installation of a driven pile. In clays, the disturbance causes remolding and loss of strength. With time, much of the original strength will be regained. Consequently, to obtain load test results that are practical for design, testing of piles in clay should be performed only after a lapse of at least several weeks. The effect of installing driven piles in sand is to create a temporary condition where extra resistance is developed. Shortly after the installation, however, the extra resistance is lost (stress relaxation). To obtain test results applicable for design, a period of at least several days should lapse before testing begins.

Loading applied to test piles frequently is obtained by hydraulically jacking against a supported weight box or platform (Fig. 14-34a) or against a reaction girder secured to anchor piles (Fig. 14-34b). If the jack is outfitted with a pressure gage, the magnitude of test load imposed onto the pile is read directly. However, some designers prefer that a proving ring or pressure capsule be used for measuring the load, feeling that it is more accurate.

Measurement for pile movement is related to a fixed reference mark. The support for reference marks needs to be located outside the soil zone that could be affected by pile movements.

Several different methods for performing pile load tests are in use. Probably the most common is the *slow-maintained load (slow-ML) test* (ASTM D-1143). With this procedure, the test load is applied in eight equal increments until twice the intended design load is reached. Time–settlement data are obtained for each load increment. Each increment is maintained until the rate of settlement becomes less than 0.01 inch per hour (2.5 mm per hour) or for 2 hours, whichever occurs first. The final load (double the design load) is maintained for 24 hours. Unloading also occurs in increments.

Another common procedure is the *constant-rate-of-penetration test*. In this method, the load is increased on the pile as necessary to force settlement (penetration) at a predetermined rate. A rate of 0.02 inch (5 mm) per minute is typical. The force required to achieve penetration is recorded, thus giving load–settlement data similar to the slow-ML test. This test is considerably faster than the slow-ML test.

Other general test methods include *cyclic loading*, in which each increment of load is repeatedly applied and removed (or reduced), and the *quick-maintained test*, in which the load increments are imposed for short periods of time. Pile movement for all loads, or cycles of loads, is recorded.

The load–settlement data are used to determine the design load for the pile. Frequently, the design load is obtained from a "failure load" indicated by the load test with a factor of safety applied. The definition of failure load is arbitrary; it may be taken when a predetermined amount of settlement has occurred (e.g., one-tenth of the pile diameter or a certain number of inches) or where the slope of the

(a) Weighted platform used as
   jacking reaction

(b) Anchor piles and girder used
   to provide reaction for jacking.

Figure 14-34 Typical pile load test arrangements (a) weighted platform used as jacking reaction; (b) anchor piles and girder used to provide reaction. (Source: ASTM D-1163)

load–settlement plot is no longer proportional. A method in use for the slow-maintained load test is to plot both load and settlement values on logarithmic coordinates. The results typically plot as two straight lines (see Fig. 14-35). The intersection of the two lines is referred to as the *failure load*. This is the failure load for design purposes and is not the actual failure or ultimate load.

The design factor of safety used for contract piles should relate to the extent of information known about subsurface conditions, and to the number and comparative results of pile load tests performed at different locations on the site. If soil conditions, including properties, are uniform and load tests at different areas compare well, a relatively low factor of safety could be justified (i.e., 1.5 to 2.0). If subsurface conditions and load test results are variable, a greater factor of safety is usually necessary (2 to 3) as protection against possible unexpected poorer soil conditions and lesser pile capacity.

Figure 14-35 One method of plotting pile load test data to determine pile design capacity.

Pile load, Q (log scale)

$Q_{design} = \dfrac{Q_{ultimate}}{FS}$

$Q_{ultimate}$

Pile settlement, inches (log scale)

Pile-Driving Formulae

The axial capacity of piles driven in certain types of soil can be related to the resistance against penetration developed during driving. Relating the load capacity that a pile will develop to the driving resistance is appropriate for piles penetrating soils that will not develop high pore water pressures during the installation. Such soils include free-draining sands and hard clays. In saturated fine-grained soils, high pore water pressures develop because of soil displacement and vibration caused by the driving. The strength of the soil surrounding the pile is affected. A predicted capacity based on such soils' resistance to pile penetration is different from the capacity that develops after the excess pore pressures dissipate.

Using driving data to determine pile capacity requires knowledge of the effect that a hammer blow has on the pile and supporting soil. As the top of a pile is struck with the pile hammer, the force of the blow causes a stress wave to be transmitted through the length of the pile. Some of the force of the transmitted wave is absorbed by the soil surrounding the pile shaft, while some is imparted to the soil at the pile tip. What has become known as the *wave equation method* applies wave transmission theory to determine the carrying capacity developed by a pile and the maximum stresses that result within the pile during driving.

In a wave equation analysis, the method assumes that the pile and its behavior when embedded in soil can be represented by a series of individual spring-connected weights and spring damping resistances (see Fig. 14-36). The various weight values, W, correspond to the weight of incremental sections of pile. The spring constants, K, relate to the elasticity of the pile. The spring damping, R, represents the frictional resistance of soil surrounding the shaft of the pile and the soil resistance at the pile tip. Spring damping along the shaft of the pile accounts for a gradual diminishing of the longitudinal force (from the hammer blow) that travels along the length of the pile. Spring damping at the pile tip is necessary to account for the force that remains within the pile to be transmitted at the tip.

To obtain a solution for the wave equation, it is necessary to know approximate pile length, the pile weight, cross section, and elastic properties, and the pile hammer characteristics, including efficiency, ram weight, and impact velocity, to have data on the pile cap and capblock, and to assign values for soil damping and the spring constants. Determining the effect of a stress wave traveling through the pile is a dynamics problem. However, if the effect of a pile hammer blow at one particular instant in time is selected (the reaction of each weight and spring to the

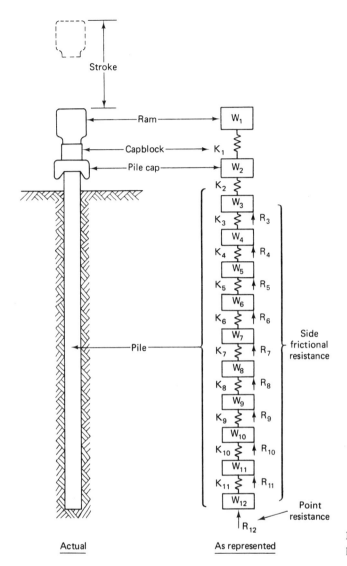

Figure 14-36 Method of representing pile for wave equation analysis [223].

Actual   As represented

forces acting on overlying weights is determined), the analysis can be handled as a statics problem. By analyzing changing conditions for successive small increments of time, the effects of the force wave traveling through the pile to the tip will be simulated. This analysis requires a numerical integration, a task conveniently undertaken by computer. Results obtained will be only for a particular pile driven by a specified pile hammer. Separate analyses are required for different conditions.

For field use, it is convenient to have the pile capacity expressed in terms of inches of penetration per hammer blow, in order to know when driving can cease. Representative results for a solution are shown in Figure 14-37. At present, a major drawback to greater application of the wave equation method lies in the practical requirement for computer use. In some cases, proper evaluation of factors such as

Deep Foundations   **425**

the equivalent spring constant and soil damping values requires driving data for the pile under study. This means that results for field control are not always available before the start of a project. This situation will change as more information on soil properties is accumulated and as more usable forms of the analysis evolve.

Wave transmission theory shows that the maximum force that can pass through a pile is related to the modulus of elasticity and mass density of the pile material and the cross-sectional area, in a term referred to as *pile impedance*:

$$\text{Pile impedance} = \rho v A \tag{14-37}$$

where impedance = ability of a pile to pass a longitudinal (axial) force by wave transmission resulting from a pile hammer blow.

ρ = mass density of the pile material, γ_{pile}/g (γ_{pile} is the pile material's unit weight; g is the acceleration of gravity).

v = velocity of longitudinal wave propagation, $\sqrt{E/\rho}$ (E is modulus of elasticity for the pile material).

A = cross-sectional area of pile.

If it is assumed that pile driving occurs with a hammer capable of delivering adequate energy, greater capacity is possible with piles having greater impedance values. Other comparative effects of pile impedance are shown by Figure 14-38. The relative position of the curves indicates that high pile capacities cannot be achieved when low-energy driving hammers or piles having low impedance values are used.

Wave transmission theory also explains other occurrences noted in pile driving. If the soil at the pile tip is very hard or compact, some of the stress wave may be reflected back along the pile. As a result, tensile stress (as well as compressive stress) may develop within the pile during driving. If a pile material is weak in tension (e.g., poorly reinforced concrete), tension cracks may develop near the top of the pile. If the pile penetrates through firm soil into soft material, tensile stresses may develop near the tip and cause damage to the end section of the pile.

The pile foundations for a project may be designed by engineering personnel, but the installations are handled by specialty contractors who frequently receive the job as the result of a bidding procedure. Pile foundation contractors typically possess a variety of driving equipment. If the contractor is required to provide a description of his proposed driving system *before* beginning the field work, the designer can introduce this information along with soil parameters (assumed or developed from boring data) into the wave equation to evaluate the adequacy and effects of the proposed driving procedure (e.g., can the hammer efficiently drive

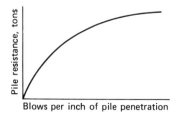

Figure 14-37 Relation between pile capacity and driving resistance indicated by wave equation.

Figure 14-38 Relationship among pile capacity, pile impedance, and equipment used for pile driving [181].

the piles to the desired depth, will the piles be overstressed during driving, etc.). If problems are indicated, the proposed driving equipment can be changed before it is brought to the construction site.

Expressions relating pile capacity to driving resistance have also been developed from work-energy theory and are simpler to apply than the wave equation. Such pile-driving formulae have been in use since at least the mid-nineteenth century. A basic assumption for these driving formulae is that the kinetic energy delivered by the pile-driving hammer equates to the work done on the pile (work defined as the product of force and distance), or

$$(W_h)(H)(\text{Eff.}) = (\text{pile resistance})(\text{pile penetration per hammer blow})$$

$$(14\text{-}38)$$

where W_h = weight of pile hammer ram.
 H = height of ram fall.
Eff. = efficiency of pile hammer.

For application, these formulae need to include corrections to account for energy losses during driving that are caused by factors such as elastic compression of the pile, soil, capblock, and cushion, and by heat generation. Variations in the many pile formulae that have been proposed result because of the different methods for handling these energy losses.

The assumption of work-energy theory to develop pile-driving formulae does not properly consider the effect of impact on a long member such as a pile; therefore, such formulae will not be theoretically correct. However, some expressions that include empirical energy loss correction factors have shown a reliability for predicting the axial capacity of piles, particularly those driven in cohesionless soil. Some of these formulae are lengthy and complicated (e.g., Hiley formula [44]) and are not reported herein. Load test studies on piles in sand indicate that the simple-to-use Danish formula is as reliable as any of the more complicated formulae [3]:[9]

[9]Some test data is available to indicate that the Danish formula can also apply for piles embedded in cohesive soil [82]; at the present level of experience, use of this driving formula should be limited to projects where pile load tests are performed to correlate load-carrying capability.

Deep Foundations   **427**

$$Q_{\text{ult}} = \frac{W_h H (\text{Eff.})}{S + \frac{1}{2} S_0} \quad \text{(Danish formula)} \tag{14-39a}$$

where Q_{ult} = axial capacity of the pile.
    S = average penetration of the pile from the last few driving blows (pile "set").
    S_0 = elastic compression of the pile
$$= \left[\frac{(2)(\text{Eff.})(W_h HL)}{AE} \right]^{1/2}$$
    L = length of pile.
    A = cross-sectional area of pile.
    E = modulus of elasticity for pile material.

Where the formula is used, a factor of safety of three should be applied ($Q_{\text{design}} = \frac{1}{3} Q_{\text{ult}}$).

During pile installation, it is convenient to know when a desired capacity has been obtained and driving can cease. The pile formula above can be rearranged to indicate the final set, usually inches per blow, that provides the design capacity:

$$S = \left[\frac{(W_h H)(\text{Eff.})}{3 Q_{\text{design}}} \right] - \frac{1}{2} S_0. \tag{14-39b}$$

If the set is to be in inches per blow, all lengths should be expressed in inches. Similarly, the units for the weight of ram and pile capacity have to be the same.

ILLUSTRATION 14-13. Steel pipe piles intended to provide a design capacity of 50 tons are used at a construction site underlain by cohesionless soils. Preliminary analysis indicates that the required pile length will be between 45 and 50 ft. If the Danish formula will be used as a field control during driving to indicate when the desired capacity is obtained, what should be the set under the last driving blows? Pile installation will be accomplished with a Vulcan Model 0 hammer having a rated driving energy of 24,375 ft-lb.

Assume a pile length of 50 ft. Pile cross section = 10 in.^{2}, $E_{\text{steel}} = 29 \times 10^6$ psi.

$$\text{Set } S = \frac{W_h H \times \text{Eff.}}{3 Q_{\text{design}}} - \frac{1}{2} S_0.$$

where $S_0 = \sqrt{\dfrac{2 \times \text{Eff.} \times W_h HL}{AE}}$

$$= \left[\frac{(2)(24{,}375 \text{ ft-lb})(50 \text{ ft})(144 \text{ in.}^2/\text{ft}^2)}{(10 \text{ in.}^2)(29 \times 10^6 \text{ lb/in.}^2)} \right]^{1/2} = 1.1 \text{ in.}$$

Therefore,

$$\text{Set } S = \frac{(24.375 \text{ ft kip})(12 \text{ in./ft})}{(3 \times 50 \text{ tons} \times 2 \text{ k/ton})} - \frac{1}{2}(1.1 \text{ in.})$$

$$= 0.98 \text{ in.} - 0.55 \text{ in.} = 0.43 \text{ in.} \approx \tfrac{1}{2} \text{ in.}$$

One of the most widely known pile-driving formulae is the *Engineering News* (ENR) formula, presented in the late nineteenth century for determining the capacity of timber piles. The formula is not reported herein, because it does not have application for existing pile-driving methods. The use of the ENR formula should be discouraged. Though it has a theoretical factor of safety of 6, various load test programs have indicated that the actual factor of safety can range from less than 1 (representing pile failure at less than the expected capacity) to about 20.

SUPERVISION OF FOUNDATION CONSTRUCTION

Since foundations frequently are covered or completely buried soon after their construction, there is limited opportunity for noting and correcting improper work or detecting conditions not in accord with design assumptions. To minimize the risk of problems resulting from improper or inadequate foundation construction, the practice of having such work guided (or supervised) by personnel with soil mechanics training is increasing.

The responsibilities of such personnel would include matching soil and groundwater conditions observed in excavations with the conditions indicated by the borings used for design. For projects where shallow foundations are being installed, the proper location, size, and depth should be verified. The bottoms of excavations should be examined prior to concrete placement to ensure that disturbed or muddy soil is not left in place; compaction or removal can be ordered if such conditions are observed.

Where drilled foundations are being installed, the bottom of the excavation and soil exposed in the walls should be examined whenever conditions permit. Depth to, or bearing in, a proper soil stratum should be verified. Proper location, dimensions, and installation of required reinforcing steel should also be verified.

With driven-pile foundations, driving records (the continuous record of blow count versus depth) should be kept for all piles. The size and length of piles should be verified. Detailed information on the equipment used for driving the piles should be obtained.

Personnel doing supervision work should keep a written record (daily logs or reports) of activities, observations, and decisions regarding the foundation work. Copies frequently are expected to be forwarded to the designer's office. Written records can serve as a diary of the construction progress, and frequently serve as a reference if disputes develop.

PROBLEMS

14-1. A long footing, 3 ft wide, is to be installed 4 ft below grade. Drained shear tests indicate that the supporting soil has a cohesive strength of 1000 psf and the angle of internal friction is 20°. The soil rigidity index is greater than the critical index. The soil unit weight is 115 pcf and the water table is deep. Calculate the safe bearing capacity, applying a factor of safety of 3 to the general bearing capacity equation. Assume that the backfill is not well compacted and the depth factors do not apply.

14-2. Determine the wall loading that can be carried by a long footing, 1 m wide and located 1.5 m below the ground surface. Strength tests indicate that the soil has a cohesion of 58 kN/m² and an angle of internal friction of 20°. The soil unit weight is 18 kN/m³. The soil above the footing is well compacted, and the depth factors will apply. The soil rigidity index is greater than the critical index. The water table is expected to rise to the ground surface. Use a factor of safety equal to 3 with the extended general bearing capacity equation.

14-3. For the conditions described, calculate the soil rigidity index:
   (a) Soil modulus of elasticity is 150 ksf, Poisson's ratio is 0.40, soil unit weight is 115 pcf, cohesion is 600 psf, and angle of internal friction, ϕ, is 28°. Find the rigidity index for a point 10 ft below the soil surface.
   (b) The modulus of elasticity is to be estimated from the results of a consolidation test where C_c is 0.35 over the pressure range between 50 and 100 kN/m² and the value of e_0 is 1.40. Poisson's ratio is 0.30. In place, the soil has a unit weight of 17 kN/m³, cohesion equal to 60 kN/m², and angle of internal friction equal to 15°. Find the rigidity index for a point 4 m below the soil surface.
   (c) The modulus of elasticity is 18 ksf, Poisson's ratio is 0.45, the soil cohesion is 1200 psf (undrained shear), and the soil unit weight is 105 pcf. Find the rigidity index for a point 8 ft below the soil surface.
   (d) The modulus of elasticity is 200 ksf, Poisson's ratio is 0.30, the angle of internal friction is 35°, and the soil unit weight is 122 pcf. Find the rigidity index for a point 10 ft below the soil surface.

14-4. A square footing is to be designed to carry a column load of 1000 kN. The footing will be installed at a shallow depth on clay soil whose undrained shear strength (cohesion) is 96 kN/m². The water table is deep. The soil rigidity index value is 30. If a factor of safety of 3 is used with the extended general bearing capacity equation, what size footing should be provided?

14-5. A square footing is to be provided in order to support a 350-kip column loading. If the footing is to be located on the surface of a cohesionless soil deposit, what size foundation is required? The soil has a unit weight of 125 pcf, and the angle of internal friction is 36°. The rigidity index for the soil zone near the ground surface is 100. It is expected that the water table could rise to the ground surface. For the design, apply a factor of safety equal to 3 to the extended bearing capacity equation.

14-6. A footing for an existing building is 6 ft square (6 ft × 6 ft) and 3 ft below the surface. A proposed building alteration would require this footing to carry a loading of 400 kips. Is the footing of adequate size? Soil investigation indicates that the foundation soils have an angle of internal friction of 35° and a unit weight of 120 pcf. The soil rigidity index value is 150. The soil above the base of the footing is well compacted, and the foundation depth factors can be applied. Use a factor of safety equal to 3 with the extended general bearing capacity equation.

14-7. Design a square footing to carry a column load of 750 kN. The footing is to be installed 1 m below the ground surface on a sand whose angle of internal friction is 33° and unit weight is 18 kN/m³. The soil rigidity index value is 125. Assume that the backfill soil is not well compacted and depth factors do not apply. The water table is very deep. Use a factor of safety of 3 with the extended bearing capacity equation.

14-8. What loading could a rectangular foundation, 4 ft by 8 ft, support if it is located on the surface of a soil where drained shear tests indicate a cohesion of 500 psf and an angle of internal friction of 20°? The soil unit weight is 110 pcf. The soil rigidity index value is 25. The water table is deep. Use a factor of safety equal to 3 with the extended general bearing capacity equation.

14-9. A heavy machine is to be provided with a temporary concrete pad foundation that needs to have a length equal to twice the width. The foundation will be installed close to the ground surface on a clay soil; undrained shear tests indicate that the cohesion is 2500 psf. The soil rigidity index is 75. The machine weighs 1200 kips. To have a factor of safety of 3, what size foundation should be constructed?

14-10. Two building columns (a wall column and an interior column) are to be supported on a common rectangular (combined) footing. The wall column imposes a loading of 120 tons; the interior column carries 200 tons. The columns are 16 ft apart. The end of the footing near the wall cannot project more than 3 ft beyond the centerline of the wall column. Using an allowable soil bearing pressure of 4000 psf, give the length and width of foundation that should be provided.

14-11. A long footing, 1 m wide, has its base inclined 10° from the horizontal. The footing bears on the surface of a soil where drained shear tests show a cohesion of 500 psf and an angle of internal friction of 25°. The soil rigidity index value is 50. What load acting normal to the foundation base can be imposed if a factor of safety equal to 3 is used with the extended general bearing capacity equation?

14-12. A long footing is to be constructed in the slope of a clay hillside that makes an inclination of 30° with the horizontal. The cohesion of the clay is 1500 psf, and the unit weight is 105 pcf. If the slope stability factor is zero, and the D/B ratio is close to zero, what width footing is required to support a wall loading of 8000 pounds per foot of length? Use a factor of safety of 3.

14-13. A long footing, 3 ft wide, is located on the slope of a 30° hill. The hill is sand that has an angle of internal friction of 35° and a unit weight of 115 pcf. If a D/B ratio of 1 is assumed, what wall loading can the footing carry? Use a factor of safety of 3.

14-14. A 4-ft-wide long footing is located at the top of a slope. The slope inclination is 30°. The hill is sand with an assumed angle of internal friction of 30°. If the D/B ratio is 1 and the b/B ratio is also 1, what loading can be imposed on the footing? Use a factor of safety of 3.

14-15. Soil borings indicate that a building site is underlain by clean fine to coarse sand. The following standard penetration test information is obtained from a boring log: At 2-ft depth, N is 12; at 6-ft depth, N is 14; at 10-ft depth, N is 18; at 14-ft depth, N is 20; at 20-ft depth, N is 25; at 25-ft depth, N is 26. No groundwater was encountered. It is planned to construct a square footing 4 ft deep to carry a 300-kip column load near to this boring location. If a 1-in. settlement is tolerable, what size foundation should be provided? What size footing should be provided if the groundwater table was about at footing level?

14-16. Static cone penetrometer resistance data obtained from a building site underlain by sand show an average q_c value of 100 kg/cm². From this information, estimate the size of square footing necessary to support a column load of 250 kips. Assume that the footing will be placed approximately 4 ft deep and that a 1-in. settlement is tolerable.

14-17. Static cone penetrometer resistance data indicate that a building site is underlain by an overconsolidated clay. The average q_c value in the upper 20 ft of soil is 75. Using this information, estimate the cohesion of the soil and a safe bearing capacity for shallow square footings.

14-18. A 14-in.-diameter pipe pile is driven 50 ft into a dry loose sand whose unit weight is 105 pcf. The angle of internal friction is 33°. Compute the safe axial downward loading, using the statical analysis. Apply a factor of safety of 2.

14-19. A 12-in.-square prestressed concrete pile is to be installed in sandy soil for a marine structure. The pile will be 40 ft long. It will be jetted 30 ft and driven the last 10 ft. The water table is at the ground surface. The saturated soil weight is 120 pcf. The angle of internal friction is 35°. For these conditions, assume that the critical depth for computing effective soil stresses is twenty pile diameters. Calculate the safe axial downward loading, using the statical analysis and a factor of safety of 2.

14-20. Timber piles are to be used as friction piles at a site underlain by a deep deposit of clay soil whose cohesion is 1000 psf and unit weight is 105 pcf. For a pile embedded 30 ft, having a tip diameter of 8 in. and a 14-in. butt diameter, calculate the axial capacity, assuming skin friction only. Use a factor of safety of 2.

14-21. A 12-inch steel H-pile (HP) is driven 60 ft into clay soil as follows: From zero to 30 ft, the cohesion is 800 psf and the unit weight is 105 pcf; below 30 ft, the cohesion is 2000 psf and the unit weight is 115 pcf. Assume that the upper clay layer is normally consolidated and the deeper clay is overconsolidated. Determine the axial capacity of the pile, using a factor of safety of 2. Compute the shaft capacity, assuming that skin friction is developed on the surface of the rectangle (12-in. square) that encloses the pile.

14-22. A 14-in.-diameter pipe pile is driven 50 ft into overconsolidated clays having the following properties: From zero to 20 ft, the cohesion is 1500 psf and the soil unit weight is 110 pcf; below 20 ft, the cohesion is 2500 psf and the soil unit weight is 120 pcf. Calculate the downward and upward axial capacity of the pile, applying a factor of safety of 2.

14-23. A four-pile group consists of 12-in.-square prestressed concrete piles 35 ft long. The piles are driven into an overconsolidated clay whose cohesion is 2000 psf and soil unit weight is 115 pcf. The pile spacing is $2\frac{1}{2}$ diameters. The water table is at the ground surface. Using a factor of safety of 2, find the capacity of the pile group.

14-24. For an offshore project, a steel pipe pile with an outside diameter of 18 in. penetrates 150 ft through normally consolidated clays. Soil conditions are as follows: From zero to 50 ft, the cohesion is 800 psf and the saturated soil unit weight is 105 pcf; from 50 to 100 ft, the cohesion is 1500 psf and the saturated unit weight is 115 pcf; below 100 ft, the cohesion is 2400 psf and the saturated unit weight is 125 pcf. The water table is above the soil surface. Using the lambda method, determine the axial capacity of the pile, using a factor of safety of 2.

14-25. A drilled-shaft foundation is to be constructed in clay soils having the following properties: From zero to 30 ft, the cohesion is 1000 psf and the soil unit weight is 105 pcf; below 30 ft, the cohesion is 2500 psf and the unit weight is 115 pcf. The foundation is to extend to a total depth of 36 ft. A 3-ft-diameter shaft will be used with a belled (underreamed) bottom 6 ft in diameter. Assume that the bell forms a 60° angle with the horizontal plane. Compute the design downward capacity if

(a) The excavation is drilled dry.

(b) It is necessary to use a bentonite slurry during drilling.

14-26. A 12-in.-square prestressed concrete pile is driven 50 ft. Under the last blow of a Vulcan 010 hammer, the pile penetrates 0.25 in. Using the Danish pile-driving formula, what safe design load is indicated? Is this size hammer proper for this type and length pile?

14-27. The Danish pile-driving formula is to be used for field control of a pile installation. Steel pipe piles penetrating approximately 40 ft are to provide a design capacity of 60 tons. Each pipe has a net cross-sectional area of 20 in.^{2}. What should be the set under the last blow of a MKT-11B3 hammer to obtain the desired axial capacity?

14-28. The following data are obtained from a slow-ML pile load test. Plot the load and settlement information on logarithmic coordinates and, from the plot, determine the "failure load."

Load (tons)	Settlement (in.)
25	0.05
50	0.15
75	0.26
100	0.40
125	0.60
150	0.80
175	0.95
200	1.55
225	2.45

chapter 15

Stability of Unsupported Slopes

The stability of sloped land areas and the potential for failure, or landslide, is a concern where movements of existing or planned slopes would have an effect on the safety of people and property or the usability and value of the area. The region affected by slope failure is not necessarily the slope's immediate area; landslides have dammed up rivers and caused upstream flooding, and mass earth movements into large bodies of water also have created huge tidal waves that have devastated areas great distances away.[1]

Existing slopes that have been stable can experience significant movement, termed *slope failures* or *landslides*, when natural or man-induced conditions cause a change in the forces that act at the sloped area. *Changed natural conditions* can result from the occurrence of earthquake, subsidence of underground caverns, erosion, a general slope weakening because of the development of tension cracks or shrinkage cracks that are followed by water intrusions, a variation in the elevation of groundwater or a change in the slope's subsurface flow, which creates new seepage forces, or the weakening of buried soil or rock seams because of groundwater flow or chemical waste leachate. Typical *man-induced changes* include increased loading on a slope or near its crest, removal of earth below the toe of a slope, and removal of material from a slope so as to make it steeper. Short-term as well as permanent changes can be the cause of slope failures.

Planned slope topography develops where the site grading for a construction project requires a change in elevation from one area to another within the confines

---

[1]For example, a sudden slide into Italy's Vaiont Reservoir (1963) produced a wave on the order of 300 ft (100 m) high, which then overtopped the reservoir dam and caused great destruction in the region downstream.

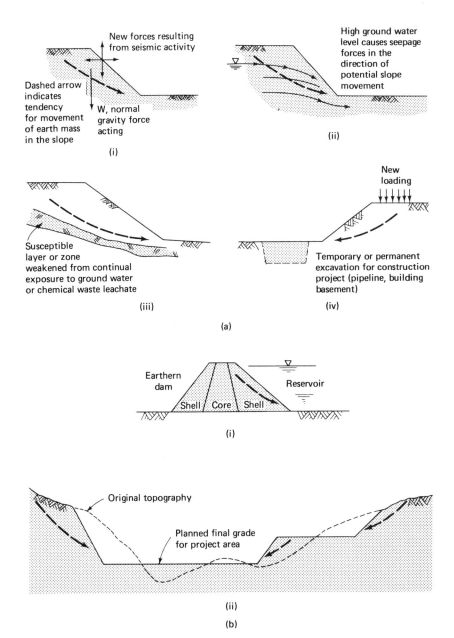

Figure 15-1 (a) Illustrations of changed conditions for existing slopes; (b) illustrations of new slopes resulting from construction.

of the project and at locations where a construction area is to be joined to the surrounding topography through the creation of new slopes or modification of existing ones. Typical of those jobs that include topography modification are earthmoving, excavation, and embankment projects such as for highways, airfields, railroads, and dams. Figure 15-1 illustrates these various conditions.

Stability of Unsupported Slopes   **435**

TYPES OF SLOPE MOVEMENTS

Movements of sloped soil masses can be classified into broad categories, depending on the type of motion relative to the adjacent or underlying earth. *Slide* refers to the occurrence where the moving mass is rather well defined and separated from the underlying and adjacent earth by a plane, or a zone comprising a number of adjacent planes, where slippage results. The slippage plane or zone represents the continuous surface where the maximum shear strength of the earth material has been reached, with the result that large displacement occurs. The failure mass remains essentially intact, although it may fracture into subunits.

Slides are classified as *rotational* or *translational* in accord with the shape and directional movement of the soil mass. *Rotational slides* are associated with natural slopes and constructed embankments of homogeneous materials possessing cohesion; the failure surface is curved, with the failed mass characteristically slumped in the toe area of the original slope (Fig. 15-2a). Rotation occurs about an imaginary axis in space, one that is aligned parallel to the slope. *Translational slides* are associated with slopes of layered materials where the mechanism of slippage occurs along a weak plane or zone that possesses a downward dip (Fig. 15-2b) and in cohesionless soil slopes where a change in conditions (such as seepage) occurs. Unlike the rotational slide, whose movement tends to cease when the mass reaches the slumped position, the translational slide can continue over a long distance. In the course of its movement, the sliding mass may remain essentially intact or subdivide.

Block or wedge failure refers to the displacement of an intact mass of soil because of the action of an adjacent zone of earth. Distinct blocks and wedges of soil may become separated from the adjoining earth because of the presence of cracks, fissures, or joints, or because materials having different properties are involved. Block failures may be included within translational slides as well as within the lateral spreads described below. The occurrence has also been noted in natural slopes and embankments where the failure block rests on a weak soil plane (see Fig. 15-2c).

More complex types of soil mass movements are *flows* and *spreads* (Figs. 15-2d and e). A *flow* involves lateral movement of soil having the characteristics of a viscous fluid, although the actual consistency of the moving mass may vary from very wet to dry. A flow tends to retain less definition than does a sliding mass; slip surfaces within the mass are continuously developing and disappearing. *Spread* refers to the occurrence of multidirectional lateral movements by a fractured soil mass. The causes are similar to those for translational slides, involving a buried plane or zone that becomes too weak to resist the tendency for movement due to gravity forces or other factors. Earthquakes are a typical cause of lateral spreads.

Methods of analysis to evaluate the stability of existing and planned slopes using principles of engineering mechanics have concentrated on earth slides (i.e., rotational, translational, and block movements). Means for evaluating an area's susceptibility to a flow or spread occurrence have relied principally on interpretation of geologic conditions or, in the case of earth-moving projects such as hydraulic fills, on the properties and conditions of the fill and foundation materials. Analytical

(a) Rotational

(b) Translational

Weak seam or stratum

(c) Block and wedge

Weak seam or zone

(d) Flow

Source area

Main track

Depositional area

(e) Spread

Firm clay

Soft clay with water bearing silt and sand layers

Firm clayey gravel

Figure 15-2 Types of slope movements. (After Varnes [262])

437

procedures in common use for studying slides are discussed in the following sections. The relatively simple condition of isotropic soils and uniform slopes of infinite extent is discussed initially. The major portion of the chapter then discusses methods for analyzing the more commonly encountered condition of slopes that are of finite extent and are composed of either isotropic, nonisotropic, or layered soils that are cohesionless or that possess cohesion.

ISOTROPIC SOILS AND UNIFORM SLOPES OF INFINITE EXTENT

For purposes of analysis, slopes extending a great distance in the height and length direction are considered to be of infinite extent. With uniform slopes of infinite extent, the analysis of forces affecting stability is considerably simpler than the analysis for a slope of limited extent. However, the procedures for studying the uniform slope of infinite extent in isotropic soil also serve as an introduction to methods for analyzing the more involved condition where slopes are of limited extent and are composed of nonisotropic (nonuniform) soils.

Cohesionless Soil   For a uniform slope composed of dry cohesionless soil, the forces acting on an incremental slice taken above the plane where sliding is assumed are as shown in Figure 15-3. The shear strength of the soil in the slope is expressed as

$$\tau = \bar{\sigma} \tan \phi \qquad (10\text{-}1b)$$

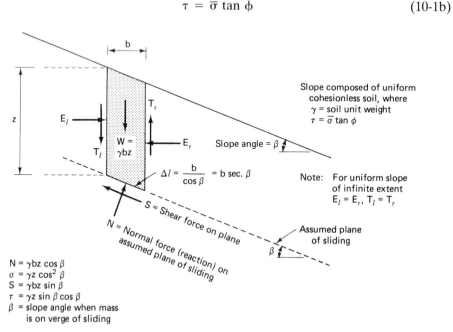

$N = \gamma bz \cos \beta$
$\sigma = \gamma z \cos^2 \beta$
$S = \gamma bz \sin \beta$
$\tau = \gamma z \sin \beta \cos \beta$
β = slope angle when mass is on verge of sliding

Figure 15-3 Description of forces acting on representative slice of cohesionless soil in uniform slope of infinite extent.

where τ is the maximum shearing strength or resistance that can be developed on the plane where $\bar{\sigma}$, the effective compressive stress (i.e., intergranular stress), is acting. The angle of internal friction, ϕ, is a property of the soil affected by particle size, shape, and mineralogical composition.

For a uniform slope of limited extent, the tangential forces (T_l and T_r) and the lateral forces (E_l and E_r) acting on a slice of incremental width are equal. When the slope is on the verge of sliding along the assumed plane, all forces acting on the slice are in equilibrium. Summing forces in the horizontal direction to obtain the relationship between S and N gives

$$\Sigma F_H = 0$$

$$S \cos \beta = N \sin \beta$$

$$S = N \frac{\sin \beta}{\cos \beta} = N \tan \beta$$

The maximum total shearing resistance that can be developed by the soil on the assumed plane of sliding is

$$\tau(\Delta l) = \bar{\sigma}(\Delta l) \tan \phi$$

where $\bar{\sigma}(\Delta l)$ is the maximum effective normal force N that can act on the plane. For the slice to be on the verge of sliding (at the limit of an equilibrium condition), the value of S on the base of the slice is equal to the maximum shearing resistance that can be developed by the soil,

$$S = \tau(\Delta l)$$

or

$$N \tan \beta = N \tan \phi$$

The limit of the equilibrium condition for other slices in the slope exists simultaneously when the relationship among W, N, and S is identical to that just shown. This condition is satisfied only where the failure plane and slope surface are parallel. Therefore, the maximum slope angle before sliding occurs is

$$\tan \beta = \tan \phi$$

or

$$\beta = \phi \text{ (for dry cohesionless soil)} \qquad (15\text{-}1)$$

Thus, when β equals ϕ, the factor of safety (the ratio of forces resisting sliding to those causing sliding) based on the shear strength of the soil is one. For slopes that have an inclination less than ϕ, the factor of safety is greater than one. Where i is the actual slope angle, existing or planned, the factor of safety against sliding is expressed as

$$FS = \frac{\tan \phi}{\tan i} \qquad (15\text{-}2)$$

Isotropic Soils and Uniform Slopes of Infinite Extent **439**

Procedures for performing stability analysis based on the concepts just discussed have been termed the *limit equilibrium method* of analysis. In its present scope, the method involves the determination of the total shear strength that is required or mobilized (i.e., utilized) by the soil along an assumed slip surface in order to maintain slope equilibrium; a factor of safety against sliding is then indicated as the ratio of total shear strength available (the maximum strength of the soil) to the total shear strength that is required or mobilized for the equilibrium condition.

If the slope is submerged, the effective unit weight of soil in the slice is reduced to the buoyant or submerged unit weight. The values of N or S on each slice will be reduced proportionately. The shearing resistance that can be developed within the soil is correspondingly reduced because of the decreased value of $\bar{\sigma}$. The result is that the maximum safe slope angle for a completely submerged slope is the same as for an unsubmerged slope of dry soil, provided that no flow of water is occurring through the slope.

For the condition where the submerged slope is subject to flow that travels parallel to the slope's surface, the resulting seepage forces contribute to those forces that act to cause sliding, and the maximum safe slope angle becomes

$$\tan \beta = \frac{\gamma_{sub}}{\gamma_{total}} \tan \phi \qquad (15\text{-}3a)$$

where γ_{total} is the wet soil unit weight above water and γ_{sub} is the submerged or buoyant soil weight. Since the submerged unit weight for many soils is on the order of half the weight above water, Equation 15-3a becomes

$$\tan \beta = \tfrac{1}{2} \tan \phi \quad \text{(approximately)} \qquad (15\text{-}3b)$$

Equations 15-3a and 15-3b indicate the condition for the factor of safety to be one. The factor of safety for lesser slopes can be determined from

$$FS = \frac{\gamma_{sub} (\tan \phi)}{\gamma_{total} (\tan i)} \begin{array}{l} \text{(for submerged slope of} \\ \text{cohesionless soil} \\ \text{subject to ground-} \\ \text{water flow)} \end{array} \qquad (15\text{-}4)$$

where i is the actual angle of the existing or planned slope.

Relating to safe slopes of cohesionless soils above the water table, certain conditions frequently observed in practice warrant consideration. Where the soil is dense because of past geologic conditions or method of placement, the peak value of ϕ is significantly greater than the ultimate value (refer to Chapter 10). Relatively steep slopes of dense cohesionless soil are susceptible to sliding if external forces, such as from earthquake or blasting operations, disturb the dense condition and ϕ is reduced from the peak to the ultimate value (Fig. 15-4; also refer to Figs. 10-16 and 10-17). A slope stabilized at an inclination angle equal to the *ultimate* value of ϕ is considered to be at the angle of repose, the slope angle resulting when a dry cohesionless soil is loosely dumped. Slopes composed of damp cohesionless soil also require certain cautions. Damp cohesionless soils possess shear strength

Figure 15-4 Relative failure envelopes (or shear strength values) due to difference in peak and ultimate Ø values.

Figure 15-5 Effect of capillary moisture on shear strength of cohesionless soil.

from apparent cohesion (Fig. 15-5) due to the presence of water menisci and capillary tension in addition to the strength in effect due to ϕ. The ability to obtain steep slopes in new excavations of such cohesionless deposits is a common occurrence. However, this extra strength disappears if the moisture evaporates or the slope becomes saturated or submerged. The result is that a zone of instability is created. A changed condition of seeping water (e.g., the result of a rising groundwater table or percolating surface water from rain or snow) can be responsible for the failure of steep slopes through the effect of seepage forces and erosion. For the rather common condition of a natural granular deposit containing some silt and clay materials, the movement of water can flush such "fines," which have been contributing a bonding or cohesive strength to the slope mass (see Fig. 15-6).

Soils Possessing Cohesion Soils possessing cohesion have their shear strength expressed as

$$\tau = c + \overline{\sigma} \tan \phi \qquad (10\text{-}3)$$

Referring to Figure 15-3, note that the shear stress acting on the base of the slice is

$$\tau = \gamma z \sin \beta \cos \beta$$

Figure 15-6 Illustrations of steep slopes and unusual slope configurations that are possible, for a limited time period, in granular deposits. In left photo, note accumulation of fallen material at base of slope.

for the nonsubmerged case. When the soil mass is in equilibrium but on the verge of sliding,

$$\gamma z \sin \beta \cos \beta = c + \bar{\sigma} \tan \phi$$

By substituting the value of $\gamma z \cos^2 \beta$ for $\bar{\sigma}$, obtain the relationship

$$\gamma z \sin \beta \cos \beta = c + \gamma z \cos^2 \beta \tan \phi$$

If the factor of safety against sliding is taken as the ratio of the soil shear *strength available* to the shear *stress acting* on the plane, a value of unity is obtained by substitution of the just discussed shear strength and shear stress values; that is,

$$FS = 1 = \frac{c + \gamma z \cos^2 \beta \tan \phi}{\gamma z \sin \beta \cos \beta} = \frac{c}{\gamma z \sin \beta \cos \beta} + \frac{\tan \phi}{\tan \beta} \qquad (15\text{-}5a)$$

For a slope of inclination i (where i is less than the angle β), the factor of safety is obtained from

$$FS = \frac{c}{\gamma z \sin i \cos i} + \frac{\tan \phi}{\tan i} \quad \text{(nonsubmerged case)} \qquad (15\text{-}5b)$$

For a completely submerged slope, the soil unit weight term in Equation 15-5b must be γ_{sub}. When the full height of the slope is subject to groundwater flow parallel to the surface of the slope, the factor of safety is determined from

$$FS = \frac{c}{\gamma z \sin i \cos i} + \frac{\gamma_{sub} \tan \phi}{\gamma_{total} \tan i} \quad \begin{array}{l} \text{(submerged slope} \\ \text{subject to ground-} \\ \text{water flow} \end{array} \qquad (15\text{-}5c)$$

In practical encounters, most earth slopes are not isotropic nor of infinite extent. Safe inclinations for finite slopes comprised of isotropic cohesionless soils *can* be determined by utilizing the procedures for infinite slopes. For nonisotropic slopes and slopes comprising soil possessing cohesion (clays and mixed soils) that are of finite extent, the methods presented in the sections that follow are required.

SLOPES OF FINITE EXTENT—SOILS POSSESSING COHESION

Investigators examining failed slopes that consisted of isotropic deposits possessing cohesion (clays and mixed soils) have noted that, typically, the failure mass moved downward and outward relative to the slope's original position by sliding along a curved plane of slippage. These observed slip surfaces have been approximately but not truly circular in shape, the actual curvature being greatest near the center of the slippage arc and least in the upper section of arc. A result of this information is that many of the methods of analyses that have evolved to study the stability of not-yet-built and not-yet-failed slopes have assumed that a plane of failure would follow along a circular arc because of this shape's probable close approximation to any actual failure plane and, also, for mathematical convenience. Other shape failure planes, such as the logarithmic spiral, have been assumed in attempts to define the failure mass more accurately, but results have not differed significantly from those based upon the circular slip surface. Found to be more crucial to the study of a slope's stability is the proper evaluation of the involved soil's shear strength and the determination of pore water pressures that exist in the slope. Realistically, the practical ability to obtain highly precise subsurface information, such as high definition of the soil profile and related soil strength properties and pore pressure values, does not match the analytical precision possible within available slope stability theories. In recognition of this, approximations and practical assumptions have been incorporated into many analyses to simplify computational procedures. Nevertheless, these methods for slope stability evaluation provide results of good accuracy and practical value.

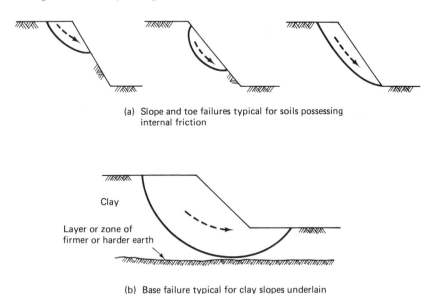

(a) Slope and toe failures typical for soils possessing internal friction

(b) Base failure typical for clay slopes underlain by deep, hard stratum

Figure 15-7 Types of rotational slides occurring in slopes comprising homogeneous soils.

Types of Rotational Slides in Isotropic Soils   The strength properties of the soil composing the slope have an effect on the general location of the slip surface. Where the soils possess significant internal friction (mixed soils and primarily cohesionless soil), the failure arc is shallower than for the condition where an isotropic mass of soft or normally consolidated clay exists (Fig. 15-7). The plane of sliding for slopes of soil having internal friction passes through the face of the slope or involves but little of the zone below the level of the toe. In contrast, failures in isotropic clay deposits involve a slippage plane that extends some distance below the elevation of the toe (classified as a base failure) and is often tangent to a deep hard or firm layer. Generally, and on a relative basis, failure of the flatter slopes involves a deeper failure zone than the steeper slopes.

Stability Analysis—General Concepts   Where the stability of a sloped earth mass is to be studied for the possibility of failure by sliding along a circular slip surface, the principles of engineering statics can be applied to determine if a stable or unstable condition exists. When the total sliding mass is assumed to be cylindrical or spoon-shaped (Fig. 15-8), a unit width extending along the face of the slope is taken for analysis, and the slip surface of the slope cross section is the segment of a circle (Fig. 15-9a). Forces that would affect the equilibrium of the assumed failure mass are determined, and *moments* of these forces with respect to a point representing the center of the slip circle arc (the point is actually an axis in space parallel to the face of the slope) are computed. With this procedure, the weight of soil in the sliding mass being considered as well as external loading on the face and top of the slope contribute to the moments acting to cause movement. Resistance to sliding is provided by the shear strength of the soil on the assumed slip surface (see Fig. 15-9b).

A computational method used to indicate if failure (sliding) occurs is to compare moments that would resist movement to those that tend to cause movement. The maximum shear strength possessed by the soil is used in the calculation

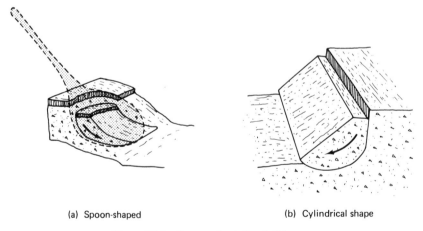

(a) Spoon-shaped   (b) Cylindrical shape

Figure 15-8   Shapes of rotational slides.

(a) Section of slope having a unit
width assumed for analysis
shown in (b)

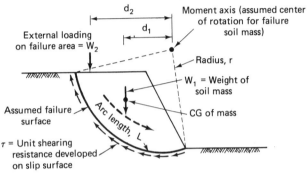

Moment causing sliding = $(W_1 \times d_1) + (W_2 \times d_2)$
Moment resisting sliding = $\tau \times L \times r$

(b) Description of forces acting on an
assumed slope failure mass

Calculations for Factor of Safety

(a) Let $\tau = \tau_{max}$ (maximum soil
shearing strength)

$$FS = \frac{\tau_{max} \times L \times r}{(W_1 \times d_1) + (W_2 \times d_2)}$$

(b) Let τ_{req} = shear strength
required for equilibrium

so that $\tau_{req} \times L \times r = (W_1 \times d_1) + (W_2 \times d_2)$

$$\tau_{req} = \frac{(W_1 \times d_1) + (W_2 \times d_2)}{L \times r}$$

$$FS = \frac{\tau_{max}}{\tau_{req}}$$

Figure 15-9 Description of terms and
basic method for slope stability analysis.

of the resisting moment. Failure is indicated when moments causing motion exceed those resisting motion. The factor of safety against sliding or movement is expressed as

$$FS = \frac{\text{Moments resisting sliding}}{\text{Moments causing sliding}} \qquad (15\text{-}6a)$$

Slopes of Finite Extent—Soils Possessing Cohesion   **445**

An *FS* of unity implies that the assumed failure mass is on the verge of sliding. A variation to this method for studying slope stability involves determining the shear strength required to have sliding moments and resisting moments balance (equilibrium). The shearing resistance required along the slip surface is compared to the shear strength that can be developed by the soil. If the soil shearing strength that can be developed by the soil is greater than the shearing resistance required for equilibrium, failure does not occur. With this method, the factor of safety against sliding is

$$FS = \frac{\text{Shear strength possessed by the soil}}{\text{Soil shear strength required for equilibrium}} \qquad (15\text{-}6b)$$

The factor of safety indicated by this method is a value based on the soil's shear strength; this method is used in most of the mathematical slope stability theories.

A number of analytical methods have been developed that utilize the basic concepts discussed above but differ in the procedure for handling various forces influencing equilibrium or in assigning practical simplifying assumptions. The methods indicated below are commonly referred-to procedures and are discussed in the following sections of this chapter.

PARTIAL LISTING OF PROCEDURES FOR ANALYZING SLOPE STABILITY

Procedure	Typical applications and limitations	Comments on usage
Basic method	Circular failure surfaces in isotropic clay slopes	Nonrigorous method; hand calculator solution practical
Fellenius method of slices	Circular failure surfaces, all soil types	Nonrigorous method; hand calculator solution practical
Bishop method of slices	Circular failure surfaces, all soil types	Rigorous method; computer program best for solution
Simplified Bishop method	Circular failure surfaces, all soil types	Semirigorous method; hand calculator solution practical
Morgenstern-Price method of slices	Circular and noncircular failure surfaces, all soil types	Rigorous method; computer required for solution
Spencer method of slices	Circular and noncircular failure surfaces, all soil types	Rigorous method; computer required
Janbu method of slices	Circular and noncircular failure surfaces, all soil types	Widely used for noncircular failure surface; computer best for rigorous method but chart aids make hand calculator solutions practical

Computational aids (i.e., charts and curves) that simplify the effort related to determining the stability of slopes composed of isotropic soils are also available, and their use is discussed in later sections of the chapter.

Strength Properties for Analysis—Clay and Mixed Soils   The shear strength of a *clay* soil is related to the soil's stress history (e.g., normally consolidated or overconsolidated), the effective or consolidation stress presently acting, and the pore water pressure condition existing, along with the opportunity for pore water drainage to occur. Use of the soil strength value determined from the in situ condition—for example, the total stress case, where $\phi = 0$ and $\tau = c$, values as would be obtained from unconsolidated-undrained shear tests (Fig. 10-22 and 10-23) and unconfined compression tests (Fig 10-35)—is considered appropriate for analysis of end-of-construction stability and short-term stability. This total stress analysis, conventionally referred to as the $\phi = 0$ condition, is utilized when dealing with normally consolidated soils but should not be applied to the study of over-consolidated and fissured or jointed deposits. Studies dealing with the long-term stability of slopes and the short-term stability where overconsolidated or jointed-fissured soils exist require use of shear strength properties applicable to the effective stress condition. With the effective stress being the net intergranular compressive stress excluding pore water pressure, the relationship among total stress, effective stress, and pore water pressure in a soil mass is

$$\text{Total stress} = \text{Effective stress} + \text{Pore water pressure}$$

or
$$\sigma = \bar{\sigma} + u \qquad \text{(refer to Eqs. 8-3, 8-4)}$$

A practical reason for using the total stress ($\phi = 0$) analysis to study *newly constructed* slopes relates to the difficulty in selecting a pore pressure because the values are changing as drainage of the newly opened slope takes place. Realistically, it is simpler to work with a concept of total stress where, provided that *excess* pore pressures do not exist, the total stress is defined from

$$\sigma = \gamma_{\text{total}} z \qquad \text{(refer to Eqs. 8-1, 8-3)}$$

where γ_{total} is the total soil weight including pore water and z is the depth to the plane under analysis.

The shear strength of mixed and clay soils (soils possessing cohesion) *based on the effective stress*, is

$$\tau = c' + (\sigma - u) \tan \phi_{\text{true}} = c' + \bar{\sigma} \tan \phi_{\text{true}}$$

where c' and $\tan \phi_{\text{true}}$ are values obtained from either consolidated–drained shear tests or consolidated–undrained tests when pore water pressures u are measured (see Fig. 15-10). The magnitude of c' is often small for normally consolidated and

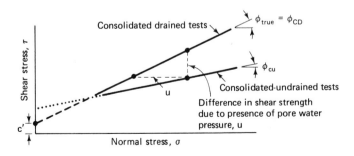

Figure 15-10 Qualitative comparison of shear strength envelope from consolidated–undrained tests.

lightly overconsolidated clay soils, and a zero value can be conservatively assigned in the slope analysis that uses effective stress parameters.

Basic Method for Stability Analysis   With an isotropic clay slope, the factor of safety for a selected failure mass and slip surface can be determined by direct use of Equation 15-6a or 15-6b when the condition for the $\phi = 0$ case is under study (see Illustration 15-1).[2] For this case, the total shear strength considered is the value of cohesion, c, from undrained shear tests (i.e., unconsolidated-undrained tests or unconfined compression tests). Knowledge of the effective stresses existing on the slip surface is not a requirement for analysis, since they do not influence the shear strength value used. However, where a soil possesses internal friction (ϕ is not zero) that contributes to the shearing resistance along a slip surface, computational procedures include determining the effective normal stress at points along the assumed slip surface in order to provide values for shear strength (resistance) available from the $\bar{\sigma} \tan \phi$ factor. A procedure for analyzing slopes that include soils possessing internal friction, the *method of slices*, is discussed in later sections.

ILLUSTRATION 15-1   An unsupported slope is planned as indicated by the sketch for an area where a deep homogeneous clay soil deposit exists. What is the factor of safety against sliding for the trial slippage plane indicated?

Area of sliding mass = 2270 sf (by planimeter)
W = (2270 sf × 1 ft)(100 pcf) = 250,000 lb.

Arc length = $\dfrac{85°}{360°} (\pi D) = \dfrac{85°}{360°} (3.14)(150 \text{ ft.}) = 112 \text{ ft.}$

Calculations for Factor of Safety

(i) FS based on ratio resisting to causing moments:

$$FS = \frac{cLr}{Wd} = \frac{(1.1 \text{ ksf})(112 \text{ ft.})(75 \text{ ft.})(1 \text{ ft. width})}{l(250K)(33 \text{ ft})}$$

$$FS = 1.12$$

(ii) FS based on soil shearing strength:

let τ_{req} = shear strength required for slope equilibrium

$$Wd = \tau_{req} \, Lr$$

$$\tau_{req} = \frac{Wd}{Lr} = \frac{250k \times 33 \text{ ft.}}{112k \times 75 \text{ ft.}} = 0.985 \text{ ksf}$$

$$FS = \frac{\tau_{max}}{\tau_{req}} = \frac{c}{\tau_{req}} = \frac{1.1 \text{ ksf}}{0.985 \text{ ksf}} = 1.12$$

---

[2]The area (volume) of earth in an assumed failure mass can be obtained by using a plenimeter if a to-scale drawing of the slope is used. The center of gravity of the failure mass can be determined by using principles of engineering mechanics for locating the centroid of an irregular shape.

The location of the moment axis has a significant effect on the computed factor of safety because it establishes the position and length of the assumed slip surface and the size of the sliding soil mass. It may be necessary to perform the stability computation for a number of assumed slip surfaces to locate the moment axis that identifies the most critical slip circle (the slip surface giving the lowest factor of safety is the one most susceptible to an actual failure; see Fig. 15-11a). A grid pattern can be utilized to systematically change the location of moment centers. By labeling each point on the grid with its calculated factor of safety, contours representing equal values for the factor of safety can be established (similar to the procedures that land surveyors use to establish map contours by obtaining ground surface elevations in the field at points on a grid pattern). By plotting these points and sketching contours on an *as-you-proceed* basis, the locations of the more critical moment centers and slip surfaces become apparent; the procedure helps eliminate unnecessary random attempts to identify the most critical slippage arc (Fig. 15-11b).

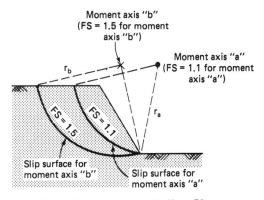

(a) Location of moment axis affects FS

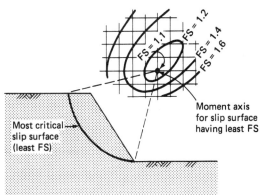

(b) Use of grid to establish FS contours to help locate most critical slip surface

Figure 15-11 Effects of moment axis location on claculated factor of safety and method to establish most critical slip surface.

Slopes of Finite Extent—Soils Possessing Cohesion **449**

Methods of Slices—Fellenius Method Where the slip surface under study for a soil slope passes through soil materials whose shear strength is based upon internal friction and effective stress, the method of slices is recognized as a practical means to account for the expected variation in shearing resistance that develops along the different portions of the assumed slippage arc. The procedure is applicable to slopes in isotropic soils, layered soils, and nonisotropic soils. Credit for the method and its application is given to Wolmar Fellenius as a result of his publications relating to analysis of soil slides [77].

The procedure involves dividing a mass assumed to be involved in a slope slide into vertical slices, as indicated in Figure 15-12a. The width for each slide is arbitrarily selected, and slices do not have to be of equal width. For practical convenience, the section of base arc for each slice should pass across only one soil type, and the slice width should be limited so that the curved base can be approximated by a straight line.

Figure 15-12b, showing the free-body diagram of a representative slice, serves as the basis for arriving at the expression for determining a slope's factor of safety.

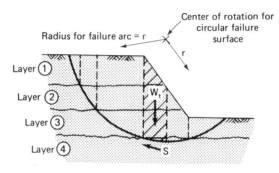

(a) Selection of slices so base arc passes through only one soil type

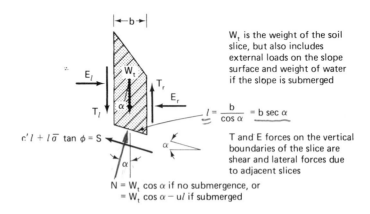

W_t is the weight of the soil slice, but also includes external loads on the slope surface and weight of water if the slope is submerged

$$l = \frac{b}{\cos \alpha} = b \sec \alpha$$

T and E forces on the vertical boundaries of the slice are shear and lateral forces due to adjacent slices

$N = W_t \cos \alpha$ if no submergence, or
$= W_t \cos \alpha - ul$ if submerged

(b) Forces acting on the individual slice

Figure 15-12 Basis of slope stability analysis by method of slices.

The *total* weight of soil in the slice, including the weight of water even when the slope is submerged, plus any external loading acting on the slope surface, comprises the W_t term shown in Figure 15-12. W_t is resolved into components tangent and normal to the base of the slice. With this method, the effects of the T and E forces on the sides of the slice are neglected. The factor of safety is the ratio of moments, with respect to the center for the sliding arc, resisting sliding to those causing sliding. For the slice of Figure 15-12b, the moment due to shearing resistance on the slip surface is

$$M_{\text{resisting}} = (S)(r)$$

where S is the total shearing force and r is the radius of the circular slip arc. The shearing resistance on the base of each slice is

$$S = \tau l = l(c' + \bar{\sigma} \tan \phi)$$

where $\bar{\sigma} = (W \cos \alpha / l)$ if the soil is not submerged; therefore,

$$S = c'l + \left(\frac{W \cos \alpha}{l}\right) l \tan \phi = c'l + W \cos \alpha \tan \phi$$

and the resisting moment is

$$M_{\text{resisting}} = r \left(c'l + W \cos \alpha \tan \phi\right)$$

The normal component of W_t passes through the center of rotation, giving a zero moment. The tangential component of W_t acts to cause sliding, giving

F × d (Lever Arm) = r.

$$M_{\text{causing}} = (W_t \sin \alpha)r$$

The factor of safety for the slope, obtained by summing the resisting and causing moments for all slices, and noting that the radius r appears in both the numerator and denominator, is

$$FS = \frac{r \, \Sigma \, [c'l + W_t \cos \alpha \tan \phi]}{r \, \Sigma \, W_t \sin \alpha}$$

b. Sec α = l.

or

$$FS = \frac{\Sigma \, [c'b \sec \alpha + W_t \cos \alpha \tan \phi]}{\Sigma \, W_t \sin \alpha} \tag{15-7}$$

(4)

If the slope is submerged or if the groundwater table is at an elevation above the toe, pore water pressures u will act on the base of those slices that extend below water. This neutral pressure u reduces the effective stress and hence the shearing resistance acting along the base of such slices. In applications of the Fellenius method, it has been found most practical to account for the neutral pressure effect by using the submerged unit weight for soil located below water when the value of W_t in the numerator of Equation 15-7 is calculated.[3] The W_t term for the de-

[3]Mathematically, the numerator should be $[c'l + (W \cos \alpha - ul) \tan \phi]$. The ul term could be larger than the $W \cos \alpha$ term if the slope is submerged, indicating a negative effective stress and shear, which is unreasonable. Recall from Chapter 8 that pore pressure $u = \gamma_w z_w$, where z_w is the depth below the water surface.

nominator continues to be determined by using the total (wet) weight of soil for each slice.

The analytical procedure for determining the resisting and causing moment is similar with each slice. A tabulated computational procedure, which can include graphical methods to determine the magnitude of a slice's weight components, has been found useful in obtaining values for Equation 15-7 when a slope stability study is performed with "longhand" methods (assisted by a hand calculator). The use of computers for aiding analyses (methods not presented in this text) is becoming widespread. Computer programs conventionally refer to an X–Y coordinate system for defining the geometry of the slope and the failure surface and slices being considered. Most programs include iteration instructions to systematically move the moment centers and establish new trial failure arcs for checking the effect on the factor of safety.

ILLUSTRATION 15-2.   Using the *Fellenius method*, calculate the factor of safety against sliding for the slope and trial failure surface shown in the sketch.

Computing Weight of Slices

$$W_a = \frac{26 \text{ ft} \times 14 \text{ ft}}{2} \times 110 \text{ pcf}$$
$$= 20.1^K/\text{ft.}$$

$$W_b = (26 \text{ ft} \times 27 \text{ ft} \times 110 \text{ pcf})$$
$$+ \left(\frac{27 \text{ ft} \times 19 \text{ ft}}{2} \times 120 \text{ pcf}\right)$$
$$= 108^K/\text{ft.}$$

$$W_c = \left(\frac{26 \text{ ft} + 6 \text{ ft}}{2} \times 26 \text{ ft} \times 110 \text{ pcf}\right)$$
$$+\left(\frac{19 \text{ ft} + 24 \text{ ft}}{2} \times 26 \text{ ft} \times 120 \text{ pcf}\right) =$$
$$= 112.8^K/\text{ft.}$$

$$W_d = \left(\frac{6 \text{ ft} \times 6 \text{ ft}}{2} \times 110 \text{ pcf}\right)$$
$$+ \left(\frac{6 \text{ ft} + 26 \text{ ft}}{2} \times 19 \text{ ft} \times 120 \text{ pcf}\right)$$
$$+ \left(\frac{26 \text{ ft} \times 5 \text{ ft}}{2} \times 120 \text{ pcf}\right)$$
$$= 40.3^K/\text{ft.}$$

slice	Base in Layer	W_t k/ft	tan φ	c' psf	b ft	α°	sec α	cos α	sin α	$c'b$ sec α (k/ft)	W_t cos α tan φ (k/ft)	W_t sin α (k/ft)
a	A	20.1	.325	350	14	62	2.13	.469	.883	10.44	3.06	17.75
b	B	108.0	.675	0	27	33	1.192	.839	.545	0	61.16	58.86
c	B	112.8	.675	0	26	12	1.022	.978	.208	0	74.46	21.54
d	B	40.3	.675	0	26	−12	1.022	.078	−.208	0	26.60	−8.38
									Σ	10.44	165.79	89.77

$$FS = \frac{\Sigma \, [c'b \sec \alpha + W_t \cos \alpha \tan \phi]}{\Sigma \, W_t \sin \alpha} = \frac{10.44 \text{ k/ft} + 165.79 \text{ k/ft}}{89.77 \text{ k/ft}} = 1.96$$

Bishop Analysis   A method of analysis presented by A. W. Bishop [26] utilizes the method of slices and considers forces to be acting on each slice, as shown in Figure 15-13. The requirements of equilibrium are applied to the slices comprising the slope, with the factor of safety against a slope failure then being defined as the ratio of the maximum shear strength possessed by soil on the trial slippage plane ($\tau_{\text{available}}$) to that shearing resistance necessary for equilibrium ($\tau_{\text{mobilized}}$), or

$$FS = \frac{\tau_{\text{available}}}{\tau_{\text{mobilized}}}$$

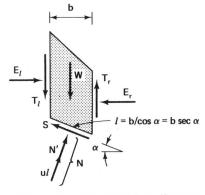

W = Total weight of soil in slice, plus surcharge if present
N = N' + ul
where N = total normal force
 N' = effective normal force
 ul = force due to pore water pressure
 u = pore water pressure acting on base
  of slice equal to $\gamma_w z_w$, where z_w
  is the depth below the water surface

Figure 15-13 Representative slope slice with forces assumed in Bishop method of analysis.

Slopes of Finite Extent—Soils Possessing Cohesion

If the shear strength of the soil is

$$\tau_{available} = c' + (\sigma - u) \tan \phi = c' + \bar{\sigma} \tan \phi$$

the shearing resistance mobilized (i.e., required) for equilibrium is then

$$\tau_{mobilized} = \frac{1}{(FS)} [c' + (\bar{\sigma} - u) \tan \phi]$$

Equation 15-8 provides the factor of safety for a trial or assumed failure arc and is obtained by summing slice forces in the *vertical* direction. The development of this equation is shown in the boxed insert below. The final form of the equation is the result of considering that the total influence of tangential forces on the sides of slices is small enough to be neglected without having great effect (i.e., the influence of $\Sigma [T_l - T_r]$ is small). The procedure for slope stability analysis that includes incorporating the simplifying assumption is referred to as the *simplified Bishop method*:

$$FS = \frac{\Sigma \dfrac{1}{m_a} [c'b + (W - ub) \tan \phi]}{\Sigma W \sin \alpha} \qquad \begin{array}{l} \text{Simplified} \\ \text{Bishop method (15-8)} \end{array}$$

The m_a factor represents a grouping of terms as defined in the Bishop development (boxed insert). Values of m_a can be obtained from Figure 15-14.

Comparisons between the simplified method and a rigorous solution that includes the effects of T_l and T_r indicate that the simplified method gives results that are slightly conservative (i.e., the simplified Bishop gives a lower factor of safety).

With the Bishop method, the factor of safety appears on both sides of the

Figure 15-14 Values of m_a for Bishop equation.

Stability of Unsupported Slopes   Chap. 15

equation to evaluate the stability of a trial failure mass. The procedure for solution involves *assuming* a value for the factor of safety term in the right side of the equation, using Figure 15-14 to expedite the computations. When the proper factor of safety has been used for the trial, the value for the left side of the equation will equal the value assumed for the right side. Practically, precise agreement is not required to obtain a factor of safety value considered valid for the assumed slip surface. The result is for a particular trial failure mass, however, and, as indicated previously, a series of trials is usually required to identify the slope section and slippage plane most susceptible to actual failure or having the lowest factor of safety.

A limitation to the Bishop method is that it provides unrealistically high factors of safety when the negative angle alpha ($-\alpha$) for the lower slope area slices approaches a value of about 30°. This condition can develop where an assumed center of rotation is above the vicinity of the slope's crest or where deep failure circles are being investigated.

Comparisons between the simplified Bishop and Fellenius methods indicate that, generally, the Bishop factor of safety will usually be slightly greater than that obtained with the Fellenius method. (The Fellenius method gives the smaller, more conservative value.) However, whereas the Bishop method provides overly high and inaccurate factors of safety when the negative angle alpha ($-\alpha$) is large, the Fellenius method tends to provide overly conservative (low) values.

MATHEMATICAL DEVELOPMENT OF THE BISHOP EQUATION FOR SLOPE STABILITY

For equilibrium, moments about center of rotation which act to cause sliding and act to resist sliding must balance:

$$\Sigma\, Wx = \Sigma\, Sr = \Sigma\, \tau/r$$

Letting

$$FS = \frac{\tau_{available}}{\tau_{mobilized}},$$

get

$$\Sigma\, Wx = \Sigma\, \frac{1}{(FS)}\left[c' + \left(\frac{N}{l} - u\right)\tan\phi\right](rl)$$

$$FS = \frac{\Sigma\, r}{\Sigma\, Wx}[c'l + (N - ul)\tan\phi]$$

since

$$x = r\sin\alpha$$

$$FS = \frac{\Sigma\,[c'l + N'\tan\phi]}{\Sigma\, W\sin\alpha} \quad Ⓐ$$

Summing vertical forces acting on the slice, obtain:

$$W = N'\cos\alpha + ul\cos\alpha + S\sin\alpha + (T_r - T_l)$$

Slopes of Finite Extent—Soils Possessing Cohesion

since $S = \tau_l$

$$W = N' \cos\alpha + ul\cos\alpha + (T_r - T_l) + \frac{1}{(FS)}\left[c' + \left(\frac{N}{l} - u\right)\tan\phi\right]/\sin\alpha$$

$$W = N' \cos\alpha + ul\cos\alpha + (T_r - T_l) + \frac{C'/\sin\alpha}{(FS)} + (N - ul)\frac{\tan\phi\sin\alpha}{(FS)}$$

$$W = N' \cos\alpha - ul\cos\alpha + (T_r - T_l) + \frac{c'/\sin\alpha}{(FS)} + N'\frac{\tan\phi\sin\alpha}{(FS)}$$

$$W - ul\cos\alpha + \frac{c'/\sin\alpha}{(FS)} - (T_r - T_l) = N'\left[\cos\alpha + \frac{\tan\phi\sin\alpha}{(FS)}\right]$$

since $b = l \cos\alpha$

$$N' = \frac{W - ub - \dfrac{c'l\sin\alpha}{(FS)} - (T_r - T_l)}{\cos\alpha + \left(\dfrac{\tan\phi\sin\alpha}{(FS)}\right)}$$

Substituting N' into Eq. Ⓐ from above, obtain

$$FS = \frac{\Sigma\left\{c'l + \tan\phi\left[\dfrac{W - ub - \dfrac{c'l}{(FS)}\sin\alpha - (T_r - T_l)}{\cos\alpha + \dfrac{\tan\phi\sin\alpha}{(FS)}}\right]\right\}}{\Sigma W \sin\alpha}$$

If the effect of $\Sigma(T_r - T_l)$ is assumed to be small and is neglected, and letting

$$m_a = \cos\alpha + \frac{\tan\phi\sin\alpha}{(FS)} = \left(1 + \frac{\tan\phi\tan\alpha}{(FS)}\right)\cos\alpha, \text{ obtain}$$

$$FS = \frac{\Sigma\left\{c'b\sec\alpha + \left[\dfrac{(W - ub)\tan\phi - \dfrac{c'b}{(FS)}\tan\phi\tan\alpha}{m_a}\right]\right\}}{\Sigma W \sin\alpha}$$

$$FS = \frac{\Sigma\dfrac{1}{m_a}\left\{(c'b\sec\alpha)\left(\cos\alpha + \dfrac{\tan\phi\sin\alpha}{(FS)}\right) - \dfrac{c'b}{(FS)}\tan\phi\tan\alpha + (W - ub)\tan\phi\right\}}{\Sigma W \sin\alpha}$$

$$FS = \frac{\Sigma \dfrac{1}{m_a}\left\{c'b \sec \alpha \cos \alpha + \dfrac{c'b \sec \alpha \tan \phi \sin \alpha}{(FS)} - \dfrac{c'b \tan \phi \tan \alpha}{(FS)} + (W - ub) \tan \phi\right\}}{\Sigma \, W \sin \alpha}$$

Since $\sec \alpha = \dfrac{1}{\cos} \alpha$

$$FS = \frac{\Sigma \dfrac{1}{m_a}\left\{c'b\left[\dfrac{\cos \alpha}{\cos \alpha} + \left(\dfrac{\tan \phi}{FS}\right)\left(\dfrac{\sin \alpha}{\cos \alpha}\right) - \dfrac{\tan \phi \tan \alpha}{(FS)}\right] + (W - ub) \tan \phi\right\}}{\Sigma \, W \sin \alpha}$$

and noting $\dfrac{\sin \alpha}{\cos \alpha} = \tan \alpha$, obtain

$$FS = \frac{\Sigma \dfrac{1}{m_a}\left\{c'b + (W - ub) \tan \phi\right\}}{\Sigma \, W \sin \alpha} \tag{15-8}$$

[*End of derivation*]

ILLUSTRATION 15-3. For the soil slope and trial failure surface of Illustration 15-2, calculate the factor of safety against sliding using the *simplified Bishop method*. The factor of safety by the Bishop method is expected to be greater than indicated by the Fellenius method. Preliminary calculations indicate a value of about 2. If a factor of safety equal to 2 is assumed

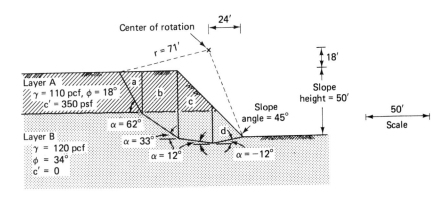

Slopes of Finite Extent—Soils Possessing Cohesion

Slice	Base in Layer	W (k/ft)	$\tan \phi$	c' (psf)	b (ft)	$\alpha°$	$\sin \alpha$	ub (k/ft)	m_a if FS = 2	$\frac{1}{m_a}[c'b + (W - ub)\tan\phi]$ (k/ft)	$W \sin \alpha$ (k/ft)
a	A	20.1	.325	350	14	62	.883	0	0.82	$(^1/_{0.82})(4.6 + 6.53) = 13.93$	17.75
b	B	108.0	.675	0	27	33	.545	0	1.03	$(^1/_{1.03})(72.9) = 70.78$	58.86
c	B	112.8	.675	0	26	12	.208	0	1.03	$(^1/_{1.03})(76.14) = 73.92$	21.54
d	B	40.3	.675	0	26	−12	−.208	0	0.93	$(^1/_{0.93})(27.20) = 29.20$	−8.38
									Σ	187.83	89.77

Assuming a factor of safety equal to 2,

for Layer A, $\dfrac{\tan \phi}{FS} = \dfrac{0.325}{2} = 0.16$

for Layer B, $\dfrac{\tan \phi}{FS} = \dfrac{0.675}{2} = 0.34$

for Layer A, $\qquad \dfrac{\tan \phi}{FS} = \dfrac{0.325}{2} = 0.16$

for Layer B, $\qquad \dfrac{\tan \phi}{FS} = \dfrac{0.675}{2} = 0.34$

$$FS = \frac{\sum \dfrac{1}{m_a}[c'b + (W - ub)\tan \phi]}{\sum W \sin \alpha} = \frac{187.83 \text{ k/ft}}{89.77 \text{ k/ft}} = 2.09$$

The assumed factor of safety is close to the calculated value; therefore, the calculation is considered adequate. (Were the *FS* close to unity, additional calculations would be performed to improve the accuracy of the answer.) Actual *FS* for this trial slip surface is about 2.05.

Other Methods of Circular Arc Analysis   A number of investigators have developed analytical procedures for slope analysis that are similar in basic approach to the Bishop method but differ in the handling of interslice forces. Two methods that are widely referred to are from the work of Spencer [237] and Morganstern-Price [175]. Spencer's analysis assumes that the forces on the sides of the slices are parallel (Fig. 15-16a). The Morganstern-Price analysis imposes normal and shear forces on the slice sides and also includes water pressure effects (Fig. 15-15b). Both methods satisfy the requirements of equilibrium in regard to forces and moments that act on a slice. (Recall that the Bishop method required equilibrium of slice forces for only the vertical direction.) Slope stability evaluations utilizing the mathematically rigorous Spencer and Morganstern-Price methods are complex because of the form of their equations and the application procedure. Practically, computer programming is required for solution. However, slope stability charts that significantly simplify the analytical procedure have been developed from the computer-required methods; such charts are presented in a later section of the chapter.

Under comparison, the methods that handle the slice side forces differently do not differ greatly in the indicated factor of safety. Such results imply that slope stability evaluations are not sensitive to the manner in which the slice forces are considered to be acting.

Though means of analysis such as the Fellenius and simplified Bishop methods are not considered to provide the precision of the rigorous methods, the use of such hand-calculation methods retains a practical importance for performing independent checks on results from complex programs, for use when a computer is not available, and for preliminary evaluations or routine checks to determine if a slope requires greater study.

Slopes of Finite Extent—Soils Possessing Cohesion

(a) Spencer assumption   (b) Morganstern-Price assumption

Figure 15-15 Description of forces acting on the free-body of a slope slice.

Noncircular Slip Surfaces   In areas where the topography varies (the slope is not uniform or well defined) or where the subsurface is stratified or otherwise nonisotropic, the soil zone most susceptible to a sliding failure may not be properly represented by a circular arc (Fig. 15-16a). An analytical procedure that permits flexibility in locating the plane of slippage is required. The Spencer and the Morganstern-Price methods referred to for circular arc analysis also have application for the noncircular slip surface but require solution by computer. A generalized method for slice analysis of noncircular slip surfaces advanced by Janbu [16, 18] is for computer solution, but the method is also adaptable to hand-calculation solutions when a simplified procedure (which still provides results of a practical accuracy) is utilized.

    The Janbu method assumes that forces acting on each slice will be as indicated in Figure 15-16b. By applying the requirements of moment equilibrium and force equilibrium in the horizontal and vertical directions to each slice, and imposing the necessity for equilibrium in the horizontal direction to the entire assumed failure mass, an expression for the slopes factor of safety is written

$$FS = \frac{\Sigma \left[b\tau \sec^2 \alpha \right]}{\Sigma \left[W + (T_l - T_r) \right] \tan \alpha} \tag{15-9a}$$

$$\text{where } \tau = \frac{\left[c' + \left\{ \dfrac{W + (T_l - T_r)}{b} - u \right\} \tan \phi \right]}{\left(1 + \dfrac{\tan \alpha \, \tan \phi}{(FS)} \right)}$$

This factor of safety is in reference to the shear strength of the soil along the assumed slippage plane. When the term m_a is included (introduced for the Bishop

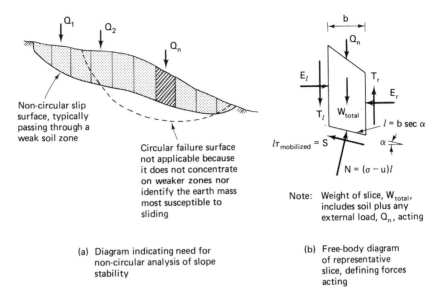

(a) Diagram indicating need for
non-circular analysis of slope
stability

(b) Free-body diagram
of representative
slice, defining forces
acting

Figure 15-16 Noncircular slippage plane for slope stability analysis, Janbu method.

analysis, Fig. 15-14), the expression for determining the factor of safety for a slope
mass under study becomes

$$FS = \frac{\Sigma \, [c'b + \{W + (T_l - T_r) - ub\} \tan \phi] \, \dfrac{1}{(\cos \alpha)(m_a)}}{\Sigma \, [W + (T_l - T_r)] \tan \alpha} \qquad (15\text{-}9b)$$

The factor of safety term appears in both sides of Equation 15-9. Trial values are
selected, and, as with the Bishop method, the factor of safety has been properly
determined when both sides of the equation are in practical agreement. For solution, Equation 15-9 requires values for the tangential forces, T_l and T_r, which
also are determined by a trial-and-error process. All other terms of the expression
can be obtained from the geometry of each slice and the involved soil properties.
However, the simplified method for the Janbu analysis initially neglects the interslice forces and then modifies the calculated factor of safety for their effect by
applying an empirically determined correction factor. The final form of the equation
with the modification is

$$FS = \frac{f_0 \, \Sigma \, [c'b + (W - ub) \tan \phi] \, \dfrac{1}{(\cos \alpha)(m_a)}}{\Sigma \, (W \tan \alpha)} \qquad (15\text{-}10)$$

where the correction factor f_0 is obtained from Figure 15-17. (See Illus. 15-4).

ILLUSTRATION 15-4.   For the soil slope and trial failure surface shown, calculate
the factor of safety, using the simplified Janbu method. Preliminary calculations
indicate a factor of safety of about 1.5; use $FS = 1.4$ for first trial.

Slopes of Finite Extent—Soils Possessing Cohesion   **461**

Slice	b (m)	c' kN/m²	α deg	$\tan \alpha$	$\cos \alpha$	$\tan \phi$	u kN/m²	W kN/m	m_a	$[c'b + (W - ub)\tan\phi]\dfrac{1}{\cos\alpha\, m_a}$ (kN/m)	$W\tan\alpha$ (kN/m)
a	3.0	12	53	1.327	.602	.325	0	108	0.80	$[(12 \times 3) + (108)(.325)]\dfrac{1}{(.602 \times 0.80)} = 152$	143
b	11.5	12	24	.445	.914	.325	0	1139	1.01	$[(11.5 \times 12) + (1139 \times .325)]\dfrac{1}{(.914 \times 1.01)} = 551$	507
c	8.5	12	18	.325	.951	.325	0	957	1.02	$[(8.5 \times 12) + (957 \times .325)]\dfrac{1}{(.951 \times 1.02)} = 414$	366
d	9.5	14.4	12	.213	.978	.364	7.35	813	1.03	$(9.5 \times 14.4) + (813 - 7.35 \times 9.5)(.364)]\dfrac{1}{(.978 \times 1.03)} = 404$	191
e	3.5	14.4	−13	−.231	.974	.364	9.8	126	0.92	$[(3.5 \times 14.4) + (126 - 9.8 \times 3.5)(.364)]\dfrac{1}{(.974 \times .92)} = 94$	−29
										Σ 1615	1178

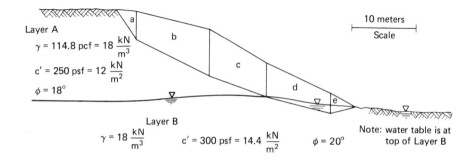

Layer A
$\gamma = 114.8 \text{ pcf} = 18 \frac{kN}{m^3}$

$c' = 250 \text{ psf} = 12 \frac{kN}{m^2}$

$\phi = 18°$

Layer B
$\gamma = 18 \frac{kN}{m^3}$ $c' = 300 \text{ psf} = 14.4 \frac{kN}{m^2}$ $\phi = 20°$

10 meters Scale

Note: water table is at top of Layer B

Computing Weight of Slices

$b = 3 \text{ m}$

(a) $\alpha = 53°$ 4 m

$W_a = \left(\frac{3 \text{ m} \times 4 \text{ m}}{2} \times 18 \frac{kN}{m^3} \right)$

$= 108 \text{ kN/m}$

$b = 11.5 \text{ m}$ 4 m

(b) $\alpha = 24°$ 7 m

$W_b = \left(11.5 \text{ m} \times 5.5 \text{ m} \times 18 \frac{kN}{m^3} \right)$

$= 1139 \text{ kN/m}$

$b = 8.5 \text{ m}$ 7 m   10 m

(c) $\alpha = 18°$ 5.5 m

$W_c = \left(8.5 \text{ m} \times 6.25 \text{ m} \times 18 \frac{kN}{m^3} \right)$

$= 957 \text{ kN/m}$

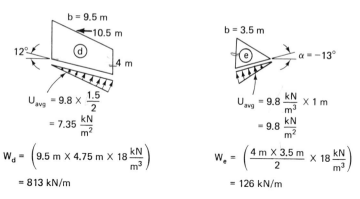

$b = 9.5 \text{ m}$ ←10.5 m

12°   (d)   4 m

$U_{avg} = 9.8 \times \frac{1.5}{2}$

$= 7.35 \frac{kN}{m^2}$

$W_d = \left(9.5 \text{ m} \times 4.75 \text{ m} \times 18 \frac{kN}{m^3} \right)$

$= 813 \text{ kN/m}$

$b = 3.5 \text{ m}$

(e) $\alpha = -13°$

$U_{avg} = 9.8 \frac{kN}{m^3} \times 1 \text{ m}$

$= 9.8 \frac{kN}{m^2}$

$W_e = \left(\frac{4 \text{ m} \times 3.5 \text{ m}}{2} \times 18 \frac{kN}{m^3} \right)$

$= 126 \text{ kN/m}$

Note: For FS = 1.4,
Layer 1, $\frac{\tan \phi}{(FS)} = 0.23$
Layer 2, $\frac{\tan \phi}{(FS)} = 0.26$

For $d/L = {}^4\!/_{40} = 0.1$, get $f_0 = 1.04$

Therefore, $FS = f_0 \left(\frac{1615 \text{ kN/m}}{1178 \text{ kN/m}} \right)$

$= 1.04(1.37) = 1.42 \pm$ (ok), compares with assumed FS.

Slopes of Finite Extent—Soils Possessing Cohesion

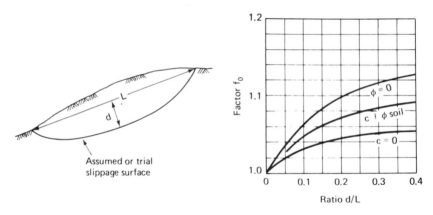

Figure 15-17 Correction factor, f_o as a function of d/L ratio.

Effect of Tension Cracks   Tension cracks developing along the crest or face of a slope (a condition most often anticipated where cohesive soils exist) can influence the slope's stability. In an analysis, zero soil shearing resistance is assigned to the section of slippage plane affected by tension cracks. If the tension crack(s) could fill with water, a hydrostatic pressure distribution is assumed to exist in the crack, and this pressure contributes to those forces and moments acting to cause slope movement. Frequently, however, tension cracks have minor influence on a slope's computed factor of safety, but these cracks may provide the opportunity for water to reach otherwise buried earth layers whose strength may be weakened by such exposure, an effect requiring consideration in the slope analysis.

Sliding Block Analysis   Natural earth slopes consisting of stratified materials and earthern embankment structures constructed on stratified soil foundations can experience failure due to sliding along one or more of the weaker layers (Fig. 15-18). Failures of this type often occur when changed conditions in an area cause susceptible layers to become exposed to, or saturated by, water. Exposure to moisture can cause physical breakdown and weakening of some earth materials, such as fine-grained sedimentary deposits, and saturation may cause a stratum's shear strength to be reduced because of increased pore water pressures.

Where the potential for the occurrence of a block slide is under study, the factor of safety with regard to the shear strength of the soil on the assumed sliding plane is, for the conditions described in Figure 15-18a, with no pore pressure effects on the block,

$$FS = \frac{cL + W \cos \alpha \tan \phi}{W \sin \alpha + E} \tag{15-11}$$

where E can be approximated as $0.25 \, \gamma_{soil} z^2$ for cohesionless soil and $0.5 \, \gamma_{soil} z^2$ for cohesive soil (refer to Fig. 15-18b).

If the formation of a tension crack along the top of the slope permits the development of water pressures in the crack and the slippage zone, as described by Figure 15-18b, the factor of safety is expressed as

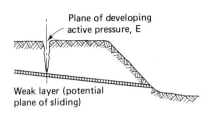

Plane of developing active pressure, E

Weak layer (potential plane of sliding)

E = Lateral force from zone of soil against vertical plane forming end of sliding block

FBD of sliding block

(a) Contribution to failure along weak plane by active pressure zone at top of sliding block

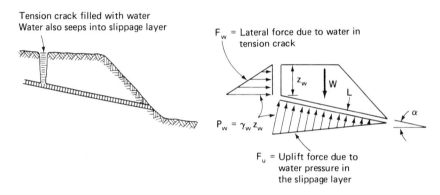

Tension crack filled with water
Water also seeps into slippage layer

F_w = Lateral force due to water in tension crack

$P_w = \gamma_w z_w$

F_u = Uplift force due to water pressure in the slippage layer

(b) Failure along a weak plane where water pressure develops in the tension crack and slippage layer

Figure 15-18 Block failure for a soil slope.

$$FS = \frac{cL + [W \cos \alpha - F_u - E_w \sin \alpha] \tan \phi}{W \sin \alpha + F_w \cos \alpha} \qquad (15\text{-}12)$$

where F_w is the force due to water pressures in the tension crack, equal to 0.5 $\gamma_{\text{water}} z^2_{\text{water}}$, and $F_u = 0.5 \; \gamma_{\text{water}} z_{\text{water}} L$.

Sections of soil embankments have been known to fail by translation along a weak foundation zone or layer, the force responsible for movement resulting from lateral soil pressures developed within the embankment itself. In the case of earth dams, the zone of slippage may develop only after the dam has impounded water for a period, with seepage through the eventual slippage zone being responsible for weakening to the extent that a failure can occur. For the conditions shown in Figure 15-19, the factor of safety against block translation is evaluated from

$$FS = \frac{S}{E_l - E_r + P_{w_1} - P_{w_2}} \qquad (15\text{-}13)$$

Slopes of Finite Extent—Soils Possessing Cohesion

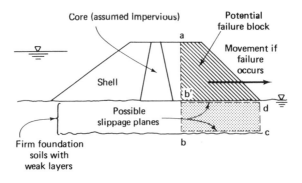

Core (assumed impervious)

Potential failure block

a

Movement if failure occurs

Shell

b'

Possible slippage planes

d

c

b

Firm foundation soils with weak layers

(a) Structure and possible sliding blocks

W = weight of soil in failure block plus any loading on slope
E = earth force from lateral soil pressure

Potential failure block

a

E_l

W

L

b'

d

S

U = total uplift

Uplift pressure diagram

(b) Forces acting where failure block slides on embankment base

a

E_l

W

b'

b

P_{w1}

d

L

c

E_r

P_{w2}

U = total uplift

(c) Forces acting where failure block slides on weak foundation layer

Figure 15-19 Description of conditions for sliding block analysis of embankments.

where $S = cL + (W - U) \tan \phi$ on sliding plane b'-d or b-c.

$E_l \cong$ force of active earth pressure on plane a-b' or a-b.

$E_r \cong$ force of passive earth pressure on plane c-d.

$P_{w1.2} \cong$ force of lateral water pressure on plane b'-b, c-d.

$U =$ uplift force on plane b'-d or b-c.

With this method, the uplift and lateral water pressure determinations are evaluated from flow nets or other seepage studies.

Upstream zones as well as downstream zones should be studied for stability. Though the effect of water on the upstream embankment increases the weight W, and the lateral pressures of the impounded water oppose block translation, the uplift force

U is considerably greater for upstream zones. As with other categories of sliding failures, determining the size and location of the section most susceptible to movement is typically a trial-and-error procedure, because the most critical zone is not always obvious.

COMPUTATIONAL AIDS—SLOPE STABILITY CHARTS

Taylor Charts   Slope stability charts to simplify the computational procedure involved in studying slopes comprised of isotropic cohesive or mixed soils have been developed by a number of investigators. The earliest charts to receive widespread usage are those from the work of Taylor (246, 247), whose results are based upon application of the friction-circle method of analysis.[4] This procedure for analysis follows convention in that it assumes that the resistance to a circular mass's tendency to slide is developed by the cohesion and internal friction of the soil on the slippage plane. In an incremental slices analysis of a slope (Fig. 15-20), the reaction on the slice base results from resolution of the normal (i.e., intergranular) force and the frictional shearing force. At slippage, this resultant reaction acts at an angle ϕ to the normal. The extended line of action for the resultant is a tangent to the friction-circle located at the center of rotation for the sliding mass, see Figure 15-20: Properties of the friction circle are defined in that figure. At the limit of the equilibrium condition for the slice, the soil cohesion c, the resultant R (which includes the effect of internal friction ϕ), and the weight of the soil W are in balance (Fig. 15-20c). This requirement for equilibrium is extended to an entire trial failure

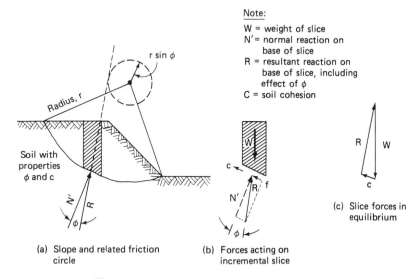

Note:
W = weight of slice
N' = normal reaction on base of slice
R = resultant reaction on base of slice, including effect of ϕ
C = soil cohesion

(a) Slope and related friction circle

(b) Forces acting on incremental slice

(c) Slice forces in equilibrium

Figure 15-20   Basis for the friction circle analysis.

[4]Wolmar Fellenius' 1936 paper, "Calculation of the Stability of Earth Dams" (2nd Congress on Large Dams, Washington, D.C.) also included charted curves relating slope stability to slope geometry and soil properties, Ref. 77.

mass and relates total weight, total cohesion, and total friction-related reactive force. Values for these factors that will provide an equilibrium condition reflect the geometry of the assumed failure mass and the properties of the involved soil. In his work, Taylor introduced a slope stability number N_s to group factors that affect the safe inclination of a soil's slope,

$$N_s = \frac{c}{\gamma H_{\max}} = \frac{c}{\gamma H_{\text{actual}}(FS)} \tag{15-14}$$

where N_s = slope stability number (dimensionless).
$\quad\quad c$ = soil's cohesion (psf, kN/m^2).
$\quad\quad \gamma$ = soil unit weight (pcf, kN/m^3).
$\quad\quad H$ = slope height (ft, m).

Where a slope is at limit equilibrium (sliding is impending), a unique relationship exists between its height and inclination and the soil properties (γ, c, ϕ). This relationship provides the curves of Figure 15-21a and b. These curves are for slopes where the soils are uniform with depth and isotropic. It is important to recognize that natural deposits of cohesive soils do not tend to possess constant strength and density through large vertical distances; under conditions giving normally consolidated and overconsolidated deposits, the strength and density of such soils typically increase with depth. However, constructed embankments often are homogeneous, whereas natural deposits possessing homogenity may exist or may be assumed in practical applications if limited heights are considered.

The Taylor curves are based upon a *total stress analysis*,[5] and the related soil strength values are obtained from undrained shear tests. These charts, therefore, are applicable for the end-of-construction and short-term stability category of analysis, where slope drainage and resulting changes in pore pressures and intergranular stresses do not have time to occur. In applications, the curves are often utilized to determine the safe inclination for an identified slope height, or the maximum height allowable when a particular inclination is desired. The H term in Equation 15-14 can be used to determine the maximum safe height based upon slope inclination and soil properties, which then can be compared to an actually existing or planned height. When the actual height is less than the maximum, the factor of safety is

$$FS = \frac{H_{\max}}{H_{\text{actual}}} \tag{15-15a}$$

This factor of safety is actually a value based upon the ratio of maximum cohesion possessed by the soil ($c_{\max}$) to the cohesion required for stability (c_{reqd}):

$$FS = \frac{c_{\max}}{c_{\text{reqd}}} \tag{15-15b}$$

For slopes composed of ϕ plus c soils, the slope's factor of safety in regard to the soil's internal friction is one when a test-determined value of ϕ is used to enter the stability chart. Where it is desired to have an equal factor of safety for both cohesion

---

[5]Total stress equals effective stress plus neutral stress due to pore water pressure.

Figure 15-21 Taylor slope stability curves for total stress analysis [246, 247].

(a) For φ = 0° soils

(b) For c plus φ soils

and internal friction, the actual values of c and ϕ are both divided by the factor of safety, and the charts are then entered with these new values.

ILLUSTRATION 15-5. A slope 40 ft (12 m) high has a face inclination of 50°. Undrained shear strength tests on the soil indicate that the cohesion is 500 psf (24 kN/m²) and ϕ is 15°. The unit weight is 110 pcf (17.3 kN/m³). What is the factor of safety (in regard to cohesion only)?

For $i = 50°$, $\phi = 15°$, get $N_s = 0.095$ (Fig. 15-21b):

$$FS = \frac{c}{\gamma H_{act} N_s} = \frac{500 \text{ psf}}{(110 \text{pcf})(40 \text{ ft})(0.095)} = 1.2$$

The critical height (maximum height) is

$$H_{max} = (FS)H_{act} = (1.2)(40 \text{ ft}) = 48 \text{ ft} \cong 15 \text{ m}$$

or, since

$$N_s = c/\gamma H_{max},$$

$$H_{max} = \frac{c}{\gamma N_\gamma} = \frac{500 \text{ psf}}{(110 \text{ pcf}) (0.095)} = 48 \text{ ft}$$

ILLUSTRATION 15-6. What inclination is required where a slope 10 m high is to be constructed and must possess a factor of safety of 1.25 (this factor of safety is to apply to both c and ϕ)? The soil properties are

$$\gamma = 16.5 \text{ kN/m}^3, \qquad c = 16.8 \text{ kN/m}^2, \qquad \phi = 10°$$

$$N_s = \frac{c}{\gamma H_{act}(FS)} = \frac{16.8 \text{ kN/m}^2}{(16.5 \text{ kN/m}^3)(10 \text{ m})(1.25)} = 0.082$$

and $\qquad \phi_{chart} = \dfrac{\phi}{(FS)} = \dfrac{10°}{1.25} = 8°$

For $N_s = 0.082$, $\phi = 8°$, obtain slope angle $i \cong 28°$ (Fig. 15-21b).

ILLUSTRATION 15-7. What is the factor of safety for a 45° slope 40 ft high in a clay soil ($\phi = 0°$, $c = 1000$ psf, $\gamma = 110$ pcf) where a rock stratum exists 40 ft beneath the toe elevation?

$$D = \frac{DH}{H} = \frac{(40 + 40) \text{ ft}}{40 \text{ ft}} = 2$$

For $i = 45°$, $D = 2$, $\phi = 0°$, obtain $N_s = 0.178$ (Fig. 15-21a).

$$FS = \frac{c}{N_s \gamma H_{act}} = \frac{1000 \text{ psf}}{(0.178)(110 \text{ pcf})(40 \text{ ft})} = 1.28$$

Also note, $nH \cong (1.6)(40 \text{ ft}) \cong 64 \text{ ft}$

Figure 15-21a and b can also be used to study submerged slopes and slopes subject to sudden drawdown. For evaluating the stability of a *submerged slope*, the only modification to procedures previously outlined is that the submerged soil unit weight be used in determining the value of N_s. The *sudden drawdown* case occurs where a submerged embankment (e.g., a dam) has a rapid drop in the level of the impounded water. This drawdown condition is often the most critical for an embankment, for seepage forces resulting when water drains out of an embankment are additive to the ever-present gravity forces acting to cause slope sliding.[6] With the sudden drawdown case, a modified value of ϕ, indicated as ϕ_{dd}, is necessary, but other factors remain as defined earlier. For practical purposes, the modified ϕ is obtained from

$$\phi_{dd}^\circ = \frac{\gamma_{sub}}{\gamma_{total}} (\phi^\circ) \tag{15-16}$$

where γ_{sub} = submerged soil unit weight.
γ_{total} = total or wet soil unit weight.

ILLUSTRATION 15-8. Determine the factor of safety (in regard to cohesion only) for a submerged embankment 100 ft high (30.5 m) whose upstream face has an inclination of 30°. The soil properties are γ_{total} = 120 pcf (18.85 kN/m³), c = 700 psf (37.6 kN/m²), ϕ = 10°.
For i = 30°, ϕ = 10°, obtain N_s = 0.075 (Fig. 15-21a).

$$FS = \frac{c}{N_s \gamma_{sub} H_{act}} = \frac{700 \text{ psf}}{(0.075)(\frac{120}{2} \text{ pcf})(100 \text{ ft})} = 1.56$$

What is the factor of safety if the embankment experiences the effects of a sudden drawdown?

$$\phi_{dd} = \frac{\gamma_{sub}}{\gamma_{total}} (\phi) = \frac{60 \text{ pcf}}{120 \text{ pcf}} (10°) \cong 5°$$

For i = 30°, ϕ = 5°, obtain N_s = 0.11.

$$FS = \frac{c}{N_s \gamma H_{act}} = \frac{700 \text{ psf}}{(0.11)(120 \text{ pcf})(100 \text{ ft})} = 0.53 \text{ (failure)}$$

Taylor's analysis also includes a procedure to locate the slope's most critical failure circle, information that is of practical importance for identifying the horizontal area and vertical zone involved with and affected by a side. Figure 15-22 provides data necessary to locate the critical circle where relatively steep slopes are under study (where the failure arc passes through the toe of the slope). Data for the flatter slopes, where the critical circle passes through the base and whose location is affected by hard substrata, are not developed. However, for soils having zero internal friction (ϕ = 0), the center of the critical circle is located above the midpoint of the slope.

[6]Also see further discussion of drawdown in section on Morganstern's chart, page 480.

Angle of Internal Friction	SLOPE INCLINATION, $i°$									
	$i = 90°$		$i = 75°$		$i = 60°$		$i = 45°$		$i = 30°$	
$\phi°$	$\alpha°$	$\theta°$	$\alpha°$	$\theta°$	$\alpha°$	$\theta°$	$\alpha°$	$\theta°$	$\alpha°$	$\theta°$
0	47.6	30.2	41.8	51.8	35.3	70.8	*	*	*	*
5	50	28	45	50	38.5	69	31.2	84.2	*	*
10	53	27	48	47	41	66	34	79.4	25	88
15	56	26	50	46	44	63	36.1	74.4	27	78
20	58	24	53	44	46.5	60.4	38	69	28	61
25	60	22	56	44	50	60	40	62	29	50

*Critical circle is a base circle, not a toe circle

Figure 15-22 Data for locating center of critical slip circle for toe failures (Taylor analysis, $0 = 0$ case [246]).

Cousins's Charts

For the evaluation of long-term stability, slope analyses must be performed in terms of effective stresses and pore water pressures acting on the slippage plane. Soil properties for such analysis (c' and ϕ) are obtained from drained shear tests. A number of investigators have produced stability charts from effective stress studies of slopes exposed to a variety of conditions. Charts developed by Cousins Ref. 49, incorporating some work of earlier investigators, have application to a wide range of practical conditions and deal in easily calculated parameters.

Effective stress analysis and related stability charts consider pore pressure and intergranular forces separately. It has been found convenient to handle the influence of pore pressures in terms of a pore pressure ratio, r_u, which is defined as the ratio of pore water pressure to total soil overburden pressure at a particular depth (typically the slippage plane) in the soil mass (see Fig. 15-23).

$$r_u = \frac{u}{\sigma_v} = \frac{\gamma_w h}{\gamma_{soil} z}$$

Cousins's charts (Fig. 15-24a through o) are based upon the friction circle method of analysis discussed earlier in regard to the Taylor charts. The Cousins stability number is defined as

$$N_s = \frac{\gamma H_{act}(FS)}{c'} \tag{15-17}$$

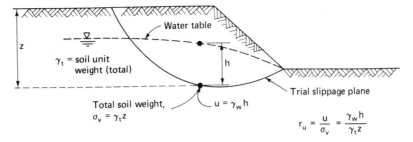

Figure 15-23 Definition of terms for calculating pore pressure ratio, r_u.

which is the reciprocal of the Taylor ratio. Cousins also uses the parameter $\lambda_{c\phi}$ to group terms relating to soil properties and slope height, where

$$\lambda_{c\phi} = \frac{\gamma H \tan \phi}{c'} \tag{15-18}$$

A depth factor, D, shown on the charts and applicable to the study of base type failures, is

$$D = \frac{\text{Vertical distance from top of slope to lowest point on slippage arc, } V}{\text{Height of slope, } H}$$

When the slope is subject to the effects of seepage, the pore pressures and pore pressure ratios will vary along the slippage plane. A weighted average for r_u must be applied when the charts are used. Such a determination involves obtaining the pattern of flow through the slope, then using that information to develop contours of the pore pressure ratio. On a scaled drawing of the slope, the location of the slip circle and the pore pressure contours are superimposed; a judgment can then be made on the average r_u value to use in computations (see Fig. 15-25)

ILLUSTRATION 15-9. Find the factor of safety for a slope where the following conditions exist:

Slope inclination, $i = 30°$, height $= 40$ ft (12 m)
Cohesion, $c' = 200$ psf (9.6 kN/m²)
Angle of internal friction, $\phi = 20°$
Unit weight, $\gamma = 110$ pcf (17.3 kN/m³)
Pore pressure ratio, $r_u = 0.2$ (assume that value was estimated from a pore pressure ratio diagram, as illustrated in Fig 15-25)
Find

$$\lambda_{c\phi} = \frac{\gamma H \tan \phi}{c'} = \frac{(110 \text{ pcf})(40 \text{ ft})(\tan 20°)}{200 \text{ psf}} = 8$$

Checking possibility of base failure

For $r_u = 0$, use Fig. 15-24e,
  get $D = 1$, $N_s = 26$

Checking possibility of toe failure

For $r_u = 0$, use Fig. 15-24b,
  get $D = 1.03$, $N_s = 27$

(continued)

Computational Aids—Slope Stability Charts

473

(a) Notation of terms

(b) Toe circle, $r_u = 0$

Figure 15-24 Cousins charts for stability numbers and locating critical circles [49].

For $r_u = 0.25$, use Fig. 15-24f,   For $r_u = 0.25$, use Fig. 15-24c
   get $D = 1$, $N_s = 22$ get $D = 1.03$, $N_s = 22$

Failure arc passes very close to the toe (based on least N_s), use $D = 1.0\,(+)$.
   If $r_u = 0.2$, N_s for stability computation $= 23$ (by interpolation of above N_s values).

(continued page 481)

(d) Toe circle, $r_u = 0.5$

(c) Toe circle, $r_u = 0.25$

Figure 15-24 (*Continued*)

475

(f) Circles with specified depth factor, $r_u = 0.25$

(e) Circles with specified depth factor, $r_u = 0$

Figure 15-24 (*Continued*)

476

(h) X and Y coordinates for toe circles, $r_u = 0$

$\dfrac{X}{H} \tan i$ and $\dfrac{Y}{H} \tan i$

$r_u = 0$

$\dfrac{X}{H} \tan i$

$\dfrac{Y}{H} \tan i$ ····· Toe Circles

(g) Circles with specified depth factor, $r_u = 0.5$

Stability Number, N_s

$r_u = 0.5$

D = 1 ---

D = 1.25 ----

D = 1.5 ----

Toe Circles

Figure 15-24 *(Continued)*

(j) X and Y coordinates for toe circles, $r_u = 0.50$

(i) X and Y coordinates for toe circle, $r_u = 0.25$

Figure 15-24 (*Continued*)

(l) X and Y coordinates for circles with depth factor of 1, $r_u = 0.25$

(k) X and Y coordinates for circles with depth factor of 1.0, $r_u = 0$

Figure 15-24 (*Continued*)

(n) X and Y coordinates for circles with depth factor of 1.25, $r_u = 0$

(m) X and Y coordinates for circles with depth factor of 1, $r_u = 0.5$

Figure 15-24 (*Continued*)

480

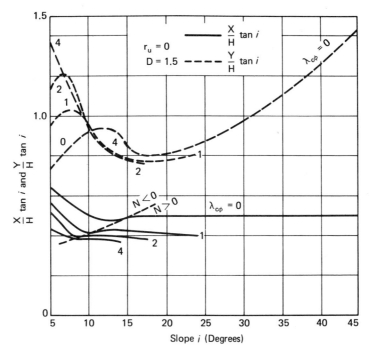

(o) X and Y coordinates for circles with depth factor of 1.5, $r_u = 0$

Figure 15-24 (*Continued*)

$$FS = \frac{N_s c'}{\gamma H} = \frac{(23)(200 \text{ psf})}{(110 \text{ pcf})(40 \text{ ft})} = 1.05$$

Coordinates of center for failure circle, if a toe failure is assumed as a close approximation:

For $r_u = 0$, $(X/H) \tan i = 0.10$
$(Y/H) \tan i = 1.2$ (from Fig. 15-24h)

For $r_u = 0.25$, $(X/H) \tan i = 0.15$
$(Y/H) \tan i = 1.1$ (from Fig. 15-24i)

$= 0.15$
$(Y/H) \tan i = 1.1$

Therefore, for $r_u = 0.2$, use

$$(Y/H) \tan i = 1.18, \text{ or } Y = (1.18)(40 \text{ ft})\left(\frac{1}{\tan 30°}\right) = 81.8 \text{ ft}$$

$$(X/H) \tan i = 0.14, \text{ or } X = (0.14)(40 \text{ ft})\left(\frac{1}{\tan 30°}\right) = 9.7 \text{ ft}$$

Morganstern Charts for Rapid Drawdown   Stability charts applicable to the case of reservoir embankments subject to drawdown have been developed by

Computational Aids—Slope Stability Charts

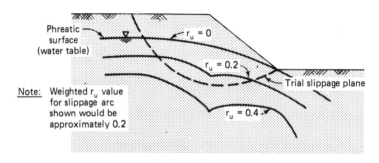

Figure 15-25 Illustration of procedure to show pore pressure ratios in reference to slippage arc for determining weighted r_u value.

Morganstern [173]. The drawdown condition is typically more critical than either the submerged or the nonsubmerged condition for embankments containing cohesive soils. Immediately after the reservoir level is lowered, a combination of potentially dangerous conditions exists: The weight of the embankment soil has changed from a submerged to the much heavier saturated state, while high pore water pressures are retained in the embankment along with the lower effective intergranular stresses as a carryover from the previously submerged condition, and seepage forces from pore water draining out of the slope act in the general direction of other gravity forces that tend to cause sliding. Morganstern's charts are based upon an effective stress analysis utilizing the method of slices. This work assumes that the soil properties are constant throughout the embankment and that the full slope height had been submerged prior to drawdown (refer to Fig. 15-26a). Factors of safety against sliding can be computed for a complete drawdown[7] and for intermediate levels of drawdown. For a complete drawdown, the least factor of safety is for a slip circle passing tangent to the rigid base (Fig.15-26b). Realistically, complete drawdowns occur infrequently. When a partial drawdown is studied, the location of the most critical slip circle is determined by a trial procedure (Fig. 15-26c and Illus. 15-10).

The parameter $c'/\gamma H$ used by other investigators has also been applied by Morganstern, and his charts are in terms of this value and slope inclination (Fig. 15-27). Factors of safety are determined directly from the curves. Values of $c'/\gamma H$ differing from those presented can, for practical purposes, be obtained by interpolation.

ILLUSTRATION 15-10. (a) Find the factor of safety when an 80-ft-high (24.4-m) embankment with a three-to-one upstream slope experiences a complete drawdown. Soil properties are

$$\gamma_{\text{total}} = 125 \text{ pcf } (19.62 \text{ kN/m}^3), \qquad c' = 250 \text{ psf } (12 \text{ kN/m}^2), \qquad \phi = 30°$$

$$\frac{c'}{\gamma H} = \frac{250 \text{ psf}}{(125 \text{ pcf})(80 \text{ ft})} = 0.025$$

[7]Recall that Taylor's charts can also be used to evaluate the stability for a slope subject to a *complete* drawdown.

(a) Embankment with terms and assumptions defined

(b) For full drawdown, use	(c) For partial drawdown, check
$H_e = H_{max}$	different values of H_e to find
$L = H_{max}$	minimum factor of safety
$\dfrac{L}{H_e} = 1$	(these different values of H_e used in L/H and $c/\gamma H$ ratios)

Figure 15-26 Terms and assumptions in Morganstern's stability analyses for rapid drawdown.

For a complete drawdown, the most critical value of $L/H_e = 80$ ft/80 ft, obtain $FS = 1.2$ (see Fig. 15-26b and Fig. 15-27).

(b) Find the factor of safety when the drawdown is half of embankment height. (Assume that the slip is tangent to the embankment base.)

$$H_e = 80 \text{ ft}, \qquad \frac{c'}{\gamma H} = 0.025$$

For $L/H_e = \dfrac{(0.5)(80 \text{ ft})}{(80 \text{ ft})} = 0.5$, obtain $FS = 1.52$.

(c) Assume that the slip circle is through the face of the slope and passing tangent to a horizontal plane at the depth L used in (b) above (refer to Fig. 15-26b).

$$H_e = \frac{80 \text{ ft}}{2} = 40 \text{ ft}, \qquad \frac{c}{\gamma H_e} = \frac{250 \text{ psf}}{(125 \text{ pcf})\left(\dfrac{80 \text{ ft}}{2}\right)} = 0.05$$

For $L/H_e = \dfrac{40 \text{ ft}}{40 \text{ ft}} = 1$, obtain $FS = 1.45$.

Variation in Shear Stress and Factor of Safety   The factor of safety computed by the limit equilibrium method of analysis is the average value developed

Computational Aids—Slope Stability Charts

Figure 15-27 Morganstern stability curves for rapid drawdown [173].

along the length of the slippage arc under study. However, it is recognized that the factor of safety (in regard to the maximum soil shear strength) actually varies at different locations along the slippage plane, because the state of stress within and beneath a slope varies considerably. Figure 15-28 illustrates how the increase in the soil zone stressed so to be at its ultimate shear strength occurs when a slope is heightened by excavating below the toe. Even in natural slopes that have long been stable, zones where the soil is near or at the ultimate shear strength probably exist. Increases in slope loading are then forced into being supported by the soil zones still at low stresses, for at or near the ultimate strength a soil deforms plastically and is unable to develop additional shearing resistance unless large strains (movements) occur. A concern with slopes where low factors of safety exist is that changes in loading conditions may cause the heavily stressed plastic zones to expand through enough of the slope and base region to have slippage occur.

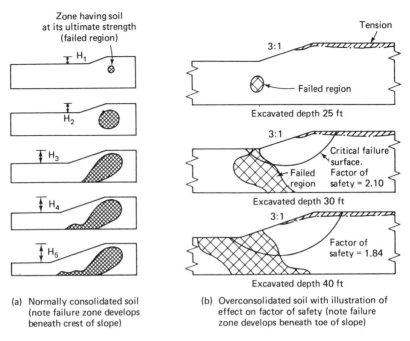

Zone having soil
at its ultimate strength
(failed region)

Tension

3:1

H_1

Failed region

Excavated depth 25 ft

H_2

3:1

Critical failure
surface.
Factor of
safety = 2.10

Failed
region

H_3

Excavated depth 30 ft

3:1

H_4

Factor of
safety = 1.84

H_5

Excavated depth 40 ft

(a) Normally consolidated soil
(note failure zone develops
beneath crest of slope)

(b) Overconsolidated soil with illustration of
effect on factor of safety (note failure
zone develops beneath toe of slope)

Figure 15-28 Patterns of increase in failure zone as slope height increases [70].

IMPROVING STABILITY OF SLOPES

Practical considerations can require that slopes susceptible to sliding have their stability improved to make the area usable and safe. Slope areas that have experienced sliding in the past should be considered likely to undergo further movement if loading conditions change. Ancient slides are viewed with the same or greater concern than presently stable areas where an analysis predicts sliding (e.g., where a very low factor of safety is indicated).

A variety of procedures have been successfully used in the past to stabilize slopes. A history of unsuccessful procedures also exists. Generally, corrective or preventative measures involve reducing the mass or loading that contributes toward sliding, improving the shear strength of the earth in the failure zone, and constructing or installing elements that will provide resistance to movement. The procedure best for a given slope is related to the type of soil in the slope, the thickness and depth of materials involved in sliding, the groundwater conditions, the areal extent requiring stabilizing, the space available to undertake corrective changes, the topographical conditions in the vicinity of the slope, and the tendency for changes such as the advent of seismic and vibratory loadings to occur.

Where area is available, slope flattening, as indicated in Figure 15-29a, can be performed to reduce the weight of the mass tending to slide. When it is anticipated that a base failure could occur, resistance to movement can be increased by

(a) Slopes flattened or benched

(b) Berm provided at toe

(c) Protection against erosion provided at toe

(d) Lowering of groundwater table to reduce pore pressures in the slope

(e) Use of driven or cast-in-place piles

(f) Retaining wall OR sheetpiling OR cylinder piles provided to increase resistance to sliding

(g) Plan for building design to aid slope stability

Figure 15-29 Methods to improve and protect slope stability.

the placement of a berm below the toe of the slope (Fig. 15-29b). If the zone below the toe is susceptible to severe erosion, an occurrence that would undermine the toe area and remove earth that provides resistance to sliding, a protective rockfill blanket and riprap can be installed (Fig. 15-29c).

High groundwater and pore water pressures in the slope affect the soil shearing resistance that can be developed. Methods to lower the zone of subsurface water and intercept surface water to prevent infiltration and erosion, and to reduce seepage forces, are depicted in Figure 15-29d.

Where cohesionless soils exist, the shearing strength of the slope material can be improved through densification by use of explosives or vibroflotation or Terra-probe procedures. For cohesive soils, shear strengths have been improved by consolidation, and water-content reduction has been achieved through surcharging (which may include wick drains), electro-osmosis, and thermal drying.

Grouting and injection methods have been utilized to add cementing or bonding agents into specific soil zones where a weak condition was critical to the stability of the slope.

Driven piles, sheetpiling, and retaining walls have been installed to provide lateral support and increase the resistance for slopes tending to slide (Fig. 15-29e and f).

In the interest of economy, improvement and protective methods such as slope flattening and drainage control conventionally are preferred and generally receive first consideration. Soil stabilization methods and the use of piling or retaining walls are expensive procedures, typically utilized where limited areas require stabilizing.

Where building construction is planned for the vicinity of a slope, the procedure depicted by Figure 15-29g should be followed wherever possible to have the effects of building loading act to benefit slope stability.

PROBLEMS

15-1. An area of planned construction is underlain by sandy soil whose angle of internal friction is 35°.

    (a) What is the maximum safe slope angle for this soil if there is no groundwater flow?

    (b) If it is assumed that groundwater flow could occur through the slope, approximately what slope angle should be considered as the allowable maximum?

15-2. Indicate probable reasons why slopes in cohesionless soils may be made at inclinations steeper than the soil's angle of repose.

15-3. **(a)** What would be the factor of safety for an infinitely long slope having an inclination of 25° in an area underlain by firm cohesive soils ($\gamma = 18$ kN/m^3) but having a thin weak layer 5 m below and parallel to the slope surface ($\gamma = 16$ kN/m^3, $c = 20$ kN/m^2, $\phi = 15°$ for the weak layer)?

    (b) If groundwater flow could occur parallel to the slope, what factor of safety would result?

15-4. Determine a slope's factor of safety for a circular arc trial failure plane that has a 35-m radius with a center of rotation located 20 m vertically above the slope's midpoint. The slope has an inclination of 45° and a vertical height of 20 m. Soil borings indicate that a uniform clay soil with γ = 16.5 kN/m³ and c = 55 kN/m² (ϕ = 0°) exists in the area. The force (weight) of the failure mass is 9900 kN per meter of length (length perpendicular to the cross section). The horizontal distance between the center of rotation and the cg of the failure mass is 11 m. Use the basic method for the stability analysis.

15-5. (a) Utilizing the basic method for a stability analysis, determine a slope's factor of safety against a rotational slide for the following conditions:
—Slope height is 50 ft.
—Slope inclination is 40°.
—Trial failure arc center of rotation is 40 ft above slope midpoint; radius of failure arc is 80 ft.
—Soil profile determined from top of slope shows clay soil from 0 to 100 ft (γ = 16 kN/m³, c = 45 kN/m², ϕ = 0°).
—A line loading of 3 kips per ft of length of slope acts along the top of the slope 20 ft from the edge.
—The failure mass involves 3725 ft³ of soil per foot of slope, and the horizontal distance from the cg of the failure mass to the center of rotation is 26 ft.

(b) Find the most critical failure circle and the least factor of safety for the above conditions by systematically changing the point representing the center of rotation used in part (a) by 10 ft horizontally and 10 ft vertically (suggested class project in which each student checks one or two trial failure circles).

15-6. (a) Using the Fellenius method of slices for slope analysis, calculate the factor of safety against a rotational slide for the following conditions:
—Slope inclination is $2H$ to $1V$.
—Trial failure arc center of rotation is 35 m above slope midpoint; arc passes through toe of slope.
—Slope height is 25 m.
—Soils are uniform to great depth (drained shear tests indicate ϕ = 15° c' = 15 kN/m², γ = 17 kN/m³); water table is very deep.
—Use five slices, approximately equal in width.

(b) Calculate the factor of safety for the above conditions but assuming a fully submerged slope (water level even with the top of the slope).

15-7. (a) Determine the factor of safety for the slope conditions indicated in Problem 15-5(a) by using the Bishop method, but with soil whose properties are γ = 16 kN/m³, c' = 10 kN/m², ϕ = 20°.

(b) Solve Problem 15-5b using the simplified Bishop method, with soil in the slope having properties as for Problem 15-7a.

15-8. Using the simplified Janbu method, determine the factor of safety for stability of a slope and potential failure mass identified by the following description:
—Slope inclination is 30°; surface level at top of slope.
—Slope height is 20 m; soil unit weight γ is 17 kN/m³.
—Buried thin weak layer (the assumed plane of sliding) extends back from the toe of slope at an inclination of 20° for a horizontal distance of 40 m, then upward at a 45° inclination until it intersects the ground surface (c' = 12 kN/m², ϕ = 18°).

15-9. A sliding block analysis is to be made for an earth embankment structure as depicted by Figure 15.20. Determine the factor of safety against sliding along the base of the embankment (Fig. 15-20b) for the conditions indicated below:

—Distance $b'd$ or $L = 130$ m.

—Distance $ab' = 40$ m.

—Slope inclination $3H$ to $1V$.

—Unit weight of compacted earth in embankment $= 18$ kN/m³.

—Active pressure on plane a-b' computed using $K_a = 0.4$.

—Uplift pressure at point $b = 10\gamma_w$ and zero at point d.

—Shear strength on assumed weak plane b'-d based on $c = 20$ kN/m² plus $\phi = 20°$.

15-10. **(a)** Determine the factor of safety for a 45° slope 30 m high in an area where a uniform clay exists, using $c = 96$ kN/m², $\phi = 0$, $\gamma = 17$ kN/m³. A rock stratum exists 45 m below the toe of slope. Use Taylor stability charts for the total stress case.

(b) What inclination is required to have a factor of safety of 1.2 for a slope 40 m high in an area where uniform soils exist ($c = 25$ kN/m², $\phi = 12°$, $\gamma = 16.5$ kN/m³)? The factor of safety is to apply to the angle of internal friction as well as cohesion. Use Taylor stability charts.

(c) A reservoir embankment 25 m high consists of compacted earth, where $\gamma = 19$ kN/m³, $c = 40$ kN/m², $\phi = 10°$. The embankment has a slope of $3H$ to $1V$. What is the factor of safety if a sudden drawdown of the reservoir occurs? Use Taylor stability charts.

15-11. **(a)** Using Cousins's stability charts, determine the factor of safety for a slope where the following conditions exist:

—Slope inclination is 30°; height is 30 m.

—Soil cohesion $c' = 20$ kN/m², $\phi = 20°$, $\gamma = 20$ kN/m³.

—Pore pressure ratio $r_u = 0$.

(b) Locate the position (coordinates) for the center of the critical failure circle.

(c) Determine the factor of safety for the slope described in (a), except that $r_u = 0.25$, and locate the center of the critical failure circle.

15-12. **(a)** Using the Morganstern stability curves for rapid drawdown, determine the factor of safety for a reservoir embankment subject to suddent drawdown where the following conditions exist:

—Inclination of upstream slope is $2\frac{1}{2}H$ to $1V$.

—Embankment height is 60 m; reservoir level is completely drawn down.

—Embankment soil properties are $\gamma = 20$ kN/m³, $c' = 30$ kN/m², $\phi = 20°$.

(b) Determine the factor of safety if the drawdown was to a level 30 m below the top of the embankment.

## chapter 16

Lateral Pressures and Retaining Structures

Structures and components of structures whose major design function is to resist lateral forces are common to private and public works projects. Historically, the magnitude and effect of lateral forces represent one of the earliest structural problems to be studied analytically. Lateral forces most typically develop against structures from the presence of soil or water against vertical sections. Retaining walls and foundation walls are representative of structures that serve principally to support or resist an adjacent mass of earth, whereas dams are identified with facilities used to retain bodies of water. Frequently these structures must be capable of resisting forces resulting from the presence of both soil and water; the design for foundation walls and retaining walls considers water as well as soil pressures where a high groundwater table exists, whereas for earth dams the internal lateral soil pressures are important to the structural stability. Retaining structures for waterfront facilities, such as bulkheads, cofferdams, and quay walls, conventionally must consider the effects of both soil and water pressures in their design. Representative retaining-type structures are depicted in Figure 16-1.

Earth retaining structures are common where a project requires that changes in the ground surface elevation be achieved abruptly because space is not available or cannot be used for the construction of stable earth slopes—for example, retaining walls where highway and railroad routes require an elevation different from the surrounding terrain. For walls that make up the subsurface components of structures, the major portion of the design loading usually results from the lateral pressures of soil or water that exist immediately adjacent to the structure as necessary for its utility or function—for example, walls for basements of buildings and walls for ship-loading facilities. The most familiar water retaining structures are

(a) Highway retaining wall

(b) Building basement walls

(c) Bridge abutments

(d) Earth dam

(e) Waterfront bulkhead

Figure 16-1 Representative types of structures subject to lateral soil and water pressures.

for impounding bodies of water for municipal use and power generation, but also are used to protect or create land areas.

Lateral Earth Pressure and Retaining Walls

STATE OF STRESS IN THE SOIL MASS

The magnitude of the lateral soil pressure that can exist or develop in a soil mass is related to the strength and stress–strain properties of the material and deformations that occur within the mass as a result of a lateral movement.

At-Rest Pressure In a homogeneous and isotropic soil mass of infinite extent bounded by a level ground surface, as illustrated by Figure 16-2a, the vertical and horizontal stresses shown on the representative element are principal stresses. For the condition where the soil deposit is normally consolidated (the existing overburden pressure represents the maximum vertical pressure the soil mass has been subjected to in its history) the vertical principal stress is equal to the weight of the overburden, or

(a) Subsurface stresses in soil mass of infinite extent

(b) Horizontal and vertical stresses related to failure envelope, for the at-rest condition

(c) Lateral pressure distribution against smooth, rigid, unyielding wall which replaces part of original soil mass (no lateral movements within soil mass)

Figure 16-2 Subsurface stresses relating to the at-rest condition.

$$\sigma_v = \gamma_{\text{soil}} Z \quad \text{or} \quad \gamma_t Z \qquad (8\text{-}1)$$

where the groundwater table is below the depth Z and no seepage or buoyancy forces exist. If the overburden acting as part of the soil mass were to increase, the vertical stress σ_v would also increase, and the soil would be subject to vertical compression as a result. Deformation in the lateral direction would not occur, however, because, through increasing, the horizontal stress on all volumetric elements would be equal and opposite in magnitude and direction, effecting a lateral restraint. For this condition the relationship between horizontal stress σ_h and vertical stress σ_v is indicated by

$$\frac{\sigma_h}{\sigma_v} = \frac{v}{1-v} \cong 1 - \sin \phi \qquad (16\text{-}1a)$$

or

$$\sigma_h = \sigma_v \left(\frac{v}{1-v} \right) \cong \sigma_v \, (1 - \sin \phi) \qquad (16\text{-}1b)$$

where v is Poisson's ratio[1] and ϕ is the angle of internal friction for the soil. The ratio of σ_h to σ_v in a soil mass is termed the coefficient of lateral earth pressure, K. Where no lateral deformations occur in the soil mass, the value expressed by Equation 16-1a is considered the *at-rest* condition for which the earth pressure coefficient is designated K_0. Therefore,

$$\sigma_h = K_0 \sigma_v \quad \text{(at-rest condition)} \qquad (16\text{-}1c)$$

Representative values of K_0 for generalized soil categories are shown in Table 16-1.

The relation of subsurface stresses to the soil's limiting strength for a typical at-rest condition is shown by the Mohr's circle plot of Figure 16-2b, which indicates that a state of equilibrium is maintained. If a smooth unyielding wall (a wall of infinite rigidity) could be embedded into the soil mass of Figure 16-2a and the soil to one side then removed without causing change in the previously established soil conditions, the lateral pressures acting against the wall would increase uniformly with depth, achieving a pressure distribution as shown in Figure 16-2c. Letting p_0 represent pressure at any depth against the wall that results from the retained soil mass, Equation 16-1c becomes, for the at-rest condition,

$$p_0 = \sigma_h = K_0 \sigma_v = K_0 \gamma_t z \qquad (16\text{-}2a)$$

TABLE 16-1 REPRESENTATIVE VALUES OF K_0

Soil type	K_0
Granular, loose	0.5–0.6
Granular, dense	0.3–0.5
Clay, soft	0.9–1.1 (undrained)
Clay, hard	0.8–0.9 (undrained)

[1] Recall from engineering mechanics that Poisson's ratio relates strain in a lateral direction to the strain in a longitudinal direction that occurs as a result of load applied in the longitudinal direction.

State of Stress in the Soil Mass

Figure 16-3 Conditions for submerged soil: Lateral pressure is total of soil plus water pressure.

and the total lateral force P_0 is the area of the pressure diagram, or

$$P_0 = \frac{1}{2}K_0\gamma_t H^2 \tag{16-2b}$$

whose resultant acts at a depth $\frac{2}{3}H$.

Effect of Submergence   Where soil is below the groundwater table, the intergranular (i.e., effective) stress $\bar{\sigma}_v$ between soil particles at any depth is reduced by the magnitude of the water pressure u at the same depth, in accord with Equation 8-4,

$$\bar{\sigma}_v = \gamma_t z - u = \sigma_v - u \tag{8-4}$$

Submergence influences the lateral pressures being exerted on a wall as in Figure 16-3 in two manners. The submerged soil unit weight or effective vertical stress is used with Equations 16-1c and 16-2, the result being that, compared to the non-submerged condition, the lateral soil pressure decreases. However, the presence of water also causes hydrostatic pressures to act against the submerged section of the wall, where the value of such pressure at any depth is a product of the unit weight of water γ_w and the depth below the surface of the water table. The hydrostatic pressure diagram is triangular, and the total lateral force is equal to the area of the diagram. Comparing cases between water or no water existing behind a wall, the presence of a water table with the combined effect of hydrostatic pressure and (reduced) lateral soil pressure causes a greater total lateral force to act on the wall.

ILLUSTRATION 16-1.   Calculate the total lateral force acting against a smooth unyielding wall that retains a cohesionless soil, assuming that no lateral deformation occurs in the soil mass and the at-rest condition applies. Properties of the retained soil and location of the groundwater table are indicated on the sketch.

Total lateral pressure against wall = area of soil pressure and water pressure diagrams

$$= (150 \text{ psf} \times \tfrac{3}{2} \text{ ft}) + \left(\frac{150 \text{ psf} + 300 \text{ psf}}{2}\right)(6 \text{ ft}) + (\tfrac{1}{2})(375 \text{ psf})(6 \text{ ft})$$

$$= 225 + 1350 + 1125 = 2700 \text{ lb per ft of wall length}$$

(*Note*: If the water table was below the wall, the total lateral soil pressure would be $[9 \text{ ft} \times 116 \text{ pcf} \times 0.43][\tfrac{1}{2} \times 9 \text{ ft}] = 2025$ lb per ft of wall.)

Active and Passive Lateral Pressures: Basic Considerations If the frictionless, infinitely rigid wall of Figure 16-2c is allowed to move away from the retained soil mass a slight distance (Fig. 16-4a), the soil starts to expand in the lateral direction, following the movement of the wall. Shearing resistance developed within the soil mass because of the soil's shear strength acts opposite to the direction of the expansion, the result being that the lateral soil pressures on the wall *decrease*, becoming less than the at-rest pressures. When lateral movement adequate to develop the soil's maximum shearing resistance occurs (see Fig. 10-16 for a generalized stress–strain relationship), the lateral earth force on the wall will be a minimum for that retained soil mass. The minimum lateral soil pressure condition based on the soil's shear strength is the *active pressure* p_a, and the active lateral pressure coefficient is K_a. The procedure for determining the theoretical minimum pressure that results with a *dry cohesionless soil* is indicated by the Mohr's circle plot in reference to the soil's failure envelope (Fig. 16-4b), whereby

$$\frac{p_a}{\sigma_v} = \frac{1 - \sin \phi}{1 + \sin \phi} = \tan^2\left(45 - \frac{\phi}{2}\right) = K_a \qquad (16\text{-}3a)$$

or

$$p_a = \sigma_v K_a = \sigma_v \left(\frac{1 - \sin \phi}{1 + \sin \phi}\right) = \sigma_v \tan^2\left(45 - \frac{\phi}{2}\right) \qquad (16\text{-}3b)$$

where p_a is the active lateral soil pressure at the depth where σ_v acts.

The *total* lateral force P_A resulting from active soil pressures against the wall is (Fig. 16-4e)

$$P_A = \frac{1}{2} \gamma_t H^2 K_a \qquad (16\text{-}3c)$$

State of Stress in the Soil Mass

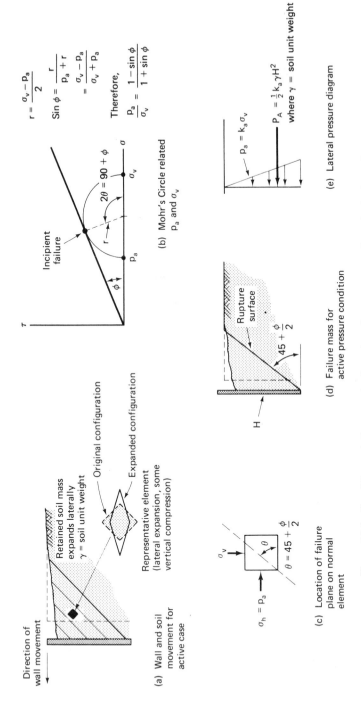

$$r = \frac{\sigma_v - p_a}{2}$$

$$\text{Sin } \phi = \frac{r}{p_a + r}$$

$$= \frac{\sigma_v - p_a}{\sigma_v + p_a}$$

Therefore,

$$\frac{p_a}{\sigma_v} = \frac{1 - \sin \phi}{1 + \sin \phi}$$

(b) Mohr's Circle related p_a and σ_v

$2\theta = 90 + \phi$

Incipient failure

σ_v

r

p_a

ϕ

τ

σ

$p_a = k_a \sigma_v$

$P_A = \frac{1}{2} k_a \gamma H^2$

where γ = soil unit weight

(e) Lateral pressure diagram

Rupture surface

$45 + \dfrac{\phi}{2}$

H

(d) Failure mass for active pressure condition

Direction of wall movement

Retained soil mass expands laterally γ = soil unit weight

Original configuration

Expanded configuration

Representative element (lateral expansion, some vertical compression)

(a) Wall and soil movement for active case

σ_v

θ

$\theta = 45 + \dfrac{\phi}{2}$

$\sigma_h = p_a$

(c) Location of failure plane on normal element

Figure 16-4 Conditions relating to active lateral earth pressure case for cohesionless soil.

496

Figure 16-4c also shows the inclination of potential failure planes in the laterally expanding soil mass. When shearing strains reach values corresponding to the soil's maximum shearing strength, incipient planes of failure are at an angle of $45 + \dfrac{\phi}{2}$ degrees to the horizontal. This angle is used to identify the soil zone which contributes to the lateral force on the wall when the fully active pressure condition is reached (Fig. 16-4d). Within this zone, an infinite number of failure planes (planes of sliding) oriented at the $45 + \dfrac{\phi}{2}$ degree angle exist. The distribution of lateral pressures with depth is indicated by Figure 16-4e.

Where the soil possesses *internal friction plus cohesion, c,* from the presence of cohesive material or moisture, the Mohr's circle-failure envelope relationship for the active pressure condition is, from Fig. 16-5a,

$$p_a = \sigma_v \tan^2\left(45 - \frac{\phi}{2}\right) - 2c \tan\left(45 - \frac{\phi}{2}\right) \tag{16-4a}$$

and the total force against the wall P_A is indicated by the area of the pressure diagram

$$P_A = \frac{1}{2}\gamma_t H^2 \tan^2\left(45 - \frac{\phi}{2}\right) - 2cH \tan\left(45 - \frac{\phi}{2}\right) \tag{16-4b}$$

For saturated clay soils analyzed under conditions where the undrained shear strength applies (refer to U–U tests of Figure 10-25), ϕ is zero and Equation 16-4a reduces to

$$p_a = \sigma_v - 2c \tag{16-4c}$$

and Equation 16-4b becomes

$$P_A = \frac{1}{2}\gamma_t H^2 - 2cH \tag{16-4d}$$

The resulting pressure distribution is similar to that indicated by Fig. 16-5b.

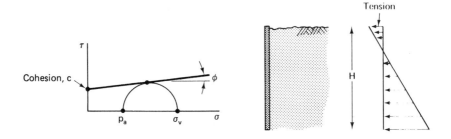

(a) Relationship between σ_v and p_a indicated on Mohr's Circle

(b) Theoretical distribution of active pressure against wall

Figure 16-5 Active lateral pressure case for soil possessing cohesion and internal friction.

State of Stress in the Soil Mass

If the wall of Figure 16-2c moves into the retained soil mass, the soil compresses in the lateral direction (Fig. 16-6a), with the soil shearing resistance acting to oppose the lateral compression. When sufficient lateral movement occurs, the maximum shearing strength of the soil is mobilized and the reaction of the resulting lateral earth pressure on the wall will be a maximum. The maximum lateral pressure condition is the *passive pressure*, and the lateral pressure coefficient is K_p. The relationship between vertical stress and passive lateral stress where a level, dry cohesionless soil mass exists is shown on the Mohr's circle presentation of Figure 16-6b. For a *dry cohesionless soil*, the ratio of lateral to vertical stress for the passive pressure condition is

$$\frac{p_p}{\sigma_v} = \frac{1 + \sin \phi}{1 - \sin \phi} = \tan^2 \left(45 + \frac{\phi}{2} \right) = K_p \tag{16-5a}$$

or

$$p_p = \sigma_v K_p = \sigma_v \left(\frac{1 + \sin \phi}{1 - \sin \phi} \right) = \sigma_v \tan^2 \left(45 + \frac{\phi}{2} \right) \tag{16-5b}$$

where p_p is the passive lateral soil pressure at the depth where σ_v acts.

The force of the passive pressure P_p against the wall becomes, for *cohesionless* soil (Fig. 16-6b)

$$P_p = \frac{1}{2} \gamma H^2 K_p \tag{16-5c}$$

For soils possessing *internal friction and cohesion, c,* the passive pressure, is (see Fig. 16-6c),

$$p_p = \sigma_v \tan^2 \left(45 + \frac{\phi}{2} \right) + 2c \tan \left(45 + \frac{\phi}{2} \right) \tag{16-6a}$$

and the force of the passive soil pressure against the wall becomes (see Fig. 16-6c)

$$P_p = \frac{1}{2} \gamma_t H^2 \tan^2 \left(45 + \frac{\phi}{2} \right) + 2cH \tan \left(45 + \frac{\phi}{2} \right) \tag{16-6b}$$

For saturated clay soils being analyzed for the condition of undrained shear ($\phi = 0°$)

$$p_p = \sigma_v + 2c \tag{16-6c}$$

and the total lateral soil force P_p becomes

$$P_p = \frac{1}{2} \gamma_t H^2 + 2cH \tag{16-6d}$$

For the passive pressure condition, the maximum shearing stresses develop on planes which are at an angle of $45 - \frac{\phi}{2}$ degrees to the horizontal. This angle defines the passive soil zone or failure wedge associated with passive resistance as well as the orientation of the infinite number of incipient failure planes within the passive zone.

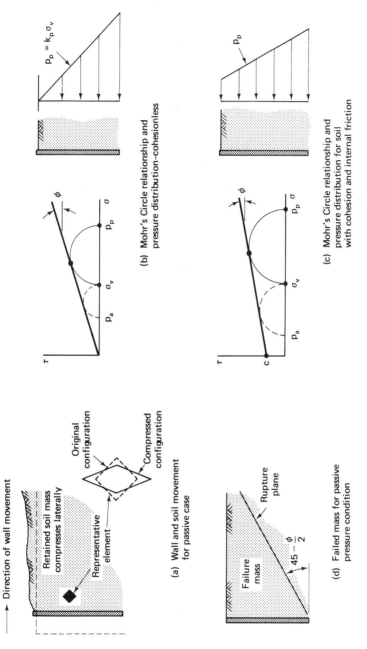

(a) Wall and soil movement for passive case

Direction of wall movement

Retained soil mass compresses laterally

Original configuration

Compressed configuration

Representative element

(b) Mohr's Circle relationship and pressure distribution–cohesionless

$p_p = k_p \sigma_v$

(c) Mohr's Circle relationship and pressure distribution for soil with cohesion and internal friction

p_p

(d) Failed mass for passive pressure condition

Rupture plane

Failure mass

$45 - \dfrac{\phi}{2}$

Figure 16-6 Conditions for passive pressure case.

If the ground water table is within the soil mass retained by a wall, the submerged soil unit weight is used in the calculations to determine the active or passive soil pressure, and, the lateral water pressure is additive, as discussed in the preceding section and shown in Illustration 16-1.

EARTH PRESSURES AGAINST RETAINING WALLS

Classical Theories   Two classical theories covering earth pressure against retaining walls, the Rankine[2] and the Coulomb[3] analyses, still serve as the basis for determining lateral soil pressures as they affect retaining wall design.

Rankine's theory, for the general case of a sloping cohesionless backfill, obtains a relationship between lateral and vertical stress such as that which exists in a soil mass of infinite extent having a uniform slope (see Fig. 16-7a), and assumes that a similar stress condition would exist against the back of a retaining wall used to support the slope. This assumption requires that friction between a wall and the retained soil be nonexistent or have insignificant effect on the shearing stresses which develop in the soil behind the wall. This creates conditions identical to those used as the basis for Equations 16-3 and 16-4, and for a level soil mass, the Rankine expression corresponds. For a wall supporting a uniformly sloping backfill of *dry cohesionless* soil, the *Rankine active pressure* p_a against the wall is

$$p_a = \sigma_v \cos i \, \frac{\cos i - \sqrt{\cos^2 i - \cos^2 \phi}}{\cos i + \sqrt{\cos^2 i - \cos^2 \phi}} \tag{16-7a}$$

(a) Vertical and lateral stress
    for Rankine condition

(b) Lateral pressure distribution

Figure 16-7 Lateral pressures defined for Rankine active pressure condition.

[2]"On the Stability of Loose Earth," V. J. M. Rankine, Philosophical Transactions of the Royal Society, Vol. 147, London, 1857.

[3]"Essai sur une Application des Regles de Maximis et Minimus a' Quelques Problemes de Statique Relatifs a' Architecture," C. A. Coulomb, presented 1773, published Memoires de Mathematiques et de Physique presentes a l'Academie des Sciences par divers savents, et lus dans ses Assemblees, Vol. 7, 1776.

where i represents the slope inclination angle, and p_a acts parallel to the slope surface.

The force P_A against a retaining wall of height H that results from the Rankine *active* condition (Fig. 16-7b) becomes

$$P_A = \frac{1}{2}\gamma_t H^2 \cos i \, \frac{\cos i - \sqrt{\cos^2 i - \cos^2 \phi}}{\cos i + \sqrt{\cos^2 i - \cos^2 \phi}} \qquad (16\text{-}7b)$$

The *passive* pressure by the Rankine theory is

$$p_p = \sigma_v \cos i \, \frac{\cos i + \sqrt{\cos^2 i - \cos^2 \phi}}{\cos i - \sqrt{\cos^2 i - \cos^2 \phi}} \qquad (16\text{-}8a)$$

and the force P_p imposed against a wall of height H that results from the Rankine passive condition is

$$P_p = \frac{1}{2}\gamma_t H^2 \cos i \, \frac{\cos i + \sqrt{\cos^2 i - \cos^2 \phi}}{\cos i - \sqrt{\cos^2 i - \cos^2 \phi}} \qquad (16\text{-}8b)$$

The *Coulomb theory*, for the active lateral pressure resulting from a retained mass of *cohesionless* soil, considers that a failure wedge forms behind the wall by sliding on a plane generally similar to that indicated by Figure 16-4d. As the retaining structure moves away from the soil mass, permitting its lateral expansion, a resulting vertical compression of the soil failure wedge and the relative movement between the wall and soil causes friction to develop on the back of the wall. The resultant of this friction and lateral soil pressure force P_A acts at an angle ψ measured normal to the face of the wall, as indicated by Figure 16-8. This resultant also establishes the magnitude and direction of the wall *reaction* against the soil failure wedge. When the failure wedge of cohesionless soil is satisfactorily retained by a

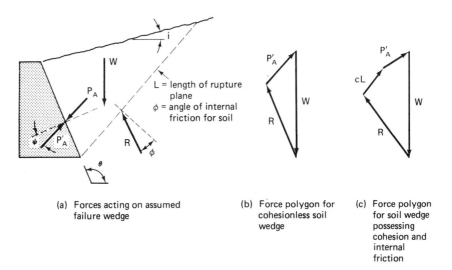

(a) Forces acting on assumed failure wedge

(b) Force polygon for cohesionless soil wedge

(c) Force polygon for soil wedge possessing cohesion and internal friction

Figure 16-8   Description of terms relating to Coulomb active pressure condition.

Earth Pressures Against Retaining Walls

wall, three forces acting on the wedge—the effect of gravity on the wedge's volume (W, the weight of the wedge), the reaction of the wall on the wedge (P_A), and the soil reaction on the wedge's failure plane (R)—are in equilibrium. When the unit weight and angle ϕ for the retained soil and the angle ψ for the wall reaction are known (see Table 16-2), the force P_A imposed on the wall as a result of the active pressure wedge can be determined for any assumed failure wedge by a simple vector addition as shown in Fig. 16-8b. The magnitude of the force P_A acting on the wall will be affected by the size of the assumed failure wedge but also by the slope of the wall face and the angles ϕ and ψ. The actual active pressure condition for a given wall results from that unique failure wedge which provides the greatest numerical value for the force P_A. Determining the proper value for P_A can be accomplished by the trial-and-error procedure of analyzing a series of assumed failure wedges having different sizes. However, where the slope of the soil backfill is uniform and the back of the retaining wall is a plane surface such as indicated in Figure 16-8, the critical failure wedge is triangular and the following expression can be used to directly calculate the force resulting from active soil pressures against the wall.

TABLE 16-2 REPRESENTATIVE VALUES FOR WALL FRICTION ANGLES

Wall material	Soil type	Wall-friction angle ψ, degrees
Concrete or masonry	Fine to coarse sand, sand and gravel, (clean)	$30\pm$
	Fine sand, silty sand, clayey sand	$25\pm$
	Silt, sandy silt, silt–clay, clay	$20\pm$
Poured concrete (formed)	Fine to coarse sand, sand and gravel (clean)	$25\pm$
	Fine to medium sand, sand–silt–gravel mixture	$20\pm$
	Sand–silt, sand–clay mixture	15–18
Steel sheeting	Coarse sand, sand–gravel mixture (clean)	22
	Fine to medium sand, sand–silt–gravel mixture	17
	Silt, sand–silt, sand–clay mixture	12–14
Wood	Cohesionless (sands and silts)	$15\pm$

$$
P_A = \frac{1}{2}\gamma_t H^2 \left[\frac{\sin(\theta - \phi)\left(\dfrac{1}{\sin\theta}\right)}{\sqrt{\sin(\theta + \psi)} + \sqrt{\dfrac{\sin(\phi + \psi)\sin(\phi - i)}{\sin(\theta - i)}}} \right]^2 \tag{16-9}
$$

When the retained soil mass possesses cohesion as well as internal friction, the vector addition representing equilibrium for forces acting on the failure wedge must include the total cohesive resistance, cL, acting on the rupture plane (Fig. 16-8c). The procedure for determining the actual force imposed on the wall reverts to the trial-and-error process of assuming different failure wedges, and then selecting that wedge which produces the largest P_A value.

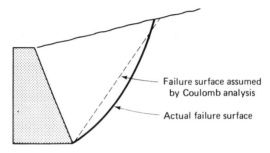

Figure 16-9 Assumed and actual failure surfaces for active pressure condition in Coulomb analysis.

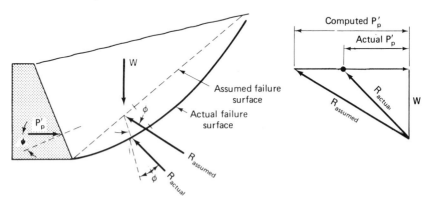

Figure 16-10 Assumed and actual failure surfaces for passive pressure condition and effect on Wall-Coulomb analysis.

Whereas the Coulomb theory assumes a plane failure surface for the active soil zone, actual rupture surfaces tend to be slightly curved (Fig. 16-9). The effect is that the lateral force calculated by Equation 16-9 is slightly low. Typically the discrepancy is minor, and considering the variations that tend to exist in a retained soil mass (which affect soil properties and wall friction), the Coulomb procedure for arriving at the effects of active pressure provides a practical accuracy.

The value of P_A computed from the Coulomb theory is slightly greater than the value obtained from the Rankine theory for similar conditions. However, the lateral pressure resultant for the Rankine condition acts parallel to the wall's retained slope, whereas the resultant from the Coulomb analysis acts at a greater inclination because of the wall friction factor. The consequence is that the Rankine analysis typically creates the more severe condition when the stability of a retaining wall is evaluated, an effect that results in a slightly more conservative wall design.

For the *passive* pressure case, the movement of the retaining wall is toward the soil mass, and the resultant of the lateral pressure and wall friction P_p is inclined downward. The reaction on the plane of rupture within the soil mass is at an angle opposing movement (Fig. 16-10). When the back of the retaining wall is planar and the retained soil has a uniform inclination so that the failure mass is triangular in shape, the Coulomb equation for the force resulting from the passive pressure, P_p, of a *cohesionless* soil becomes

Earth Pressures Against Retaining Walls

$$P_p = \frac{1}{2} \gamma_t H^2 \left[\frac{\sin(\theta + \phi)\left(\dfrac{1}{\sin\theta}\right)}{\sqrt{\sin(\theta - \psi)} - \sqrt{\dfrac{\sin(\phi + \psi)\sin(\phi + i)}{\sin(\theta - i)}}} \right]^2 \qquad (16\text{-}10)$$

The shape of the actual rupture surface within the retained soil mass is influenced by the soil friction developing on the back of the retaining wall. Where the magnitude of friction is low so that the angle ψ is small, the rupture surface is approximately planar. As the angle ψ increases, however, the lower zone of the failure wedge becomes curved. For values of ψ up to about one-third of ϕ, Equation 16-10 closely approximates the actual lateral pressure force, but as ψ becomes larger, the error in the computed lateral force becomes increasingly greater, whereby the actual passive resistance is less than the computed value (see Fig. 16-10). For the larger wall friction angles, analysis of the force resulting from passive pressure should be based on a curved surface of rupture [247].

Practical Considerations   Walls for buildings and structures that support an adjacent zone of soil as well as free-standing retaining walls normally are designed to resist an at-rest or active lateral soil pressure. In designs, passive soil pressures typically are considered only as reactionary loading, resisting movement where a structural element is moved toward or into a soil mass as an effect of the primary design load; for example, soil along the front of a retaining wall _foundation_ tends to develop passive resistance if the supported soil mass causes the wall to move laterally outward (Fig. 16-11). Since lateral movement in a retained soil mass is necessary for the active and passive pressure conditions to develop, structural elements, such as basement walls and bridge abutments whose design requires or assumes that the wall remains rigid without deflection or translation and where connecting framing components act to keep the structure stationary, need to consider lateral soil pressures corresponding to the _at-rest_ condition. At-rest pressures

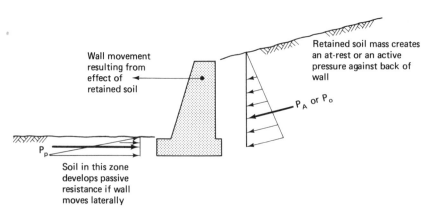

Figure 16-11   Zones tending to develop active and passive lateral pressures.

for the case where backfill against the wall is placed and compacted in layers tend to be greater than with uncompacted fill and natural deposits.

Figure 16-12 shows the general relationship between retaining wall movements and lateral pressures. This presentation illustrates the important fact that lateral pressures change gradually in accord with wall movement, and reach the fully active or passive condition only when adequate movement has occurred. Until such movement is achieved, the lateral pressure acting is intermediate between the at-rest and active or at-rest and passive value. The extent of movement required for a soil mass to reach the passive condition is considerably greater than for the active condition. The pressure variations indicated by Figure 16-12 are for the short-term condition; changes back toward the at-rest pressure can occur over an extended duration, particularly with cohesive soils but also with some cohesionless soils.

For free-standing retaining walls, movement adequate to develop a lateral force corresponding to the active pressure or passive pressure condition can occur by rotation or translation (Fig. 16-13).

Active case lateral pressure distributions that result with a *cohesionless backfill* and wall rotation or translation are shown in Figure 16-14. Since retaining wall behavior conventionally expected corresponds to the condition represented by Figure 16-14a or 16-14b, these cases serve as the basis for most designs. The condition for Figure 16-14c could result where unusual areal settlement occurs or where a rotational slide which is deep seated and below the base of the wall occurs (a condition discussed in Chapter 15).

Figure 16-12 Lateral pressure condition related to wall movement.

Figure 16-13 Wall movements that produce the active and passive pressure conditions.

Earth Pressures Against Retaining Walls

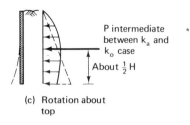

Figure 16-14 Pressure distributions for cohesionless soil related to type of wall movement.

Methods of backfill placement and the category of granular soil have an important effect on the lateral pressures that eventually act on the wall. Over the long term, lateral pressures will correspond to the theoretical active condition when coarse granular backfill is used but not compacted. When the backfill directly behind the retaining wall is compacted, a common procedure intended to increase the angle of internal friction ϕ and theoretically to reduce the K_a value, final lateral pressures may actually reach or exceed at-rest values. The procedure of placing and compacting the soil in layers causes lateral squeezing and progressive wall deflection as the height of backfill is being increased, one result being that the postconstruction movement necessary to achieve the active condition does not occur. There is also evidence to indicate that even when lateral pressures resulting from a retained granular soil decrease to theoretical active values as wall movement occurs, the pressures subsequently increase with time and approach at-rest values [41]. Further wall movement may occur as a result, and the repetitive occurrence of pressure increase and wall movement can lead to wall failure. The extent of change is greatest with the finer cohesionless soils.

It is common to find that retaining wall design has been on the basis of the theoretical active soil pressure condition indicated by Figure 16-13(a). However, because of the typical modern procedure of placing and compacting retaining wall backfill, and factors that influence the retained soil mass's shear stress–strain behavior and its ability to help support itself over an extended duration, this conventional or established design procedure does not apply to all wall construction. Where wall movement must be limited or where continuous wall movement cannot be tolerated, design on the basis of a lateral pressure condition in the at-rest range is more appropriate than assuming an active pressure condition. Further, if a limited zone behind the wall represents the excavation which is subsequently backfilled, the full Rankine–Coulomb failure wedge may not have space to develop. Additionally, the natural soil slope adjacent to the work area behind the wall often has earlier experienced some lateral movement as a result of having been unsupported temporarily, and that zone may not be capable of providing the further shearing resistance necessary for the full active pressure condition to develop against the wall. For this situation and with the backfill compacted in layers (Fig. 16-15), the lateral pressures assumed for design should correspond to at least the at-rest pressure condition.

The expression from theory for the active lateral pressure resulting from a retained *cohesive soil* is given by Equation 16-4a, whereby

$$p_a = \gamma_t Z \tan^2 \left(45 - \frac{\phi}{2} \right) - 2c \tan \left(45 - \frac{\phi}{2} \right) \qquad (16\text{-}4a)$$

Where conditions for the undrained shear strength apply, ϕ is zero and the above equation reduces to

$$p_a = \gamma_t z - 2c \qquad (16\text{-}4c)$$

These expressions imply that the lateral pressure imposed on a wall by the uppermost zone of a retained clay is zero. The internal cohesion enables the soil mass to resist shearing stresses developing as lateral support is removed, in effect providing some self-support. The theoretical active pressure is negative (the soil is considered to be in tension) to a depth z where p_a in Equation 16-4a is zero, or

$$z = \frac{2c}{\gamma_t \tan \left(45 - \frac{\phi}{2} \right)} \qquad (16\text{-}11a)$$

and for the condition where undrained shear strength applies,

$$z = \frac{2c}{\gamma} \qquad (16\text{-}11b)$$

Only below the depth z does a soil pressure develop against the wall.

Figure 16-15   Limited backfill zone effects lateral pressures against wall.

Earth Pressures Against Retaining Walls

The active pressure distribution against a retaining wall resulting from application of Equation 16-4a is shown in Figure 16-16b. This diagram helps explain why excavations in clay soils can be maintained with vertical banks without lateral supports being provided. The pressure distribution of Figure 16-16b can be assumed for supporting a cohesive soil over a *short time period*. However, two important factors limit the apparent benefit indicated by this figure and Equation 16-4a for realizing a reduced lateral force acting on a retaining structure over an *extended* duration. Tension cracks can develop in the upper soil zone, and the soil may pull away from the wall, to the depth z, affecting the theoretical pressure distribution. Should the open cracks against and near to the wall fill with water, a hydrostatic pressure can result against the wall. To compensate for the possible effect of such water pressures, a modified active pressure diagram can be assumed as indicated in Figure 16-16c for short-duration designs. For a long-term design and permanent retaining structures, the stress–strain behavior of clay in shear becomes significant. During sustained shear near a clay's maximum strength, most will creep or flow. Internal shearing resistance is retained only if progressive deformation can occur. Applying this principle of soil behavior to the force resulting against a retaining wall, lateral pressures from a clay will increase above the initially active value when movement is prevented and the soil's internal shearing resistance diminishes. For pressures that correspond to the active case to remain in effect against a retaining wall, continuous wall movement must occur. Walls designed for only the active pressure condition are subject to movement when lateral pressures increase above

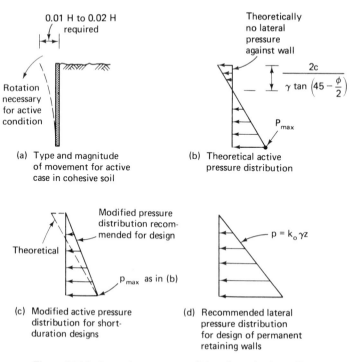

Figure 16-16 Lateral pressure conditions for cohesive soil.

Lateral Pressures and Retaining Structures   Chap. 16

(a) Lateral soil pressure distribution
where water table is below level
of wall backfill

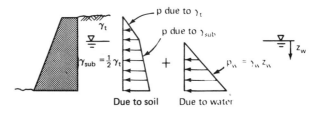

(b) Lateral pressures against wall when water
level behind wall is above base of wall

Figure 16-17 Lateral pressures affected by water behind wall.

that magnitude. After the additional wall movement does occur, the lateral pressures decrease to the active value but subsequently will again increase. The sequence of increasing pressure followed by wall movement is ongoing, and if enough wall movement occurs, failure will result. In recognition of this phenomenon, when cohesive soil must be used for backfill behind a retaining wall (the use of such soil should be avoided wherever possible), the wall should be designed to resist at least an at-rest lateral pressure, as indicated by Figure 16-16d.

Wall behavior can be further affected if a clay backfill is subject to large volume changes as its water content varies. Lateral pressures against the wall increase in periods when moisture is available and swelling occurs. Pressure changes are greatest if shrinkage cracks from dry periods have become filled with soil or debris.

Lateral soil pressures against a wall are computed by using the *effective* unit weight of the retained soil. If the groundwater level rises into the backfill behind a retaining wall because of either a changing ground water condition or percolating surface water, the lateral pressures against the wall are changed (Fig. 16-17). For soil below the water table a submerged unit weight is used, and the related lateral soil pressure becomes approximately half of the nonsubmerged value. Additionally, however, a hydrostatic pressure develops against the back of the wall. The combined effect of soil and water pressures causes overturning moments and sliding forces to be greater than for the condition of no water (refer to Illustration 16-1). To eliminate the opportunity for a great height of water to build up behind a wall, through-the wall weep holes or a collector–drainage system, or both, are commonly provided and are considered to be an essential part of the design and construction

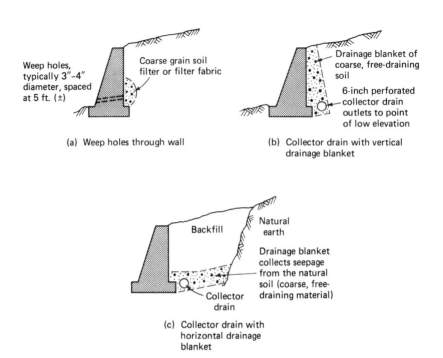

Figure 16-18 Drainage methods to prevent development of water pressures behind retaining walls.

(Fig. 16-18). Weep holes should be at least 3 inches (8 cm) in diameter, and provided with a granular soil filter or filter fabric at the back of the wall to prevent backfill erosion. The horizontal spacings normally selected range from about 4 ft to 10 ft (1.5–3 m). For tall walls, two or more rows of weep holes may be used, with a typical vertical spacing of 5 ft or about 1.5 m.

Freezing temperatures can cause ice lens formation behind the wall if water is available in the backfill. The backfill zones around weep holes are particularly vulnerable because of the hole opening and temperature conduction of the weep hole pipe if metal is used. The conduction properties of solid concrete and masonry are also high, the effect being that the back sides of such retaining walls have temperatures close to air temperatures. Coarse, non-frost-susceptible material behind the wall (Fig. 16-18b) serves to prevent the development of ice lenses in the backfill zone. A coarse drainage blanket located as indicated by Fig. 16-18c acts to prevent deep groundwater from rising by capillary action to the freezing zone behind the wall.

Retaining Walls: Design Requirements Retaining walls have been constructed of plain and reinforced concrete, masonry, laid-up stone (dry construction), timber, and metal materials. Simple walls are the gravity type, with the weight of the wall providing the required stability against the effects of a retained soil. Representative types of gravity walls are shown in Figure 16-19. The practical use of gravity retaining walls is controlled by height limitations, whereby the required wall cross section starts to increase significantly with tall heights because of effects of the approximately triangular soil pressure distribution behind the wall. Cantilever retaining walls (Fig. 16-20) incorporate a design feature which enables some of the retained soil to contribute to the stability of the structure, thereby permitting a design which requires less wall material than the equivalent height gravity type. Such walls require reinforcing steel because of the relative slenderness of the stem (i.e., vertical section) and base.

Retaining walls have also been constructed of timber and steel sheet piling, closely spaced large diameter concrete piles, and spaced H-piling with horizontal lagging of concrete or timber planks (Fig. 16-21). Cube-shaped wire mesh baskets filled with crushed rock (gabions) have been used to form gravity walls in a manner similar to that achieved by using laid-up stone (dry, no mortar) construction, although their prevalent use has been for slope protection. Figure 16-28 and the related text further discuss gabions.

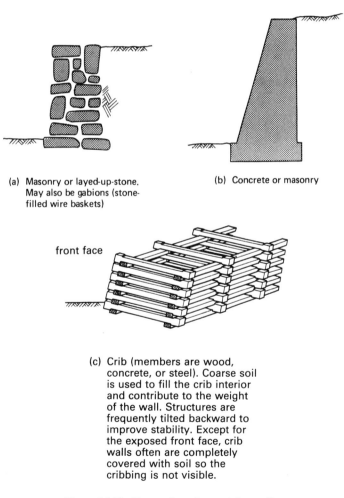

(a) Masonry or layed-up-stone. May also be gabions (stone-filled wire baskets)

(b) Concrete or masonry

front face

(c) Crib (members are wood, concrete, or steel). Coarse soil is used to fill the crib interior and contribute to the weight of the wall. Structures are frequently tilted backward to improve stability. Except for the exposed front face, crib walls often are completely covered with soil so the cribbing is not visible.

Figure 16-19 Types of gravity retaining walls.

Earth Pressures Against Retaining Walls

(a) Cantilever section indicating general principle whereby backfill assists stability

(b) Semi-gravity type

(c) Cantilever

(d) Counterfort or buttress wall (counterfort wall has buttress located on backfill side, while buttress wall has buttresses along front side)

Figure 16-20 Cantilever-type retaining walls.

Retaining walls are long structures. The usual design procedure is to analyze a section one unit in length, with the unit length selected being an increment where the wall section begins to repeat; walls whose general cross section is constant for a long length would consider a segment one foot or one meter in length, whereas a counterfort or buttressed wall would consider a section that extends the center-to-center distance between buttresses. The height of soil to be retained will usually vary along the length of the wall, and with homogeneous backfill and foundation conditions the most severe design loading occurs where the height is greatest. The wall cross section required for this crucial location is also assumed for adjacent locations, although the actual height constructed may be lower. For long walls of varying height requirements, a separate design can be provided for the different segments in order to economize on materials. Conversely, for concrete walls of limited length that retain an approximately constant height of soil, the critical cross section may be used for the entire wall, because savings related to labor and forming procedures associated with constructing the wall offset the extra material used. A benefit resulting from this latter approach is that the average theoretical structural factor of safety across the full length of retaining wall is greater than the design factor of safety.

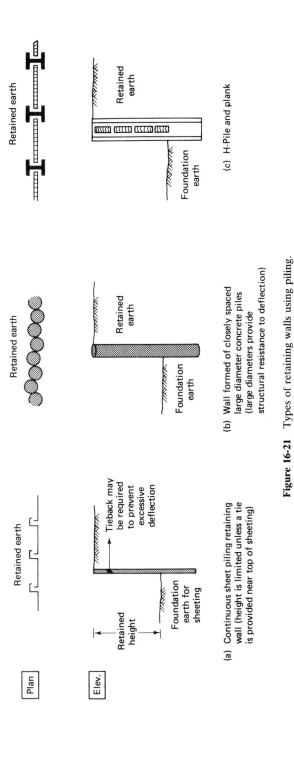

Retained earth

Plan

Elev.

Retained height

Foundation earth for sheeting

Tieback may be required to prevent excessive deflection

(a) Continuous sheet piling retaining wall (height is limited unless a tie is provided near top of sheeting)

Retained earth

Retained earth

Foundation earth

(b) Wall formed of closely spaced large diameter concrete piles (large diameters provide structural resistance to deflection)

Retained earth

Retained earth

Foundation earth

(c) H-Pile and plank

Figure 16-21 Types of retaining walls using piling.

A proper retaining wall design satisfies the following requirements:

1. The structural components of the wall (the base and the stem) are capable of resisting the internal shears and bending moments developing as a result of soil and other loading.
2. The wall structure is safe against overturning.
3. The wall structure is safe against sliding.
4. The bearing capacity of the foundation material supporting the wall is not exceeded.
5. Settlement and distortion of the wall due to compression of the foundation soil are limited to a tolerable value.

All factors relating to the stability of a retaining wall are affected by the magnitude of the lateral earth pressure. For design, then, it is important to know the properties of the backfill and to be assured that wall movement, if necessary for the design lateral pressures to develop, can actually occur. For instance, if a gravity or cantilever wall is founded on rock or a very firm or compact soil (Fig. 16-23a), rotational movement (Fig. 16-14a) will probably not occur; such walls are designed with the assumption of an at-rest pressure. In a design analysis, the position of the lateral pressure resultant at the back of a wall is as indicated in Figure 16-22.

The analysis for shear forces and bending moments acting on the vertical section of a wall is similar to the procedure for analyzing a structural beam carrying a distributed loading (Fig. 16-23b). The stability against overturning is evaluated by comparing moments about an assumed axis of rotation (typically the toe of the wall) which result from forces acting to cause overturning and forces acting to resist overturning (Fig. 16-23c). The ratio of moments resisting to those causing overturning is the factor of safety against overturning; a value of 2 or greater is normally desired. The stability against sliding is evaluated by comparing forces causing sliding to those resisting sliding (Fig. 16-23d). The ratio of the forces resisting to the forces causing is the factor of safety against sliding; a desired minimum value of 1.5 is typical.

(a) Gravity wall   (b) Cantilever wall

Figure 16-22 Position of lateral pressure resultant for stability analysis.

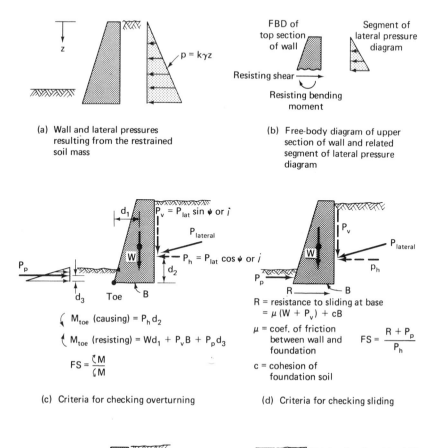

(a) Wall and lateral pressures resulting from the restrained soil mass

(b) Free-body diagram of upper section of wall and related segment of lateral pressure diagram

M_{toe} (causing) $= P_h d_2$

M_{toe} (resisting) $= W d_1 + P_v B + P_p d_3$

$$FS = \frac{\complement M}{\complement M}$$

(c) Criteria for checking overturning

R = resistance to sliding at base
$= \mu (W + P_v) + cB$

μ = coef. of friction between wall and foundation

$$FS = \frac{R + P_p}{P_h}$$

c = cohesion of foundation soil

(d) Criteria for checking sliding

P_{max} less than $P_{allowable}$

(e) Typical soil bearing pressure distribution as a result of lateral pressures against wall

(f) Weight of wall and backfill can cause wall to settle

Figure 16-23 Summary of conditions to check during retaining wall designs.

Foundation bearing pressures are computed by following the procedures for determining stress distributions where an axial loading and bending moment act in combination on a structural section. The position of the foundation reaction is first located from

$$d = \frac{\Sigma M_{\text{toe}}}{\Sigma V} \quad \text{or} \quad \frac{\Sigma M_{\text{heel}}}{\Sigma V}$$

where ΣM = algebraic sum of moments about the wall's toe or heel.
$\quad\quad \Sigma V$ = vertical component of the foundation reaction including the weight of the wall and backfill, and vertical component of the lateral soil pressure.
$\quad\quad d$ = distance from toe or heel to point where foundation reaction is applied.

Desirably, the d distance is located within the middle third of the base so that the wall loading is spread across the entire base (theoretically, no tensile stresses will develop). An eccentricity distance, e, which is the distance from the center of the wall base to the position where the foundation reaction acts, is then determined from

$$e = \frac{b}{2} - d$$

where b = width of wall base.
The foundation pressure p_f at the toe and at the heel can be calculated by using

$$p_f = \frac{V}{(b)(1)} \pm \frac{Ve\left(\frac{b}{2}\right)}{\left(\frac{1}{12}\right)(1)(b^3)} = \frac{V}{b} \pm \frac{6Ve}{b^2} \tag{16-12}$$

If the foundation reaction V is located to the toe side of the base's center, the plus sign is used in Equation 16-12 to compute pressure at the toe while the negative sign is used to calculate the pressure at the heel, and vice versa. The computed values are then compared to allowable bearing pressures determined from bearing capacity equations or other information. Wall settlement or movement expected as a result of the weight of the wall and backfill loading being imposed on an area can be evaluated from settlement analysis based on the compressibility of the foundation soils (Fig. 16-23f).

Relating to consideration of foundation pressure and settlement, the capability of the foundation soils underlying the location of a retaining wall *and* its backfill may actually be the aspect most crucial to achieving a satisfactory performance in areas where clay exists. Studies of retaining wall performances have indicated that clay foundations were involved in the majority of failures [187]. The undrained shearing strength and bearing capacity of the foundation deposit should be evaluated to ensure that the in situ conditions will be capable of supporting the loading to result from the wall and backfill. Strength gain can be expected when foundation clays are subject to new loading, but changes associated with consolidation normally occur very slowly.

ILLUSTRATION 16-2. A simple retaining wall of masonry supports a sand backfill as shown by the sketch. Assuming an active lateral pressure condition, determine the stability of the wall.

$$P_A = \tfrac{1}{2}\gamma H^2 K_a = \tfrac{1}{2}(125 \text{ pcf})(12 \text{ ft} \times 12 \text{ ft})(0.25) = 2250 \text{ lb per ft of length}$$

$$P_v = P_A \sin 35° = 1290 \text{ lb/ft} = 18.86 \text{ kN/m}$$

$$P_h = P_A \cos 35° = 1840 \text{ lb/ft} = 26.91 \text{ kN/m}$$

1. $\Sigma\, M_{\text{toe}}$ to determine stability against overturning

$$\circlearrowleft (1840 \text{ lb/ft})\left(\frac{12 \text{ ft}}{3}\right) = 7360 \text{ ft-lb per ft of wall's length,}$$

$$\text{or, } (26.91 \text{ kN})\left(\frac{3.66}{3}\text{ m}\right) = 32.83 \text{ kN-m per m of wall's length.}$$

$$\circlearrowright (1290 \text{ lb/ft} \times 4 \text{ ft}) + \left(150 \text{ pcf} \times 4 \text{ ft} \times 1 \text{ ft} \times 12 \text{ ft} \times \frac{4}{2}\text{ ft}\right) =$$

$$= 5160 + 14{,}400 = 19{,}560 \text{ ft-lb per ft of wall's length.}$$

$$\text{or, } \left(18.86 \frac{\text{kN}}{\text{m}}\ (1.22 \text{ m}) + \left(23.55 \frac{\text{kN}}{\text{m}^3}\right)(1 \text{ m})(1.22 \text{ m})(3.66 \text{ m})\left(\frac{1.22}{3}\text{ m}\right) = \right.$$

$$= 87.14 \text{ kN-m per m of wall's length}$$

$$FS \text{ against overturning} = \frac{19{,}560 \text{ ft-lb}}{7{,}360 \text{ ft-lb}} = \frac{87.14 \text{ kN-m}}{32.83 \text{ kN-m}} = 2.6\pm$$

2. $\Sigma\, F$ in horizontal direction to determine stability against sliding

$$\leftarrow F_{\text{causing}} = 1840 \text{ lb/ft} \quad\text{or}\quad 26.91 \text{ kN/m}$$

Earth Pressures Against Retaining Walls

$\rightarrow F_{\text{resisting}} = cB = (1000 \text{ psf})(4 \text{ ft}) = 4000 \text{ lb per ft of wall's length.}$

$\text{or} \left(48 \dfrac{\text{kN}}{\text{m}^2} \times 1.22 \text{ m} \right) = 58.56 \text{ kN per m of wall's length.}$

$FS \text{ against sliding} = \dfrac{F_{\text{resisting}}}{F_{\text{causing}}}$

$= \dfrac{4000 \text{ lb}}{1840 \text{ lb}} = \dfrac{58.56 \text{ kN}}{26.91 \text{ kN}} = 2.2 \pm$

3. Determining foundation pressures

$\Sigma M_b = (1840 \text{ lb/ft} \times 4 \text{ ft}) + (7200 \text{ lb/ft} \times 2 \text{ ft})$

$= 21{,}760 \text{ ft-lb per ft of length,}$

$\text{or} \ (26.91 \text{ kN/m})(1.22 \text{ m}) + (23.55 \text{ kN/m}^3)(3.66 \text{ m})(1.22 \text{ m})(1.22 \text{ m}/2)$

$= 97 \text{ kN-m per m of length.}$

$\Sigma V = 7200 \text{ lb/ft} + 1290 \text{ lb/ft} = 8490 \text{ lb/ft}$

$\text{or} \ (105.1 + 18.9) \text{ kN/m} = 124 \text{ kN per m of length.}$

$d = \dfrac{\Sigma M}{\Sigma V} = \dfrac{21{,}760 \text{ ft-lb/ft}}{8490 \text{ lb/ft}} = 2.56 \text{ ft,} \quad \text{or } 97 \text{ kN-m/m124 kN/m} = 0.78 \text{ m}$

B = 4 ft or 1.22 m

1 ft or 1 m

$I_{xx} = \frac{1}{12} (1 \text{ ft}) (4 \text{ ft} \times 4 \text{ ft} \times 4 \text{ ft}) = 5.33 \text{ ft}^4 = 0.15 \text{ m}^4$

I for wall section

V = 8490 lb/ft. = 124 kN/m

e = 256 ft − 2.0 ft = 0.56 ft.

$P_b = (2122 - 1783) \text{ psf}$
$= 339 \text{ psf} = 16 \text{ kN/m}^2$

$Pa = \dfrac{V}{A} + \dfrac{M \ (B/2)}{I} = \dfrac{V}{A} + \dfrac{Ve \ (B/2)}{I}$

$= \dfrac{8490 \text{ lb}}{4 \text{ ft} \times 1 \text{ ft}} + \dfrac{(8490 \text{ lb})(0.56 \text{ ft})(4/2)}{5.33 \text{ ft}^4}$

$= 2122 + 1783 = 3906 \text{ psf} = 187 \text{ kN/m}^2$

ILLUSTRATION 16.3. Check the stability and determine the bearing pressures beneath the base for the cantilever retaining wall shown.

Sand backfill, $\phi = 35°$, $\gamma = 130$ pcf
Use k = 0.4 since backfill is placed and
   compacted in layers and limited
   work area behind wall interferes
   with development of active wedge

Silty sand foundation
   $\gamma = 115$ pcf, $\phi = 30°$
   Assume $\mu = 0.5$ for sliding

Neglect passive
pressure at toe

$$P_{\text{lateral}} = \tfrac{1}{2}\gamma H^2 K = \tfrac{1}{2}(130 \text{ pcf})(22 \text{ ft} \times 22 \text{ ft})(0.4)$$

$$= 12{,}585 \text{ lb per ft of wall length}$$

1. ΣM_{toe} to check stability against overturning

$$\curvearrowleft \left(10{,}900 \text{ lb} \times \frac{22 \text{ ft}}{3}\right) = 79{,}935 \text{ ft-lb per ft of wall length}$$

$$\curvearrowright (6300 \text{ lb})(10 \text{ ft}) + (145 \text{ pcf})(1 \text{ ft})(10 \text{ ft})(2 \text{ ft})\left(\frac{10 \text{ ft}}{2}\right)$$

$$+ (145 \text{ pcf})(1 \text{ ft})(18 \text{ ft})(2 \text{ ft})(3 \text{ ft}) + (6 \text{ ft})(1 \text{ ft})\left(\frac{18 + 20}{2} \text{ ft}\right)(7.1 \text{ ft})(130 \text{ pcf})$$

$$= 198{,}385 \text{ ft-lb per ft of wall length}$$

$$FS \text{ against overturning} = \frac{198{,}385 \text{ ft-lb}}{79{,}935 \text{ ft-lb}} = 2.5 \pm$$

2. ΣF in horizontal direction to check sliding

$$\leftarrow F_{\text{causing}} = 10{,}900 \text{ lb per ft of wall length}$$

$$\rightarrow F_{\text{resisting}} = 0.5 \, [(2 \text{ ft} \times 10 \text{ ft} \times 1 \text{ ft} \times 145 \text{ pcf})$$

$$+ (2 \text{ ft} \times 18 \text{ ft} \times 1 \text{ ft} \times 145 \text{ pcf})$$

$$+ (6 \text{ ft} \times 19 \text{ ft} \times 1 \text{ ft} \times 130 \text{ pcf}) + 6300 \text{ lb}]$$

$$= 15{,}320 \text{ lb per ft of length}$$

$$FS \text{ against sliding} = \frac{15{,}320 \text{ lb}}{10{,}900 \text{ lb}} = 1.4 \pm$$

3. Determining foundation pressures

$$\Sigma M_a = 198{,}385 \text{ ft-lb} - 79{,}935 \text{ ft-lb} = 118{,}450 \text{ ft-lb}$$

$$\Sigma V = (145 \text{ pcf})[(2 \text{ ft})(1 \text{ ft})(18 \text{ ft}) + (2 \text{ ft})(1 \text{ ft})(10 \text{ ft})]$$

$$+ \left(\frac{20 + 18}{2}\right) \text{ft}(6 \text{ ft})(1 \text{ ft})(130 \text{ pcf}) + 6300 \text{ lb} = 29{,}240 \text{ lb}$$

Earth Pressures Against Retaining Walls **519**

$$d = \frac{\Sigma\, M_a}{\Sigma\, V} = \frac{118{,}450 \text{ ft-lb}}{29{,}240 \text{ lb}} = 4.05 \text{ ft}$$

$$e = \frac{b}{2} - d = \frac{10 \text{ ft}}{2} - 4.05 \text{ ft} = 0.95 \text{ ft}$$

I for wall section

1 ft

$I_{xx} = \frac{1}{12}$ (1') (10' × 10' × 10') = 83.3 ft^4

B = 10 ft

B/2 = 5 ft

V = 29,240 lb

a   b

d = 4.05 ft   e = 0.95 ft.

$p_b = 2924 - 1667 = 1257$ psf

$$P_a = \frac{V}{A} + \frac{Ve\,(B/2)}{I}$$

$$= \frac{29{,}240}{(10 \times 1)} + \frac{(29{,}240)\,(0.95)\,(10/2)}{83.3}$$

$$= 2924 + 1667 = 4591 \text{ psf}$$

Surface Loads near Wall   Loadings placed on the ground surface behind a retaining wall cause lateral pressures against the wall that are additive to those pressures created by the backfill and, if applicable, a high water table. If an areal load of uniform intensity q occurs, a uniform *increase* in the lateral pressures acting against the wall, equal to qK, develops (Fig. 16-24). The lateral-pressure coefficient K used for the wall backfill also applies to the areal load.

A concentrated load Q will cause a lateral pressure distribution against the wall which is generally as indicated by Figure 16-25. The lateral pressure resulting

Area loading of intensity q (psf or kN/m^2)

$k\sigma_v$ Kq

+

Lateral pressure   Lateral pressure due
due to backfill   to areal loading

Figure 16-24 Influence of areal loading on wall pressures.

m	R	Y
0.2	$0.78\dfrac{Q}{H}$	0.59 H
0.4	$0.78\dfrac{Q}{H}$	0.59 H
0.6	$0.48\dfrac{Q}{H}$	0.48 H

Figure 16-25 Pressure distribution against vertical wall resulting from point load, Q.

at any point along the height of the wall directly in front of the load can be closely approximated by

$$p_Q = \left(\frac{Q}{H^2}\right)\frac{(0.28n^2)}{(0.16 + n^2)^3} \quad \text{for } m \le 0.4 \tag{16-13a}$$

$$p_Q = \left(\frac{Q}{H^2}\right)\frac{(1.77\ m^2n^2)}{(m^2 + n^2)^3} \quad \text{for } m > 0.4 \tag{16-13b}$$

If a line load of intensity q acts behind a wall, a pressure distribution against the back of the wall is created, as generally shown by Figure 16-26. The lateral pressure at points along the height of the wall can be approximated from

$$p_q = \left(\frac{q}{H}\right)\frac{(0.20n)}{(0.16 + n^2)^2} \quad \text{for } m \le 0.40 \tag{16-14a}$$

$$p_q = \left(\frac{q}{H}\right)\frac{(1.28)m^2n^2}{(m^2 + n^2)^2} \quad \text{for } m > 0.4 \tag{16-14b}$$

In these equations, the units for p_Q and p_q are in accord with the units used for Q or q, and H.

Terzaghi-Peck Charts for Backfill Pressures Where small, routine projects are involved, the designer may have little or no information about a wall's

m	R	Y
0.2	0.55q	0.60 H
0.4	0.55q	0.58 H
0.6	$\dfrac{0.64q}{m^2 + 1}$	0.52 H

Figure 16-26 Pressure distribution against vertical wall resulting from line load of intensity q.

Earth Pressures Against Retaining Walls

backfill, or the source of backfill may be subject to change. Job economics may limit or preclude investigation of backfill properties and control of its placement. For low retaining walls such as those bordering highways and railroads, where stability is the principal concern but wall movements and backfill settlements are not critical, Terzaghi and Peck have presented charts for estimating backfill pressures as related to general soil categories. Their information, evolving from a coupling of theoretical concepts and evaluation of the performance of existing walls, is shown in Figure 16-27. These curves are considered suitable for the design of walls up to about 20 ft (6 m) in height. Such charts are limited to providing realistic but safe values of lateral pressures due to soil backfill. The designer must still include provisions for drainage and consider the possibility of soil freezing and swelling behind the wall. Importantly, the designer must independently obtain information about the character and strength of the area's foundation soils to evaluate their adequacy for supporting the wall and backfill.

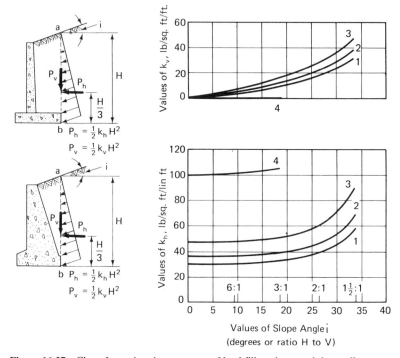

Figure 16-27 Chart for estimating pressure of backfill against retaining walls supporting backfills with plane surface. Use of chart limited to walls not over about 20 ft (6m) high. Curves refer to different soil types: (1) Backfill of coarse-grained soil without admixture of fine particles, very permeable, as clean sand or gravel. (2) Backfill of coarse-grained soil of low permeability due to admixture of particles of silt size. (3) Backfill of fine silty sand, granular materials with conspicuous clay content, and residual soil with stones. (4) Backfill of very soft or soft clay, organic silt, or silty clay. (After Terzaghi and Peck. From *Foundation Engineering* by Peck, Hanson, and Thornburn, by permission of John Wiley and Sons, Inc., publisher [185].)

Gabion Retaining Walls   Gabions are large steel wire mesh baskets filled with stone (Fig. 16-28a). The units[4] can be assembled, like building blocks, to construct retaining wall, slope protection, and waterfront protection structures. Gabions are assembled and filled with the desired size and gradation of rock material at the job site. Conventionally, a wall structure is built by placing an empty basket in position, filling it with rock, then placing and filling the next basket, and so on (Fig. 16-28b). Each newly placed basket is attached by wire to the adjacent and underlying gabions.

A gabion structure obtains most of its stability and resistance to erosive forces from the gabion's rock fill. Virtually all of the resistance to earth or water forces acting against a completed structure is provided by the friction and interlocking which develops within a basket's rockfill and between the rockfill surfaces of the individual gabion units. Structurally, the main purpose of the gabion basket is to keep the rock materials assembled in place.

A gabion retaining wall offers the advantage that it is a flexible structure which can tolerate foundation settlement and lateral movements while still retaining stability. The open structure of the rockfill permits water to move through the wall, a feature that prevents the occurrence of high water pressures behind the wall. However, tall walls may still be constructed with a drain system behind the wall to prevent seepage effects that could reduce stability. Compared to concrete construction, the gabion structure may show economy in construction time and overall cost.

A gabion retaining wall is analyzed as a gravity wall. The conventional design procedures discussed previously in the chapter are used to determine the lateral forces that will act against the structure. Resistance to sliding and overturning is checked for each section of wall (along each row of gabions) and for the full wall height as with the analysis of a masonry retaining wall. Walls usually follow either

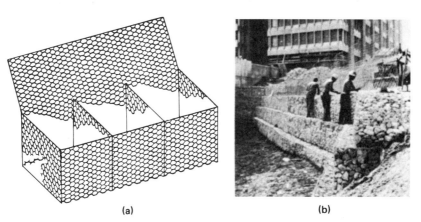

(a)   (b)

Figure 16-28   Illustration of gabion unit and installation procedure: (a) Gabion basket; (b) wall under construction. (Courtesy Maccaferri Gabions, Inc.)

[4]Basket sizes range from approximately 6 ft (2 m) to 12 ft (4 m) in length and are 3 ft (1 m) in width and 3 ft (1 m) in depth. Internal diaphragms or dividers are included so that the interior cells do not become too large; small cells limit internal movement of the rock fill.

(a) Straight front face

(b) Stepped front face

Figure 16-29 Typical designs for gabion retaining walls.

the straight-front-face, step-rear-face design, or the stepped-front-face, straight-rear-face design (Fig. 16-29). Walls usually will be tilted slightly backward, say to a slope of $1H$ to $10V$, to improve the stability insofar as being affected by the angle of the lateral soil pressure resultant.

Reinforced Earth Retaining walls and embankments have been built of earth reinforced with strips, fabrics, or fibers of various materials so as to increase the shear strength and supporting properties of the constructed mass. The use of reinforced earth for engineered structures as pioneered by the Reinforced Earth Company® involves reinforcing metal or fabric strips integrated with a granular earth fill which is placed and compacted in layers. A facing material, typically of thin metal or concrete panels, is used to form the exposed boundary or face of the reinforced earth structure and prevent the loss of fill material. The facing is mechanically fastened to the reinforcing strips. A reinforced earth structure is constructed systematically, layer by layer. Reinforcing strips are placed on the surface of each fill layer and connected to the face paneling, then covered with the next soil layer, a procedure that ensures the design number and location of reinforcing strips. Facing panels are placed as the height of fill progresses. The schematic diagram of Figure 16-30a illustrates the basic components of reinforced earth construction, while Figure 16-30b shows a project in progress. Variations of the *tied-back face panel retaining wall* concept exist and are available from other commercial organizations; usually the differences relate to the type of embedded strip or to the type and connection of the face paneling.

The friction or bond developed between the soil fill and strip surfaces provides the resistance required to hold the face panels in place. In terms of design, the lateral pressures exerted on the facing by the granular fill are opposed by the frictional resistance developed along the surface of the reinforcing strips. In effect, then, the reinforced earth mass retains itself, even though a sharp discontinuity (the vertical facing) exists. The lateral soil pressure imposed on the facing is approximately equal to the active lateral pressure indicated by conventional earth pressure theory. The required total surface area for each layer of reinforcing can be determined by computing the increment of lateral pressure developed by each soil layer. Typically, the width of fill and length of strips perpendicular to the wall facing is on the order of 0.8 of the fill height. However, the fill width and strip

(a)

(b)

Figure 16-30 (a) Basic components of reinforced earth construction. (b) Reinforced earth embankment under construction. (Courtesy of the Reinforced Earth Company)

length must extend back beyond any potential failure plane that could result from outward movement of the facing.

Reinforced earth structures that function as retaining walls and for stabilizing earth slopes (including earth dam structures) can offer a cost advantage compared to conventional retaining structures. Part of this cost advantage relates to the condition that, generally, reinforced earth structures do not require special foundations, often being built directly on natural ground. The structures normally retain stability where foundation settlement or wall deflections occur, provided that movements are not excessive.

The design of a reinforced earth structure requires consideration of the effective life of material used for the reinforcing. Metals that experience only limited

Earth Pressures Against Retaining Walls   **525** corrosion or nondegradable fabrics are preferred. Design must also ensure that the reinforced earth structure will not be part of or cause an areal failure, such as a slope stability failure that passes outside the limits of the reinforced earth structure.

EXCAVATION BRACING

Excavations for subsurface construction must consider procedures for preventing cave-in of the perimeter earth and protection of adjacent outlying areas against ground subsidence and lateral movement during the construction period. Where shallow excavations and excavations in open or undeveloped areas are made, the periphery of the excavation can simply be sloped at a safe inclination to ensure stability of the resulting embankment. With deep excavations, however, the safe sloping of soil banks may involve considerable distance beyond the limits of the work area and require that large volumes of earth be removed and subsequently replaced; such procedures can be expensive and time consuming, and may create a problem of storage. In developed or built-up regions there simply may not be adequate space for sloping outside the excavation perimeter; in urban locations, excavations frequently extend to the property line or are required to be adjacent to an existing structure. Protection of the excavation perimeter and surrounding region for these situations then necessitates some system for vertically bracing the earth walls of the excavated area. Sheeting and bracing is frequently used.

A braced sheeting system when completed consists of a relatively flexible sheeting material, installed vertically against the excavation walls, and the bracing that provides the lateral support to hold the sheeting in place. Either partially or wholly, the sheeting support is installed prior to excavating. Bracing is provided as the excavation proceeds and the face of the sheeting components becomes exposed. A variety of materials, methods, and procedures have been used to achieve the required support bracing, the choices being influenced by factors such as subsurface conditions, excavation depth, working space, conditions surrounding the constructions site, availability and cost of materials, equipment and labor force available, climate and season, construction timetable, and ingenuity of the construction contractor or designer. There are three basic categories of braced sheeting in common use—vertical wood sheeting, interlocking steel sheeting, and soldier beam with horizontal timber sheeting. Each grouping offers both advantages and disadvantages.

Wood and *steel* sheeting (Fig. 16-31) is driven to a depth that will be below the base of the excavation prior to excavating in the construction area. Lateral support to resist the pressure of earth behind the sheeting is provided by horizontal bracing termed *struts* or diagonal bracing termed *rakers* which are positioned transverse to the sheeting line and within the excavated area. Lines of continuous horizontal members extending along the face of the sheeting, termed *wales*, are provided at the time the struts or rakers are installed (and are also supported by them) to reinforce the sheeting between the strut or raker locations. The installation of strut and wale bracing takes place as excavation proceeds; that is, the upper section of sheeting is the first to be braced, with subsequent bracing for the lower sheeting provided as the excavation progresses (Figs. 16-32 and 16-34). Diagonal

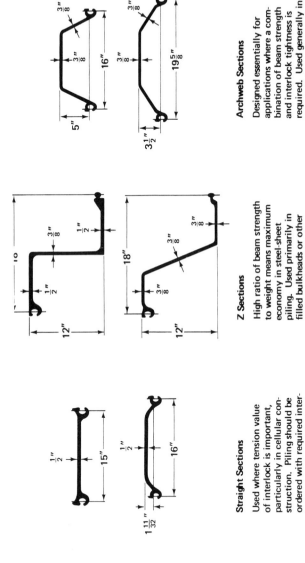

Straight Sections

Used where tension value of interlock is important, particularly in cellular construction. Piling should be ordered with required interlock strength specified and type of structure indicated.

Z Sections

High ratio of beam strength to weight means maximum economy in steel-sheet piling. Used primarily in filled bulkheads or other walls requiring high beam strength.

Archweb Sections

Designed essentially for applications where a combination of beam strength and interlock tightness is required. Used generally in light bulkheads, internally braced single wall cofferdams, cut-off walls.

Figure 16-31 Representative steel sheeting sections.

527

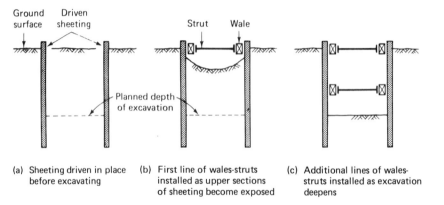

Figure 16-32 Procedure for bracing sheeting with struts and wales.

bracing (rakers) is used where horizontal struts cannot extend across the width of a large excavation because of the great span or because a too-cumbersome interior framework would be required to support the struts. Diagonal bracing obtains its interior support at the base elevation of the excavation (see Figs. 16-33 and 16-34). This requires at least some deep excavation before bracing is provided, a procedure that can be safely accomplished by initially excavating at a slope only

Figure 16-33 Procedure for bracing sheeting with wales and rakers.

Figure 16-34 Steel sheeting with crosslot or strut bracing (upper section of photo) and raker bracing (lower section of photo). (Courtesy Spencer, White, and Prentis)

the central area of the construction site. A berm or wedge of earth is left against the sheeting. The rakers can then be installed as removal of the berm progresses, or, alternatively, in trenches dug between the sheeting and interior excavation. A conventional soldier beam and timber lagging system consists of vertical steel H-piles (the soldier beam) which are driven to a penetration below the excavation's planned base elevation before digging begins. Piles may be positioned with the flanges parallel or perpendicular to the excavation wall. As excavation proceeds, timber plank lagging is inserted between or behind the piles if the flanges are parallel to the excavation (similar to the representation shown in Figure 16-21c, or held by clips against the front of the pile when the flanges are perpendicular to the excavation. The strut or raker and wale bracing is placed as for a sheeting installation.

Vertical wood sheeting, consisting of planks 3 in. to 4 in. thick, is, practically speaking, used for excavation extending no deeper than about 20 ft (6 m). Where the soil has properties that permit an excavation wall of limited depth to support itself temporarily, the wood sheeting can be installed in the open or perhaps partially completed excavation to provide support as required by law and to protect adjacent ground. With deep excavations the sheeting typically is driven in place with sheet piling hammers, and the size of this equipment must be limited to prevent over-stressing and damage to the wood. Soil displacement tends to be rather great during the driving of wood sheeting, one effect being that very firm and dense soils as well as gravel or boulder materials cannot be penetrated. In deep excavations, the sheeting bracing must be closely spaced because of the relatively low strength of the wood, an arrangement that subsequently may interfere with construction work within the excavation.

Interlocking steel sheeting offers the advantages of being able to be driven to great depths through many soil types without suffering damage. As an excavation wall, it acts to prevent the inflow of groundwater from behind it (for such cases

Excavation Bracing   **529** the sheeting and bracing must be designed to resist water pressures as well as soil pressures). Steel sheeting cannot be used to penetrate earth that includes boulders, and there can be difficulty with gravelly material. Similarly, fill containing heavy debris or large objects such as broken concrete and timbers cannot be penetrated. A major disadvantage is cost on those projects where the sheeting cannot be withdrawn for use elsewhere; for example, with projects in urban areas, pulling of the sheeting when the substructure is completed could result in damage to the new construction or could disturb the ground and structures surrounding the construction site.

Steel soldier beam and horizontal timber sheeting is considered to be a flexible system with respect to installation. The H-pile soldier beams can penetrate problem soils more easily than sheeting; some freedom in spacing is permitted when local obstructions are encountered. Strut and wales normally can be the same size member as the soldier beam, simplifying on-site storage and handling of these members. The lagging (timber planks 3–4 in. thick) is wedged between the pile flanges or behind the back flange as the excavation deepens. Commonly, the soldier beams are left in place to become an integral part within a poured concrete foundation wall for the permanent structure. When lagging is installed behind the back flange, it acts as the back form for construction of the concrete wall. During its installation, the lagging may be placed so as to create open horizontal spacings 1–2 in. wide, to permit drainage of the surrounding area and prevent hydrostatic pressures from developing against the back of the sheeting. Hay is often used in the space between lagging when seeping water tends to erode or wash in soil from behind the sheeting. An advantage to having drained earth behind the sheeting is the higher shear strength and lesser lateral pressure. Disadvantages include the effects of seepage forces, which contribute to lateral earth movement and consolidation–settlement of the retained earth mass.

Generally, the use of continuous steel sheeting is preferred for excavations deeper than about 25 ft or 8 m, especially where soft clays exist at and below the lower zones of the planned excavation, because the embedded sheeting improves the stability of the excavation foundation.

Bracing within an excavation interferes with the construction activities which must take place inside the excavated area. A relatively recently developed but now widely applied method, which eliminates the need for interior bracing, involves the use of tiebacks (Fig. 16-35), which extend into the earth behind the sheeting. Essentially, the tieback is a tensioned rod or cable connected to the sheeting or lagged wall plus an anchor embedded into soil or rock *outside* of the excavation area for establishing resistance to lateral forces imposed against the sheeting. Figure 16-36 illustrates a soldier beam–lagging system secured with tiebacks.

Alternatives to the use of driven sheeting for protecting the perimeter of an excavated area are available. Concrete walls constructed to support the earth excavation can also serve as all or part of the permanent foundation wall for the permanent structure. Unformed concrete walls can be created by utilizing drilled cast-in-place pile installation procedures. Alternatively, where firm cohesive soils exist, unsupported narrow trenches can be excavated and filled with concrete. When trenches are deep, or will extend through granular or soft clay soils as well as the

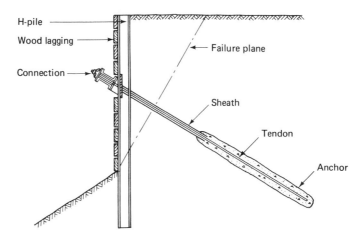

Figure 16-35 Typical earth tieback. Anchor is located outside potential failure zone.

water table, *slurry trench* construction can be performed (Fig. 16-37). This procedure involves excavating the trench while simultaneously keeping a heavy, viscous slurry (typically a bentonite clay–water mixture) present in the excavation to exert a lateral pressure that retains the trench's soil wall. Concrete is then tremied into the trench from the bottom up in a manner that displaces the slurry and prevents mixing. Reinforcing steel often is included, being placed into the slurry-filled trench before the concrete is poured. A tieback system or interior bracing is used to support the new concrete walls temporarily when the interior excavation is made.

Lateral Pressures for Designing Bracing   The top struts for sheeting bracing are normally installed before much earth is removed from the excavation area. The struts are wedged or jacked into position, a procedure that places each brace

Figure 16-36 Tiebacks used to support steel soldier beam and timber lagging installation. (Photo courtesy of Spencer, White, and Prentis)

Excavation Bracing

(a)

(b)

Figure 16-37 (a) Sequence of slurry-trench (slurry-wall) construction. (Diagram courtesy of Spencer, White, and Prentis) (b) Tied-back concrete walls constructed by slurry wall procedure. (Photo courtesy of Bencor Corportation of America Foundation Specialist)

in compression and forces the sheeting outward from the excavation, acting to prevent a subsequent inward deflection. The compression in the strut before it receives sheeting load is termed *prestress*. As excavation proceeds, some inward deflection (toward the excavation) of the lower sheeting occurs before the lower struts can be placed. This described sequence of excavation and bracing results in a lateral soil pressure distribution against the sheeting (Fig. 16-38), that generally is similar to the parabolic distribution that occurs when a retaining wall rotates about its top.

Figure 16-38 Mode of deflection and lateral pressure distribution for sheeting supporting a vertical cut.

(a) Typical deflection for braced sheeting

(b) Generalized representation of lateral pressures against sheeting

Forces developed in the struts of braced excavations provided for sand and clay soils have been measured. Pressure distributions against the sheeting have been approximated by assuming that each strut supports a sheeting area extending vertically and horizontally halfway to adjacent struts. The results of such studies have established patterns of pressure distribution but also show marked variation in magnitudes, even when measured in the same soil deposit. Factors found to influence the pressure distribution include the speed at which excavation progresses and the care taken when bracing is installed, as well as soil type and properties. The effects of all variables have not been clearly established, however. Nevertheless, the results of field studies serve as the basis for developing earth pressure diagrams which can be used to design bracing for new work. The pressure distribution diagrams recommended for design (Fig. 16-39) actually represent an envelope that encompasses the field-determined pressure diagrams. Such design pressure diagrams are conventionally referred to as *apparent pressure diagrams* to differentiate them from test-determined diagrams. Use of the diagrams provides conservative but not necessarily uneconomical design of struts.

The procedure for the design of struts used to brace excavation sheeting reverses the process used to develop the apparent pressure diagram, as shown by Figure 16-40. This figure indicates that the effect of the lower embedded segment of sheeting does not require consideration when the bracing is designed by reference to the apparent pressure diagram.

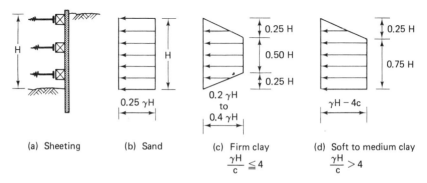

Figure 16-39 Apparent pressure diagrams for designing strut loads for braced vertical sheeting (after Peck).

Excavation Bracing

Figure 16-40 Pressure zones assumed for calculating strut loads.

The apparent pressure diagram represents conditions for a completed bracing system. Struts, and rakers as well, are conventionally designed on the assumption that the maximum load could exceed the planned load at some time during installation of the bracing or after its completion if a construction mishap results in damage to some bracing or if unforeseen loading conditions occur in the area surrounding the excavation. A 50% overload is a common assumption.

Relating to the surface elevation at the bottom of an excavation, a surcharge pressure effect exists at this elevation behind the sheeting from the height of the retained soil. There is a resulting tendency for soil beneath the excavation base to be pushed upward, as occurs with a bearing capacity failure (Fig. 16-41). The occurrence is most likely where clay soils exist. A heaving of the base is accompanied by lateral movement of the lower sheeting. With large movement, significant settlement of the ground surrounding the excavation also occurs.

With excavations in clay, the strength for the case of undrained shear applies to the conditions that exist during the construction period. Since the bearing capacity of clay in undrained shear is controlled by its cohesion, c, the safe excavation depth in regard to bottom heave is similarly related.[5] Heave is expected to be small when $\gamma H/c$ values (the ratio of surcharge pressure to soil shear strength) are less than 6. Where the ratio exceeds 8, significant and possibly uncontrolled heave is anticipated, and a standard bracing system should not be used. The ratio of excavation depth to clay shear strength also affects the lateral pressures developing

Figure 16-41 Loss of stability in bottom of excavation when surcharge effect is excessive.

[5]Recall that the ultimate bearing capacity of clay q_{ult} when a condition of undrained shear prevails is close to 6c.

against the sheeting as indicated by the design recommendations of Figures 16-39c and 16-39d.

Where a firm stratum underlies the excavation area and is reasonably close, the danger of bottom heave can be eliminated by extending sheeting close to or into the firm material. If soft clays extend a great distance below the excavation, increasing the sheeting penetration offers little benefit unless the excavation is narrow. Excavations in sand typically do not experience a problem with bottom heave. However, instability of the base can occur in a pumped excavation where a groundwater table rises high behind the sheeting and the resulting seepage into the excavation area causes high uplift pressures.

Compared to strut bracing, diagonal bracing and tiebacks involve differences in method that affect lateral pressures against the sheeting. Where the uppermost section of sheeting is not directly braced, some freedom for movement exists and the lateral pressures may initially be less than indicated by the pressure diagrams obtained from measurements of strut bracing. However, lateral pressures may subsequently increase because of soil creep and the effects of surface activities adjacent to the excavation area. In the absence of data relevant to the design of diagonal or tieback support for a particular project, the apparent pressure diagrams of Figure 16-39 can be referred to for estimating the horizontal component of the axial force in rakers and tiebacks. Because tiebacks are typically provided at spacings closer than those used for interior braces, an overload to one tie easily results in redistribution to or sharing of load with adjacent ties. It has been found that tiebacks do not require the conservatism used for interior bracing. Consequently, tiebacks commonly are designed to resist 80 percent of the loading indicated by the earth pressure envelopes developed for interior bracing (i.e., 80% of the loading indicated by diagrams such as Figure 16-39). A further comparative advantage of tieback construction is that the close spacing results in smaller shear forces and bending moments being developed in the sheeting, an occurrence that permits sheeting having a lighter cross section to be used.

The horizontal and vertical spacing of braces has an effect on the deflection that sheeting experiences. Large deflections are possible where the bracing is widely spaced. It is important to recognize that lateral movement of a retained soil also results in ground settlement. For excavation work in developed areas, where settlement or shifting of ground will endanger nearby facilities, the bracing system should be designed to keep the sheeting rigid and movement minimized.

ANCHORED BULKHEADS

The category of structure termed the anchored bulkhead is commonly used for marine and waterfront structures such as wharfs, piers, waterfront retaining walls, floodwalls, and breakwaters. The anchored bulkhead, structurally used for supporting a soil mass that often is adjacent to a body of water, consists of a vertical wall having its lower section embedded in earth and a tie or anchor near its top for support and to limit deflection. Steel sheet piling is the material most typically used for the bulkhead wall, but timber and concrete are also common. For marine work, interlocking sheeting has the advantage that it can be driven into place through an existing depth of water, eliminating the requirement to first isolate and dewater an area to permit construction of the bulkhead.

When an area is to be used as a docking facility for shipping, the location for the bulkhead is often dredged first to provide the desired water depth (draft). If soft soils exist below dredging depth, they should be removed and replaced with granular fill to a depth which will be below the sheeting's tip elevation, so that better support is provided. Soil placed behind the sheeting to create a land surface should be cohesionless material. Weak natural soil behind the bulkhead should be removed prior to placement of the granular fill if future settlement would create a problem in the use of that area. (For example, buildings, utilities, and rail or vehicle roads to be located on the fill area could be damaged by settlement due to compression of weak natural soil left in place beneath the fill.)

Various methods of providing the anchor system for supporting the upper section of sheeting have been developed. As most typically designed, the upper support generally consists of horizontal wales that extend the plan length of the sheeting plus steel tie rods that connect the wales to anchors capable of providing the necessary resistance to pull imposed by the sheeting (Fig. 16-42). Blocks and walls that serve as anchors develop their resistance primarily from passive soil pressures.

A number of procedures are in use for representing the lateral pressures acting against wood and steel sheetpiling, a requirement for determining the required sheeting embedment and strength and the anchor resistance. The *free-earth-support method*, considered the most conservative of the methods shown in Figure 16-43, assumes that the sheeting acts as a vertical beam that receives its top support from the anchor and bottom support from soil in front of the bulkhead (Fig. 16-43a). Forces act on the sheeting only from lateral soil pressures and the anchor pull; it is assumed that water pressures in front of and behind the sheeting will balance. The lateral pressures due to a retained cohesionless soil fill conventionally have been assumed to be active pressures, but recent studies suggest that the at-rest pressure distribution may be more appropriate. In a design analysis, the anchor pull on the sheeting is taken as a moment center, and moments due to the lateral pressure of the retained earth are compared to moments of passive soil pressure in front of the sheeting. An adequate depth of penetration D is achieved when these moments balance, and the theoretical factor of safety is one. The required anchor tension is subsequently determined as the difference between the lateral soil forces acting behind and in front of the sheeting. For construction, the actual penetration is commonly increased to be 1.5 to 2 times the calculated value of D. The sheeting section is designed to resist the shear forces and bending moments that are indicated as a result of the anchor pull and lateral pressures acting along its length.

Usual designs call for drainage holes to be included in the sheeting so that water levels behind and in front of the sheeting are always similar even though tidal changes occur. If means for rapid drainage are not provided, the design should consider the additional lateral force that would develop because of unbalanced hydrostatic pressures.

(a) Common anchoring system
utilizing anchor blocks

(b) Continuous
wall anchor

(c) Individual spaced
piles as anchor

(d) Compression and tension piling

(e) Tension piles used
as rakers

Figure 16-42 Methods and procedures for providing tiebacks.

The *fixed-earth-support method* considers the lowest section of sheeting to be fixed in the earth, similar to the manner in which a cantilever beam is fixed at its wall support. For analysis or design, an extra lateral resistance based on passive pressures developing against the land side of the sheeting's lower section is assumed to exist, and to be additional to the conventional at-rest and passive soil pressures, as shown in Figure 16-43b. To design a bulkhead, an estimated sheeting length is analyzed for deflections and a proper embedment has been reached when the deflection at the depth D is zero. The procedure typically requires a number of trials and is a laborious and time-consuming method unless some computational aid or computer program is available. Compared to the free-earth-support method, greater sheeting penetrations are required, but the use of lighter and more economical sheeting sections usually results.

Anchored Bulkheads

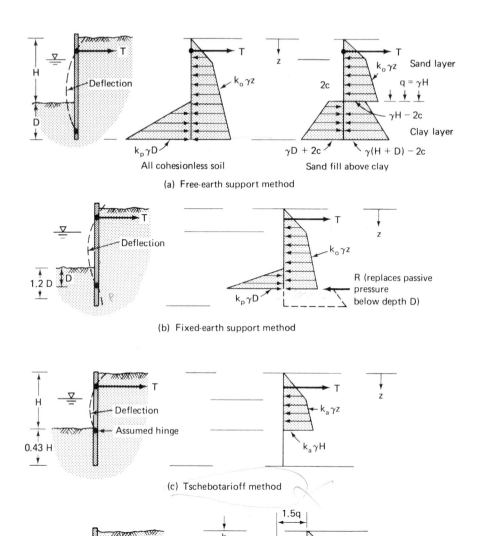

(a) Free-earth support method

(b) Fixed-earth support method

(c) Tschebotarioff method

(d) Danish rules method

Figure 16-43 Methods to represent lateral pressures against sheeted bulkheads.

The *Tschebotarioff method* (Fig. 16-43c) recommends a penetration equal to 0.43 of the sheeting support height. The sheeting section and anchor system is then designed on the basis that active soil pressures exist above the dredge line and a hinge is present at the dredge line. The *Danish rules* method, based on an "active-arching" lateral pressure distribution acting against the sheeting (Fig. 16-43d), was developed from studies on flexible bulkheads that indicated that bending was less than the values predicted by the free-earth-support method. However, the pressure distribution is appropriate only for the case where there is no anchor yield. This method is considered the least conservative of the four procedures discussed.

The occurrence of a bulkhead failure because the steel sheeting was over-stressed in bending is rare. Where stability problems have occurred, the cause usually has been failure of the anchor system or has been related to inadequate soil support along the embedded lower section. Anchor failures often originate with the tie rod. If the bulkhead fill settles, as is typical, the tie rod deflects. Although steel tie rods normally can deflect without problem, the connection at the anchor, or more probably at the sheeting, may be overstressed. Hinged connections represent one method used to prevent the overstress problem. Bulkhead failure due to inadequate penetration can result during construction as the procedure of placing fill behind the sheeting causes the various effects of the retained material to increase. Instability can occur if the passive pressure resistance below the dredge line is inadequate, or if a rotational slide precipitated by the weight of the fill (discussed in Chapter 15) develops behind the bulkhead and passes beneath the sheeting. Failure due to similar causes can also occur after construction is completed if the site's foundation includes weak cohesive soil. Projects that require dredging and filling after the bulkhead sheeting is in place should have filling on both sides progress evenly. For existing facilities, protection against scour and overdredging is necessary to prevent loss of material that provides embedment for the sheeting.

WATER-RETAINING STRUCTURES: DAMS

Dams, structures that serve to retain water for storage and utilization purposes or to protect land areas, represent one of civilization's oldest category of major constructed facilities. In current times, dams are an essential component of water supply systems, hydroelectric power facilities, and flood control projects; they also serve to create reservoirs for recreational and navigational use and for sediment retention. Frequently, a dam provides multipurpose service.

At present, there are more than 60,000 known dams in service in the United States. Over 95 percent of this number have been constructed during the twentieth century. Early dams typically were for water supply systems or hydroelectric usage, whereas many of the recently built dams have been for flood control and recreational use. For the future, new dams will be needed for water supply, flood control, and recreational use; additionally, with the concern over the availability and cost of energy, dams for providing new sources of hydroelectric power are being studied and proposed for many areas.

Dams for permanent facilities (as compared to temporary dams involved with construction projects) typically have been of masonry, concrete, earth fill or rockfill construction, although timber and steel materials have also been used. Of the United States dams, some 7000 are masonry or concrete, and more than 53,000 are earth fill or rockfill.[6] Certain advantages and disadvantages are associated with the construction, function, and operation of dams built of each of these materials. The selection for a given project is influenced by the dam's purpose, the location and site conditions including area available, construction conditions including materials and labor available as well as climate, and cost. Concrete, masonry, and rockfill dams require strong foundations such as rock or firm incompressible soil, whereas earth fill dams can be designed for locations where the foundation material is less firm.

A dam facility must include a spillway and outlet works (Fig. 16-44). The spillway enables excess reservoir water—water above the reservoir's design elevation but lower than the crest of the dam's impounding section—to move safely past the dam. Outlet works permit water to be drawn from the normal reservoir pool as required for a water supply, for generating hydropower, or for navigation

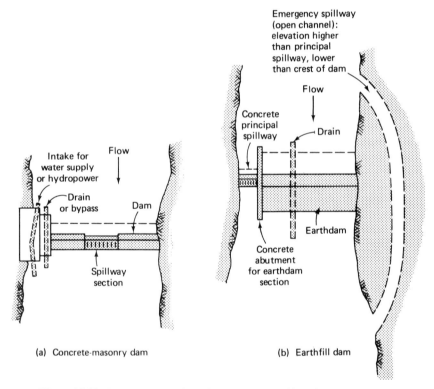

Figure 16-44 Plan representation of components and locations for concrete and earthfill dams.

[6]Personal communication, J. A. Gomez. Stetson-Harza Engineering Company, Utica, NY; derived from U.S. Army Corps of Engineers data.

purposes, and also enables the reservoir to be drained for dam repair or other purposes. Concrete and masonry dams often are designed so that part of the length will also serve as the spillway; the construction material can withstand the effects of flow over the section. In contrast, earth fill and rockfill dams should not be topped because of the probability that erosion and loss of section would result. For these dams, special spillway structures are required so that the reservoir's excess water will flow around or through the dam before cresting (i.e., topping) can occur. Because of such requirements, dams for sites where flow is great, as along rivers, commonly are concrete or masonry, since the structure can be easily designed to spill large volumes of water without danger to the structure itself. Earth fill and rockfill dams typically are used for locations where the spill volume under normal operation is limited, such as with storage reservoirs for water supply and recreational lakes. These projects often include a principal spillway possessing limited capacity, while a relatively inexpensive emergency spillway, such as a grassed open channel, is provided to bypass large excess flows, such as those which occur in time of flood. Bypass channel spillways may involve large volumes of excavation that desirably could be used for constructing the dam itself.

Concrete and masonry dams can be gravity type, buttress type, or arch dams (Fig. 16-45). Gravity dams, owing to their stability against overturning and sliding forces that act on the structure to the mass of the dam section, are usually most practical where limited heights of water are to be impounded.[7] Buttress and arch dams are considered appropriate for medium-height and high dams; compared to the gravity type, buttress and arch dams will economize on materials but require advanced design and construction techniques.

Earth fill and rockfill dams obtain their overall structural stability from the large mass of soil or rock comprising the structure. These structures are expected to permit at least some leakage to occur. Means are necessary to keep such flow within the limits required for stability and protection of downstream areas, or in arid regions to control the loss of valuable water. To restrict through-the-dam flow, impervious barriers or zones are incorporated into the dam's cross section. Drains and filters are also designed into the dam so that seepage which does occur can be collected and carried off without affecting stability. A barrier or cutoff is also extended into the zone below the dam if the site includes a soil or rock foundation that would otherwise permit an undesirable volume of seepage.

Earth Fill Dams   Earth fill dams are classified as homogeneous or zoned (Fig. 16-46). A homogeneous section is most appropriate where the soil used for its construction has a relatively low permeability after placement (e.g., soils with adequate silt or clay content). Zoned earth fill dams generally consist of coarse-soil outer zones or shells (e.g., predominantly sand, gravel, and possibly cobble materials) and a relatively impermeable internal zone or core of fine-grained soil.[8]

---

[7]Designations according to height are somewhat arbitrary, but a height of 80 ft (25 m) can be assumed as order-of-magnitude division between the low and moderate-height categories.

[8]The design of zoned earth dams in the early twentieth century frequently showed a "puddled" core consisting of a blend of clay and sand–gravel materials to be placed and rolled in layers.

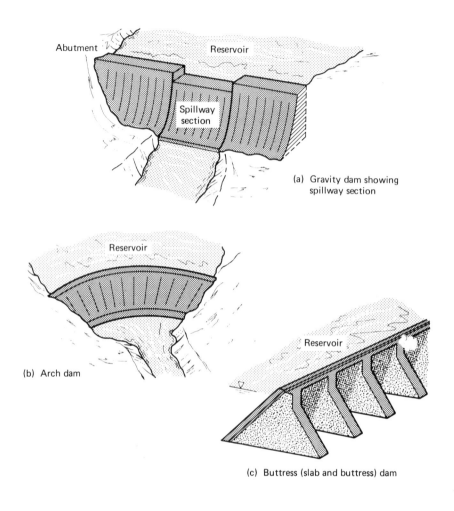

(a) Gravity dam showing
spillway section

(b) Arch dam

(c) Buttress (slab and buttress) dam

(d) Multiple arch (buttresses) dam

Figure 16-45 General categories of concrete-masonry dams.

Where a very coarse material can be provided separate from the smaller coarse-grained material (e.g., cobbles or gravels can be separated from gravels or sands), a zoning of the shell should be planned, with the coarsest material being used for the outermost section. Practically speaking, even the materials provided for large homogeneous dams show a variation in grading, and for that occurrence the finer material should be placed near the center of the dam while the coarser materials are used for the shell zones. When a dam is designed as a homogeneous earth fill section, a blanket of cobbles or large gravel, or a slab of Portland cement concrete, bituminous concrete, or soil cement is provided for the *upstream slope* as protection against the erosive effects of wave action, fluctuations in reservoir level including

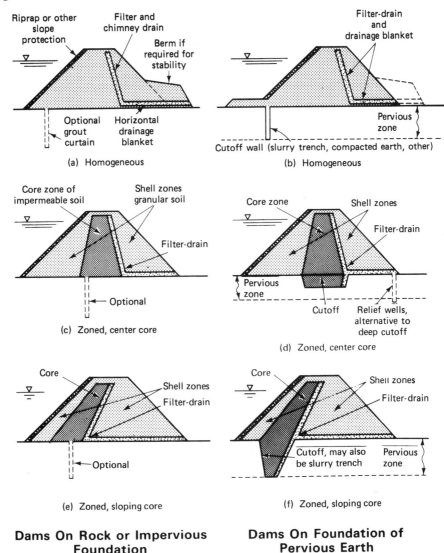

Figure 16-46 Typical earth dam sections.

Water-Retaining Structures: Dams

intentional drawdowns, and ice and rainfall. Downstream slopes of homogeneous dams can be provided with a filter blanket of coarse material so rain and snow melt will not cause surface erosion. Grasses and other low-height vegetation are also used on the downstream slope as erosion protection. Trees should not be permitted on slopes, because an uprooting during storm periods could begin a serious erosion. Deep tree roots could encourage through-dam seepage by shortening the seepage path.

For zoned designs the moderately sloping fine-grained core (Fig. 16-46e and 16-46f) is considered to provide a more stable section than the severe sloping or vertical core. Failures which do occur in earth fill sections often are slip-circle slides (Chapter 15) which pass through one of the slopes. A core zone is commonly the weakest material in the dam, and the moderately sloping core represents the optimum shape for obtaining benefit from the weight of water against the dam's upstream slope while limiting adverse effects from seepage moving through the core.

Earth dams as total structures are subject to settlement as the lower sections and probably also the foundation material compress under the weight of the overlying embankment. Upon reservoir filling, additional settlement and some lateral movement occur because of the effect of the impounded water above and against the dam. The soil mass making up the dam is deformed as a result of these movements. If the dam is properly designed and constructed, movements between adjacent sections are limited, and no adverse effect on the structural stability results. Cracks may form,[9] particularly near the interface of zones, because of the different reaction to loading by the different materials. However, properly designed soil transition zones will permit self-healing to occur in areas where seepage begins to move through cracks.

Concrete core walls to serve as the internal barrier to seepage are no longer being recommended for use, except possibly for very low dams. Concrete core walls are susceptible to cracking as settlement of the dam structure occurs.

For homogeneous and zoned dams, drains such as those represented in Figure 16-46 are included to collect and carry away any through-the-dam seepage that develops. Alternatively, for the zoned design represented by Figure 16-47, the downstream zoning of properly graded pervious materials can serve as the filter drain to collect seepage for harmless disposal downstream. Internal drains also should be zoned to act as filters[10] so that the seeping water does not carry soil particles from the core into the drain and shell zone (e.g., the filter zone closest to a silt–clay core may consist of a cohesionless silt or fine sand, while the outer zones of the filter drain consist of clean, coarse sand).

Cutoff walls into the foundation strata to prevent seepage beneath the dam can be an extension of the impermeable core zone if the cutoff excavation to the desired depth can be made dry, a requirement to permit proper placement including

---

[9]The condition where cracks develop within the dam section because of reservoir water pressures acting against the upstream slope, or because seepage under pressure enters a small crack and enlarges it, is referred to as *hydraulic fracturing*.

[10]Filters will need to satisfy the gradation requirements for filter material discussed in Chapter 6.

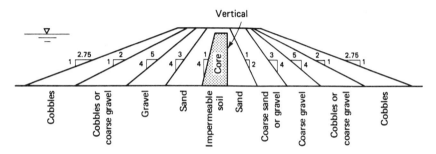

Figure 16-47 Illustration of zoned design for a granular earth fill dam. The downstream sand and gravel zones can also serve as drains for seepage.

compaction of the soil cutoff and its filter drain. Steel sheetpiling has been widely used as a cutoff in the past, although sheeting installed into coarse soils has proven to be a risky choice susceptible to developing open joints and tears that permit locations for high-gradient seepage to occur. Concrete cutoff walls similarly are not recommended.

Where a foundation zone extends below the water table and a cutoff excavation cannot be adequately dewatered to permit dry construction, slurry trench methods can be considered. A bentonite clay slurry is used during the excavation process to temporarily support the trench walls against cave-in; then a fine-grained–coarse-grained soil mixture including some slurry material is placed to obtain a wall of impermeable backfill. Such slurry trench backfill is not highly compacted and is subject to settlement under loading. Consequently, the best location for the slurry trench cutoff is in the vicinity of the upstream toe to minimize the weight of the dam and water overburden. Steel sheeting can be installed within the backfilled slurry trench as added protection.

An alternative to the foundation zone cutoff for controlling *deep* under-dam seepage is to use a system consisting of drains and relief wells located beneath the downstream slope, near the toe, to intercept and collect seepage and prevent the development of piping through the foundation and erosion at the toe (Fig. 16-46d).

Earth fill dams should be constructed by placing and compacting the soil in relatively thin layers.[11] Hydraulically placed earth fills are not recommended because of the relatively loose, weak, and unstable condition of the fill. Almost any soil type can be used for the compacted earth fill with the exception of material with organic content. Highly plastic clays are not recommended for use, however, because of a practical difficulty with handling and compacting. Similarly, dispersive clays should not be used because of the great susceptibility to erosion and piping which can lead to loss of embankment once leakage commences.

Experiences have shown that satisfactory strength and performance are achieved if the compacted density of the earth fill is in the range of 95–100 percent of the

[11]The layer thickness that can be properly compacted relates to the soil type and compaction equipment. Fine-grained soils probably will require that layers be no greater than 1 ft in thickness, whereas clean granular soils may permit layers approaching 2 ft in thickness where vibratory compactors are used.

maximum density obtainable from the Standard Proctor moisture–density relationship (i.e., compaction test). Design slopes range from about 2.5 horizontal to 1 vertical where granular soil shell zones are used to about 4 horizontal to 1 vertical for homogeneous silt–clay embankments. Fine-grained soil should be placed at a water content 1–2 percent drier than the optimum moisture indicated by the compaction test results, particularly for the lower zones of high dams, to prevent the development of excess pore water pressures when the weight of the overlying dam and water storage causes an expected soil compression. In the early history of earthwork construction, with embankments of limited height, it was common to compact the earth fill at water contents slightly above the optimum, anticipating that a moist fill would be more flexible and less brittle than a dry mass and therefore less subject to cracking when settlement occurred. Compared to crack formation, however, there is greater concern over effect on stability if high pore water pressures develop in the dam section (a condition that limits the soil shear strength that can develop). It is felt that the proper design of soil filter transition zones prevents the danger of serious crack–leakage problems.

Earth fill dams may be exposed to ice loading and earthquake forces. Ice formed at the reservoir surface normally does not have great direct structural effect on a dam's stability, because it tends to slide upward on the embankment's upstream slope. The danger associated with ice lies in its potential for eroding or otherwise damaging the riprap or other face material.

Analytical methods that predict the behavior of earth dams when subject to earthquake are not precise.[12] Dam failures have resulted when sliding occurred on a weak foundation or when direct structural damage resulted because fault movement affected the foundation. Failures have also been caused by embankment sloughing or cracking followed by a dam break, or by overtopping where large settlement occurred or when slides into the reservoir area created a water wave that topped the dam. However, evaluation of the performance of dams that have experienced earthquake indicates that, generally, rolled earth embankments that include plastic cohesive soils and are located on firm foundations retain stability when subject to moderate earthquake forces. The effects of repeated seismic loads are not well established, however.

Rockfill Dams   Rockfill dams include features that make them generally similar to earthfill dams. A rockfill dam is one where placed rock is responsible for providing all or most of the necessary strength and stability required for proper performance of the structure. Rockfill dams may include soil zones.

Rockfills use large-size quarried or natural rock but also include smaller-soil-size materials such as gravels and sands. Rockfill dams have been constructed in thick lifts by loosely dumping the material in place but also by spreading and compacting the material in layers of limited thickness. Loosely dumped thick lifts—various projects have used lifts anywhere from about 10 ft (3 m) to 60 ft (18 m)—that included large materials in the 6- to 8-ft or 2-m size range have proved to

[12]The paper "Considerations in the Earthquake-Resistant Design of Earth and Rockfill Dams," H. Bolton Seed, *Geotechnique*, September 1979, provides a good evaluation of factors and procedures that apply to earthquake design for dams.

create stable structures, provided that the rockfill is sluiced with large volumes of high-pressure jetted water. (The volume of water used has typically been 3–4 times the volume of the placed rockfill.) Apparently the great volume of water flushes fines from within the dumped rock mass, so better edge-to-edge contacts for the large fragments develop, while simultaneously the prolonged inundation softens rock edges and corners so that fracture occurs, which causes settlement but also produces a greater interlocking of materials with greater strength for the rockfill mass. Compared to dry placement, the sluicing procedure reduces postconstruction settlements. Typically, the postconstruction settlement for sluiced rockfills has been on the order of 1 percent of the embankment height.

The alternative procedure of constructing a rockfill by spreading and compacting the fill in relatively thin layers is preferred for dams where stability or leakage problems would constitute a hazard to life or valuable property. Better control over the fill materials and the resulting in-place condition is achieved with compacted layer techniques, and, where zoning is required, provides a practical approach for constructing what is designed. Layers on the order of 3 ft or 1 m thick, comprising materials whose maximum size does not exceed layer thickness, are considered practical for achieving desired compaction densities. Vibratory compactors on the order of 10 tons in size have proved to be effective for compacting such rockfill layers. Moisture can be added during placement, but moisture content variations are less crucial for compaction of rockfill than for earth fill. In fact, one general advantage of rockfill construction is that it is less affected by adverse weather than earth fill or concrete construction. With either sluiced or compacted layer construction, rockfills can be constructed to relatively steep slopes (e.g., on the order of 1 or 1.5 horizontal to 1 vertical), although flatter slopes are often provided.

As with earth fill embankments, some settlement and lateral movement of a compacted rockfill dam are expected when the reservoir is filled. Settlements for properly constructed compacted rockfills are expected to be less than 1 percent of the embankment height. Where the length is limited, rockfill dams have been constructed with a slight upstream curvature to the longitudinal axis, so lateral movements occurring as a result of reservoir water load would cause compression within the structure, an effect that would tend to close developed vertical cracks.

Rockfill dams require an impervious upstream face or an impermeable core to control leakage. When provided with an impervious upstream face, the embankment is referred to as a *diaphragm section*. Surfaces of reinforced Portland cement concrete and bituminous concrete are typical for present-day projects, but wood timbers and steel plates have also been used successfully. If possible, the concrete diaphragm is placed toward the end of the construction period to minimize the effect of embankment movements, which could cause cracks to occur in the facing.

Where an impermeable core is to serve as the barrier to seepage, soil of low permeability is typically selected. Bituminous concrete has also been used. Internal cores can be sloping or vertical zones which are compacted in thin layers as for earth fill dams. Soil core zones require adjacent soil transition filter zones to prevent particle migration when seepage flows occur. Similarly, a bituminous concrete core zone should be bounded by transition filter zones in the event cracking occurs. Portland cement concrete cores are not recommended for high dams because of their rigidity and the probability of extensive cracking when embankment settlement occurs. The Portland cement concrete core, if used, should be bounded by transition filter soil zones. Because of embankment settlement, it is expected that cracking will occur within the soil or concrete cores and the adjacent soil transition zones, but such cracks will fill with soil (self-heal) where the transition filters have been properly designed.

Using an upstream face for the impervious barrier offers the advantage that the vertical component of weight from the overlying reservoir water acts to increase the stability of the dam structure. A disadvantage is that postconstruction settlement will cause cracking in the facing. If repair becomes necessary, however, relatively easy access is available. The facing also effectively provides necessary upstream slope protection, but its exposed location tends to hasten deterioration and the need for repair.

Rockfill dams sited on previous soil foundations can have cutoffs similar to those used for earth fill dams to control underdam seepage. Diaphragm sections constructed on rock foundations use a footwall anchored into the rock or a grout curtain of closely spaced drilled-and-pressure-grouted holes at the upstream toe. Earth core rockfill dams on rock foundations can use a grout curtain beneath the earth core to control foundation seepage. Where the surficial zone of foundation rock is fractured, a grout blanket can be used as a seal in place of or to complement the grout curtain.

Concrete and Masonry Dams   Concrete and masonry dams are appropriate where part of the dam must also function as a spillway, as with a run-of-river structure, or where the area taken up by the cross section must be limited, or where earth or rockfill material is scarce, or where site topography makes a concrete masonry structure a more economical choice than the earth fill or rockfill (such as where a narrow rock canyon exists and the side channel spillway necessary with an earth fill dam cannot be economically built).

Categories of concrete or masonry dams include the gravity dam, the arch dam, and the buttress dam. In modern construction, reinforced concrete is most conventionally used. The mass of the gravity dam section provides the resistance to the overturning and sliding effects that develop from the loadings that act on the structure, similar to gravity retaining walls. Gravity dams are suitable where the required height is not exceptionally great. Arch dams, relatively thin in section, retain stability against reservoir loading because of the curved alignment which effectively puts the longitudinal axis of the dam in compression. Arch dams are considered appropriate for narrow valley locations, where the ratio of length to height is small, say 5 or less. The buttress dam essentially consists of a sloping upstream slab supported by buttresses that transmit the effects of reservoir loading to the foundation soil or rock. The sloping upstream face, at a relatively steep angle, such as 45°, enables part of the reservoir loading to contribute to the dam's stability. Buttress dams are of two basic designs—the flat slab section with buttress, and the multiple arch. With the slab–buttress structure, each flat slab section and each buttress can be considered to be a separate component. In contrast, the multiple-arch design results from buttresses that thicken as they get closer to the dam's upstream face and crest, in effect blending into the face slab and crest. The downstream elevation of this dam shows adjacent buttresses integrated to create the multiple-arch structure. The multiple-arch design produces a rigid structure. The basic flat slab and buttress dam is considered to be a flexible structure where adjacent buttress spans can tolerate some differential foundation settlement without harmful effect, provided that slab joints falling along each buttress centerline remain watertight if movement does occur. Buttress dams are considered most appropriate for long dams of moderate to high height. Compared to gravity dams, the buttress structure economizes on materials but involves greater labor and forming costs.

In addition to loading resulting from impounded reservoir water, dams are designed to also resist the effects of other forces that may act, including ice load, reservoir silting, uplift against the base, and earthquake.

Ice loading represents a winter condition that can occur when a frozen reservoir surface experiences temperature change. As an ice sheet expands, a lateral force is imposed against the upstream side of the dam. The magnitude of the ice loading relates to the thickness of ice that undergoes temperature change (which can be less than the total ice thickness) as well as to the degrees of temperature change. For winter climates similar to those witnessed in the northernmost United States, the maximum ice load is commonly assumed as 10 kips per foot of dam length (which corresponds to a temperature change through approximately a 2-ft thickness of ice). When a dam's upstream side is at a significant slope, it is conventional to assume that an expanding ice sheet will slide up the face, with little of the lateral force acting to affect structural stability.

Silting behind a dam results as sediment carried into the reservoir area by the feeding water flow accumulates behind the dam. Silting is analyzed as a lateral earth pressure problem when the effect on dam stability is evaluated. A submerged unit weight appropriate for loose soil (e.g., 40 pcf) and a lateral pressure coefficient equal to 0.5 can be used when computations are performed.

An uplift force will develop against the base of a dam if underdam seepage occurs. The uplift pressure acting at different points along the base relates to the pattern of seepage through the foundation strata and the water levels behind and in front of the dam, as can be studied from a flow net analysis (Chapter 6). For the design of a dam situated on a foundation of soil or permeable rock, it is also common to assume an uplift force based on a full headwater hydrostatic pressure acting at the structure's upstream corner and a hydrostatic pressure based on the tailwater elevation acting at the downstream corner; pressures along the base vary uniformly between these limits, resulting in a trapezoidal uplift pressure pattern. Uplift computed by this simplified procedure will be somewhat greater than actual, but the result has a conservative effect on design.

Where a dam's foundation is to be embedded in sound rock, the magnitude of uplift that will develop is uncertain. If the rock is very sound and impervious, seepage would be very low and uplift pressures would require a very long period of time to develop. Alternatively, if the rock is layered or jointed, uplift could act on sections or slabs of the foundation rock that are larger than the base width of the dam, and cause a total uplift force greater than would develop directly against the dam's base. Nevertheless, it is common *during design* to assume that uplift pressures for dams situated on rock will relate directly to upstream and downstream water levels, as previously discussed.

With buttress dams, uplift pressures between buttress locations can be reduced or eliminated by use of relief wells. Since the plan area of a buttress foundation is usually small compared to the total plan area of the dam, such a procedure can remove most of the effect of uplift.

Earthquakes create ground motions that produce excitations in a structure. A result is that the equivalent of vibratory-type horizontal and vertical loads, additional to those resulting from static loading, acts on the structure. For *small* dams, the effect of seismic or shock forces on the overall structural stability can be evaluated by assuming that a static-type force P_{eq} having an effect equivalent to the earthquake acts at the dam's center of gravity, with

$$P_{eq} = Ma = \frac{W}{g} \alpha g = \alpha W \tag{16-15}$$

where M = mass of the structure.
g = acceleration of gravity.
W = weight of the structure.
a = acceleration or tendency for motion resulting from the earthquake or other seismic shock.
α = ratio of a to g, an empirically determined factor that, for horizontal earthquake, ranges from about 0.03 for areas where seismic activity is light to 0.20 where activity is great. The vertical factor is assumed to be half the horizontal factor.

In a stability analysis, the seismic forces are taken for that instant in time when they act in the direction that creates the least stable condition for the dam; that is, the horizontal component acts in the downstream direction while the vertical component acts upward.

Earthquake effects also cause the pressure of the impounded water acting against the dam to increase. The magnitude of the increase is related to the dam's upstream slope. The total increase in the horizontal water force against the back of the dam H_{ew} for an impounded height of water h is

$$H_{ew} = (0.73)C\alpha h^2 \gamma_w \tag{16-16}$$

where γ_w = unit weight of water.
C = coefficient relating to the dam's upstream slope, measured with respect to the vertical (Table 16-3).

The total increase in a dam's overturning moment M_{ew} with reference to an axis on a plane corresponding to the ground level behind the dam is

$$M_{ew} = (0.3)C\alpha h^3 \gamma_w \tag{16-17}$$

Slope of dam's upstream face (deg)	Coefficient, C
0	0.73
15	0.64
30	0.53
45	0.42

Stability Analysis for Gravity Dams   A dam must retain stability when subject to the various forces that tend to cause sliding or lateral movement, and overturning. Similarly, the dam's construction materials and foundation must not be overstressed. The stability of gravity dams can be studied through application of the basic laws of engineering mechanics (see Illustration 16-4). The stability of buttress dams can be evaluated approximately by using the methods applied to gravity dams. Stability studies for arch dams require advanced analytic procedures that are considered outside the scope of this text.

The stability analysis for gravity dams is similar to the analysis for earth retaining walls. A unit length of dam is isolated from its adjoining sections, and the design loads are applied. Where an instability against overturning exists, the overturning tends to occur by rotation about a longitudinal axis extending along the downstream toe. A safety factor against overturning is computed by relating moments of forces (with reference to the moment axis at the toe of the dam section) that resist overturning to those that cause overturning, or

$$FS \text{ against overturning} = \frac{\Sigma \text{ moments resisting overturning}}{\Sigma \text{ moments causing overturning}}$$

In general, the weight of the dam and reservoir water that can exert a *vertical* load on the dam's sloping upstream face will produce moments that resist overturning. Lateral water and soil pressures against the dam's upstream side, and ice, uplift, and earthquake effects, create loadings that act to cause overturning. Factors of safety computed by this method should be 2 or greater.

The magnitude and direction of stresses developed at the base of the dam require checking to guard against overstressing of the dam material or foundation.[13] The foundation pressure distribution diagram typically will be triangular or trapezoidal, with the maximum pressure at the downstream toe. To determine the pressure distribution, the position of the foundation reaction is first located from

$$d = \frac{\Sigma M_{toe}}{\Sigma V}$$

[13]Structurally, of course, the dam section must be capable of resisting the internal shear forces and bending moments that develop as a result of applied loads.

Water-Retaining Structures: Dams

where ΣM_{toe} = moments resisting overturning minus moments causing overturning, for one unit of the dam's length.

V = vertical component of the foundation reaction, including the weight
of the dam and water on a sloping upstream face but less any uplift
force, for one unit of dam length.

d = distance from toe to point where the foundation reaction is applied.

Desirably, the location for V falls within the middle third of the base; such a
condition theoretically ensures that compressive stresses act across the entire base.
An eccentricity distance, e, which is the distance from the center of the dam's base
to the position where the foundation reaction acts, is then determined from

$$e = \frac{b}{2} - d$$

where b = width of dam base.
The foundation pressure at the toe and at the heel of the dam is calculated from

$$P_{\text{toe}} = \frac{V}{b} + \frac{6Ve}{b^2} \qquad \text{(16-12a)}$$

$$P_{\text{heel}} = \frac{V}{b} - \frac{6Ve}{b^2} \qquad \text{(16-12b)}$$

The foundation pressures should not exceed the allowable compressive strength
of the dam material or foundation material. The pressure at the heel should not
be negative, a condition that would indicate tensile stress in the dam or a tendency
for uplifting to occur. Some small tensile resistance can be developed within concrete or where a dam's concrete is bonded to a rock foundation, but in design such
tensile resistance is normally not relied on. An indication of tension at the heel
typically would warrant a design change, such as enlarging the dam section, or a
modification, say to include a supplementary anchoring system such as steel dowels
extending from the dam into a rock foundation.

A dam's ability to resist sliding along its base is evaluated by comparing
horizontal forces that act to cause movement and those forces that resist movement.
A factor of safety against sliding is the ratio of forces resisting movement to those
causing movement, or

$$FS \text{ against sliding} = \frac{\Sigma \text{ forces resisting lateral movement}}{\Sigma \text{ forces causing lateral movement}}$$

Typically, water and soil pressures behind the dam, and ice and earthquake loadings, act to cause sliding. Resistance is provided by friction, shear, and bond
developed on the potential plane of sliding at the base of the dam. Where a gravity
dam is supported on a soil foundation, the resistance to sliding is computed from

$$\text{Sliding resistance} = \mu W + cbl \qquad \text{(16-18a)}$$

where W = the weight imposed by a unit length of the dam structure in contact
with the foundation, including reservoir water lying above the dam's

sloping faces. If uplift acts, W is the weight of the dam less the uplift force.

μ = coefficient of friction between the dam material and foundation soil (μ equals approximately $\tan \phi$).

c = cohesion of a cohesive foundation soil.

b = width of dam base in contact with the foundation.

l = length of dam section under analysis (typically one foot or one meter).

The factor of safety computed by this method should be 1.5 or greater.

Where the dam is supported on rock, the friction–shear method for determining resistance to sliding can be applied, where

$$\text{Sliding resistance} = \mu W + lb\tau \qquad (16\text{-}18b)$$

where μ = coefficient of friction between dam material and the foundation rock. Suggested values of μ range between 0.65 and 0.80 for concrete and masonry.

τ = bond or shear strength developing between the dam material and foundation rock. A value of 200 psi (1380 kN/m²) can be assumed where modern Portland cement concrete is bonded to sound clean rock. If the rock is stratified or laminated with weak seams, the shear strength of the seams should be compared to the concrete–rock bond value, and the least value assumed.

W, b, l = as defined previously.

Factors of safety computed by this method should be 4 or greater.

ILLUSTRATION 16-4. A concrete river dam also functions as a spillway. The gravity spillway section is indicated by the sketch. Determine the stability against overturning and sliding for

1. The normal winter operations condition, where the reservoir level is at the spillway elevation, and ice loading acts.
2. The normal operations condition, excluding ice but with seismic effects included.

Water-Retaining Structures: Dams

$$\text{Weight of dam} = (0.150 \text{ kcf})[(16 \text{ ft})(70 \text{ ft})(1 \text{ ft}) + (\tfrac{1}{2})(70 \text{ ft})(56 \text{ ft})(1 \text{ ft})$$
$$+ (10 \text{ ft})(72 \text{ ft})(1 \text{ ft})] = 570 \text{ k/ft of length}$$

$$M_{\text{toe}} \text{ due to mass of dam} = (0.150 \text{ kcf}) \left[(10 \text{ ft})(72 \text{ ft})(1 \text{ ft}) \left(\frac{72 \text{ ft}}{2} \right) \right.$$

$$+ (\tfrac{1}{2})(56 \text{ ft})(70 \text{ ft})(1 \text{ ft}) \left(\frac{2 \times 56 \text{ ft}}{3} \right)$$

$$\left. + (16 \text{ ft})(70 \text{ ft})(1 \text{ ft}) \left(\frac{16 \text{ ft}}{2} + 56 \text{ ft} \right) \right] = 25{,}616 \text{ ft-kip per ft of length}$$

M_{toe} causing overturning due to upstream water, ice, and uplift

$$= (4.99 \text{ ksf})(1 \text{ ft}) \left(\frac{80 \text{ ft}}{2} \right) \left(\frac{80 \text{ ft}}{3} \right) + (7.5 \text{ k/ft})(1 \text{ ft})(79 \text{ ft})$$

$$+ (4.99 \text{ ksf})(1 \text{ ft}) \left(\frac{72 \text{ ft}}{2} \right) (\tfrac{2}{3} \times 72 \text{ ft})$$

$$= 5325 + 593 + 5751 = 11{,}669 \text{ ft-kip per ft of length}$$

Normal Operations Case

1. *FS* against overturning $= \dfrac{\Sigma M_a \text{ (resisting)}}{\Sigma M_a \text{ (causing)}} = \dfrac{25{,}616 \text{ ft-kip/ft}}{11{,}669 \text{ ft-kip/ft}} = 2.2$

Position of resultant measured from toe

$$d = \frac{\Sigma M_a}{\Sigma V} = \frac{(25{,}616 \text{ ft-kip} - 11{,}669 \text{ ft-kip})}{\text{wt.dam} - \text{uplift}} = \frac{13{,}947 \text{ ft-kip/ft}}{(570 \text{ k/ft} - 180 \text{ k/ft})}$$

$d = 35.8$ ft from (a) axis at toe . . . (satisfactory, within middle-third of base)

$$P_{\text{toe}} = \frac{\Sigma V}{A} + \frac{Ve \dfrac{b}{2}}{I}$$

$$= \frac{(390\text{k})}{(72 \text{ ft} \times 1 \text{ ft})} + \frac{(390\text{k})(0.2 \text{ ft})(36 \text{ ft})}{31{,}104 \text{ ft}^4}$$

$$= 5.41 + 0.09 = 5.50 \text{ ksf}$$

$$P_{\text{heel}} = 5.41 - 0.09 = 5.32 \text{ ksf}$$

2. *FS* against sliding (shear–friction method)

$$= \frac{\mu(\Sigma V) + \tau bl}{\text{lateral water force and ice force}}$$

$$= \frac{(0.65)(570\text{k} - 180\text{k}) + (0.200 \text{ ksi})(72 \text{ ft})(1 \text{ ft})(144 \text{ in}^2/\text{ft}^2)}{(\frac{1}{2} \times 4.99 \text{ ksf} \times 80 \text{ ft}) + (7.5 \text{ k/ft})}$$

$$= \frac{253\text{k} + 2072\text{k}}{208\text{k}} = 11 \pm \ldots \text{(adequate, greater than 4)}$$

Seismic Effects Added to Normal Operations Loadings

Additional overturning M_a due to seismic effects on dam mass

$$= 0.05 W\bar{y} + 0.025 W\bar{x} = (0.05)(570\text{k})(31.4 \text{ ft}) + (0.25)(570\text{k})(44.94 \text{ ft})$$
$$= 1535 \text{ ft-kip per ft of length}$$

Additional M_a due to reaction between dam and reservoir water (refer to Eq. 16-17)

$$= (0.30)(0.73)(0.0624 \text{ kcf})(0.05)(80 \text{ ft})(80 \text{ ft})(80 \text{ ft})(1 \text{ ft wide})$$

$$= 350 \text{ ft-kip}$$

3. *FS* against overturning $= \dfrac{25{,}616 \text{ ft-kip/ft}}{(5325 + 5751 + 1535 + 350) \text{ ft-kip/ft}} = 1.98$

4. *FS* against sliding

$$= \frac{\mu(\Sigma V) + \tau bl}{(\text{lat water force}) + (\alpha W_{\text{dam}}) + \left(\begin{array}{c}\text{Seismic reaction between dam} \\ \text{and water, from Eq. 16-16}\end{array}\right)}$$

where lateral water force $\cong 200$ k,
and $\alpha W_{\text{dam}} = 0.05 \, (570\text{k}) \cong 29$ k,
and seismic reaction from Eq. 16-16
$= (0.73)(0.05)(0.0624 \text{ kcf})(.73)(80 \text{ ft})(80 \text{ ft})(1 \text{ ft})$
$= 11$ k.

The substitution of values gives

$$FS = \frac{0.65[570k - (0.025)(570k) - 180k] + 2072k}{200k + 29k + 11k} = 9.7$$

Stone Wall and Earth Dams Low dams that consist of a wall of laid-up stone backed with an earthen embankment that extends into the impounding area have been used successfully in regions where fieldstone was abundant and low cost was a condition for construction (Fig. 16-48). Existing dams of this type appear not to be the result of engineering design but, rather, to represent an evolution to dimensioning that retains stability under a variety of adverse conditions, including leakage and overtopping. The stone walls of satisfactory dam structures have been thick in relation to their height. Structurally, the wall acts as a retaining wall to help support the upstream-side soil embankment. The stone wall also serves as a noneroding section for times that the dam is topped, ensuring continued stability.

Study of a series of existing dams in New England [101] indicates that the stone wall and earth dam retains stability even when overtopping occurs, provided the ratio of an open-jointed wall thickness to height is 0.35 or greater, and the earthen embankment behind the wall (the *e* distance) is more than half the wall height. When the back of the wall is sealed against seepage, a condition that increases lateral pressures against the wall, the wall thickness-to-height ratio should be at least 0.45.

PROBLEMS

16.1. Define lateral pressure, and indicate the requirements for the at-rest lateral pressure condition.

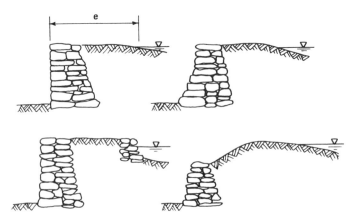

Figure 16-48 Typical cross-sections for stonewall and earth dams (after Healy [101]).

16-2. Assuming that a rigid, unyielding wall can be inserted into a soil mass where the at-rest lateral pressure condition exists, explain the effect that soil submergence will have on the total lateral pressure that acts against the wall.

16-3. Calculate the magnitude of lateral force resulting from an active soil pressure against the back of a frictionless wall 6 m (approximately 20 ft) high. The surface behind the wall is level, with the retained soil having an angle of internal friction equal to 37° and a unit weight of 18 kN/m³ (approximately 115 pcf).

16-4. A 10-m-high concrete retaining wall having a vertical backface supports a cohesionless soil backfill with an inclination of 30° with the horizontal. The retained soil has the following properties:

$$\gamma = 17 \text{ kN/m}^3, \qquad \phi = 35°$$

   (a) Calculate P_A, using the Rankine theory.
   (b) Calculate P_A, using the Coulomb theory, assuming a wall–friction angle equal to 30°.

16-5. A 10-m-high retaining wall is required to support a clay backfill having a level surface, where γ equals 17 kN/m³ and the cohesion equals 45 kN/m². Referring to Figure 16-16, compare the total lateral force resulting from the retained soil, for
   (a) The theoretical active pressure condition.
   (b) The modified active pressure distribution recommended for short-term design.
   (c) The pressure distribution recommended for permanent retaining wall design.

16-6. Explain why at-rest lateral soil pressure conditions and not active lateral pressures should be assumed for the design of basement walls and permanent retaining walls.

16-7. A 6-m-high retaining wall having a cross section depicted by Figure 16-23 is to be designed to support a backfill consisting of predominantly coarse-grained soil, containing some silt but no clay. The surface of the retained soil has a slope of 3 horizontal to 1 vertical. Using the Terzaghi–Peck charts, determine the magnitude of P_h and P_v that can be assumed for designing the wall. Provide a sketch of the wall, indicating the magnitude and location of these two forces.

16-8. A 20-ft retaining wall is to be used to support a Terzaghi–Peck type 1 backfill (Fig. 16-27). The wall cross-section is similar to that shown in Illustration 16-3, except that the base is 8 ft instead of 10 ft. The backfill surface is level. Determine the factor of safety against overturning and against sliding (using $\mu = 0.5$), and the foundation pressure distribution (reaction against the base).

16.9 Braced vertical sheeting is to be used for an open-trench excavation as applied for the construction of a section of subway tunnel that extends through medium stiff clay ($c = 42$ kN/m², $\gamma = 17$ kN/m³). The excavation will be 12 m deep and supported by three rows of struts. The top strut will be level with the ground surface, with the second strut 3 m down and the third strut 7 m down from the ground surface. The struts will be positioned at 3.5-m center-to-center spacing (plan view spacing). Calculate the force in each strut.

16.10. A sheetpile bulkhead for a shipping channel is used to support a fill that extends 25 ft higher than the channel bottom. The fill and channel bottom consist of granular soil where γ is 120 pcf and ϕ is 35°. Determine the required depth of sheetpile embedment, using the free-earth-support method (Fig. 16-43a). The anchor will be 5 ft below the top of the fill, and the design depth for the channel water is 18 ft.

16.11. A concrete gravity dam 25 ft high is used to create a lake in an area where a small river flows. The dam will also function as a spillway, and the design height for the water behind the dam can be assumed level with the crest. The dam has a cross-sectional shape similar to that shown in Illustration 16-4, with the top width equal to 4 ft and the bottom width equal to 22 ft. The downstream face slopes uniformly to intersect the indicated base dimension. The dam is situated on a rock foundation, with the downstream water level considered to be at the rock surface. Applying a 5-kip per lineal foot ice loading at the crest of the dam and using μ equal to 0.75, determine

(a) The factor of safety against overturning.
(b) The factor of safety against sliding.
(c) The location of the resultant passing through the base.

chapter **17**

Loads on Buried Conduits

Conduits constructed for carrying materials such as water supplies, sewage, natural and storm water flows, and fuels, or items such as electrical supply and communications cables, may have much or all of their length underground. Structurally, buried conduits need to be capable of supporting all external loadings that develop as a result of the underground location, such as the effects of the overlying earth, and internal forces that occur if the transported material is under pressure. Conduit strength required because of an internal pressure is determined by applying strength of materials-engineering mechanics principles. External loading resulting because of buried location and the method of construction–installation is discussed in this chapter.

The loading on an underground conduit and therefore its required strength will be influenced by factors such as the buried depth, rigidity of the conduit, method of installation including the backfilling or covering procedures, preparation of conduit bedding, live or dead loads expected from overlying structures, and the transit effects of moving vehicles.

Loadings on conduits that occur as a result of being buried beneath earthfills are evaluated by using the Marston theory (based on the results of research on underground conduits conducted during the first third of the twentieth century at the Iowa Engineering Experimental Station, Iowa State College, under Director Anson Marston). The Marston theory recognizes that the loading on a buried conduit is related to the weight of earthfill located directly above it, but also considers that vertical shearing forces develop within the fill that, depending on the relative compression between the soil above and surrounding the conduit, act to increase or decrease the effects of the fill.

The early Iowa Engineering Experiment Station research established two broad categories of buried conduits—*ditch conduits*, installed where the original ground surface is retained, and *projecting conduits*, installed below or within earthen embankments constructed on top of an area's natural ground surface. *Ditch conduits* refer to installations in narrow ditches or trenches which are subsequently backfilled to final grade (Fig. 17-1a, b, c). The *projecting conduit* classification refers to installations for any area where an earth embankment will be placed above the conduit, regardless of whether the conduit is at, below, or above the site's original grade (Fig. 17-1d, e, f). Underground conduits located in areas where the original grade has been lowered are classified as ditch conduits (Fig. 17-1 b). Sanitary and storm sewer lines, and water and gas supply lines, are typically ditch-conduit-type installations; culverts for highway, airfield, and railroad embankments illustrate a common projecting-conduit-type installation.

Loading on Ditch Conduits The ditch conduit classification applies to installations in narrow ditches or trenches, say not wider than two or three times the conduit diameter. Backfill placed over the conduit to return the trench area to the original grade will tend to settle unless it has been placed and compacted in thin layers. Any tendency for downward movement of the backfill results in the development of frictional or shearing resistance along the backfill's vertical boundaries—that is, the vicinity of the original trench walls. Where cohesionless soils are involved, the boundary resistance relates to the lateral earth pressure acting on the vertical boundaries and the coefficient of sliding friction between the backfill and trench wall. This shearing or frictional resistance causes part of the backfill weight to be transmitted to the zones outside the original trench limits. In effect, an arching action occurs. The result is that the load transmitted onto the buried conduit is less than the weight of the overlying backfill.

The relationship between the weight of backfill placed in a ditch and the loading that eventually is imposed onto a buried rigid conduit can be established by applying the requirements of equilibrium to forces acting on a free-body diagram of the trench. With reference to Figure 17-2, a summation of vertical forces affecting the ditch element shown gives

$$W + dW + 2V = W + \gamma B_d(dh)$$

$$W + dW + (2)(\sigma_h\mu')(dh) = W + \gamma B_d(dh)$$

$$W + dW + (2)\left(K\frac{W}{B_d}\right)\mu'(dh) = W + \gamma B_d(dh)$$

$$dW = \gamma B_d(dh) - 2K\left(\frac{W}{B_d}\right)\mu'(dh)$$

where W = vertical load on any horizontal plane measured at a depth h.
K = lateral pressure coefficient, σ_h/σ_v.
μ' = coefficient of sliding friction between the backfill material and the trench wall.
γ = unit weight of soil backfill.

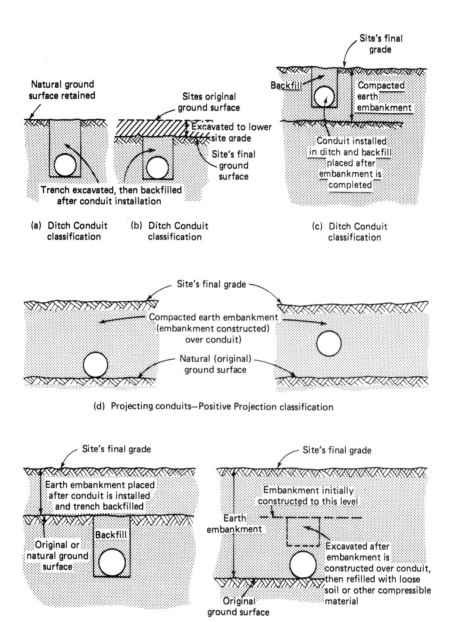

(a) Ditch Conduit classification

(b) Ditch Conduit classification

(c) Ditch Conduit classification

(d) Projecting conduits—Positive Projection classification

(e) Projecting conduit—negative Projection classification

(f) Projecting conduit—Induced Trench classification

Figure 17-1 Classifications of buried conduit installations.

Figure 17-2 Forces in effect for ditch conduit condition—basis for developing load equations.

σ_h = lateral pressure acting at a depth h.
B_d = width of trench.

Solution of this differential equation in terms of the load W_c that acts across the top of the conduit gives[1]

$$W_c = \frac{\gamma B_d^2}{2K\mu'} - \frac{\gamma B_d^2}{2K\mu'}\left(\frac{1}{e^{2K\mu'(H/B_d)}}\right)$$

$$W_c = \gamma B_d^2\left(\frac{1 - e^{-2K\mu'(H/B_d)}}{2K\mu'}\right) \tag{17-1a}$$

where e is the base of natural logarithms, or

$$W_c = \gamma B_d^2 C_d$$

where
$$\tag{17-1b}$$

$$C_d = \frac{1 - e^{-2K\mu'(H/B_d)}}{2K\mu'}$$

Values of C_d for various H/B_d and $K\mu'$ factors can be obtained from Figure 17-3.

If the conduit is *flexible* or otherwise capable of vertical deformation under load *and* the side fill zones are well compacted, the imposed loading is

$$W_c = \gamma B_c B_d C_d \tag{17-1c}$$

where B_c = conduit diameter.

[1]In the original solution of this equation, it was assumed that the K value was equal to the active lateral pressure coefficient, while μ' values were taken as the tangent of the backfill soil's angle of internal friction ϕ. However, the lateral pressure exerted at the wall line of a backfilled trench likely is close to the at-rest pressure if at least some compaction is accomplished, while the average coefficient of sliding friction between a compacted backfill and natural soil may be less than tan ϕ because shearing strains would be limited. The product of the $K\mu'$ term for these latter conditions is not expected to differ greatly from the originally assumed value.

The development of Equation 17-1 and the C_d values shown on Figure 17-3 assume that the arching effect is achieved without soil cohesion acting. Some cohesive resistance is expected in the vicinity of the trench wall where the excavation and backfill involve cohesive soil, but the time rate for its development is difficult to predict. Since the presence of soil cohesion would reduce the backfill loading on a buried conduit, the assumption of the no-cohesion condition for designing a conduit to carry backfill loading is conservative.

Conduit loads indicated by Equation 17-1 represent ultimate loadings, which often require a time period of months or years to reach. The loading following installation may be but 80–90 percent of the expected ultimate load. The time-dependent increase in loading is believed to relate to soil strains (deformations) occurring in the zones along the vertical boundaries of the original trench wall following the initially developing friction or shear stresses, a relaxation occurrence that reduces the soil shearing resistance and transfers weight back to the soil volume overlying the conduit.

If the trench backfill is placed in thin layers that are compacted to high densities, it will not settle relative to the surrounding undisturbed earth, and arching action does not take place. For this condition, the loading on the conduit should be assumed to be equal to the full weight of backfill. If there is a possibility that

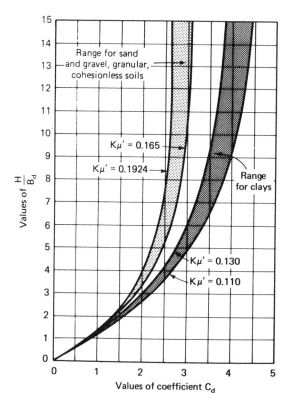

Figure 17-3 Coefficient C_d for ditch conduits.

the natural deposit surrounding a well-compacted trench backfill will settle more than the fill, the conduit loading should be computed by assuming the method for projecting conduits described in a following section.

Where a conduit trench is dug with sloping sides, the B_d value for use with Equation 17-1 is the width of trench across the plane corresponding to the top of the conduit (Fig. 17-4a). If a very wide ditch exists or has been provided, the fill loading on the conduit can be minimized by installing the conduit in a narrow subditch, as indicated by Figure 17-4b.

Positive Projecting Conduits   The *positive projecting* classification is defined as the condition where a conduit projects above the original ground surface in an area blanketed by earth fill.

Where a conduit is embedded under a height of embankment, there is a tendency for some differential settlement to occur between the fill zone directly overlying the conduit and the soil to the sides of this zone. If each incremental layer of embankment soil undergoes compression because of the weight of the overlying fill, and a rigid conduit has been installed, the total compression of the full embankment section to either side of the conduit will be greater than the total compression of the embankment zone directly over the conduit because of the greater fill height involved; that is, the settlement of the fill zone directly above the conduit is less than the settlement of the side zones. Conversely, if the conduit deflects significantly under the weight of the embankment fill, the settlement of the fill zone overlying the conduit will be greater than the settlement to the sides of the conduit.

The differential movement between the soil overlying the conduit and the adjacent embankment results in the development of shearing stresses on vertical planes that pass through the fill roughly in line with the sides of the conduit. Where the soil directly above the conduit settles more than the adjacent zones, the action of the shearing resistance on the central zone is upward (Fig. 17-5a) and the loading onto the conduit is less than the weight of fill directly overlying the conduit (similar to the occurrence for ditch conduits). When the soil zone above the conduit settles

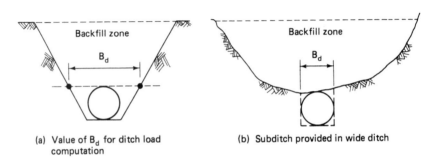

(a) Value of B_d for ditch load computation

(b) Subditch provided in wide ditch

Figure 17-4   Ditches with sloping sides.

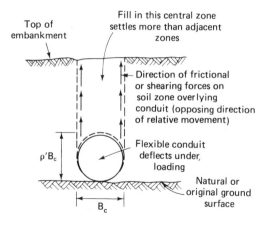

(a) Center zone settles more
than side zones

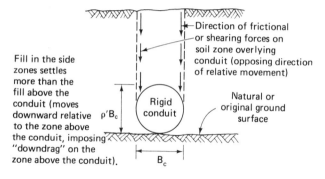

Fill in the side
zones settles
more than the
fill above the
conduit (moves
downward relative
to the zone above
the conduit, imposing
"downdrag" on the
zone above the conduit).

(b) Side zones settle more
than central zone

Figure 17-5 Effect of relative
settlement on direction of shearing
resistance within embankment—positive
projecting conduits.

less than the adjacent zones, the shearing resistance acts downward on the center zone (Fig. 17-5b), and the loading imposed onto the conduit is greater than the weight of fill that directly overlies the conduit.

As an aid for determining the direction of the shearing resistance that acts *on* the soil volume overlying the conduit, reference is made to relative settlements measured from a critical plane (Fig. 17-6). The critical plane is defined as a horizontal plane in the fill material that is level with the top of the conduit at the time embankment construction is begun, before settlements occur. If the critical plane subsequently settles more than the top of the conduit settles or deflects (Fig. 17-6a), the direction of the shearing resistance on the soil volume above the conduit is downward, and vice versa (Fig. 17-6b).

(a) Soil above conduit settles
less than adjacent zones

(b) Soil above conduit settles
more than side zones

Figure 17-6 Factors that affect settlement ratio, r_c.

    A settlement ratio, considering the various factors that contribute to settlement measured at the critical plane and at the top of a conduit (see Fig. 17-6), has been established for determining the relative movement between the critical plane and top of conduit,

$$\text{Settlement ratio, } r_c = \frac{(\delta_m + \delta_g) - (\delta_f + d_c)}{\delta_m} \qquad (17\text{-}2)$$

where r_c = settlement ratio for the positive projecting condition.
    δ_m = compression of the sidefill on the sides of the conduit (in the pB distance only).

δ_g = settlement of the embankment subgrade adjacent to the conduit.

δ_f = settlement of the subgrade beneath the conduit (the conduit foundation).

d_c = vertical deflection of the conduit.

The settlement ratio is a negative value when the conduit settles more than the critical plane. This is the condition that results in shearing resistance acting upward on the soil volume overlying the conduit; it is similar to the situation for ditch conduits discussed earlier in the chapter. The loading on the conduit thus is less than the weight of the directly overlying fill. When the settlement ratio is a positive value, the loading imposed onto a conduit is greater than the weight of fill directly above it.

For construction projects, the individual terms included in the settlement ratio equation are difficult or impractical to determine. The empirically determined values shown in Table 17-1, established from observation and experience data, are considered suitable for design purposes.

The shearing stresses acting on the vertical planes that represent the side boundaries of the soil zone directly overlying a conduit do not necessarily extend to the top of the embankment where a high fill exists. Differential settlements, and the resulting shear stresses, between the soil zones above and outside the conduit are greatest at the top of the conduit and progressively decrease toward the surface of the embankment. This occurrence relates to the manner in which the effect of compressive strains accumulate with increasing depth. As the stress transfer creates an arching action of cumulative effect between the soil above the conduit and the adjacent zones, a horizontal plane develops at some height above the conduit where the *differential* vertical strains and related shearing stresses diminish to zero. At this height, designated H_e, settlement of the soil zone above the conduit is equal to the settlement of the adjacent zones, and a plane of equal settlement is established. No differential settlement occurs within the embankment soil above the plane of equal settlement.

An expression for H_e can be obtained by equating the total vertical movement that occurs in the embankment zones above and to the sides of the conduit. The total soil movement above the conduit is the sum of the total compression of soil above the conduit plus the deflection of the conduit top. The vertical movement

TABLE 17-1 DESIGN VALUES FOR SETTLEMENT RATIO
(after Spangler, [236])

Conditions	r_c, Settlement ratio
Rigid culvert on foundation of rock or unyielding soil	+1.0
Rigid culvert on foundation of ordinary soil	+0.5 to +0.8
Rigid culvert on foundation of material that yields with respect to adjacent natural ground	0 to +0.5
Flexible culvert with poorly compacted side fills	−0.4 to 0
Flexible culvert with well-compacted side fills[a]	−0.2 to +0.8

[a]Not well established.

in the embankment zones adjacent to the conduit is the total compression of soil above the critical plane plus settlement of the critical plane. Mathematically, the equating of settlements is

$$
\left[\frac{1}{2K\mu'} \pm \left(\frac{H}{B_c} - \frac{H_e}{B_c} \pm \frac{r_c\rho'}{3} \right) \right] \frac{e^{\pm 2K\mu'(H_e/B_c)} - 1}{\pm 2K\mu'} + \frac{1}{2} \left(\frac{H_e}{B_c} \right)^2 \cdots
$$

$$
+ \frac{r_c\rho'}{3} \left(\frac{H - H_e}{B_c} \right) e^{\pm 2K\mu'(H_e/B_c)} - \frac{1}{2K\mu'} \left(\frac{H_e}{B_c} \right) \mp \left(\frac{H}{B_c} \right) \left(\frac{H_e}{B_c} \right) = \pm r_c\rho' \frac{H}{B_c} \qquad (17\text{-}3)
$$

In Equation 17-3, the upper plus or minus signs apply when the settlement ratio, r_c, is positive, while the lower signs apply when r_c is negative. The term ρ' is a *projection ratio* (Fig. 17-5) where the dimension from the original ground surface to the top of the conduit is taken as $\rho' B_c$ (i.e., ρ' is the distance between the original ground surface and top of conduit expressed as a function of the conduit diameter).

Based on comparison of actual embankment height and H_e, and the possibility of the settlement ratio's being positive or negative, four different conditions are encountered with conduit installations:

1. The *complete ditch condition*, when the embankment height is less than H_e and r_c is negative.
2. The *complete projection condition*, when the embankment height is less than H_e and r_c is positive.
3. The *incomplete ditch condition*, when the embankment height is greater than H_e and r_c is negative.
4. The *incomplete projection condition*, when the embankment height is greater than H_e and r_c is positive.

These different possible conditions are illustrated in Figure 17-7.

For the complete ditch or complete projection condition, the shearing stresses acting on the vertical planes passing upward from the sides of the conduit extend to the top of the embankment. (Recall that this condition also occurs with ditch conduit installations.) With the incomplete ditch or incomplete projection condition, the shearing stresses extend only to the plane of equal settlement, which is below the embankment surface.

The Marston theory establishes the expressions for loading on positive projecting conduits as

$$
W_c = \gamma B_c^2 C_c \qquad (17\text{-}4a)
$$

where, for the *complete* projection or ditch condition,

$$
C_c = \frac{e^{\pm 2K\mu'(H/B_c)} - 1}{\pm 2K\mu'} \qquad (17\text{-}4b)
$$

and for the *incomplete* projection or ditch condition

$$
C_c = \frac{e^{\pm 2K\mu'(H_e/B_c)} - 1}{\pm 2K\mu'} + \left(\frac{H}{B_c} - \frac{H_e}{B_c} \right) e^{\pm K\mu'(H_e/B_c)} \qquad (17\text{-}4c)
$$

Figure 17-7 Possible combinations of relative embankment height and settlement ratio, for conduit installations.

The positive signs apply where r_c is positive (projection conditions), while the negative signs apply when r_c is negative (ditch conditions).

Determination of the vertical distance representing the plane of equal settlement and the conduit loads through use of Equations 17-3 and 17-4 can be cumbersome and time-consuming. As for the ditch conduit analysis, the solution of these equations is simplified by use of a diagram, as shown in Figure 17-8. Values of C_c can be obtained when the H/B_c ratio and the product obtained by combining the settlement and projection ratio terms are known. The positioning of the curves is not sensitive to the range of $K\mu'$ values expected with field installations, and the diagram shown provides adequate accuracy for practical problems. On Figure 17-8, the point where the curves labeled "complete ditch" or "complete projection condition" separate from the incomplete condition curves establishes the H/B_c ratio when H equals H_e.

Negative Projecting Conduits The *negative projecting* condition occurs where a conduit is installed in a trench below the original ground surface of an area which

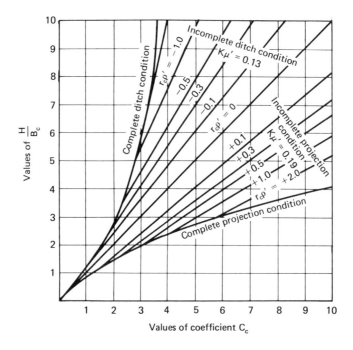

Figure 17-8 Coefficient C_c for positive projecting conduits.

then is blanketed with earth embankment (Fig. 17-9). For this case, the critical plane is located level with the original ground surface, and the settlement ratio for the negative projection condition is

$$r_c' = \frac{\delta_g - (\delta_d + \delta_f + d_c)}{\delta_d} \tag{17-5}$$

where r_c' = settlement ratio for the negative projecting condition.
δ_g = settlement of the original ground surface.
δ_d = settlement of backfill in the trench.
δ_f = settlement of the conduit foundation.
d_c = vertical deflection of the conduit.

Normally the settlement of the critical plane in the trench fill overlying the conduit is greater than the settlement of the natural ground surface adjacent to the trench. Thus, the shearing stresses act upward on the vertical boundaries of the trench backfill, and the settlement ratio is negative.

The expression for loading imposed onto the conduit is

$$W_c = \gamma B_d^2 C_n \tag{17-6a}$$

where

$$C_n = \frac{e^{-2K\mu'(H/B_d)} - 1}{-2K\mu'} \quad \text{when } H \le H_e \tag{17-6b}$$

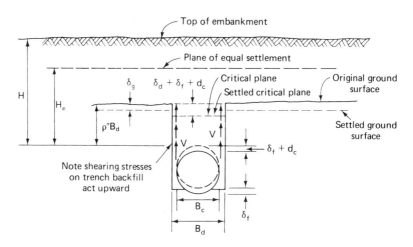

Figure 17-9 Conditions defined for negative projecting conduit.

and

$$C_n = \frac{e^{-2K\mu'(H_e/B_d)} - 1}{-2K\mu'} + \left(\frac{H}{B_d} - \frac{H_e}{B_d}\right) e^{-2K\mu'(H_e/B_d)} \quad \text{when } H > H_e \quad (17\text{-}6c)$$

The curves presented in Figure 17-10a, b, and c can be used to obtain values of C_n for various r_c' and ρ'' values. The projection ratio ρ'' for the negative projecting condition is the distance from the top of the conduit to the natural ground surface in terms of the conduit diameter (see Fig. 17-9). Values of the settlement ratio r_c' for negative projecting conditions have not been well defined. In the absence of information about field conditions, a design value of -0.5 is commonly assumed for r_c'.

Induced Trench   Loads imposed on conduits installed in the positive projecting condition under high embankments are greater than the conduit loads that result when a negative projecting condition exists. The *induced trench* method, Figure 17-11, can be used to effectively reduce the loading that develops on conduits placed under high earth fills. Initially, the conduit is installed and blanketed with a limited thickness of earth fill, as for a normal positive projection condition. Soil placement is temporarily halted when it reaches a height above the conduit equal to one to two times the conduit diameter. At that stage, a trench is excavated directly above the conduit and then is backfilled with compressible material, an undertaking that creates the situation for a negative projection condition. Materials such as very loosely placed earth fill or baled straw have been used to cause the desired trench backfill settlement, a condition that forces an arching action in the overlying embankment, with the result that loading onto the conduit is minimized.

Equations 17-6a, b, c can be used for the induced trench condition by substituting values of B_c in place of B_d. The diagrams of Figure 17-10 correspondingly apply.

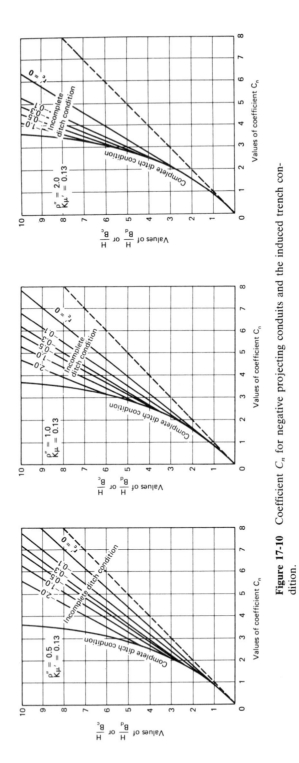

Figure 17-10 Coefficient C_n for negative projecting conduits and the induced trench condition.

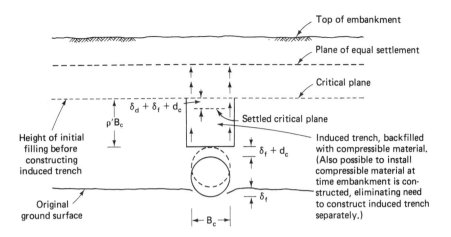

Plane of equal settlement

Critical plane

$\delta_d + \delta_f + d_c$

$\rho' B_c$

Settled critical plane

Height of initial
filling before
constructing
induced trench

$\delta_f + d_c$

Induced trench, backfilled
with compressible material.
(Also possible to install
compressible material at
time embankment is con-
structed, eliminating need
to construct induced trench
separately.)

Original
ground surface

δ_f

$\leftarrow B_c \rightarrow$

Figure 17-11   Conditions for induced trench.

Tunneled Conduits   Conduits may be required to pass beneath existing embankments or hilly areas where it is most practical to use tunneling or jacking
methods for the installation (see Fig. 17-12) instead of the open trench method
(e.g., culvert or sewer installation beneath a highway or railroad which is providing
service that cannot be disrupted). The load on a conduit installed by tunneling or
jacking, as shown in Figure 17-13, is

$$W_c = \gamma B_t^2 C_t - 2cB_t C_t \qquad (17\text{-}7)$$

(a)   (b)

Figure 17-12   Equipment and working pit for a horizontal boring-jacking installation. Jacking precedes auger by slight distance to prevent loss of ground above
sleeve. (a) Extra section of sleeve being placed in preparation for jacking. (b)
Head-on view of boring-jacking machine. New sleeve section with boring auger is
to right of machine.

Chap. 17   Loads on Buried Conduits

Ground surface or top
of embankment

H

Tunnel or jacked sleeve

Installed conduit

|←— B_t —→|

Figure 17-13 Description of terms applicable to a jacked or tunneled installation.

where B_t = width or diameter of the tunnel or jacked opening.

  c = cohesive strength of the soil overlying conduit tunnel.

  C_t = load factor equal to C_d, the same factor used for ditch conduits (see Eq. 17-1b and Fig. 17-3).

Loads on Surface above Conduits   Except for deep installations (large H/B ratios), the effect of loads applied on the surface above a buried conduit will be transmitted through the earth to the conduit structure. Typical of this occurrence are surface loads from trucks and automobiles, aircraft, and railroad stock.

The influence of concentrated or uniformly distributed loadings acting on a *soil surface* above a buried conduit can be determined by application of the methods discussed in Chapter 8, with the Boussinesq distribution applying for most situations. The subsurface stress distribution which results from loads applied through a highway or airport pavement, or a railroad track-ties-ballast system, is less clearly understood, however. Pavements and railroad track systems are themselves structures whose function, in part, is to spread out surface loadings. The underground distribution which results relates to the physical characteristics of the pavement or rail system (such as thickness and rigidity), and magnitude and imposition area (e.g., tire contact area) of wheel or axle loads. Recommended procedures for design analysis by involved engineering and technical-trade organizations[2] have generally considered surface loads to act over some prescribed area whose size increases with depth, a procedure which results in decreasing magnitudes of stress as depth increases, similar to the effects resulting from the sixty-degree approximation method discussed in Chapter 8. Procedures required for analysis of highway, airport, or railroad related projects can be somewhat unique. Concerning recommendations for design, it is most appropriate that reference be made to the design standards which serve as the governing criteria for the project, such as the American Association of State Highway and Transportation Officials (AASHTO) design manuals for highway work and American Railway Engineering Association (AREA) design manuals for railroad work.

---

[2]For example, American Association of State Highway and Transportation Officials (AASHTO), American Railway Engineering Association (AREA), Portland Cement Association (PCA), Water Pollution Control Federation (WFCF), American Society of Civil Engineers (ASCE), Federal or State Department of Transportation (DOT), American Concrete Pipe Association, and so on.

Compared to static loads, moving loads create an impact whose effect is greater than that of the involved dead load. For underground conduits the effects of impact are greater where a soil surface exists than where a paved surface is present. If the impact factor is defined as a multiplier for a dead load in order to account for the moving effect, an impact factor on the order of 1.5 is considered appropriate for determining subsurface stresses resulting from truck traffic on unpaved roads, whereas a vehicle impact factor of unity can be assumed for conduits more than three feet below a paved highway.

In general, surface loads diminish rapidly with depth under structural pavements. Conduits covered by a few feet of earth fill plus a structural pavement are commonly considered to be adequately protected from the effects of vehicle loads; the preferable soil cover ranges from about 3 ft where rigid-class concrete pavements are provided to about 5 ft for flexible-class pavements. Realistically, the greatest structural danger to conduits beneath highways, airport runways, and railroads probably occurs during embankment construction, when the conduit has little or no protective cover and heavy equipment is operating. During construction, embankment culverts should be protected with a temporary soil covering some 3 or more feet thick, or the culvert area can be permanently covered with adequate fill installed with the aid of light equipment before heavy equipment begins operating in the area. The regions to the sides of the conduit should be ramped with soil, to achieve resistance to lateral movement.

Required Pipe Strength   The maximum loading that conduits are capable of carrying is affected by factors such as the conduit material and shape, and the support of the material beneath and to the sides.

The safe loading that can be imposed onto a rigid conduit such as concrete pipe is determined by the pipe strength and the quality of the foundation bedding. Generally, better support and higher permissible loadings are obtained if the foundation is shaped to the contour of the conduit (Fig. 17-14).

The strength of plain concrete and reinforced concrete pipe as information for design is commonly obtained from results of the *three-edge bearing* test. In this test, the conduit is subjected to compressive loading applied across the diameter through narrow bearing strips on the perimeter, as indicated by Figure 17-15. Unreinforced concrete pipe is rated in terms of the ultimate load that can be applied. Reinforced concrete pipe is rated either by ultimate load or by the loading that

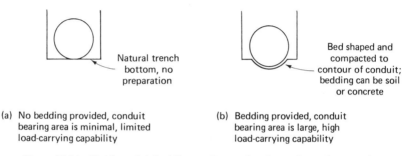

Natural trench
bottom, no
preparation

Bed shaped and
compacted to
contour of conduit;
bedding can be soil
or concrete

(a) No bedding provided, conduit
bearing area is minimal, limited
load-carrying capability

(b) Bedding provided, conduit
bearing area is large, high
load-carrying capability

Figure 17-14   Rigid conduit bedding—effect on bearing and carrying capacity.

Applied load

Rigid steel
member

Pipe
wall

Two
bearing strips

Figure 17-15 Arrangement for three-edge bearing test.

causes the formation of a 0.01-inch crack one foot in length. The pipe strength may be indicated in terms of a D-load (either D_u or $D_{0.01}$), a value obtained by dividing the three-edge bearing test load by the interior pipe diameter; the procedure is intended to provide a pipe strength classification independent of diameter.

The three-edge bearing test represents a severe loading condition that rarely develops with actual conduit installations. When the field-foundation support is better than the support provided in the three-edge bearing test, the buried pipe is capable of supporting load greater than that indicated by the test. Based on the benefit to a rigid conduit's load carrying capacity, bedding classifications have been established for the ditch conduit type of installation (Fig. 17-16). Load factors shown for each classification of *ditch conduit* (trench bedding) indicate the ratio of permissible field load to three-edge bearing test load; since the load factors for all cases are greater than one, the magnitude of allowable field loadings is greater than that for the test loads.

With *projecting conduit* installations, difficult-to-evaluate factors influence the load factor. Organizations such as the American Concrete Pipe Association have developed tables, illustrated in Figure 17-17, that provide load factors for variously shaped concrete conduits based on type of bedding, and conduit projection and settlement ratios. For planning and design purposes, it is practical to refer to such sources.

Study of the load-carrying capacity of *flexible* conduits as related to installation procedures indicates that influencing factors are not defined to the extent that practical design procedures can be provided. On the basis of experience and empirical data, manufacturers of corrugated metal pipe have developed manuals that relate pipe properties (such as gauge and type of corrugation) with installation conditions and allowable fill height, as illustrated in Figure 17-18. For planning and design, it is practical to consult such references.

ILLUSTRATION 17-1. A reinforced concrete pipe culvert 3.5 ft in diameter is required in an area where the height of embankment will be 24 ft. The culvert will

CLASS A
Reinforced A_s = 1.0% L_f = 4.8
Reinforced A_s = 0.4% L_f = 3.4
Plain $\quad\quad\quad\quad$ L_f = 2.8

B_c + 8" min.

1-1/4 B_c

12" min.

Densely compacted backfill

B_c

Plain or reinforced concrete 2000 psi min.

1/4 B_c
1/4 D max.

Concrete cradle

B_c + 8" min.

1-1/4 B_c

1/8 H
6" min

1/4 D
4" min.

B_c

d

Compacted granular material

Concrete arch

CLASS B
L_f = 1.9

Densely compacted backfill

12"

B_c

Compacted granular material

d

Granular foundation

CLASS C
L_f = 1.5

Lightly compacted backfill

1/8 H
6" min

B_c

Compacted natural granular soil or compacted granular backfill

1/6 B_c
d

Granular foundation

CLASS D
L_f = 1.1

1/8 H
6" min.

Loose backfill

B_c

Flat subgrade

Depth of bedding material below pipe

D	d (min.)
27" and smaller	3"
30" to 60"	4"
66" and larger	6"

Notes:
For Class B and C beddings, subgrades should be excavated or over excavated, if necessary, so a uniform foundation free of protruding rocks may be provided.
Special care may be necessary with Class A or other unyielding foundations to cushion pipe from shock when blasting can be anticipated in the area

Legend

B_c = outside diameter
H = backfill cover above top of pipe
D = inside diameter
d $\;$ = depth of bedding material below pipe
A_s = area of transverse steel in the cradle or arch expressed as a percentage of area of concrete at invert or crown

Figure 17-16 Bedding classes and load factors: rigid circular pipe, ditch, and negative projection installations. (After American Concrete Pipe Association [8])

CLASS A

$B_c + 8''$ min.

B_c

1/4 B_c
1/4 D min.

Concrete cradle

Notes:
For Class B and C beddings, subgrades should be excavated or over excavated, if necessary, so a uniform foundation free of protruding rocks may be provided.
Special care may be necessary with Class A or other unyielding foundations to cushion pipe from shock when blasting can be anticipated in the area

CLASS B

1.25 B_c min.

pB_c
p max. = 0.5

B_c

d

Compacted granular material

Granular foundation

CLASS C

1.25 B_c min.

B_c

1/6 B_c min.

d

Compacted granular material or densely compacted backfill

Granular foundation

CLASS D

B_c

Flat subgrade

Depth of bedding material below pipe

D	d (min.)
27" and smaller	3"
30" to 60"	4"
66" and larger	6"

Legend

B_c = outside diameter
H = backfill cover above top of pipe
D = inside diameter
d = depth of bedding material below pipe

Figure 17-17 Bedding classes and load factors, rigid pipe—positive projection and induced trench conditions. (American Concrete Pipe Association [8])

LOAD FACTORS FOR CIRCULAR PIPE
POSITIVE PROJECTION CONDITIONS

H/Bc	Class A Bedding ρ' = 0.9					Class B Bedding ρ' = 0.9					Class C Bedding ρ' = 0.9					Class D Bedding ρ' = 0.9				
	$r_c\rho'=0$	0.1	0.3	0.5	1.0	$r_c\rho'=0$	0.1	0.3	0.5	1.0	$r_c\rho'=0$	0.1	0.3	0.5	1.0	$r_c\rho'=0$	0.1	0.3	0.5	1.0
0.5	11.26	8.87	8.87	8.87	8.87	3.82	3.81	3.81	3.81	3.81	3.01	2.82	2.81	2.82	2.82	1.51	1.46	1.46	1.46	1.46
1.0	6.61	5.37	5.37	5.37	5.37	3.00	3.00	3.00	3.00	3.00	2.55	2.35	2.35	2.35	2.35	1.39	1.33	1.33	1.33	1.33
1.5	5.81	4.83	4.47	4.47	4.47	2.83	2.71	2.71	2.71	2.71	2.42	2.26	2.16	2.16	2.16	1.35	1.29	1.27	1.27	1.27
2.0	5.48	4.49	4.35	4.19	4.19	2.77	2.67	2.62	2.61	2.61	2.37	2.20	2.14	2.10	2.10	1.33	1.28	1.26	1.24	1.24
3.0	5.18	4.50	4.21	4.06	3.88	2.72	2.62	2.56	2.50	2.50	2.31	2.17	2.10	2.07	2.02	1.31	1.27	1.24	1.23	1.24
5.0	4.97	4.37	4.11	3.97	3.81	2.67	2.58	2.52	2.46	2.46	2.27	2.14	2.08	2.04	2.00	1.30	1.26	1.24	1.22	1.21
10.0	4.82	4.28	4.04	3.90	3.76	2.64	2.55	2.50	2.44	2.44	2.24	2.12	2.06	2.03	1.99	1.29	1.25	1.23	1.22	1.20
15.0	4.77	4.25	4.01	3.88	3.74	2.63	2.54	2.49	2.43	2.43	2.23	2.10	2.05	2.02	1.98	1.29	1.25	1.23	1.21	1.20

LOAD FACTORS FOR CIRCULAR PIPE
INDUCED TRENCH INSTALLATIONS

H/Bc	Class A Bedding ρ' = 0.9					Class B Bedding ρ' = 0.9					Class C Bedding ρ' = 0.9				
	$r_c=-0.1$	-0.3	-0.5	-1.0	-2.0	$r_c=-0.1$	-0.3	-0.5	-1.0	-2.0	$r_c=-0.1$	-0.3	-0.5	-1.0	-2.0
1	7.11	7.11	7.11	7.11	7.11	3.46	3.46	3.46	3.46	3.46	2.62	2.62	2.62	2.62	2.62
2	7.12	7.12	7.12	7.12	7.12	3.46	3.46	3.46	3.46	3.46	2.62	2.62	2.62	2.62	2.62
3	7.20	8.03	8.41	8.41	8.41	3.50	3.66	3.73	3.73	3.73	2.64	2.64	2.64	2.64	2.64
5	7.30	8.21	9.42	12.15	12.92	3.51	3.67	3.91	4.30	4.39	2.64	2.74	2.87	3.07	3.12
10	7.32	8.57	9.76	13.60	26.95	3.51	3.76	3.97	4.46	5.29	2.64	2.79	2.90	3.15	3.55
15	7.32	8.69	10.04	14.94	35.12	3.51	3.78	4.01	4.59	5.54	2.64	2.80	2.92	3.22	3.66
20	7.32	8.71	10.09	15.70	41.89	3.51	3.78	4.02	4.66	5.68	2.64	2.80	2.93	3.25	3.72
25	7.32	8.72	10.13	16.20	47.57	3.51	3.79	4.02	4.70	5.77	2.64	2.81	2.93	3.27	3.75

Figure 17-17. (continued)

2²/₃" × ¹/₂" CORRUGATED STEEL PIPE

H20 LIVE LOAD— ROUND PIPE*

Diameter or Span in Inches	Min.‡ Cover	Maximum Cover in Feet					
		Specified Thickness in Inches					
		0.052	.064	.079	.109	.138	.168
12		199	248	310			
15		159	199	248			
18		132	166	207			
21		113	142	178	249		
24		99	124	155	218		
27			111	138	193		
30	12-in. Minimum Cover		99	124	174		
36			83	103	145	186	
42			71	88	124	160	195
48			62	77	109	140	171
54				66	93	120	147
60					79	102	125
66					68	87	107
72						73	89
78							74
84							61
90							50
96							41

‡From top of pipe to top of subgrade.

E80 LIVE LOAD—ROUND PIPE†

Diameter or Span in Inches	Min. Cover	Maximum Cover in Feet					
		Specified Thickness in Inches					
		0.052	.064	.079	.109	.138	.168
12		199	248	310			
15		159	199	248			
18		132	166	207			
21		113	142	178	249		
24	12 inches	99	124	155	218		
27			111	138	193		
30			99	124	174		
36			83	103	145	186	
42			71	88	124	160	195
48			62	77	109	140	171
54	18 inches			66	93	120	147
60					79	102	125
66					68	87	107
72						73	89
78	24 inches						74
84							61
90							50
96							41

Figure 17-18 Height of cover limits—corrugated steel pipe. (Courtesy Armco Inc., [15])

DITCH INSTALLATIONS
2²/₃" × ¹/₂" CORRUGATED STEEL PIPE
H20 LIVE LOAD*

Diameter of Pipe (inches	Depth of Trench to Top of Pipe					
	1-15 (ft.)	16-20 (ft.)	12-25 (ft.)	26-30 (ft.)	31-35 (ft.)	36-40 (ft.)
12 to 48	.064"	.064"	.064"	.064"	.064"	.064"
54	.079"	.079"	.079"	.079"	.079"	.079"
60	.079"	.079"	.079"	.079"	.079"	.079"
66	.079"	.079"	.079"	.079"	.079"	.079"
72	.079"	.079"	.079"	.079"	.079"	.079"
78	.109"	.109"	.109"	.109"	.109"	.109"
84	.109"	.109"	.109"	.109"	.109"	.109"
90	.109"	.109	.109"	.138"	.168"	.168"
96	.109"	.109"	.138"	.138"	.168"	.168"
102	.138"	.138"	.138"	.138"	.168"	.168"

*Typically assumed live load condition for highway culverts.
†Typically assumed live load condition for railroad culverts.

Figure 17-18 *(Continued)*

be installed as a positive projecting conduit where the subgrade is shaped to the contour of the pipe so the Class C bedding condition is provided.

Determine (a) the embankment loading on the conduit, and (b) the strength of pipe required based on the $D_{0.01}$ load classification.

(a). For an inside diameter of 3.5 ft, assume an outside diameter = 4 ft.

$$H/B_c = \frac{20.4 \text{ ft}}{4.0 \text{ ft}} = 5.1 \quad \text{and} \quad r_c\rho' = (+0.5)(0.9) = +0.45$$

From Figure 17-8, obtain $C_c \cong 7.5$

Therefore, $W_c = \gamma B_c^2 C_c = (115 \text{ pcf})(4 \text{ ft} \times 4 \text{ ft})(7.5) = 13,800 \text{ lb/lineal ft}$

(b) From Figure 17-17, obtain load factor for installed pipe $\cong 2.05$

$$D_{0.01}\text{load} = \frac{13,800 \text{ lb/ft}}{(\text{load factor})(\text{I.D.})} = \frac{13,800 \text{ lb/ft}}{(2.05)(3.5 \text{ ft})} = 1924 \text{ lb per linear foot of}$$
inside diameter
(the required pipe
strength based on
$D_{0.01}$ load classification)

PROBLEMS

17.1. Prepare a summary tabulation for the major categories of conduit installation which, in a general manner, indicates whether loading from an overlying soil fill is less or more than the weight of soil in the prism directly overlying the conduit (i.e., use column titles of *conduit condition* and *conduit loading less/more than overlying soil prism*).

17-2. A 3-ft-diameter conduit is installed in a trench 6 ft wide and 20 ft deep at a location where granular soils exist. The soil unit weight is 115 pcf.
(a) What soil load results if the conduit is concrete and the backfill is slightly compacted?
(b) What loading onto the conduit is to be expected if the backfill is well compacted?
(c) Approximately what backfill load results if a corrugated metal conduit is used?

17-3. A 4-ft-diameter culvert is to be located directly on the ground surface of an area (no prepared bedding) where a 24-ft soil embankment will be constructed. Assume that the embankment soil will have an average unit weight equal to 125 pcf.
(a) What loading is expected if the culvert is concrete and the natural ground surface is rock?
(b) What loading is expected where the culvert is corrugated metal and the soil fill to the sides is poorly compacted?
(c) Determine the H_e distances for the conditions described in (a) and (b).

17-4. A corrugated metal conduit is to be installed in a trench excavated below the natural grade in an area where a 5-m height of fill is later to be placed. Determine the soil overburden load expected to be imposed onto a 1-m-diameter conduit if the trench is 1.5 m wide and 2 m deep. Assume a soil unit weight of 18 kN/m³.

17-5. A 1.5-m-diameter steel pipe is jacked horizontally through a highway embankment so that there will be no interference to the existing traffic. The top of the jacked section will be 4 meters below the embankment surface. What loading is imposed onto the pipe from the overlying embankment? Assume that the embankment soil weighs 19 kN/m³, has an angle of internal friction ϕ equal to 30°, and a cohesion c equal to 9 kN/m².

17-6. A concrete conduit, 5 ft OD and 4.5 ft ID, is installed in a 20-ft deep, 8-ft wide trench whose bottom is prepared so as to provide a class-B bedding. What conduit strength, based on the $D_{0.01}$ load, is required? Assume unit weight of backfill is 120 pcf.

17-7. A 5-ft-diameter corrugated steel pipe is to be used as a culvert beneath a 50-ft height of highway embankment. For the $2\frac{2}{3}$-inch by $\frac{1}{2}$-inch corrugated sections, what is the *minimum* wall thickness that should be used? (Refer to Figure 17-18.)

Glossary

Adsorbed water Water bound to soil particles because of the attraction between electrical charges existing on soil particle surfaces and (dipole) water molecules.

Aquifer A water-bearing layer of soil or permeable rock.

Arching The transfer of stress from a yielding part of a soil mass to an adjacent, less yielding or restrained part of the mass.

Atterberg limits The liquid limit, plastic limit, and shrinkage limit for soil. The *water content* where the soil behavior changes from the liquid to the plastic state is the liquid limit; from the plastic to the semisolid state is the plastic limit; and from the semisolid to the solid state is the shrinkage limit.

Backfill Soil material placed back into an area that has been excavated, such as against structures and in pipe trenches.

Bearing capacity The pressure that can be imposed by a foundation onto the soil or rock supporting the foundation.

Boring The method of investigating subsurface conditions by drilling into the earth. Frequently, soil or rock samples are also extracted from the boring for classification and testing.

Borrow Soil or rock material obtained from an off-site source for use as fill on construction projects.

Caisson Large structural chamber used to keep soil and water from entering into a deep excavation or construction area. Caissons may be installed by being sunk in place or by systematically excavating below the bottom of the unit to the desired depth.

Capillarity The movement of water, due to effects other than gravity, through very small void spaces that exist in a soil mass. Water movement occurs in very small channels such as capillary-sized openings because of the affinity between soil and water, which acts to increase the boundary of contact between the two materials, and the surface tension property developed by water in contact with air. Capillary flow can occur in a direction opposite to that of the pull of gravity.

Chemical weathering The process of weathering whereby chemical reactions such as hydration, solution, oxidation, and ion exchange break down and possibly change rock and soil materials.

Clays (clay minerals) Very small soil particles having a crystalline (layered) structure, created as the result of the chemical alteration of primary rock minerals. Most clay particles, because of their mineralogical composition, are flat or platelike in shape, with a large surface area to mass ratio. Clay particle dimensions are often smaller than 2μ.

Coarse-grained soil Those soil types having particles large enough to be seen without visual assistance. The coarse-grained materials include the sand and gravel (or larger) soil particles.

Cohesion The bonding or attraction between particles of fine-grained soil that creates shear strength.

Compaction The process of increasing the density or unit weight of a soil (frequently fill soil) by rolling, tamping, vibrating, or other mechanical means.

Compressibility The change, or tendency for change, that occurs in the thickness of a soil mass when it is subjected to compressive loading.

Conduit Pipe that is buried in a soil mass or passing through a soil embankment, and carries water or other fluid materials, electrical cables, and the like.

Consolidation The process by which compression of a newly stressed clay soil occurs simultaneously with the expulsion of water present in the soil void spaces. Initially, the newly imposed stress acting on the clay is imparted onto the water in the soil voids (pore water), and not onto the soil particles. Because of the increased pressure, the water is gradually forced out of the soil. As the pore water pressure is reduced, the magnitude of stress being imposed onto the soil particles is correspondingly increased. Compression of the clay layer occurs only as rapidly as pore water can drain from the soil, and this is related to the permeability of the soil layer.

Density The mass per unit of volume. In reference to soil, the term often also indicates weight per unit volume and is synonymous with unit weight.

Dewatering The procedure used to remove water from a construction area, such as pumping from an excavation or location where water covers the planned working surface; the procedure used to lower the groundwater table in order to obtain a "dry" area in the vicinity of an excavation that would otherwise extend below water.

Dispersive clays Clay soils that defloculate in still water and erode when exposed to a low-velocity flow of water. A clay-pore water system that has a high concentration of sodium ions tends to have high dispersivity.

Ditch conduits Conduits installed in narrow ditches or trenches that are subsequently backfilled.

Drawdown The lowering of the level of the groundwater table that occurs in the vicinity of a water well (on dewatering equipment) when it is pumped.

Dynamic compaction Procedure whereby surface and near-surface zones of soil or fill are compacted by dropping a heavy weight (commonly 5 to 15 tons) from a relatively great height (drops of 30 to 100 ft are typical). Multiple poundings are provided at each drop location, and closely spaced drop locations are utilized to improve a construction site.

Earth pressure Normally used in reference to the lateral pressure or force imposed by a soil mass against an earth-supporting structure such as a retaining wall or basement wall, or on a fictitious vertical plane located within a soil mass. The *coefficient* of earth pressure refers to the ratio of lateral pressure to vertical pressure existing at a point in a soil mass.

Effective stress   The actual particle-to-particle contact stress (or pressure) existing between soil grains. This stress compensates for the possible buoyancy influence of water pressure. Effective stress relates directly to the shear strength possessed by a soil.

Expansive clays   Clay soils that experience significant volume expansion in the presence of water and shrink upon drying. Clays including the montmorillonite mineral are especially noted for their volume-change characteristics.

Fill   Earth placed in an excavation or other area to raise the surface elevation. Also referred to as earth fill or soil fill. *Structural earth fill* refers to the material that is placed and compacted in layers in order to achieve a uniform and dense soil mass which is capable of supporting structural loading.

Fines or **Fine-grained**   Refers to silt- and clay-sized particles that exist in a soil mixture.

Flow line   The path of travel traced by moving water as it flows through a soil mass.

Flow net   A pictorial method used to study the flow of water through a soil. Used to indicate the paths of travel followed by moving water and the subsurface pressures resulting from the presence of the water.

Footing   Type of foundation typically installed at a shallow depth and constructed to provide a relatively large area of bearing onto the supporting soil.

Friction, internal   The particle (solid to solid) friction developed by cohesionless soils, and the property responsible for most of the shear strength which this type of soil can develop. The angle of internal friction, ϕ, refers to the arc tan value of the sloped line that results from graphing the relationship between shear strength and the imposed normal stress for a soil. This strength property also applies to fine-grained soils when the effect of consolidation or drainage on the shearing resistance of those soils is being studied.

Gabions   Stone-filled steel wire baskets which can be assembled or stacked like building blocks to act as retaining walls or provide slope and erosion protection.

Geofabrics   Synthetic fabrics used as filters, drains, or reinforcements in earthwork projects.

Groundwater table   The surface of the underground supply of water. Also referred to as the *phreatic surface*.

Head   Shortened form of the phrase *pressure head*, referring to the pressure resulting from a column of water or elevated supply of water. Pressure would be computed from $\gamma_w h$, where γ_w is the unit weight of water and h is the height or elevation of the water supply. The h term is the pressure *head*.

Heave   Upward movement of soil and foundations supported on soil, caused by expansion occurring in the soil as a result of such factors as freezing or swelling due to increased water content. *Frost heave* refers to the vertical soil movement that occurs in freezing temperatures as ice layers or lenses form within the freezing soil and cause the soil mass to expand.

Hydraulic gradient   Mathematical term indicating the difference in pressure head existing between two locations divided by the distance between these same locations. Given the designation i.

In situ   Refers to soil when it is at its natural location in the earth and in its natural condition.

Isotropic   Pertaining to a soil whose properties are the same in all directions.

Landslide   The relatively rapid lateral and downhill movement of a generally well-defined earth mass or land form due to gravitational forces.

Laterite   The category of residual soil formed from the weathering of igneous rock in tropical regions that through the process of its formation, will include high concentrations of iron and aluminum sesquioxides with low concentrations of silica.

Limit equilibrium A method of analysis used to evaluate the stability of soil mass (such as in a slope or foundation support) that could be involved in movement associated with failure. The method involves determining the soil shear strength on an assumed failure surface as required to maintain equilibrium or stability, and compares this value with the actual shear strength of the soil; this comparison indicates if equilibrium will exist or if the limits of equilibrium will be exceeded.

Liquefaction Loss of strength occurring in saturated cohesionless soil exposed to shock or vibrations when the soil particles momentarily lose contact. The material then behaves as a fluid.

Mechanical weathering The process of weathering whereby physical forces, such as frost action and temperature changes, break down or reduce rock to smaller fragments without involving chemical changes.

Mineral A naturally formed chemical element or compound having a definite chemical composition and usually a characteristic crystal form.

Penetration test Term generally applied to subsurface investigative methods for determining a strength-related property of a soil by measuring the resistance to advancement of penetration or boring equipment.

Permafrost The permanently frozen ground located in the northern regions of the earth.

Permeability The ability of water (or other fluid) to flow through a soil by traveling through the void spaces. A high permeability indicates flow occurs rapidly, and vice versa.

Pier Category applied to columnlike concrete foundations, similar to piles. The pier is generally considered the type of deep foundation that is constructed by placing concrete in a deep excavation large enough to permit manual inspection. Pier is also used frequently to indicate heavy masonry column units which are used for basement-level and substructural support.

Pile The relatively long, slender, columnlike type of foundation that obtains supporting capacity from the soil or rock some distance below the ground surface.

Pipe bedding Preparation of the surface that is to support a buried conduit. Established bedding classes consider effects of contouring the supporting surface to the shape of the pipe, extent of compaction, and placement of a supporting material such as concrete or gravel. Generally, preparation of bedding reduces the stresses that will develop in the pipe (conduit) from an overlaying fill.

Piping Erosion by subsurface water moving through a soil zone, which results in the formation of continuous tunnels or "pipes" through which water then travels rapidly. Progressive erosion or cave-in of the ground results. The condition is associated with the movement of water through permeable dam foundations.

Plane strain A state of strain in which all displacements that arise from deformation are parallel to one particular plane.

Plasticity Term applied to fine-grained soils (particularly clays) to indicate the soils' (plus included water's) ability to flow or be remolded without raveling or breaking apart.

Plate tectonics The concept that the earth's outer zone consists of a small number (10 to 25) of large thick plates that "float" on a viscous underlayer and can move more or less independently. The continents are carried on the plates and move with them; oceans are similarly carried on the plates and expand or shrink as the distances between continents change.

Poisson's ratio   The ratio of lateral unit strain to the longitudinal unit strain in a body that has been stressed longitudinally within its elastic limit.

Pore pressure   Water pressure developed in the voids of a soil mass. *Excess pore pressure* refers to pressure greater than the normal hydrostatic pressure expected as a result of position below the water table.

Porosity   The term to indicate the relative volume of open space (pores or voids) existing within the total volume occupied by a soil or rock mass. Mathematically, porosity n is equal to the volume of void spaces divided by total volume of the soil or rock material (the total volume consists of the volume of void spaces plus the volume of solids).

Pressuremeter   An instrument used to determine the in situ strength of a soil zone through measurement of the pressure-related lateral expansion of a flexible cylinder that is at a known depth in a borehole.

Projecting conduits   Conduits in areas where earth fill or earth embankment will be placed above the installation.

Radon   An invisible, odorless, tasteless gas formed from the decay of uranium, radium, and polonium found in some rock, soil, and waste materials.

Reinforced earth   Earth structures such as embankments, retaining walls, and dams which are constructed in layers reinforced with fabrics, strips, or fibers to increase the strength of the soil mass.

Relative density   Term applied to sand deposits to indicate a relative state of compaction compared to the loosest and most dense conditions possible.

Retaining wall   A vertical structure designed to resist the lateral pressure of soil and water behind it.

Revetment   A facing or layering of stone, concrete, or other durable material built to protect an embankment or shore structure from wave erosion.

Rollers, compaction   The category of construction equipment utilized to compact (or densify) soil by rolling it. The compaction force typically results from the heavy weight of the equipment and/or vibrations transmitted from the equipment into the soil.

Sand   The category of coarse-grained soil whose particle sizes range between about 0.07 mm and 5 mm in diameter.

Seepage   Generally refers to the quantity of water flowing through a soil deposit or soil structure such as an earth dam. Also may refer to the quantity of subsurface water leaking into a building's underground (basement) area.

Seismic   Pertaining to an earthquake or earth vibration, including one that is artificially induced.

Seismic exploration   The method of determining subsurface soil and rock conditions (without excavation) by inducing a shock wave into the earth and measuring the velocity of the wave's travel through the earth material. This *seismic velocity* indicates the type of earth material.

Settlement   The downward vertical movement experienced by structures or a soil surface as the underlying supporting earth compresses.

Shear strength   The ability of a soil to resist shearing stresses developed within a soil mass as a result of loading imposed onto the soil.

Sheetpiling   A pile with a generally flat cross section, made to interlock with adjoining sections to form a thin diaphragm wall or bulkhead; used to resist the lateral force of retained earth or water when part of temporary and permanent structures.

Sieve Pan or traylike equipment having a screen or mesh bottom; used in laboratory or field work to separate particles of a soil sample into their various sizes.

Silt The category of fine-grained soil particles (individual soil grains whose particle size is smaller than 0.07 mm or too small to be seen without visual aid) whose mineralogical composition remains similar to the rock they were derived from.

Soil sampler The equipment used to extract soil samples from borings or test pits made in a subsurface investigation.

Soil stabilization Treatment of soil to improve its properties; includes the mixing of additives and other means of alterations such as compaction or drainage.

Sump Small excavation or pit provided in the floor of a structure, or in the earth, to serve as a collection basin for surface water and near-surface underground water.

Terra-probe A method of compacting thick surficial sand zones through the use of a vertically vibrating tubular probe; the probe is vibrated to the desired depth, then slowly withdrawn while continuing to vibrate. Closely spaced probe locations are utilized to compact a construction site.

Till Description given to glacially transported soil formations consisting of a heterogeneous mixture of fine-grained and coarse-grained material.

Unit weight The weight per unit volume of a material such as soil, water, concrete, etc. Typically expressed as pounds per cubic foot (lb/ft^3), grams per cubic centimeter (g/cm^3), or kilonewtons per cubic meter (kN/m^3).

Vibroflotation A method of compacting thick surficial sand zones through the use of a horizontally vibrating cylinder termed a *Vibroflot®*. The Vibroflot® is jetted to a desired depth and slowly brought to the surface while it continues to vibrate. The process typically compacts the soil in a 5-ft zone surrounding the Vibroflot®, and a series of penetrations are provided to compact a construction site. Sand is added to the zone surrounding the Vibroflot® to make up the volume lost by compaction.

Void ratio The total volume occupied by a soil mass includes the soil particles plus void spaces (which in nature always exist between the particles because of their irregular shape). The void ratio is the ratio of the void space volume to the volume of soil solids.

Water content The ratio of the quantity of water in a soil (by weight) to the weight of the soil solids (dry soil), typically expressed as a percentage.

Well point The perforated end section of a wellpipe that permits the groundwater to be drawn into the pipe for pumping.

References

1. Abdun-Nur, E. A. *A Standard Classification of Soils as Prepared by the Bureau of Reclamation.* ASTM Special Technical Publication No. 113. 1950.
2. Acker, W. L. III. *Basic Procedures for Soil Sampling and Core Drilling.* Scranton, Pa.: Acker Drill Company, 1974.
3. Agerschou, H. A. "Analysis of the Engineering Pile Formula." *Journal of Soil Mechanics and Foundations Division, ASCE* [American Society of Civil Engineers] *88*, No. SM5, October 1962.
4. Akroyd, T. N. W. *Laboratory Testing in Soil Engineering.* London: Soil Mechanics Limited, 1964.
5. Aldrich, H. P. "Precompression for Support of Shallow Foundations." *Journal of Soil Mechanics and Foundations Division, ASCE, 91*, No. SM2, March 1965.
6. Aldrich, H. P. "Selection of Foundation Systems." *Soil Mechanics Lecture Series.* Foundation Engineering, Soil Mechanics and Foundations Division, Illinois Section, ASCE, and Department of Civil Engineering, Northwestern University, Evanston, Illinois, 1969.
7. American Cyanamid Company. *AM-9 Chemical Grout, Technical Data.* Wayne, N.J.: Author.
8. American Concrete Pipe Association. *Concrete Pipe Design Manual.* Vienna, Va.: Author, 1978.
9. American Society of Civil Engineers. "Uplift in Masonry Dams." Transactions, ASCE, 117, 1952.
10. American Society of Civil Engineers. "Ice Pressure against Dams, A Symposium." Transactions, ASCE, 119, 1954.
11. American Society of Civil Engineers (ASCE), Committee on Definitions and Standards of the Geotechnical Engineering Division. "SI Units for Geotechnical Engineering." *Journal of Geotechnical Engineering, ASCE, 109,* No. 12, December 1983.
12. Anderson, R. D. "Foster Vibrator." *Proceedings, Design and Installations of Pile Foundations and Cellular Structures.* Lehigh, Pa.: Envo Publishing Company, Lehigh University, 1970.
13. Antevs, E. *Maps of the Pleistocene Glaciations.* Geological Society of America, Bulletin 40, 1929.

14. Armco Drainage and Metal Products. *Handbook of Drainage and Construction Products*. Middletown, Ohio: Armco.

15. Armco, Inc. *Armco Corrugated Steel Pipe and Pipe Arch Manual*. Middletown, Ohio: Armco Metal Products Division, 1980.

16. Armento, W. J. "Criteria for Lateral Pressures for Braced Cuts," *Proceedings Performance of Earth and Earth-Supported Structures, Soil Mechanics and Foundations Division, ASCE and Purdue University, 1,* Part 2, June 1972.

17. *Asphalt Handbook*. College Park, Maryland: The Asphalt Institute.

18. Baguelin, F.; J. F. Jezequel; and D. H. Shields. *The Pressuremeter and Foundation Engineering*. Clausthal, Germany: Trans Tech Publications, 1978.

19. Baker, C. N., and F. Kahn. "Caisson Construction Problems in Chicago," *Journal of Soil Mechanics and Foundations Division, ASCE, 97,* No. SM2, February 1971.

20. Barron, R. "Consolidation of Fine-Grained Soils by Drain Wells." *Transactions, American Society of Civil Engineers, 113,* 1948.

21. Basore, C. E., and J. D. Boitano. "Sand Densification by Piles and Vibroflotation." *Journal of Soil Mechanics and Foundations Division, ASCE, 95,* No. SM6, November 1969.

22. Baver, L. D. *Soil Physics*. New York: Wiley, 1956.

23. Bell, J. M. "Dimensionless Parameters for Homogeneous Earth Slopes." *Journal of Soil Mechanics and Foundations Division, ASCE, 92,* No. SM5, September 1966.

24. Berezantzev, V. G.; V. S. Kristoforov; and V. N. Golubkov. "Load Bearing Capacity and Deformation of Piled Foundations." *Proceedings of the Fifth International Conference on Soil Mechanics and Foundation Engineering*. Paris, 1961, Vol. 2.

25. Bertram, G. E. "Design Requirements and Site Selection." *Design and Construction of Earth Structures, Soil Mechanics Lecture Series*. Soil Mechanics and Foundation Division, Illinois Section, ASCE, and Civil Engineering Department, Illinois Institute of Technology, Chicago, 1966.

26. Bishop, Alan W. "The Use of the Slip Circle in the Stability Analysis of Slopes." *Geotechnique, 5,* No. 1, 1955.

27. Bishop, A. W., and N. R. Morganstern. "Stability Coefficients for Earth Slopes." *Geotechnique, 10,* No. 4, 1960.

28. Brennan, T., and B. Turner. "Radon's Thrust Can Be Subdued." *Solar Age*, May 1985.

29. Brennan, T., and B. Turner, "Defeating Radon." *Solar Age*, March 1986.

30. Broms, Bengt. "Lateral Earth Pressures Due to Compaction of Cohesionless Soils." In A. Kedzi, ed., *Proceedings of the Fourth Budapest Conference on Soil Mechanics and Foundation Engineering*. Budapest: Akademiai Kiado, 1971.

31. Brown, D. R., and J. Warner. "Compaction Grouting." *Journal of Soil Mechanics and Foundations Division, ASCE, 99,* No. SM8, August 1973.

32. Brown, R. E. "Vibroflotation Compaction of Cohesionless Soils." *Journal of Geotechnical Engineering Division, ASCE, 103,* No. GT12, December 1977.

33. Brown, R. E., and A. J. Glenn. "Vibroflotation and Terra-Probe Comparison." *Journal of Geotechnical Engineering Division, ASCE, 102,* No. GT10, October 1976.

34. Bureau of Reclamation. *Design of Small Dams*, 2nd ed. Washington, D.C.: U.S. Department of the Interior, 1973.

35. Bussey, W. H. "Foundation Evaluation and Treatment." *Design and Construction of Earth Structures, Soil Mechanics Lecture Series*. Soil Mechanics and Foundation Division, Illinois Section, ASCE, and Civil Engineering Department, Illinois Institute of Technology, Chicago, 1966.

36. Carpenter, J. C. and E. S. Barker. "Vertical Sand, Drains for Stabilizing Muck-Peat Soils." *Transactions, American Society of Civil Engineers, 124,* 1959.

37. Carson, A. B. *General Excavating Methods.* New York: McGraw-Hill, 1961.
38. Casagrande, A. "Research on the Atterberg Limits of Soils." *Public Road, 13,* October 1932.
39. Casagrande, A. "Classification and Identification of Soils." *Transactions, ASCE, 113,* 1948.
40. Casagrande, L. "Electro-Osmotic Stabilization of Soils." *Journal of the Boston Society of Civil Engineers,* January 1952.
41. Casagrande, L. "Comments on Conventional Design of Retaining Structures." *Journal of Soil Mechanics and Foundations Division, ASCE, 99,* No. SM2, February 1973.
42. Cedergren, H. R. *Seepage, Drainage and Flow Nets.* New York: Wiley, 1967.
43. Chellis, R. D. "The Relationship between Pile Formulas and Load Tests." *Transactions, ASCE, 114,* 1949.
44. Chellis, R. D. *Pile Foundations,* 2nd ed. New York: McGraw-Hill, 1961.
45. Choudbury, R. N. *Slope Analysis.* New York: Elsevier Scientific Publishing Company, 1978.
46. Christian, J. T., and W. F. Swiger. "Statistics of Liquefaction and SPT Results." *Journal of Geotechnical Engineering Division, ASCE, 101,* No. GT11, November 1975.
47. Clough, C. W. "Deep Excavations and Retaining Structures." *Analysis and Design of Building Foundations.* Lehigh Valley, Pa.: Envo Publishing Company, Lehigh University, 1976.
48. Cornell University, Geotechnical Group (F. H. Kulhawy, Principal Investigator). *Transmission Line Structure Foundations for Uplift–Compression Loading.* Electric Power Research Institute, Palo Alto, Calif., February 1983.
49. Cousins, B. F. "Stability Charts for Simple Earth Slopes." *Journal of Geotechnical Engineering Division, ASCE, 104,* No. GT2, February 1978.
50. Coyle, H. M., and L. C. Reese. "Load Transfer for Axially Loaded Piles in Clay." *Journal of Soil Mechanics and Foundations Division, ASCE, 92,* SM2, March 1966.
51. Coyle, H. M., and Castello, R. R. "New Design Correlations for Piles in Sand." *Journal of Geotechnical Engineering Division, ASCE, 107,* No. GT7, July 1981.
52. Coyle, H. M., and I. H. Sulaiman. "Bearing Capacity of Foundation Piles: State of the Art." *Highway Research Record No. 333.* Washington, D.C.: Highway Research Board, National Academy of Sciences—National Academy of Engineering, 1970.
53. Cummings, A. E.; G. O. Kerkhoff; and R. B. Peck. "Effect of Driving Piles into Soft Clay." *Transactions, ASCE, 115,* 1950.
54. D'Appolonia, D. J. "Soil-Bentonite Slurry Trench Cutoffs." *Journal of Geotechnical Engineering Division, ASCE, 106,* No. GT4, April 1980.
55. D'Appolonia, D. J.; E. D'Appolonia; and R. F. Brissette. "Settlement of Spread Footings on Sand." *Journal of Soil Mechanics and Foundations Division, ASCE, 94,* No. SM3, May 1968.
56. D'Appolonia, D. J.; R. V. Whitman; E. D'Appolonia, "Sand Compaction with Vibratory Rollers." *Journal of Soil Mechanics and Foundations Division, ASCE, 95,* No. SM1, January 1969.
57. D'Appolonia, E. "Load Transfer–Pile Clusters." *Soil Mechanics Lecture Series, Foundation Engineering.* Soil Mechanics and Foundations Division, Illinois Section, ASCE, and Department of Civil Engineering, Northwestern University, Evanston, Illinois, 1969.
58. Davisson, M. T. "Design Pile Capacity." In *Proceedings, Design and Installation of Pile Foundations and Cellular Structures.* Lehigh Valley, Pa.: Envo Publishing Company, Lehigh University, 1970.
59. DeBeer, E. E. "Bearing Capacity and Settlement of Shallow Foundations on Sand."

Proceedings, Bearing Capacity and Settlement of Foundations Symposium. Durham, N.C.: Duke University, 1967.

60. DeBeer, E. E. "Experimental Determination of the Shape Factors and the Bearing Capacity Factors of Sand." *Geotechnique, 20,* No. 4, London, 1970.

61. Deere, D. V., and F. D. Patton. "Slope Stability in Residual Soils." *Proceedings, Fourth Pan American Conference on Soil Mechanics and Foundation Engineering*, San Juan, Puerto Rico, 1971.

62. deMello, V. F. B. "The Standard Penetration Test." *Proceedings, Fourth Pan American Conference on Soil Mechanics and Foundation Engineering*, Vol. 1, Puerto Rico, June 1971 (Pub. ASCE).

63. de Rutter, J. "Electric Penetrometer for Site Investigations." *Journal of Soil Mechanics and Foundation Division, ASCE, 97,* No. SM2, February 1971.

64. *Design of Small Dams.* Denver, Colo.: U.S. Bureau of Reclamation, 1960.

65. Dewey, J. F. "Plate Tectonics." *Scientific American*, May 1972.

66. Dietz, R. L., and J. C. Holden. "The Breakup of Pangaea." *Scientific American*, October 1970.

67. *Dispersive Clays, Related Piping, and Erosion in Geotechnical Projects.* ASTM Special Technical Publications 623, J. L. Sherard and R. S. Decker, eds. Philadelphia: American Society for Testing and Materials, 1976.

68. Dobson, T. "Vibro Techniques." Conference on Geotechnical Engineering Practice, Central Pennsylvania ASCE and Pennsylvania Department of Transportation, Harrisburg, April 1986.

69. Dunham, C. W. *Foundations of Structures.* New York: McGraw Hill, 1962.

70. Dunlop, P., and J. M. Duncan. "Development of Failure around Excavated Slopes." *Journal of Soil Mechanics and Foundations Division, ASCE, 96,* No. SM2, March 1970.

71. *Earth Manual.* Denver, Colo.: Bureau of Reclamation, U.S. Department of the Interior, 1960.

72. *Earth Resistivity Manual.* Chicago: Soiltest, Inc., 1968.

73. *Engineering Properties of Lateritic Soils.* Proceedings of the Specialty Session, Seventh International Conference on Soil Mechanics and Foundations, Mexico City, Mexico. Sponsored by Asian Institute of Technology, Bangkok, Thailand, August 1969.

74. *Engineering Seismograph Instruction Manual.* Chicago: Soiltest, Inc., 1975.

75. Fang, Hsai-Yang. *Stability of Earth Slopes.* Foundation Engineering Handbook, H. F. Winterkorn and H. Y. Fang, eds. New York: Van Nostrand-Reinhold, 1975.

76. Fellenius, B. H. "Test Loading of Piles and New Proof Testing Procedure." *Journal of Geotechnical Engineering Division, ASCE, 101,* No. GT9, September 1975.

77. Fellenius, W. "Calculation of the Stability of Earth Dams." Second Congress on Large Dams, Washington, D.C., 1936.

78. Ferrians, O. J., Jr.; R. Kachadoorian; and G. Greene. *Permafrost and Related Engineering Problems in Alaska.* Geological Survey Professional Paper 678. Washington, D.C.: U.S. Department of the Interior, 1969.

79. Fletcher, G. "Standard Penetration Test, Its Uses and Abuses." *Journal of Soil Mechanics and Foundations Division, ASCE, 91,* SM4, July 1965.

80. *Foundation Piling.* Report No. 4 for the Federal Construction Council Building Research Advisory Board, National Research Council—National Academy of Sciences Pub. No. 987, Washington, D.C., 1962.

81. Fowler, J. W. "Pile Installation Case Histories." *Proceedings, Design and Installation of Pile Foundations and Cellular Structures.* Lehigh Valley, Pa.: Envo Publishing Company, Lehigh University, 1970.

82. Friels, D. R. "Pile Capacity in Cohesive Soils Computed from SPT N-Values." *Piletips.* Clifton, N.J.: Associated Pile and Fitting Corp., September–October 1980.
83. *Frost Action in Roads and Airfields.* Highway Research Board, Special Report No. 1, National Academy of Sciences—National Research Council, Pub. 211, Washington, D.C., 1952.
84. Frye, S. C. "The Protection of Piling." *Proceedings, Design and Installation of Pile Foundations and Cellular Structures.* Lehigh Valley, Pa.: Envo Publishing Company, Lehigh University, 1970.
85. Galloway, J. D. "The Design of Rockfill Dams." *Transactions, ASCE, 104,* 1939.
86. Gendron, G. J. *Pile Driving: Hammers and Driving Methods.* Highway Research Record No. 333, Highway Research Board, National Academy of Sciences—National Academy of Engineering, Washington, D.C., 1970.
87. Gibbs, H. J. "Standard Penetration Test for Sand Denseness." *Proceedings of the Fourth Pan American Conference on Soil Mechanics and Foundation Engineering,* Vol. 2, Puerto Rico, June 1971 (Pub. ASCE).
88. Gibbs, H. J., and W. G. Holtz. "Research on Determining the Density of Sands by Spoon Penetration Testing." *Proceedings of the Fourth International Conference on Soil Mechanics and Foundation Engineering,* London, 1957.
89. Golder, H. Q. "State-of-Art of Floating Foundations." *Journal of Soil Mechanics and Foundations Division, ASCE, 91,* No. SM2, March 1965.
90. Golder, H. Q. "The Allowable Settlement of Structures." *Proceedings, Fourth Pan American Conference on Soil Mechanics and Foundation Engineering,* Vol. 1, Puerto Rico, June 1971 (Pub. ASCE).
91. Golze, A. R., ed. *Handbook of Dam Engineering.* New York: Van Nostrand-Reinhold, 1977.
92. Goodman, L. S., and R. H. Karol. *Theory and Practice of Foundation Engineering.* New York: Macmillan, 1968.
93. Gould, J. P. "Lateral Pressures on Rigid Permanent Structures," 1970 Specialty Conference on Lateral Stresses in the Ground and Design of Earth Retaining Structures, ASCE, Cornell University, 1970.
94. Grand, B. A. *Types of Piles: Their Characteristics and General Use.* Highway Research Record No. 333, Highway Research Board, National Academy of Sciences—National Academy of Engineering, Washington, D.C., 1970.
95. Gray, H. "Field Vane Shear Tests of Sensitive Cohesive Soil," *Transactons, ASCE, 122,* 1957.
96. Grim, R. E. "Physico-Chemical Properties of Soils: Clay Minerals." *Journal of Soil Mechanics and Foundation Division, ASCE, 85,* No. SM2, April 1959.
97. Grim, R. E. *Clay Mineralogy,* 2nd ed. New York: McGraw-Hill, 1968.
98. Hanna, A. M., and G. G. Meyerhof, "Experimental Evaluation of Bearing Capacity of Footings Subjected to Inclined Loads." *Canadian Geotechnical Journal, 18,* No. 4, 1981.
99. Hansen, J. "A Revised and Extended Formula for Bearing Capacity." *Danish Geotechnical Institute Bulletin,* No. 28, Copenhagen, 1970.
100. Harr, M. E. *Groundwater and Seepage.* New York: McGraw-Hill, 1962.
101. Healy, K. A. "Evaluation and Repair of Stonewall-Earth Dams." *Proceedings, Safety of Small Dams, ASCE Engineering Foundation Conference,* New England College, Henniker, N.H., August 1974.
102. Hedges, C. S. "Standard Test Boring with Drilling Mud." *Proceedings, Fourth Pan American Conference on Soil Mechanics and Foundation Engineering,* Vol. 2, Puerto Rico, June 1971 (Pub. ASCE).

References **593**

103. Hirsch, T. J.; L. L. Lowery; H. M. Coyle; and C. H. Samson. *Pile Driving by One-Dimensional Wave Theory: State of the Art.* Highway Research Record No. 333, Highway Research Board, National Academy of Sciences—National Academy of Engineering, Washington, D.C., 1970.

104. Hoechst Fibers Industries Manual. *Engineering Fabrics for Geotextile Applications.* Spartanburg, N.C.: American Hoechst Corporation.

105. Holtz, W. G., and H. J. Gibbs. "Engineering Properties of Expansive Clays," *Transactions, ASCE, 121,* 1956.

106. Holtz, W. G., and H. J. Gibbs. "Discussion, Settlement of Spread Footings on Sand." *Journal of Soil Mechanics and Foundations Division, ASCE, 95,* SM3, May 1969.

107. Hough, B. K. "Compressibility as the Basis for Soil Bearing Value." *Journal of Soil Mechanics and Foundations Division, ASCE, 85,* No. SM4, August 1959.

108. Hough, B. K. *Basic Soils Engineering.* New York: Ronald Press, 1969.

109. Housel, W. S. *Checking Up on Vertical Sand Drains.* Highway Research Board Bulletin 90, National Academy of Sciences—National Research Council, Washington, D.C., 1954.

110. Housel, W. S. "Michigan Study of Pile Driving Hammers." *Journal of Soil Mechanics and Foundations Division, ASCE, 91,* No. SM5, September 1965.

111. Housel, W. S. "Pile Load Capacity: Estimates and Test Results," *Journal of Soil Mechanics and Foundations Division, ASCE, 92,* No. SM4, July 1966.

112. Hunt, C. B. "Geology of Soils, Their Evolution, Classification and Uses." San Francisco: W. H. Freeman, 1972.

113. Hunt, H. W. *Piletips, Design and Installation of Pile Foundations.* New Jersey: Associated Pile and Fitting Corporation, 1974.

114. Hvorslev, M. J. *Subsurface Exploration and Sampling of Soils for Civil Engineering Purposes.* Vicksburg, Miss.: U.S. Waterways Experiment Station, 1949.

115. Illinois Institute of Technology. *Design of Structures to Resist Earth Pressures.* Soil Mechanics and Foundation Division, Illinois Section, ASCE, and Civil Engineering Department, Illinois Institute of Technology, 1964.

116. Janbu, N. *Stability Analysis of Slopes with Dimensionless Parameters.* Harvard Soil Mechanics Series, No. 46, 1954.

117. Janbu, N. "Dimensionless Parameters for Homogeneous Earth Slopes: Discussion." *Journal of Soil Mechanics and Foundations Division, ASCE, 93,* No. SM6, November 1967.

118. Janbu, N. "Slope Stability Computations." In *Embankment Dam Engineering.* Casagrande Volume. New York: Wiley, 1973.

119. Johnson, S. J. "Foundation Precompression with Vertical Sand Drains." *Journal of Soil Mechanics and Foundation Division, ASCE, 96,* No. SM1, January 1970.

120. Johnson, S. J. "Precompression for Improving Foundation Soils." *Journal of Soil Mechanics and Foundations Division, ASCE, 96,* No. SM1, January 1970.

121. Jumikis, A. R. *Soil Mechanics.* New York: Van Nostrand-Reinhold, 1962.

122. Jumikis, A. R. *Thermal Soil Mechanics.* New Brunswick, N.J.: Rutgers University Press, 1966.

123. Jurgenson, L. "The Application of Theories of Elasticity and Plasticity to Foundation Problems." *Journal, Boston Society of Civil Engineers,* July 1954.

124. Justin, J. D. "The Design of Earth Dams." *Transactions, ASCE, 87,* 1924.

125. Kansas, University of. *Proceedings of the Eighteenth Annual Soil Mechanics and Foundations Engineering Conference,* Lawrence, Kansas, 1969.

126. Karol, R. H. "Chemical Grouting Technology." *Journal of Soil Mechanics and Foundations Division, ASCE, 94,* SM1, January 1968.

127. Kerisel, J. L. "Vertical and Horizontal Bearing Capacity of Deep Foundations in Clay." *Proceedings, Bearing Capacity and Settlement of Foundations Symposium*. Durham, N.C.: Duke University, 1967.
128. Kerisel, J. "The Bicentennial of C. Coulombs Theory of Loose Media." *Proceedings of the Eighth International Conference on Soil Mechanics and Foundations*, Moscow, 1973.
129. Kezdi, A. *Handbook of Soil Mechanics*. Amsterdam: Elsevier, 1974.
130. Kjellman, W. "Mechanics of Large Swedish Landslides." *Geotechnique, 5,* No. 1, 1955.
131. Koerner, R. M., and J. P. Welsh. *Construction and Geotechnical Engineering Using Synthetic Fabrics*. New York: Wiley, 1980.
132. Kraft, L. M.; J. A. Focht; and S. F. Amerasinghe. "Friction Capacity of Piles Driven into Clay." *Journal of Geotechnical Engineering Division, ASCE, 107,* No. 11, November 1981.
133. Kreb, R. D., and R. D. Walker. *Highway Materials*. New York: McGraw-Hill, 1971.
134. Krynine, D. P., and W. R. Judd. *Principles of Engineering Geology and Geotechnics*. New York: McGraw-Hill, 1957.
135. Kulhawy, F. H. "Analysis of a High Gravity Retaining Wall." *Proceedings, Analysis and Design in Geotechnical Engineering, Geotechnical Engineering Division, ASCE, University of Texas, 1,* June 1974.
136. Kulhawy, F. H., and T. M. Gurtowski. "Load Transfer and Hydraulic Fracturing in Zoned Dams." *Journal of Geotechnical Engineering Division, ASCE, 102,* No. GT9, September 1976.
137. Lambe, T. W. *Soil Testing for Engineers*. New York: Wiley, 1951.
138. Lambe, T. W. "The Structure of Inorganic Clay." *Journal of Soil Mechanics and Foundations Division, ASCE, 79,* October 1953.
139. Lambe, T.W. "The Engineering Behavior of Compacted Clay." *Journal of Soil Mechanics and Foundations Division, ASCE, 84,* No. SM2, May 1958.
140. Lambe, T. W., et al. "Compacted Clay—A Symposium." *Transactions, ASCE, 125,* 1960.
141. Lee, I. K., and P. J. Moore. "Stability Analyses Application to Slopes, Rigid and Flexible Retaining Structures." In I. K. Lee, ed., *Soil Mechanics, Selected Topics*. New York: American Elsevier, 1968.
142. Lee, K. L.; B. D. Adams; and J-M. J. Vagneron. "Reinforced Earth Retaining Walls." *Journal of Soil Mechanics and Foundations Division, ASCE, 99,* No. SM10, October 1973.
143. Leggett, R. F. *Geology and Engineering*, 2nd ed. New York: McGraw-Hill, 1962.
144. Leonards, G. A., et al. *Foundation Engineering*. New York: McGraw-Hill, 1962.
145. Leonards, G. A.; W. A. Cutter; and R. D. Holtz. "Dynamic Compaction of Granular Soils." *Journal of Geotechnical Engineering Division, ASCE, 106,* No. GT 1, January 1980.
146. Liao, S. S. C., and R. V. Whitman. "Overburden Correction Factors for SPT in Sand." *Journal of Geotechnical Engineering, ASCE, 112,* No. 3, March 1986.
147. Lindahl, Harry A. "Steel Pile Retaining Walls." Eighteenth Annual Soil Mechanics and Foundation Engineering Conference, University of Kansas, March 1969.
148. Lukas, R. G. "Densification of Loose Deposits by Pounding." *Journal of Geotechnical Engineering Division, ASCE, 106,* No. GT4, April 1980.
149. Lukas, R. G., and B. L. deBussey. "Pressuremeter and Laboratory Test Correlations for Clays." *Journal of Geotechnical Engineering Division, ASCE, 102,* No. GT 9, September 1976.

150. Maccaferri Gabions Inc. *Gabion Retaining Walls.* Williamsport, Md.: Author.

151. Malasheskie, G. J. "Prefabricated Drainage Systems." Conference on Innovations in Geotechnical Engineering, Central Pennsylvania ASCE and Pennsylvania Department of Transportation, Harrisburg, April 1985.

152. Marchetti, S. "In-Situ Tests by Flat Dilatometer." *Journal of Geotechnical Engineering, ASCE, 106,* No. GT3, March 1980.

153. McCarthy, D. F. *Basic Toil Testing Procedures.* Utica, N.Y.: Mohawk Valley Community College, State University of New York, 1970.

154. McClelland, B. "Design and Performance of Deep Foundations." *Proceedings of the Specialty Conference on Performance of Earth and Earth-Supported Structures,* Purdue University, ASCE, June 1972.

155. McClelland, B. "Design of Deep Penetration Piles for Ocean Structures." *Journal of Geotechnical Engineering Division, ASCE, 100,* No. GT7, July 1974.

156. McClelland, B.; J. A. Focht; and W. J. Emrich. "Problems in Design and Installation of Off-Shore Piles." *Journal of Soil Mechanics and Foundations Division, ASCE, 95,* No. SM6, November 1969.

157. Meyerhof, G. G. "The Ultimate Bearing Capacity of Foundations." *Geotechnique, 2,* No. 4, London, 1951.

158. Meyerhof, G. G. "The Bearing Capacity of Footings under Eccentric and Inclined Loads." *Proceedings, Third International Conference on Soil Mechanics and Foundation Engineering,* Zurich, 1953.

159. Meyerhof, G. G. "The Influence of Roughness of Base and Ground Water on the Ultimate Bearing Capacity of Foundations." *Geotechnique, 5,* No. 3, London, September 1955.

160. Meyerhof, G. G. "Penetration Tests and Bearing Capacity of Cohesionless Soils." *Journal of Soil Mechanics and Foundations Division, ASCE, 82,* No. SM1, January 1956.

161. Meyerhof, G. G. "The Ultimate Bearing Capacity of Foundations on Slopes." *Proceedings, Fourth International Conference on Soil Mechanics and Foundation Engineering,* London, 1957.

162. Meyerhof, G. G. "Compaction of Sands and Bearing Capacity of Piles." *Journal of Soil Mechanics and Foundations Division, ASCE, 85,* No. SM6, December 1959.

163. Meyerhof, G. G. "Some Recent Research on the Bearing Capacity of Foundations." *Canadian Geotechnical Journal, 1,* No. 1, September 1963.

164. Meyerhof, G. G. "Shallow Foundations." *Journal of Soil Mechanics and Foundations Division, ASCE, 91,* No. SM2, March 1965.

165. Meyerhof, G. G. "Bearing Capacity and Settlement of Pile Foundations." *Journal of Geotechnical Engineering Division, ASCE, 102,* No. GT3, March 1976.

166. Millar, C. E.; L. M. Turk; and H. D. Foth. *Fundamentals of Soil Science.* New York: Wiley, 1958.

167. Mitchell, J. K. "Fundamental Aspects of Thixotropy in Soils." *Journal of Soil Mechanics and Foundations Division, ASCE, 86,* No. SM3, June 1960.

168. Mitchell, J. K. "In-Place Treatment of Foundation Soils." *Journal of Soil Mechanics and Foundations Division, ASCE, 96,* No. SM1, January 1970.

169. Moore, W. S. "Experiences with Predetermining Pile Lengths." *Transactions, ASCE, 114,* 1947.

170. Moorhouse, D. C. "Shallow Foundations." *Proceedings, Specialty Conference on Performance of Earth and Earth-Supported Structures,* Purdue University, ASCE, June 1972.

171. Moorhouse, D. C., and G. L. Baker. "Sand Densification by Heavy Vibratory Com-

pactor." *Journal of Soil Mechanics and Foundations Division, ASCE, 95,* No. SM4, July 1969.

172. Moretrench Corporation. *Moretrench Wellpoint System.* Rockaway, N.J.: Author, 1967.

173. Morganstern, N. R. "Stability Charts for Earth Slopes during Rapid Drawdown." *Geotechnique, 13,* No. 2, 1963.

174. Morganstern, N. R. "Slopes and Excavations." Ninth International Conference on Soil Mechanics and Foundation Engineering, Tokyo, 1977.

175. Morganstern, N. R., and V. E. Price. "The Analysis of the Stability of General Slip Surfaces." *Geotechnique, 15,* No. 1, March 1965.

176. Mosley, E. T., and T. Raamot. *Pile Driving Formulas.* Highway Research Board, National Academy of Sciences—National Academy of Engineering, Washington, D.C., 1970.

177. Navy, Department of the. *Design Manual, Soil Mechanics, Foundations and Earth Structures.* NAVFAC DM-7, Rev. 1974.

178. Nordlund, R. L. "Bearing Capacity of Piles in Cohesionless Soils." *Journal of Soil Mechanics and Foundations Division, ASCE, 89,* No. SM3, May 1963.

179. Nordlund, R. L. "Pressure Injected Footings." *Proceedings, Design and Installation of Pile Foundations and Cellular Structures.* Lehigh Valley, Pa.: Envo Publishing Company, Lehigh University, 1970.

180. Osterberg, J. O. "Drilled Caissons—Design, Installation, Application." *Soil Mechanics Lecture Series, Foundation Engineering,* Soil Mechanics and Foundations Division, Illinois Section, ASCE, and Department of Civil Engineering, Northwestern University, Evanston, Ill. 1969.

181. Parola, J. F. "Mechanics of Impact Pile Driving." Ph.D. dissertation, University of Illinois, Urbana, 1970.

182. Parsons, J. D. "Piling Difficulties in the New York Area." *Journal of Soil Mechanics and Foundations Division, ASCE, 92,* No. SM1, January 1966.

183. Peck, R. B. "Pile and Pier Foundations." *Journal of Soil Mechanics and Foundations Division, ASCE, 91,* No. SM2, March 1965.

184. Peck, R. B., and A. R. S. Bazaraa. "Discussion, Settlement of Spread-footings on Sand." *Journal of Soil Mechanics and Foundations Division, ASCE, 95,* No. SM3, May 1969.

185. Peck, R. B.; W. E. Hanson; and T. H. Thorburn. *Foundation Engineering,* 2nd ed. New York: Wiley, 1973.

186. Peck, R. B., and H. O. Ireland. "Full Scale Lateral Load Test on a Retaining Wall Foundation." *Proceedings, Fifth International Conference on Soil Mechanics and Foundation Engineering,* 1961.

187. Peck, R. B.; H. O. Ireland; and C. Y. Teng. "A Study of Retaining Wall Failures." *Proceedings, Second International Conference on Soil Mechanics and Foundation Engineering,* 1948.

188. Peurifoy, R. L. *Construction Planning, Equipment and Methods,* 2nd ed. New York: McGraw-Hill, 1970.

189. Portland Cement Association. *Small Concrete Dams.* Portland, Ore.: Author, 1971.

190. Prandtl, L. "Uber die Harte, plastischer Korper" ("On the Hardness of Plastic Bodies"). *Nachr. Kgl. Ges. Wiss.* Gottingen, Math. Phys. Kl., 1920.

191. *Procedures for Testing Soils.* Philadelphia: American Society for Testing and Materials.

192. Proctor, R. R. "Fundamental Principles of Soil Compaction." *Engineering News Record,* August 31, September 7, September 21, September 28, 1933.

193. Ramaswamy, S. D.; M. A. Aziz; R. V. Subrahmanyan; M. H. Adul Khader; and

Seng-Lip Lee. "Treatment of Peaty Clay by High Energy Impact." *Journal of Geotechnical Engineering Division, ASCE, 105,* No. GT 8, August 1979.

194. Reese, L. C., and M. W. O'Neill. "Criteria for the Design of Axially Loaded Drill Shafts." Research Report 189-11F, Center for Highway Research, University of Texas, Austin, 1971.

195. Reese, L. C.; F. T. Touma; and M. W. O'Neill. "Behavior of Drilled Piers under Axial Loading." *Journal of Geotechnical Engineering Division, ASCE, 102,* No. GT5, May 1976.

196. Reginatto, A. R. "Standard Penetration Tests in Collapsible Soils." *Proceedings, Fourth Pan American Conference on Soil Mechanics and Foundation Engineering,* Vol. 2, Puerto Rico, June 1971 (Pub. ASCE).

197. Reissner, H. "Zum Erddruck-problem" ("The Earth Pressure Problem"). *Proceedings, First International Congress on Applied Mechanics,* 1924.

198. Richart, F. E. "A Review of the Theories for Sand Drains." *Journal of Soil Mechanics and Foundations Division, ASCE, 83,* No. SM3, July 1957.

199. Roberts, D. V. "Notes on Predetermination of Pile Capacities." *Dames and Moore Engineering Bulletin, 5,* Dames and Moore, Los Angeles, Calif., 1959.

200. Robinsky, E. I., and K. E. Bespflug. "Design of Insulated Foundations." *Journal of Soil Mechanics and Foundations Division, ASCE, 99,* No. SM9, September 1973.

201. Rodin, S. "Experiences with Penetrometer, with Particular Reference to the Standard Penetration Test." *Proceedings, Fifth International Conference on Soil Mechanics and Foundation Engineering,* Paris, 1961.

202. Rose, E. "Thrust Exerted by Expanding Ice Sheet." *Transactions, ASCE, 112,* 1947.

203. Rosenquist, I. T. "Physico-Chemical Properties of Soils: Soil–Water Systems," *Journal of Soil Mechanics and Foundations Division, ASCE, 85,* No. SM2, April 1959.

204. Rutledge, P. C. "Construction Methods and Inspection." *Soil Mechanics Lecture Series, Foundation Engineering.* Soil Mechanics and Foundations Division, Illinois Section, ASCE, and Department of Civil Engineering, Northwestern University, Evanston, Ill., 1969.

205. Rutledge, P. C. "Utilization of Marginal Lands for Urban Development." *Journal of Soil Mechanics and Foundation Division, ASCE, 96,* No. SM1, January 1970.

206. Sanglerat, G. *The Penetrometer and Soil Exploration* (English). London–New York: Elsevier, 1972.

207. Schlick, W. J. "Loads on Negative Projecting Conduits." *Proceedings, Highway Research Board, 31,* 1952.

208. Schmertmann, J. H. "Static Cone Penetrometers for Soil Exploration." *Civil Engineering, ASCE,* June 1967.

209. Schmertmann, J. H. "Static Cone to Compute Settlement over Sand." *Journal of Soil Mechanics and Foundation Division, ASCE, 96,* No. SM3, May 1970.

210. Schmertmann, J. H. "Introduction to the Marchetti Dilatometer Test." Conference on Innovations in Geotechnical Engineering, Central Pennsylvania ASCE and Pennsylvania Department of Transportation, Harrisburg, April 1985.

211. Schmid, W. E. "Low Frequency Pile Vibrators." *Proceedings, Design and Installation of Pile Foundations and Cellular Structures.* Lehigh Valley, Pa.: Envo Pubishing Company, Lehigh University, 1970.

212. Schnabel, H., Jr., and J. W. Siquorney. *Design and Installation of Earth Tiebacks.* Washington, D.C.: Schnabel Foundation Company.

213. Seed, H. B.; K. Tokimatsi; L. F. Harder; and R. M. Chung. "Influence of SPT Procedures in Soil Liquefaction Resistance Evaluations." *Journal of Geotechnical Engineering Division, ASCE, 111,* No. 12, December 1985.

214. Sherard, J. L. "Embankment Dam Cracking." In R. C. Hirschfeld and S. J. Poulos, eds., *Embankment Dam Engineering*, Casagrande Volume. New York: Wiley Interscience, 1973.
215. Sherard, J. L.; R. S. Decker; and N. L. Ryker. "Piping in Earth Dams of Dispersive Clays." *Proceedings of the Specialty Conference on Performance of Earth and Earth Supported Structures.* Purdue University and Soil Mechanics and Foundations Division of ASCE, June 1972.
216. Sherard, J. L.; L. P. Dunnigan; and R. S. Decker. "Identification and Nature of Dispersive Soils." *Journal of Geotechnical Engineering Division, ASCE, 102,* No. GT4, April 1976.
217. Sherard, J. L.; L. P. Dunnigan; and J. R. Talbot. "Basic Properties of Sand and Gravel Filters." *Journal of Geotechnical Engineering, ASCE, 110,* No. 6, June 1984.
218. Sherard, J. L. "Filters for Silts and Clays." *Journal of Geotechnical Engineering, ASCE, 110,* No. 6, June 1984.
219. Sherard, J. L.; R. J. Woodward; S. F. Gizienski; and W. A. Clevenger. *Earth and Earth-Rock Dams.* New York: Wiley, 1963.
220. Skempton, A. W. "The Colloidal Activity of Clays." *Proceedings, Third International Conference on Soil Mechanics and Foundation Engineering,* Zurich, 1953.
221. Skempton, A. W. "Soil Mechanics in Relation to Geology." *Proceedings of the Yorkshire Geological Society, 29,* Part 1, No. 3, April 1953.
222. Skempton, A. W., and J. Hutchinson. "Stability of Natural Slopes and Embankment Foundations." Seventh International Conference on Soil Mechanics and Foundation Engineering, Mexico, 1969.
223. Smith, E. A. L. "Pile-Driving Analysis by the Wave Equation." *Transactions, ASCE, 127,* 1962.
224. Smith, R. E. "Guide for Depth of Foundation Exploration." *Journal of Soil Mechanics and Foundations Division, ASCE, 96,* No. SM2, March 1970.
225. *Soil Cement Construction Handbook.* Chicago, Ill.: Portland Cement Association.
226. *Soil Cement Laboratory Handbook.* Chicago, Ill.: Portland Cement Association.
227. *Soil Density Control Methods.* Highway Research Board, Bulletin 159, National Academy of Sciences—National Research Council, Pub. No. 498, Washington, D.C., 1957.
228. *Soil Mechanics, Foundations and Earth Structures.* NAVDOCKS DM-7, Department of the Navy, Bureau of Yards and Docks, Washington, D.C.
229. Sorenson, T., and B. Hansen. "Pile Driving Formulae—An Investigation Based on Dimensional Considerations and a Statistical Analysis." *Proceedings, Fourth International Conference on Soil Mechanics and Foundation Engineering,* London, 1957.
230. Sowers, G. F. "Fill Settlement Despite Vertical Sand Drains." *Journal of Soil Mechanics and Foundations Division, ASCE, 90,* No. SM5, September 1964.
231. Sowers, G. F. "Soil Stress–Strain, Strength and Earth Pressure." *Design of Structures to Resist Earth Pressures, Soil Mechanics Lecture Series,* Soil Mechanics and Foundations Division, Illinois Section, ASCE, and Civil Engineering Department, Illinois Institute of Technology, Chicago, Ill., 1964.
232. Sowers, G. B., and G. F. Sowers. *Introductory Soil Mechanics and Foundations,* 3rd ed. New York: Macmillan, 1970.
233. Spangler, M. G. "Underground Conduits—An Appraisal of Modern Research." *Transactions, ASCE, 113,* 1948.
234. Spangler, M. G. "A Theory of Loads on Negative Projecting Conduits." *Proceedings, Highway Research Board, 29,* 1950.
235. Spangler, M. G. "A Practical Application of the Imperfect Ditch Method of Construction." *Proceedings, Highway Research Board, 37,* 1958.

References   **599**

236. Spangler, M. G. "Culverts and Conduits." In G. A. Leonards, ed., *Foundation Engineering*. New York: McGraw-Hill, 1962.

237. Spencer, E. "A Method of Analysis of the Stability of Embankments Assuming Parallel Interslice Forces." *Geotechnique, 17,* No. 1, March 1967.

238. Spencer, E. "Effect of Tension on Stability of Embankments." *Journal of Soil Mechanics and Foundation Division, ASCE, 94,* No. SM5, September 1968.

239. Spencer, E. "Circular and Logarithmic Spiral Slip Surfaces." *Journal of Soil Mechanics and Foundations Division, ASCE, 95,* No. SM1, January 1969.

240. Spencer, E. "Thrust Line Criterion in Embankment Stability Analysis." *Geotechnique, 23,* No. 1, March 1973.

241. Stearns, R. *Permafrost (Perenially Frozen Ground).* Cold Regions Science and Engineering, Part 1, Section A2, U.S. Army Materiel Command, Cold Regions Research and Engineering Laboratory, Hanover, N.H., August 1966.

242. *Stresses and Deflections in Foundations and Pavements.* Soil Mechanics and Bituminous Materials Research Laboratory, Department of Civil Engineering, University of California, Berkeley, 1965.

243. Strom, J. A. "Development of the Earth Deformation Recorder." *Dames and Moore Engineering Bulletin, 21,* Dames and Moore, Los Angeles, 1962.

244. Swatek, E. P.; S. P. Asrow; and A. M. Seitz. "Performance of Bracing for Deep Chicago Excavation." *Proceedings, Performance of Earth and Earth-Supported Structures.* Soil Mechanics and Foundations Division, ASCE, and Purdue University, *1,* Part 2, June 1972.

245. Taylor, A. W. "Physico-Chemical Properties of Soils: Ion Exchange Phenomena." *Journal of Soil Mechanics and Foundations Division, ASCE, 85,* No. SM2, April 1959.

246. Taylor, D. W. "Stability of Earth Slopes." *Journal of the Boston Society of Civil Engineers,* July 1937.

247. Taylor, D. W. *Fundamentals of Soil Mechanics.* New York: Wiley, 1949.

248. Teng, W. C. *Foundation Design.* Englewood Cliffs, N.J.: Prentice-Hall, 1962.

249. Terzaghi, K. *Theoretical Soil Mechanics.* New York: Wiley, 1943.

250. Terzaghi, K. "Effect of Minor Geologic Details on the Safety of Dams" (1929), reproduced in *From Theory to Practice in Soil Mechanics.* New York: Wiley, 1960.

251. Terzaghi, K. *From Theory to Practice in Soil Mechanics.* New York: Wiley, 1960.

252. Terzaghi, K. and R. B. Peck. *Soil Mechanics in Engineering Practice,* 2nd ed. New York: Wiley, 1968.

253. Tomlinson, M. J. "The Adhesion of Piles Driven in Clay." *Proceedings, Fourth International Conference on Soil Mechanics and Foundations Engineering,* London, 1957.

254. Tomlinson, M. J. *Foundation Design and Construction.* New York: Wiley–Interscience, 1969.

255. Touma, F. T., and L. C. Reese. "Behavior of Bored Piles in Sand." *Journal of Geotechnical Engineering Division, ASCE, 100,* No. GT7, July 1974.

256. Townsend, F. C. "Geotechnical Characteristics of Residual Soils." *Journal of Geotechnical Engineering, ASCE, 111,* No. 1, January 1985.

257. Tschebotarioff, G. P. *Foundations, Retaining and Earth Structures,* 2nd ed. New York: McGraw-Hill, 1973.

258. Tschebotarioff, G. P., Chairman. "Lateral Pressures of Clayey Soils on Structures." Specialty Session 5, *Proceedings of the Eighth International Conference on Soil Mechanics and Foundation Engineering,* Moscow, 1973.

259. Turnbull, W. J.; J. R. Compton; and R. G. Ahlvin. "Quality Control of Compacted Earthwork." *Journal of Soil Mechanics and Foundations Division, ASCE, 92,* No. SM1, January 1966.

260. Turnbull, W. J., and C. I. Mansur. "Compaction of Hydraulically Placed Fills." *Journal of Soil Mechanics and Foundations Division, ASCE, 99,* No. SM11, November 1973.
261. Tuttle, J., "Experiences with Piles in Coarse Granular Soils." *Dames and Moore Engineering Bulletin, 6,* Dames and Moore, Los Angeles, Calif., 1959.
262. Varnes, D. J. "Slope Movement and Type and Processes." *Landslide Analysis and Control.* Special Report 176. Washington, D.C.: Transportation Research Board, National Research Council, 1978.
263. Vesic, A. S. "Ultimate Loads and Settlement of Deep Foundations in Sand." *Proceedings, Bearing Capacity and Settlement of Foundations Symposium,* Duke University, Durham, N.C., 1967.
264. Vesic, A. S. "Load Transfer in Pile–Soil Systems." *Proceedings, Design and Installation of Pile Foundations and Cellular Structures.* Lehigh Valley, Pa.: Envo Publishing Company, Lehigh University, 1970.
265. Vesic, A. S. "Test on Instrumental Piles, Ogeechee River Site." *Journal of Soil Mechanics and Foundations Division, ASCE, 96,* No. SM2, March 1970.
266. Vesic, A. S. "Analysis of Ultimate Loads of Shallow Foundations." *Journal of Soil Mechanics and Foundations Division, ASCE, 95,* No. SM1, January 1973.
267. Vesic, A. S. "Bearing Capacity of Shallow Foundations." In H. F. Winterkorn and H. Y. Fang, eds., *Foundation Engineering Handbook.* New York: Van Nostrand-Reinhold, 1975.
268. Vijayvergiya, V. N., and J. A. Focht. "A New Way to Predict Capacity of Piles in Clay." Fourth Annual Offshore Technology Conference, Houston, Texas, May 1972.
269. Webb, D. L., and R. I. Hall. "Effects of Vibroflotation on Clayey Sands." *Journal of Soil Mechanics and Foundations Division, ASCE, 95,* No. SM6, November 1969.
270. Wegman, E. *The Design and Construction of Dams.* New York: Wiley, 1918.
271. Welsh, J. P. "In-Situ Testing for Ground Modification Techniques." In-Situ '86, ASCE Specialty Conference, Virginia Technical Institute, Blacksburg, June 1986.
272. Whitman, R. V. "Hydraulic Fills to Support Structural Loads." *Journal of Soil Mechanics and Foundation Division, ASCE, 96,* No. SM1, January 1970.
273. Wilson, S. D., and R. Squier. "Earth and Rockfill Dams." Seventh International Conference on Soil Mechanics and Foundation Engineering, Mexico, 1969.
274. Winterkorn, H. F., and H. Y. Fang, eds. *Foundation Engineering Handbook.* New York: VanNostrand-Reinhold, 1975.
275. Woodward, R. J.; W. S. Gardner; and D. M. Greer. *Drilled Pier Foundations.* New York: McGraw-Hill, 1972.
276. Wu, T. H. "Relative Density and Shear Strength of Sands." *Journal of Soil Mechanics and Foundations Division, ASCE, 83,* No. SM1, January 1957.

Answers to Selected Problems

2-1. $\omega = 13.2\%$
2-2. (a) $w = 20\%$; (b) $\gamma_{\text{wet}} = 116.7$ pcf, $\gamma_{\text{dry}} = 97.5$ pcf
2-3. $G_s = 2.63$
2-4. $e = 0.57$, $n = 36\%$
2-5. $e = 0.58$
2-6. $G_s = 2.68$, $e = 0.62$
2-7. $\gamma = 77$ pcf
2-8. Increase in density $= 112 - 93.5 = 18.5$ pcf
2-10. $w = 23.5\%$, $e = 0.62$, $S = 100\%$
2-11. $e = 2.31$, $S = 100\%$, $w = 85\%$
2-12. Sat $= 42\%$
2-13. $G_s = 2.57$
2-14. $e = 0.54$
2-15. $\gamma_{\text{wet}} = 135.4$ pcf, $\gamma_{\text{sub}} = 73.5$ pcf
2-16. (a) $\gamma_{\text{sub}} = 60$ pcf; (b) $\gamma_{\text{sub}} = 65$ pcf

4-2. $C_u \cong 9$
4-3. $\gamma_{\text{wet}} = 131$ pcf, $\gamma_{\text{dry}} = 114$ pcf
4-4. $D_R = 69\%$
4-5. $e_o = 0.55$, $D_r = 74\%$
4-6. (a) Water content; (b) PI $= 32\%$; (c) MH
4-7. (a) LI $= 0.33$; (b) CL–CH
4-8. (a) LI $= -0.22$; (b) CH
4-9. $V_t = 83.9$ cm^3
4-10. $G_s = 2.66$
4-11. Activity $= 0.88$, probably kaolinite

5-1. $R_H = r/2$

5-2. $R_H = 1.2$

5-7.   (a) $k \cong 0.022$ cm/sec; (b) $k \cong 0.013$ cm/sec

5-10. $k = 9.2$ cm/min

5-11. $k = .021$ ft/min $\cong .01$ cm/sec

5-12. $Q = 48.5$ cm^3

5-13. $k = 2.04 \times 10^{-4}$

5-14. $k = 9.6 \times 10^{-4}$ ft/min

5-16. $h_c = 310$ cm

5-17. $p_w = -375$ psf

5-18. $h_c = 3100$ cm; $p_w = -6350$ psf

5-19. $h_c \cong 1500$ cm

6-1. $Q = 32$ ft^3/hr $= 5700$ gal/day

6-3.   (a) 8.5 gal/day/ft wide; (b) 5.6 gal/day/ft wide

6-4. $i = 1.03$

6-6.   Drawdown slope approx. 5%, distance approx. 350 ft

7-1.   (b) $\tau_{max} = 1500$ psf, $\sigma_n = 3500$ psf; (c) $\sigma_n = 2750$ psf, $\tau = 1300$ psf

7-2. $\tau = 26$ psi, $\sigma_n = 65$ psi

7-3.   (b) $\sigma_n = 30$ psi, $\tau_{max} = 50$ psi; (c) $\sigma = 55$ psi, $\tau = 43$ psi

7-4.   (b) $\sigma_1 = 8600$ psf, $\sigma_3 = 1400$ psf; (c) $\theta = 16.9°$; (d) $\tau_{max} = 3600$ psf

7-5.   (b) $\theta = 16°$; (c) $\tau_{max} = 47$ psi

7-6. $\tau_{max} = 30$ psi, $\sigma_n = 70$ psi

7-7. $\sigma_1 = 130$ psi

7-8. $\tau_{max} = 500$ psf

7-9.   (a) $\sigma_1 = 1200$ psf, $\sigma_3 = 600$ psf; (b) $\tau_{max} = 300$ psf

7-10. $\sigma_1 = 940$ psf, $\sigma_3 = 424$ psf, $\tau_{max} = 258$ psf

8-1.   (a) $\overline{\sigma}_v = 1476$ psf; (b) $\overline{\sigma}_v = 1100$ psf, $u = 375$ psf

8-2 $\overline{\sigma}_v = 1390$ psf

8-3.   (a) $\sigma_h = 1150$ psf; (b) $\sigma_h = 580 + 1248 = 1828$ psf

8-4. $\Delta\sigma_h = 372$ psf

8-5.   Boussinesq $\sigma_v = .096$ ksf, .018 ksf, .002 ksf at $r = 0, 10, 20$ ft

8-6.   (a) Center, $\Delta\sigma_v = 1.08$ ksf; edge, $\Delta\sigma_v = 0.90$ ksf;
      (b) Center, $\Delta\sigma_v = 0.72$ ksf; edge, $\Delta\sigma_v = 0.54$ ksf

8-8.   Full tank, $\sigma_v = 4730$ psf at center

8-9.   Boussinesq, $\Delta\sigma_v = 2.20$ ksf; 60° approx., $\Delta\sigma_v = 1.54$ ksf

8-10.   Westergaard, center, $\Delta\sigma_v = 2400$ psf; edge, $\Delta\sigma_v = 1520$ psf

8-11.   (a) $\Delta\sigma_v = 540$ psf; (b) $\Delta\sigma_v = 840$ psf

8-12.   net $\Delta\sigma_v = +760$ psf

8-13.   total $\Delta\sigma_v = 3650$ psf

9-6.   (a) $a_v = 9.5 \times 10^{-5}$ ft^2/lb; (b) $C_c = 0.64$

9-9. $C_c = 0.63$
9-10.   (a) $\Delta H = 1.9$ in.; (b) $\Delta H = 3.3$ in.; (c) $\Delta H = 1$ in.
9-11. ΔH is approx. 17″
9-12. $K_v = 240$ kcf
9-13. ΔH is approx. ¾ in
9-16.   (a) $t = 5.8$ yrs; (b) $\Delta H = 0.85$ in.; (c) $t = 1.37$ yrs
9-17. $t = 6.7$ months ($\pm$)

10-1. $\phi = 31°$
10-2. $\phi = 27°$
10-3. $\phi = 37°$
10-4. $\sigma_1 = 74$ psi
10-5. $\sigma_1 = 3400$ psf ($\pm$)
10-6.   No shear failure
10-7. $\phi = 33.7°$, $\tau = 3340$ psf
10-8.   (a) $c = 1000$ psf; (b) axial load $= 2000$ psf
10-9.   Through consolidation to reduce water content
10-10. $\tau = 790$ psf
10-11. $\phi_{CD} = 29°$
10-12. $\phi_{CU} = 21.5°$, $\phi_{CD} = 30.6°$

11-11. $V_1 = 2000$ ft/sec, $V_2 = 10,000$ ft/sec, $H = 82$ ft

12-4.   (a) $\gamma_{max} = 115$ to 116 pcf, $\omega_{opt} = 15\%$ ($\pm$); (b) 7% to 20%
12-5. $\gamma_{max} = 120$ pcf, $w_{opt} = 13$ to 14%
12-8.   (a) $\gamma_{dry} = 112$ pcf, $\omega = 15\%$ ($\pm$); (b) 97.5% compaction
12-9.   (a) $\gamma_{dry} = 109$ pcf; (b) 93% compaction

14-1. $q_{des} \cong 6.0$ ksf
14-2.   wall loading $= 432$ kN per m of wall length
14-3.   (a) $I_r = 44.2$
         (b) $I_r = 4.3$
         (c) $I_r = 5.2$
         (d) $I_r = 90$
14-4.   footing size $= 2.25$ m × 2.25 m
14-5.   Foundation size $= 10.75$ ft × 10.75 ft ($\pm$)
14-6.   Design load for footing $\cong 384$ k; slightly less than 400 k required
14-7.   Square footing, 1.5 m × 1.5 m
14-8. $Q_{des} = 106$ k
14-9.   Foundation size $= 22.6$ ft × 11.3 ft ($\pm$)
14-10.   Combined footing; B $= 6.2$ ft, L $= 26$ ft
14-11. $Q = 162$ kN per m of length or 11.1 k per ft of length

14-12. $B = 4.6$ ft
14-13. $Q = 8.7$ kips per ft of length
14-14. $Q = 11.6$ kips per ft of length
14-15. (a) $q_{des} = 3.3$ tsf, $B = 7$ ft; (b) $q_{des} = 2.15$ tsf, $B = 8.5$ ft
14-16. Select $B = 5.75$ ft or 6.0 ft
14-17. $q = 5.2$ kg/cm$^2 \cong 5.2$ tsf
14-18. $Q_{des} = 85$ kips (for $K = 3$)
14-19. $Q_{des} = 77$ kips
14-20. $Q_{des} = 43$ kips
14-21. $Q_{des} = 117$ kips
14-22. $Q_{down} = 106$ kips, $Q_{up} = 94$ kips
14-23. Group $Q_{design} = 316$ kips (group action controls)
14-24. $Q_{des} = 295$ kips
14-25. $Q_{des} = 246$ kips
14-26. (a) $Q_{des} = 50$ tons; (b) weight of pile hammer satisfactory
14-27. Set $= 0.33$ inches
14-28. $Q_{failure} = 170$ tons

15-1.   (a) $\beta = \phi = 35°$; (b) $\beta = 19°$
15-3.   (a) $FS = 1.15$; (b) $FS = 0.86$
15-4. $FS = 1.11$
15-5. $FS = 1.17$
15-6.   (a) $FS \cong 1.15$; (b) FS $\cong 0.70$ (failure)
15-7.   (a) $FS \cong 1.5$
15-8. $FS \cong 1.3$
15-9. $FS \cong 3.2$
15-10. (a) $FS = 1.05$; (b) slope angle $i = 18°$; (c) $FS = 1.05$
15-11. (a) $FS = 1.03$; (b) $X = -5.2$ m, $Y = 71.2$ m; (c) $FS = 0.83$ (Fails), $X = 5.2$ m, $Y = 62.4$ m
15-12. (a) $FS \cong 0.8$ (failure); (b) $FS \cong 1.05$

16-3. $P_A = 81$ kN/m of length
16-4.   Rankine $P_A = 374$ kN/m of length; Coulomb $P_A = 378$ kN/m
16-5.   (a) $P_A = 188$ kN/m; (b) $P_A = 400$ kN/m; (c) $P_{lat} = 765$ kN/m
16-7. $P_h = 7760$ lb/ft of length, $P_v = 1940$ lb/ft of length
16-8. $FS = 1.97$ against OVT; $FS = 1.38$ against sliding
16-9.   Top strut, force $= 47.3$ kN; middle strut, $F = 394$ kN; bottom strut, $F = 567$ kN
16-10. Computed D $\cong 8$ ft; $D_{design} = 1.5(8$ ft$) = 12$ ft
16-11. FS against overturning $= 1.3$; FS against sliding $= 27$; position of resultant, $d = 5.27$ ft from toe.

17-2.   (a) W_c = 7040 lb/ft of length; (b) W_c = 11,730 lb/ft; (c) W_c = 3520 lb/ft

17-3.   (a) W_c = 17,000 lb/ft; (b) W_c = 8,000 lb/ft;
(c) H_e = 9.2 ft for (a); H_e = 8 ft for (b)

17-4. W_c = 101.3 kN/m of length

17-5. W_c = 27.5 kN/m of length

17-6. W_c = 10,800 lb/ft; $D_{0.01}$ = 1260 lb/ft of ID

17-7.   Required min. thickness = 0.109 inches

Index

Index   **613**